Landform Studies
from Australia and New Guinea

A Nation of trees, drab green and desolate grey
In the field uniform of modern wars,
Darkens her hills, those endless, outstretched paws
Of Sphinx demolished or stone lion worn away.

They call her a young country, but they lie:
She is the last of lands, the emptiest . . .

A. D. HOPE, Australia

Landform Studies from Australia and New Guinea

Edited by

J. N. JENNINGS and J. A. MABBUTT

with a Foreword by Professor E. S. Hills

CAMBRIDGE
AT THE UNIVERSITY PRESS
1967

PUBLISHED BY.
THE SYNDICS OF THE CAMBRIDGE UNIVERSITY PRESS

Bentley House, 200 Euston Road, London, N.W.1
American Branch: 32 East 57th Street, New York, N.Y. 10022

Published in Australia and New Zealand by
AUSTRALIAN NATIONAL UNIVERSITY PRESS

Printed in Australia at Burwood, Victoria by Brown, Prior, Anderson Pty Ltd
LIBRARY OF CONGRESS CATALOGUE CARD NUMBER: 67-13805

Foreword

But there is a growing pleasure in comparing the character of the scenery in different countries, which to a certain degree is distinct from merely admiring its beauty. It depends chiefly on an acquaintance with the individual parts of each view. I am strongly induced to believe that as in music the person who understands every note will, if he also possesses a proper taste, more thoroughly enjoy the whole, so he who examines each part of a fine view may also thoroughly comprehend the full and combined effect.

Charles Darwin

The Voyage of the 'Beagle'*

Darwin's approach to geomorphology, if he had developed his studies in that discipline, would clearly have been analytical. When he crossed the Blue Mountains in the summer of 1836, on his excursion to Bathurst, he was vastly impressed with the great chasms which had by some means been excavated into the plateau composed, as he observed, of thick horizontal sandstones. His imagination boggled at the thought that streams so small as those which he saw in the height of summer could have cut out such great valleys, but when he argued and finally agreed that the valleys had been excavated by the sea he was equally puzzled, as he knew that the rivers passed through very narrow gorges downstream so that if the sea had done the work it too would have been inhibited, as the terrain would have consisted of large lagoons rather than open sea. He was wrong in his interpretation of the physiography of the Blue Mountains but he was right in his views as to the origin of the coastal formation at Bald Head, on King George's Sound, Western Australia. There he correctly interpreted the so-called 'petrified forest' as calcareous concretions formed around decaying vegetable matter. It is interesting to note that in both his excursions into physiographic matters he was careful to note the structure of the rocks, even details of structure, and to base his interpretation on his views as to the processes which had operated. Darwin's failure with the Blue Mountains was due to his lack of appreciation of the effect of sub-aerial erosion over a very prolonged period—that is the time element—and also to his well-nigh complete lack of understanding of marine processes, despite his long voyage in the *Beagle*. The lessons to be derived from Darwin's work are firstly that it is necessary to identify the elements in the landscape (to which he referred), and secondly that it is necessary to have a complete genetic understanding of the formation of these elements.

An immediate difficulty emerges in that the processes that are operating now may have been different in the past in the emphasis and balance of the various forces operating. This introduces the concept of evolutionary stages in physiographic elements and the tectonic and climatic accidents that have affected a

* *A Naturalist's Voyage—Journal of Researches into the Natural History and Geology of the Countries visited during the Voyage round the World of* H.M.S. Beagle *under command of Captain Fitz Roy.* R.N.

region. Hence the need for comparative physiographic studies from which a sequence of evolutionary stages in the development of individual physiographic features, and also the development of the landscape as a whole, may be recognized. This involves a much larger element of hypothesis and theory than is the case with the recognition of landforms and the description of the processes to which they are now subjected.

Australia is unusual in that the greater portion of its area is subject to climatic conditions which are not strictly comparable with those obtaining in Europe and in those parts of North America where theories as to the physiographic evolution of landscapes have been developed. The very wide occurrence of fossil soils is a clear indication of the equally wide, if not wider, occurrence of fossil land surfaces—land surfaces which have been but little modified during the course of geological time, even since the early Tertiary period. Rainfall and temperature conditions in Australia are extremely variable from place to place and also in time. As regards rainfall there is a large area which is not only subject to extreme fluctuations but in which there is a sharp decrease in rainfall from the sources of streams towards their middle courses and their mouths. The Murray, for example, receives the Darling as its last effective tributary and flows on to the sea with practically no further surface addition to its water.

Australian physiography has developed over a hundred years within its own unique environment. Certain lines of interest have accordingly appeared as characteristic of Australian physiographic work. These are coastal physiography; the conditions in interior riverine plains with a generally sub-arid character; the various desert formations including sand ridges and gibber plains, tent hills and laterite and silcrete cappings, which are found over enormous areas of the continent; and tectonic effects, particularly the significance of faulting in landscape development as against fault-line scarps or escarpments, all of which are, in places, admirably displayed. Another area of knowledge to which Australian physiographers have added much concerns volcanic landscapes, which are widespread in eastern Australia—stream diversions, the development of lateral streams, volcanic lakes, centres of eruption, basaltic lava plains of Tertiary or Pleistocene age, have all been more minutely studied in Australia than in other countries. A good deal of our knowledge of such matters derives from the search for gold where deep leads, some of which lie beneath lava flows, were explored in subsurface workings. It was also in sub-alluvial deep leads in Victoria that the relatively flat planed-off bedrock surface lying beneath the alluvial deposits of mature streams was first discovered and is still best known.

The articles in this book are expressive of the Australian scene—volcanic landscapes, dissected mountains and pediments, coastal features and coral reefs, salt lakes, riverine plains, and riverless karst country; they also follow traditional Australian trends in discussing denudation chronology, soils and landforms, fossil soils, tectonic patterns, and regional geomorphology. A growing regional interest is indeed shown in the three papers on New Guinea, and one in fact feels a sense of deprivation in that nothing has been written on Antarctica, where Australian geologists and physical geographers have for so long played a major role in exploration. We in Australia are still at the stage of recognizing the various elements of the landscape, and describing them. We still lack sufficient precision in the cartographic representation of the land surface to add significantly to concepts of quantitative geomorphology, but on the other hand we are contributing notably to the body of organised knowledge of elements of landscape and their origin.

The resurgence of geomorphology of recent years has been linked with a growing recognition of its practical significance in geological and mineral exploration, in the understanding of soil-forming processes, and in surface and subsurface hydrology, and it may confidently be predicted that further researches along the lines discussed in this book will contribute much to the material welfare of Australia, as well as to the cultural development of Australians.

Darwin left Australia with strangely mixed feelings. He wrote,

> Farewell, Australia! you are a rising child, and doubtless some day will reign a great princess in the South; but you are too great and ambitious for affection, yet not great enough for respect.

The Australian's love for his country is scarcely to be described as affection, but there can be no doubt that those who have lived in Australia develop a certain deep feeling for the country. Nostalgia certainly affects us as much as it does people of other lands, and I believe it would be true to say that with the intellectual grappling with the problems of development, the understanding of landscape and the intimate regard that the physiographer must have for the country he studies, a certain feeling of belonging with this generally harsh land arises. Such feelings have certainly animated most of the research workers in previous decades and it is with the recognition that the work of the early geomorphologists is being continued, extended and given greater precision that I am very happy to have been asked to write a foreword to this book.

E. S. HILLS

Preface

The essays in this collection, although for the most part regionally based, draw on their settings primarily for discussion of systematic themes which reflect trends in modern geomorphology and opportunities offered by the Australian landscape. Most of the themes are discussed within the limits of a single area; however, a few of the essays range more widely and illustrate general topics by bringing together examples from a number of regional contexts. In the event, the book is neither a regional geomorphology of Australia nor a complete systematic study of landforms from an Australian standpoint.

The collection epitomizes the earlier growth and the present state of geomorphology in Australia. With some exceptions, the scientific study of scenery here until about fifteen years ago was one of broad reconnaissance accompanying the geological exploration of the continent. As in the United States and southern Africa, this was largely a natural outcome of the clear relief expression of geological structure in a predominantly dry climate, and significantly the three major publications which epitomize this early stage were written by geologists. J. T. Jutson's *Physiography of Western Australia* first appeared in 1914 and for many decades had an impact far beyond this country as a source of knowledge of arid erosion. In *The Physiography of Victoria,* published in 1940, the smaller state of Victoria provided E. S. Hills with sufficient variety of landforms for the first Australian textbook of systematic geomorphology. Ten years later appeared *The Geology of the Commonwealth of Australia* by T. Edgeworth David (ed. W. R. Browne), essentially the culmination of pre-war work, with one-third of the second volume devoted to regional physiographic accounts, state by state. Since 1950 there has been an increasing tempo of geomorphological investigation, partly as a result of accelerated geological survey, partly with the growth of university departments of geography and geology, and partly from soil studies and regional surveys carried out by CSIRO. This later phase has been much more the work of specialists and has more commonly involved detailed regional analysis. At this specialist level our knowledge of Australian landforms is patchy, and for many parts there are still only the pioneer descriptions; hence no full and uniform regional account can yet be given. Partly for the same reason and partly as a result of full commitments to current field research, it is unlikely that an Australian equivalent of Lester King's *South African Scenery* will be written for some time.

Bearing in mind this unevenness in our knowledge of Australian landforms and the inevitable gaps in regional coverage, contributors were selected and subjects suggested to them such that the contents might at least be representative of Australia, both geographically and systematically. In the result, arid, tropical semi-arid, tropical humid, temperate humid, glacial, and periglacial landforms are treated in settings ranging between Tasmania, Western Australia, and Australian New Guinea, and in structural contexts which include ancient shields, sedimentary basins, and young orogenic belts. Also, there is discussion of many of the geomorphological features which would be regarded as typically Australian;

such are the duricrusts of northern, central, and western Australia, the salt lakes and dune ridges of the deserts, pediments in a range of semi-arid and subhumid environments, and the coral reefs of the tropical coasts.

Modern tendencies in geomorphology are fairly well represented. A large number of the essays treat of morphogenesis as an expression of climate, explaining the youngest landforms as part of the present climatic pattern and older landforms as inherited from different climates of the past. The growing emphasis on the study of process is reflected in accounts of such contrasted areas as the New Guinea rainforest and the dry Flinders Ranges. Quantitative analysis of landforms, another growing point of the discipline, is here applied in studies of meander patterns and the distribution of landslides. The two essays which treat of the relationships between landforms and soils are particular instances of the increasing use of correlative deposits as a key to the history of landscape, but the theme recurs in other contributions, some of which show the value of exact dating by radiometric methods.

Omissions from the book reflect equally the history and present state of Australian geomorphology. The English reader may be surprised to find in it no account of closely stepped land surfaces or of river terraces, such as until recently dominated the British literature, but few studies of this kind have been made in Australia. Many of the gaps point to work still to be done. For instance, the problem of the anastomosing rivers of the interior plains awaits treatment on the lines of recent American studies of the hydraulic geometry of rivers and by the techniques of spectral analysis; also omitted are the Pleistocene coastal dune systems, which have still to be placed firmly in a framework of sea-level and climatic changes and of related coastal evolution.

Finally, the list of contributors is professionally indicative of past contributions to and the share of present effort in Australian geomorphology. The close association with geology continues, and no fewer than seven out of seventeen authors are geologists. However, a large part of geomorphological teaching and research is now vested in university departments of geography, which provide five authors. The two essays by pedologists are a token of the important contributions made by soil scientists to the understanding of Australian landforms in the last decade, and further to the significant application of geomorphology in pedological studies here. Five essays arise from another form of applied geomorphology, namely the integrated resource surveys of the CSIRO Division of Land Research.

J. N. JENNINGS

J. A. MABBUTT

Notes on Contributors

Dr J. L. Davies is Senior Lecturer in Geography at the University of Tasmania. He is a graduate in Geography of the University of Wales and came to Tasmania in 1954; since then his main work has been on the morphogenesis of coastlines, for which he gained his doctorate at the University of Birmingham. His approach to the geomorphology of Tasmania has been mainly a morphoclimatic one.

Dr M. J. J. Bik, is a Senior Research Scientist of the Geographical Branch, Department of Mines and Technical Surveys, Ottawa. He studied physical geography in the University of Amsterdam where his doctoral dissertation treated of the glacial landforms and deposits in part of the Austrian Alps. As Geomorphologist with the Division of Land Research, CSIRO, he took part in a resources survey in New Guinea on which this essay is based.

J. G. Speight, Research Scientist, Division of Land Research, CSIRO, graduated in Geology at the University of Canterbury in New Zealand and had some training in river hydrology before coming to Australia. His studies of river behaviour arise from regional surveys in Papua and New Guinea and from a broader concern with quantitative geomorphology.

David S. Simonett, Associate Professor of Geography, University of Kansas, has strong interests in geomorphology and soil-forming processes in the humid tropics. After graduating in Geography from Sydney University, he studied lateritic soils in the Cape York Peninsula. This work is part of a larger project in New Guinea supported by the Geography Branch, Office of Naval Research, United States Navy.

B. P. Ruxton graduated in Geology from Cambridge University, and later carried out geological surveys in the Sudan. He lectured in Geology at the University of Hong Kong, where his interest in deep weathering developed, and later at the University of Ghana. He came to Australia in 1960 as Geologist with the Bureau of Mineral Resources, and worked in the Darwin area. Subsequently he joined the Division of Land Research, CSIRO, as Senior Research Scientist and has taken part in regional surveys in Australian New Guinea.

Dr C. R. Twidale, Reader in Geography, University of Adelaide, joined the Division of Land Research, CSIRO, after graduating in Geography from Bristol University, and studied landforms in northwestern Queensland. His doctoral thesis at McGill University was in periglacial geomorphology. Since returning to Australia his research interests have centred on landforms of the dry parts of South Australia.

J. A. Mabbutt, Professor of Geography, University of New South Wales, formerly Principal Research Scientist, Division of Land Research, CSIRO, is a graduate in Geography of Cambridge University. He studied desert landforms in southern Africa whilst on the staff of the University of Capetown, and since coming to Australia has also worked mainly in the arid zone.

John Hays is Senior Geologist with the Commonwealth Bureau of Mineral Resources, Geology and Geophysics. He graduated in Geology from Leeds University and after war service carried out geological surveys, including studies of land surfaces, in Zambia from 1946 to 1957. He was resident in Darwin from 1957 to 1962.

Dr M. J. MULCAHY is Officer-in-Charge, Western Australian Regional Laboratory, CSIRO. He graduated in Forestry from the University of Aberdeen in 1949 and afterwards worked at the Macaulay Institute for Soil Research on the Soil Survey of Scotland. He came to Australia in 1954, where his research has been mainly on the principles governing the distribution of soils and soil-landscape relationships in Western Australia, with particular reference to old land surfaces.

B. E. BUTLER is Officer-in-Charge, Division of Soils, South Eastern Regional Centre, CSIRO, Canberra. After graduating in Agricultural Science from the University of Western Australia, he carried out soil surveys in many parts of southeastern Australia, including the Riverina. He has pioneered the investigation of soil layers in relation to landscape change in Australia.

J. N. JENNINGS, Professorial Fellow in Geomorphology in the Research School of Pacific Studies of the Australian National University, graduated in Geography at Cambridge University. After army service during the war, he lectured at the University of Leicester until assuming his Australian appointment in 1952. He is a past president of the Australian Speleological Federation and of the Canberra Speleological Society.

Dr R. W. GALLOWAY, Senior Research Scientist, Division of Land Research, CSIRO, graduated in Geography from Edinburgh University and spent some years on research into periglacial geomorphology in Europe and the Arctic. In Australia he has been mainly engaged on regional surveys by CSIRO, including that of the Hunter Valley in New South Wales.

C. D. OLLIER is Senior Lecturer in the Geology Department, University of Melbourne. A graduate in Geology of Bristol University, he studied soil science at Rothamsted and then made soil and geomorphological surveys for the Uganda Department of Agriculture. Prior to his Victorian work on lava caves, he has studied caves in the volcanic rocks of Mt Elgon in East Africa.

E. D. GILL is Assistant Director of the National Museum of Victoria, Honorary Secretary of the Royal Society of Victoria, a member of the INQUA Commission on Quaternary Shorelines, and Honorary Secretary of the ANZAAS Quaternary Shorelines Committee. A graduate of the University of Melbourne, he has published many papers on Quaternary history, including geology, palaeontology, archaeology, and palaeoclimatology. He has been very much concerned with the promotion of radiocarbon dating in Australia.

Dr E. C. F. BIRD is Reader in Geography at Melbourne University. A graduate of King's College, London, he came to Australia in 1957 to study the geomorphology of the Gippsland Lakes in Victoria. After a period as Lecturer in Geography and Conservation at University College, London, he returned to the Australian National University and in 1963 resumed work on coastal geomorphology.

Dr HELMUT WOPFNER, a graduate of the University of Innsbruck, came to Australia in 1956 to join Geosurveys of Australia Ltd. His present appointment is that of Supervising Geologist, Petroleum Division, South Australian Geological

Survey. He has carried out extensive field-work in the Great Artesian Basin for petroleum investigation, including much aerial reconnaissance and the first crossing of the southern Simpson Desert by motor vehicle in 1960.

DR RHODES W. FAIRBRIDGE, Professor of Geology, Columbia University, New York, is a graduate of the Universities of Oxford and Western Australia, and of Queens University (Kingston, Ontario), and has previously been a member of staff of the Universities of Western Australia, California and Illinois. His field experience is wide, including Europe, the Middle East, Northern Australia, the South Pacific and the Sudan. Wartime service in the Royal Australian Air Force Intelligence involved systematic investigation by sea and air of coral reefs to establish photo-interpretation techniques for planning military operations.

Acknowledgments

We gratefully acknowledge permission to publish granted by the Chief of the Division of Land Research, CSIRO, for Chapters 2, 3, 5, 8, and 13, by the Chief of the Division of Soils, CSIRO, for Chapters 10 and 11, by the Director of the Commonwealth Bureau of Mineral Resources, Geology and Geophysics, for Chapter 9, by the Director of the Geographical Branch, Office of Naval Research, Washington, for Chapter 3, and by the Director of the South Australian Department of Mines for Chapter 7.

Mr Alan Stewart, Chief of the Division of Land Research, CSIRO, kindly allowed the drafting of maps and diagrams for Chapters 2, 3, 5, 8, 10, 11, and 13 to be carried out in his Division; we thank the Editorial Section of this Division, in particular Mr R. W. Munyard, Mrs N. Geier, and Mrs B. Jordan, for their help. With the permission of Professor O. H. K. Spate, the cartographic work for the remainder of the book was done in the Department of Geography, Research School of Pacific Studies, Australian National University; we are grateful to Mr Hans Gunther, Mrs C. Daniels, and Mr J. Heyward for their efforts.

We have been obliged also by all those who have generously allowed their photographs to be reproduced here; attributions will be found in the captions to the plates. All other photographs were taken by the authors of the chapters to which they appertain. Mr C. S. Leslie, CSIRO Land Research Division, helped us most generously with the choice and preparation of the dustjacket photograph, and Mrs M. Bourke with the index.

Books like this, to which numerous authors contribute, give rise to many tiresome difficulties in the course of their publication; we are therefore especially indebted to the officers of the Australian National University Press for the patience and care they have exercised in their part in the making of this book.

CORRIGENDA

Page 72, line 1. Insert:

pendent variable in the multiple correlation in the expectation that in general

Page 106. For the first three lines of text read:

The residuals stand between 10 and 50 m above local baselevels, the deepest dissection observed being east of the Italowie Gorge. The upper surfaces of the mesas and plateaux slope smoothly down from the nearby uplands at angles of

Page 107. For the first three lines of text read:

In both the Brachina and Italowie Gorge areas there are several former plain levels. The large number of mesa and plateau remnants in the Brachina area especially do not fit into a small number of height ranges, even allowing for

Page 125. For lines 3 and 4 of text beneath figure read:

Silcrete
Fragmental zone
Kaolinised zone
Ferruginous zone

Pages 148, Fig. 8.2. For inset 'Figure 4' read '8.4'.

Pages 152 and 168. The figure above caption 8.5 on page 168 should be above caption 8.3 on page 152, and vice versa.

Page 171, line 12. After 'either' insert 'shortly'.

Page 205, line 32. For 'the arc of the Wessel Islands on the west.' read 'the arc of the Wessel Islands on the east.'

Page 270, Fig. 12.5. Insert: 'Scale: 2 miles to 1 inch'.

Page 302, Fig. 13.3. For insets 'Fig. 3', 'Fig. 4', 'Fig. 5' read '13.4', '13.5', '13.6'.

Page 333, line 13. For 'Gibbon' read 'Gibbons'.

Contents

Plates

7 Geomorphology of the Lake Eyre Basin

8 Denudation Chronology in Central Australia

9 Surfaces and Laterites in the Northern Territory

10 Landscapes and Soils in Southwestern Australia

11 Soil Periodicity and Landforms

B2

Figures

1

Tasmanian Landforms and Quaternary Climates

J. L. DAVIES

INTRODUCTION

The island of Tasmania is a detached portion of the eastern highlands of Australia, jutting polewards to provide the only section of the Australian landmass lying south of forty degrees of latitude (Fig. 1.1). Climatically it is often compared with Britain, but such a comparison is not particularly apt, for Tasmania lies generally ten degrees nearer the equator and is subject to significantly warmer winters and higher rates of sunshine and evaporation than are the British Isles. This is reflected in such things as a much lower rate of peat formation in post-glacial time. European homoclimes for Tasmania may most profitably be sought in northwestern Spain, where striking affinities may be found, as among the apple orchards of the Galician and Asturian rias. Comparison with Galicia is not only meaningful in terms of present-day climates: it also helps towards some initial deductions regarding the effect of the swinging Quaternary climatic belts. Many Tasmanian coastal regions may be judged warm temperate today, according to the criteria imposed by the more generally used climatic classifications (Fig. 1.2), and the climate of the island as a whole can in many ways be thought of as transitional between warm and cool temperate. The implications as far as the Quaternary is concerned seem to be that, in interglacials, something approaching a warm temperate west coast or Mediterranean type climate can be expected to have prevailed, while, in glacials, the climate is likely to have been cool temperate in the lowlands, but cold enough in the highlands for frost to be normal and, given enough precipitation, for glacier ice to form. These deductions support the direct evidence about Quaternary climates gathered so far and provide a useful background against which the influence of climatic variation on landform evolution may be discussed.

Tasmania is a mountainous island and, while variations in absolute relief have their normal effect upon temperature distribution, precipitation is the climatic element most strongly affected. Present mean annual rainfall of over 2500 mm on the west coast mountain ranges contrasts with totals of less than 750 mm and in places less than 500 mm in the rain shadow areas of the central lowlands (Fig. 1.3). Even on highland areas in the eastern half of the island, annual falls of more than 1250 mm are rare. Using the widely known criteria of Thornthwaite, Gentilli (1947) formulated superhumid, humid, and subhumid provinces (Fig. 1.4), and the

The writer is grateful to M. R. Banks and K. D. Nicolls for reading the manuscript of this chapter and suggesting improvements. This does not mean, of course, that they necessarily agree with all the interpretations offered.

relatively narrow belt covered by the humid province is a good indication of the steep precipitation gradients that exist. The isohyet for 30 inches (750 mm), which is the approximate boundary of the subhumid province, may also be taken to separate that part of the island where streams are generally perennial from

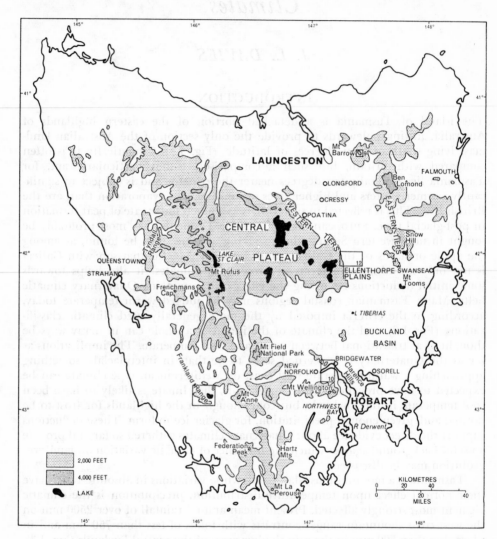

1.1   Altitudinal zones, showing places mentioned and locations of Figures 1.8, 1.9, 1.10, and 1.12

that in which they are generally non-perennial. The contrast between the stream régimes in the superhumid and subhumid provinces is important today in relation to fluvial processes, but may also have been of great significance in determining the effect which Pleistocene climatic changes had upon valley morphology. This suggestion will be returned to later.

Corresponding roughly to the precipitation dichotomy is an important structural dichotomy illustrated in Figure 1.5. Pre-Carboniferous rocks in Tasmania were strongly contorted by a number of orogenic movements, but the Carboniferous seems to have been a time of widespread and prolonged planation, so that

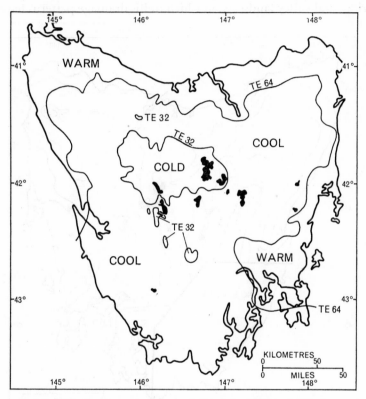

1.2 *Temperature provinces defined by Thornthwaite's temperature efficiency indices (after Gentilli 1947)*

the succeeding Permian and Triassic sediments were laid down unconformably on an extensive erosion surface. These latter sediments were intruded in the Jurassic by enormous sheet-like bodies of dolerite. The doleritic intrusions, together with the subsequent block faulting that took place at the end of the Mesozoic and beginning of the Tertiary, caused widespread dislocation, but there have been no strong fold movements in post-Carboniferous time. The pattern evident in Figure 1.5 arises from a general stripping of the post-Carboniferous cover and the uncovering of the pre-Carboniferous basement in the wetter west and northeast regions.

Two fundamental structural provinces may therefore be distinguished. The centre and southeast of the island is still covered by subhorizontal post-Carboniferous rocks, with dolerite masses commonly overlying weaker Permian and Triassic sediments, so that more or less tabular landforms have been produced (Plate Ia). The scarps bounding these tabular landforms are often related to fault trends, and drainage patterns are strongly rectangular, with stream axes commonly related both to fault directions and major joint systems. In the west and north, in contrast, the folded pre-Carboniferous basement rocks have been exposed to give rise to a ridge-and-valley landscape in which trellis drainage patterns have evolved.

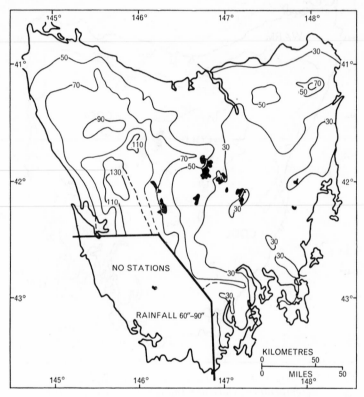

1.3   Mean annual precipitation. Isohyets in inches.

Here ranges of more resistant rocks like quartzite and conglomerate alternate with valleys cut in relatively less resistant rocks such as limestone, schist and phyllite (Plate Ib). The essential, although not absolute, distinction between the two provinces is that, in the one, landforms have developed mainly on fault structures, while in the other they have developed mainly on fold structures. The distinction is a generalised one, but sufficiently clear to allow reference, for brevity's sake, to the fault structure and fold structure provinces respectively.

The rough coincidence between the fault structure province and lower precipitation on the one hand, and the fold structure province and higher precipitation on the other, is significant in terms of landform evolution. Most important perhaps, the tabular nature of the landforms in the fault structure province has been enhanced by the relatively low density of the drainage, while, in the fold structure province, a high intensity of stream dissection has exaggerated further the narrowness of the interfluves and the steepness and frequency of the slopes.

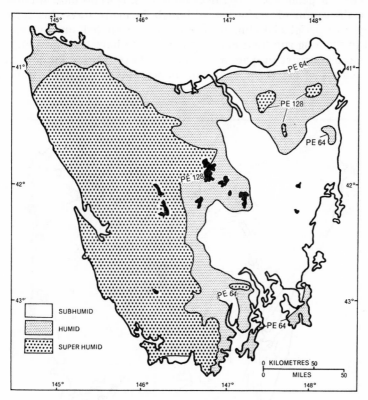

1.4 *Precipitation provinces defined by Thornthwaite's precipitation effectiveness indices (after Gentilli 1947)*

One further point of contrast may be made. This concerns the likely effect of Pleistocene climatic vicissitudes upon the landforms in the two provinces. In the wetter parts of the island, precipitation is so great that it seems unlikely that any small changes in its amount could have any significant effect. On the other hand, where precipitation is high, small changes in temperature below a crucial limit may cause the onset of glaciation. In the drier parts of the island, a relatively small change in precipitation effectiveness could have a significant effect on stream régimes and bring about changes in valley landforms. Conversely, where precipitation is low, a larger temperature swing may be necessary to cause widespread formation of glacial ice. The ensuing discussion will help to show the extent to which these deductions are borne out.

GLACIATION

The most spectacular monuments to the effect of climatic change on landform evolution in Tasmania are those highland masses reshaped in varying extent by Pleistocene glaciers. It is now over a hundred years since the effects of glaciation were first recognised, and they have received much more attention than any other aspect of climatic geomorphology. Because of this, it seems most suitable to begin with some discussion of glaciation, although in many ways this is an illogical beginning since periglacial climates preceded, surrounded, and succeeded glacial ones, and in the long run their effects may prove to have been greater. They were certainly more extensive in space and time. But at present we know so much more about the effects of glaciation that expediency almost dictates a start from this point.

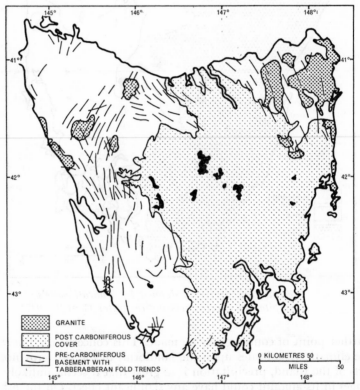

1.5 Structural provinces (based on Spry and Banks 1962)

The three-stage scheme of glaciation postulated by A. N. Lewis (summarised 1945) has been abandoned by modern workers (Jennings and Banks 1958), and no acceptable evidence has yet been adduced for more than one glacial stage. This stage may be correlated in time with the Würm-Wisconsin of the northern hemisphere on the basis of the general freshness and stratigraphic relationships of the morainic deposits (Plate Ib) and also of one radiocarbon date of 26480 ± 800 years B.P. for wood from glacial sediments in the Linda valley near Queenstown (Gill 1956). In view of the extent of the known glaciation, and recent work in New Zealand, where multiple glaciation is now well established, it seems highly probable that Tasmania was subjected to more than one glaciation, but that the last was the most extensive and so more or less obliterated the evidence of the previous ones. So far no sections of glacial deposits showing multiple stages have been found, and relatively little subsurface exploration has taken place.* For the time being then, it is necessary to discuss the geomorphic effects of glaciation in terms of one stage.

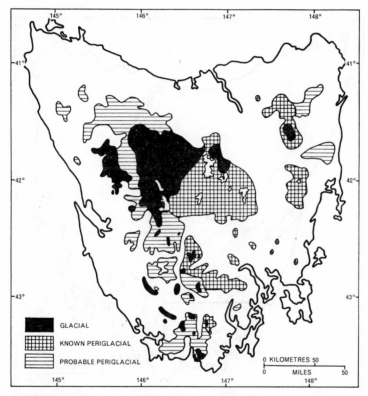

GLACIAL

KNOWN PERIGLACIAL

PROBABLE PERIGLACIAL

0 KILOMETRES 50

0 MILES 50

1.6 Distribution of Pleistocene glacial and periglacial processes

The distribution of glaciated areas is indicated in Figure 1.6 and their tendency to a westerly location is clear. One of the most outstanding character-istics of glaciation in Tasmania is the evidence for a rise in the regional snowline

* Since this essay was written, S. J. Paterson has published a paper, 'The Pleistocene drift in the Mersey and Forth valleys—probability of two glacial stages', *Pap. Proc. R. Soc. Tasm.*, **99**, 115-24, which provides the first strong evidence for more than one glacial stage. Along the Leomonthyne penstock line in the Forth valley, a well lithified tillite is found in bores to underlie an unconsolidated gravelly till.

from WSW to ENE in sympathy with the precipitation gradient. In Figure 1.7 an attempt has been made to draw isopleths for the height of the snowline at the maximum extent of glaciation towards the end of the Pleistocene by plotting, for each limited highland area, the lowest altitude at which glacial ice would appear to have formed. Generally these altitudes represent cirque floor levels. It is well known that such attempts at reconstruction are fraught with difficulty and Figure 1.7 must be approached with reservations, but it undoubtedly shows the right sort of trends, and the general conclusions reached about lowest ice-forming levels check well with results obtained independently by Derbyshire (1963) in an analysis of the altitude of the highest cirque floors between Queenstown and the Central Plateau.

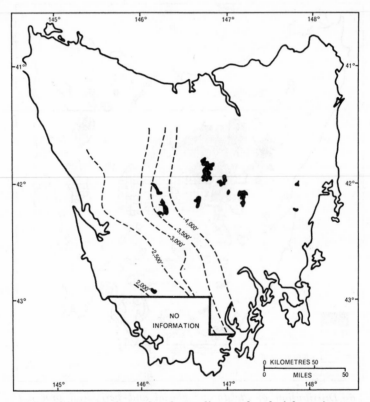

1.7   Altitude of the regional snowline at the glacial maximum (for explanation see text)

In the west the snowline was as low as 600 m in the Frankland Range, and north of Queenstown the terminal moraines of the Henty glacier lie at about 75 m above sea level. At the other extreme, on the Ben Lomond plateau in the northeast, the snowline was at about 1350 m and ice does not seem to have extended below 900 m. There was thus a difference of at least 750 m in the altitude of the snowline at either end of the island. The change in altitude was not gradual and even, but very rapid in the west, so that it rose from 600 m to 1200 m within 80 km, and took about 130 km to lift the remaining 150 m. This of course parallels the present-day precipitation gradient, in which a comparatively rapid drop from at least 3800 mm a year to about 1500 mm on the west contrasts with generally distributed aggregates of 1000 to 1250 mm for highland areas in the east. However, it does not exactly parallel the precipitation gradient; for the Pleistocene snowline gradient trends from southwest to northeast, while the precipitation gradient trends from northwest to southeast. This is because most of the total precipitation comes with northwesterly winds whereas most of the snow comes with southwesterly winds following the passage of cold fronts.

The effect of this northeastward rise in the snowline is noticeable in a number of ways. On a regional scale it combined with the texture of relief to influence the type of glacier produced. In the fault structure province, the snowline was high and sheet-type glaciers tended to form on the relatively undissected plateau tops; conversely, in the more finely dissected fold structure province, the snowline was low, and here many more cirque and stream-type glaciers appeared. Since the western glaciers descended to much lower altitudes, they interfered more with the pre-glacial drainage systems which they partially occupied, causing drainage derangement, sometimes as a result of ice damming, sometimes because of glacial deposition (Fig. 1.8).

Altitudinal variation in the snowline also has very important implications as far as the time factor is concerned, for glaciation must have started earlier and finished later in areas where the snowline was lower. The west, then, would have been glacierised longer than the east, and we can expect to find that the highest cirque glaciers in the southwestern mountains would have been the very last to disappear (Plate Ia). Such an interpretation is supported by the extremely fresh appearance of moraines in the high cirques of the Federation Peak block, for instance. As a corollary to this, we may expect highland landforms in the west to have been more modified by ice than those in the east. This difference should have been exaggerated by variations in the regimen of the glaciers concerned. Although, as a moist island little more than forty degrees from the equator, Tasmania as a whole would have experienced high rates of accumulation and ablation, these rates would have been especially great in the west, where precipitation was higher everywhere and where temperature was higher at the snowline than in the east. Higher rates of accumulation and ablation imply higher ice velocities, which in turn imply higher rates of erosion. In considering the significance of variations in the extent of landform modification by ice, this conclusion is an important one.

Superimposed on the general contrast associated with the regional snowline were systematic local variations imposed by the effect of aspect upon accumulation and ablation. While the snowline rose regionally eastwards, it was locally lower on the eastern sides of highland areas than on their western sides because of maximum snow accumulation in the lee of summits. Ranges in the west, trending along the fold axes of the Devonian Tabberabberan orogeny (Fig. 1.5), show a striking tendency to be scalloped by cirques along their sheltered eastern sides. Much less obvious is the factor of differential ablation, which tends to lower the snowline locally on south-facing slopes, relatively protected from insolation. This second factor is significant only where the first does not operate, but its effect is discernible, for instance on the Frankland Range (Fig. 1.8). The major section of the range trends NW-SE, and here all cirque-cutting has been on the eastern side, presumably as a result of the accumulation factor; but where the range has an easterly trend and insolation comes into play, the cirques appear on the southern side. In this east-trending section differential accumulation ceases to be important and differential ablation becomes significant as a factor in cirque location. It seems that the position of Lake Pedder has been in large part determined by this swing of cirque location from one side of the range to the other. The Serpentine River has been pushed to the northern edge of its valley by a series of large, low-angled, outwash fans originating in the flank of the Frankland Range. Lake Pedder lies where these outwash fans cease because of the switch in cirque location.

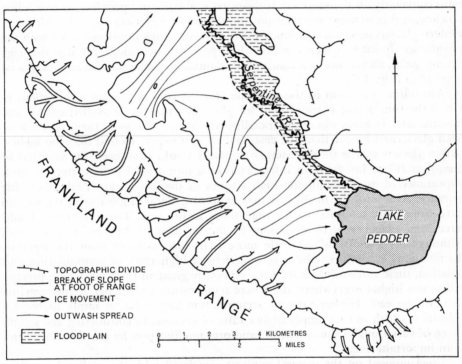

1.8   The Frankland Range and Lake Pedder, showing cirque glaciation and outwash spread

In general, glacifluvial sediments and landforms are not as extensively developed as one might expect if deductions about the high wastage rate of the ice bodies are valid. The complicating factor here is almost certainly lithology, and again something of a contrast between east and west obtains. The siliceous conglomerate and metamorphic rocks of the fold structure province tended to produce sand and small pebbles as a result both of pre-glacial weathering and glacial erosion. This material formed comparatively bulky outwash features relatively close to the area of origin. The Frankland Range fans shown in Figure 1.8 provide an example. In the fault structure province, the surface rock in the glaciated districts is overwhelmingly dolerite, and this is known to have been deeply weathered in pre-glacial times to produce very large quantities of clay. Glacial till in this province is typical boulder clay, very unlike the pebbly and sandy till of the west. Outwash deposits dominantly comprise small boulders and cobbles, the clay having been removed much further downstream by the meltwater. The volume of glacifluvial sediments close to the glaciated areas is therefore correspondingly less. This contrast is likely to have been accentuated if, as has been deduced, the western glaciers were characterised by higher erosion rates and were active longer. Other factors being equal, they can be expected to have produced a larger quantity of till relative to their size.

PLEISTOCENE PERIGLACIAL PROCESSES

In great contrast to the early recognition of the legacies of glaciation in Tasmania is the very late appreciation of the effects of periglacial processes. As recently as 1956, Jennings, in a review of Australian periglacial geomorphology, was able to comment

> although about one-fifth of the area of Tasmania is thought to have been glaciated in the Pleistocene, there is scarcely a passing reference to periglacial features to be found in the published literature on that state.

In fact, first recognition of periglacial processes seems to have been by K. D. Nicolls and his co-workers in the CSIRO Division of Soils, but to date the only published account of periglacial landforms is a short preliminary interpretation of the summit plateau of Mt Wellington (Davies 1958). It seems probable that this lack of appreciation of a group of processes which have seriously modified all the highland areas of Tasmania was one of the major reasons why the extent of Pleistocene glaciation was exaggerated by earlier workers. A. N. Lewis, the energetic pioneer and authority on glacial matters up to his death in 1943, does not seem to have recognised periglacial phenomena, and did not mention them in his writings (bibliography in Lewis 1945). He quite frequently interpreted as glacial till what we would now identify as periglacial solifluction material; for instance, this is clearly the reason for his belief (Lewis 1933, 1924) that Pleistocene glacial ice covered the southeastern segment of the Central Plateau and the summit of Mt Wellington. Both are covered with extensive mantles of solifluction material and both are areas which are now believed to have escaped glaciation.

At present, the extent of solifluction material which has moved down slopes less steep than its present angle of rest is the best indication of Pleistocene periglacial limits. Yellow-brown solifluction soils derived from dolerite have been mapped in a continuing series of Reconnaissance Soil Maps issued by CSIRO Division of Soils (Leamy 1961, the last to date, gives a list of previous issues). These soils are characterised by a yellow-brown earthy matrix containing dolerite stones and boulders, sometimes layered but largely unsorted (Nicolls 1958c). They cover much of the dolerite hill country in the centre and east of the island, and the bouldery nature of the surface layer is a most important reason for the unsuitability of this country for cultivation.

As with the glacial sediments, it has not yet been possible to identify more than one period of periglacial deposition, and that relatively recent, and the occasional presence of stony or bouldery bands suggests only degrees of reactivation within this period, which has to be equated with the Würm-Wisconsin. It must be stressed once more, however, that field workers have so far been few, and it may be that examination of periglacial deposits in section will eventually provide the best opportunity for elucidating a Pleistocene chronology.

Establishing some sort of figure for the lower limit of periglaciation in the Pleistocene is difficult, because of rapid variation with local conditions of relief, and also because of lack of accurate information from much of the island. From figures so far published and from the writer's unpublished observations, it seems safe to say that, given a sufficient amount of land higher up, all the country above 600 m was subjected to periglacial solifluction, and that this limit commonly fell to 450 m and sometimes to 300 m. These variations in altitude seem to be local, and no systematic regional variation is so far apparent. Since the processes concerned are overwhelmingly temperature-dependent, this is what one might expect, but more reliable conclusions must await further exploration and recording.

One of the basic difficulties is that of identifying the results of periglacial processes in the western part of the island. In the fault structure province, on the dominantly tabular, relatively undissected landforms of the dolerite highlands, there is an abundance of low slopes over which the effects of periglacial solifluction are readily apparent, particularly as much of the regolith is bouldery. In the rugged fold structure province, slopes are very rarely less steep than the angle of rest of the weathered material which, because it is dominantly sandy and pebbly, has a low angle of rest in any case. In the very high rainfall country of the southwest, many slopes formed on the metamorphosed quartzitic rock are completely bare, due presumably to the slow rate of decomposition of the rock relative to the high rate of removal of the small weathered particles by the abundant running water. The absence of soil creep as a significant slope-forming process, associated with the development of narrow pediments over which the sandy weathering product is washed, give these landscapes a pseudo-arid appearance. The effect of periglacial conditions upon them remains so far a matter of speculation.

Observations made in the dolerite highlands of the centre and east, then, form the basis of our present knowledge of the distribution and effect of Pleistocene periglacial processes. No evidence for the former presence of permafrost has been discovered, and in such latitudes it is not to be expected. Characteristic landforms are solifluction sheets, sometimes channelled into block streams. These may descend from rock scarps and residual stacks or tors, but often appear to originate in areas of previous deep weathering higher up. One of the best developed landscapes of this type is the unglaciated higher plateau of Mt Barrow in the northeast, lying at about 1200 m above sea level (Fig. 1.9). Here a complex system of block streams, now fossil, formed along well marked lineations in the dolerite. These presumably follow zones of preferential earlier weathering, which has isolated residual areas of sounder rock. The residual areas are of all shapes and sizes; some form large humps nearly two kilometres across, others are small and stack-like. All seem to

Ia   Mt La Perouse lies in the faulted structure province of Tasmania with nearly horizontal sandstones overlying a dolerite sill. Two cirque lakes with enclosing end moraines can be seen.

Ib   Lake Margaret lies in an area of strongly folded Palaeozoic rocks typical of the fold structure province of Tasmania, and it is surrounded by an end moraine up to 300 m high

mark stages in the isolation and sculpture of the eventual tor feature. The block streams too vary considerably in size; some are small and narrow, but three which debouch towards the southwest are particularly wide and massive. The streams often originate in back-to-back fashion in down-wasting cols, called block field saddles by the writer in a description of similar features on Mt Wellington (Davies 1958).

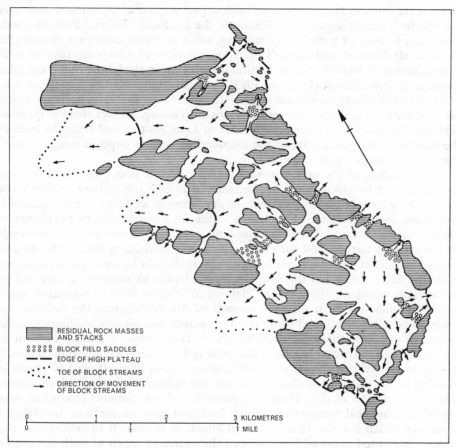

1.9   Fossil periglacial block streams on the high plateau of Mt Barrow

The block streams in dolerite country, like the solifluction sheets, consist of boulders in a matrix of clay, but in places the clay matrix is missing. The occurrence of patches, or even of fields of bare dolerite blocks, sometimes called 'ploughed fields' or 'potato fields' in Tasmania, often seems to be related to the action of runoff from rainfall and snowmelt. The channelling effect which produced the block stream in the first place also concentrates running water, which progressively carries away the interstitial clay. Where the clay has been removed, the ground surface normally shows a concave transverse profile which is

C

clearly due to subsidence. Excellent examples of this phenomenon are traversed by the road which ascends Mt Wellington.

The large-scale descent of solifluction masses in the Pleistocene seems to have been responsible for derangement of the drainage in parts of the hill country, especially where stream gradients are low. In the southeastern section of the Central Plateau and on the Eastern Tiers in the Snow Hill-Mt Tooms district, extensive swampy areas are found and interesting stream diversions may be postu- lated, these features being associated with a past régime of mass movement over the relatively gentle slopes. Lake Fenton in the Mt Field National Park may well have been formed by periglacial damming, since it drains through a narrow gap between Mt Mawson and Seager's Lookout, the sides of which are covered with large masses of dolerite boulders continuous with the material damming the lake. Lewis made two attempt (1922 and 1923) to explain Lake Fenton as a cirque lake and tried to fit it into his scheme of glaciation; but he was clearly unhappy about his explanations, and they are certainly not convincing. In fact there is no good evidence that glacial ice came near the site of Lake Fenton, and both the form of the lake basin and the nature of the surrounding surface deposits suggest a peri- glacial rather than a glacial origin.

The question of the origin of solifluction material is one to which no firm answer can yet be given. Some of the material can be traced back to free faces, where it may have been detached by frost shattering or wedging. A great deal of it must have been the result of prolonged subsurface weathering in pre-glacial or interglacial times. Local systems of cryoplanation may therefore be either one-cycle or two-cycle in nature, and sometimes perhaps a mixture of both. The upland plains of the dolerite country are known to be underlain by some metres of rotted rock, and Hale (1958) has discussed the great depths of weathering revealed by engineering works on the Central Plateau. When, in 1959, a television trans- mission station was built near the summit of Mt Wellington, the dolerite was found to be much weathered along the joint planes and pseudo-bedding planes to at least 6 m below the surface. Although, as Hale shows, a certain amount of pneumatolysis is involved in places, the great bulk of this decomposition is clearly due to downward percolation of meteoric waters along the well marked planes of jointing in the dolerite, so that core stones are isolated and progressively dimin- shed within a mass of clay. It seems certain that this is the end product of long periods of chemical weathering on the highland plateau surfaces, involving a basic rock which is liable to this form of attack. It is difficult to believe that this widely distributed material has not been the source of much of both the glacial and periglacial sediments in the fault structure province.

Following this argument, it seems logical to regard the tors of Mt Wellington for instance as two-cycle features, formed more or less in the manner suggested by Linton (1955), but this does not exclude the possibility of a one-cycle origin for some such landforms; for instance, tor-like stacks such as those within glacially eroded zones on the Ben Lomond plateau may well be completely periglacial in origin.

PRESENT-DAY PERIGLACIAL PROCESSES

Although there are no glaciers left in Tasmania today, evidence is accumulating of periglacial processes still active within limited areas. Basically, such present-day activity takes two forms. The first is nivation or snow-patch erosion, and the second is small-scale formation of patterned ground. Snow-patch erosion may be met with to a minor extent in most highland areas above about 1150 m. Here frost shattering and the removal of shattered particles by snowmelt is a common phenomenon, but well established snow-patch hollows are most evident on higher summits above about 1400 m, and especially in the southwest where the Pleistocene snowline was low. Lewis (1925) described a good example of such a feature on Mt La Perouse (Plate Ia); he found fresh striations in the Permian coal measures which he considered were due to movement of the seasonal snow mass with basal boulders (as discussed and illustrated in Costin *et al.* (1964)). A particularly fine circular snow-patch hollow is to be found cut in quartzite near the summit of Frenchmans Cap and preliminary investigation of this has been made by J. A. Peterson (unpublished). On the dolerite, with its more or less vertical jointing and horizontal pseudo-bedding, snow-patch hollows tend to be transverse and to produce ledge-like features, in contrast perhaps to the incipient nivation cirques elsewhere. No fossil nivation hollows have yet been described, but they are clearly to be expected.

The first discovery of patterned ground seems to have been recorded by Jennings (1956) from the glaciated southwestern part of the Central Plateau. Here, rudimentary hexagonal sorting on small bare patches of moraine at about 900 m was thought to be the result of present-day processes, made possible perhaps by firing of the vegetation. Since this time the writer has discovered other examples, notably developed in accumulations of weathered dolerite particles washed into small depressions by snowmelt. Rather crude miniature polygons occur near the summit of Mt Wellington, but much better examples are to be found at many points on the Ben Lomond plateau, which has a general height of about 1370 m. The polygons are about 25 cm across and are formed in weathered particles of dolerite ranging from granules to fragments up to 8 cm long. Since the particles appear to be decomposing relatively rapidly and are annually washed over by snowmelt, it is certain that the polygons are being currently produced. The lowest altitude at which the writer has found frost sorting is at 920 m on the shores of Lake Perry in the Hartz Mountains. The resulting patterns were very indistinct and, since they are formed on a seasonally uncovered section of the lake floor, may be the result of rather special circumstances.

On the Ben Lomond plateau, accumulations of finer particles including a proportion of clay display what appear to be earth polygons. These also are about 25 cm in diameter and have all the characters which Cailleux and Taylor (1954) suggest may be used to distinguish such features from desiccation cracks.

The absence of patterned ground of larger dimensions on dolerite is not surprising, for this rock breaks down relatively rapidly from boulder size to clay and intermediate sized particles are comparatively unstable and rare. On the other hand, on other rocks which might provide the right range of particle sizes, slopes are seldom slight enough to encourage patterning. That exploration of flattish non-dolerite summits may prove rewarding is suggested by Derbyshire's record (1963) of polygons 2 m in diameter at 1380 m on Mt Rufus. These are formed of sandstone particles which give a greater size range and, chemically at least, are more stable than the dolerite fragments. The polygons recorded by Derbyshire are currently active. It is in similar circumstances, though perhaps at lower levels, that fossil patterned ground, as yet unrecognised in Tasmania, may eventually be identified.

Temperature measurements made on mountain summits in recent years have shown that, above 1200 m, periglacial climates are likely to be encountered for about half the year. Recent records from a height of about 1200 m on Mt Wellington, for instance, indicate that temperatures fluctuate daily about freezing point from June to October inclusive. During the remainder of the year, the temperature rarely drops below freezing point; even so, this gives about 160 major freeze-thaw cycles a year. Although it is difficult to give a single figure, because of local variations with such factors as soil and exposure, the present treeline may be taken as lying at about 1200 m. It is above this height, then, that frost sorting is likely to be best developed. Records, such as that for Lake Perry and that by Jennings on the Central Plateau, represent exceptional cases where the vegetation has been removed or is inhibited.

COMPARISON OF LIMITS

Despite the hazards, some profit may be gained from comparing Pleistocene and present-day climatic limits from the evidence of landforms. The present-day snowline nowhere intersects the surface of the island, but near the summits of Mt Anne and Frenchmans Cap, above 1200 m, are semi-permanent snow patches which survive occasionally from one winter to the next. They suggest that here the level of permanent snow lies at about 1525 m or perhaps a hundred metres more. The comparison is with the lowest Pleistocene snowline, deduced from cirque-floor levels to have been at about 600 m around Mt Anne and at about 730 m at Frenchmans Cap. A difference of about 900 m in elevation is indicated in this rough fashion.

Comparison of periglaciation levels is even more difficult, partly because of the unreliability of the deduced Pleistocene limits and partly because one is not comparing altitudes of strictly similar phenomena. However, we may note the present lower limit of vigorous frost action in the soil of about 1200 to 1400 m, and the previously suggested lower limit of about 450 m deduced from the evidence of Pleistocene features. But this argument is a very tenuous one and provides no more than a very rough indication of the change involved.

A more soundly based comparison, and one which is much more profitable from a geomorphological point of view, is that between the Pleistocene levels for glacial and periglacial limits. We have seen that the regional snowline in the Pleistocene, being dependent on temperature and precipitation, climbed steeply from 600 m in the west to about 1200 m, and then flattened out in the centre and east. On the other hand, there is no evidence to contradict the assumption that regional periglacial limits were very much more temperature-dependent and that they were likely to have been more or less at the same altitude over the whole island. The consequences of such a deduction are that glacial action extended below periglacial limits in the west but not in the east, and that there was a longer interlude of post-glacial periglacial activity on eastern highlands than on western highlands. These are supported by the field evidence as far as it is known.

The implications are important, and clearly to be borne in mind in regional studies. Perhaps the most significant implication concerns the extent to which subsequent periglacial processes may have modified the landscape inherited from the glaciers. In the west such modification is likely to have been slight and many of the depositional landforms resulting from glaciation are actually below the presumed periglacial limit. As one goes eastwards however, on to the areas around the Central Plateau, increasing periglacial modification is to be expected. The extreme is reached on the dolerite plateau of Ben Lomond, where the regional snowline was probably never much lower than 1400 m, and therefore stood something of the order of 900 m above the periglacial limit. There must here have been an extended period of periglacial activity after the disappearance of the plateau glaciers which occupied the surface of Ben Lomond in the late Pleistocene, and this is reflected in the present-day landforms. Glacially abraded surfaces are overlain in places by streams and sheets of angular dolerite blocks. In places too, tor-like features, which it is very difficult to envisage as having escaped glaciation, rise from this surface and provide what may be the best examples of one-cycle 'paleo-arctic' tors (Palmer and Radley 1961) in the island. Although the projections out of which they are etched were probably pre-glacial and overridden by ice, their final form must be the result of post-glacial weathering and mass movement in which frost action probably took a major part.

Perhaps more important still in terms of large-scale landscape evolution is the effect of prolonged periglacial action upon the deposits left by the glaciers. On the Ben Lomond plateau the areas of glacial erosion are associated, not with morainic forms, but with what appear to be block streams. The landscape is a hybrid one and is to be compared on the one hand with typically mamillated plateau surfaces with associated moraines, such as that of the Tyndall Range on the west coast, and on the other with typical periglacial landscapes of tors and block streams such as that on the high plateau of Mt Barrow. At Ben Lomond we seem to have the general picture of mamillated surfaces topped by tor-like forms which do not represent nunataks, and with block streams descending below. The inference is that morainic material here has suffered at least some redistribution by more recent periglacial solifluction. If the inference is a proper one, it would also be applicable to some other glaciated areas in the more easterly part of the island. McKellar (1957) described rivers of talus descending to about 300 m above sea level below the Western Tiers near Poatina, and these were subsequently interpreted as periglacial block streams (Davies 1958). The plateau surface above shows clear evidence of glaciation, and much of the blocky material may thus have originated as moraine.

It is possible that redistribution of morainic material by frost action may provide part of the answer to the question of why morainic ridges are so few in the centre and east of Tasmania in comparison with the west. The western glaciers left behind a wonderful array of terminal and recessional moraine ridges, some of which are of enormous dimensions in comparison with the related glaciers, and almost perfect in form. As one goes eastwards in Tasmania however, morainic ridges become fewer until they are often strikingly absent. The eastern and southeastern limit of the Central Plateau ice sheet, for instance, is not marked by any clear-cut outmost line of moraine ridges (Jennings and Ahmad 1957) and it is difficult to discover where the bouldery ground moraine ends and where material which can be confidently identified as periglacial begins. Some reasons have already been offered why moraines should generally be larger in the west than in the east, but the question of form raises other issues. It may be that the more easterly glaciers did not attain a state of equilibrium long enough to produce ridged forms and that these are consequently confined to special situations such as the piedmont Lake St Clair; but the possibility of their degradation by periglacial processes seems worth bearing in mind when investigations are carried further.

RIVER RÉGIMES AND VALLEY FILLS

The climatic changes which so overwhelmingly influenced the development of landforms in the highlands of Tasmania may be expected to have had some effect upon the lowlands as well. Unfortunately, the geomorphology of lowland Tasmania has been much less studied even than that of the high country, and only in recent years have detailed investigations been made of landscapes nearer to sea level.

The relatively poor development of glacifluvial landforms, except perhaps in the west, has already been pointed out. No large-scale aggradational terrace systems, such as those which have been so profitably explored by New Zealand workers, have come to notice. As suggested earlier, they should be looked for particularly in the west, but exploration of this part of the island, in which there are few roads, remains minimal. What is much more in evidence are valley fills resulting from periglacial solifluction. These fills are considerably more widespread and particularly noticeable in the centre and east, where solifluction material, which chokes the headwater valleys of many of the eastern streams, is clearly continuous with that making up aggradational terraces lower down. The Northwest Bay River, for instance, rising in a large block stream on the Mt Wellington plateau, is characterised by a more or less continuous fill terrace of dolerite pebbles right down to sea level.

A good example of large-scale stream aggradation under periglacial conditions is provided along a section of the drowned River Derwent between New Norfolk and Bridgewater, where it cuts between Mt Dromedary and Mt Faulkner (Fig. 1.10). These mountains are mantled with solifluction material and the valleys of small tributaries joining the Derwent on either side contain abundant pebbles and gravels derived from this source. The present streams are incised into this material and also into large alluvial fans that were formed along the north bank. The fans disappear beneath the post-glacial fill that is progressively limiting the present river channel: they are probably graded to the low sea-level talweg of the Derwent, but their submarine extensions have not been explored.

Not all valley fill deposits are of glacial or periglacial origin, for it seems certain that there have been other, later, aggradational phases. These phases affected streams rising in low hill country, often below 300 m. The material which came into the valleys was shed from hill slopes at least as steep as its general angle of rest and could have been mobilised under the present climate. Judging by the writer's limited field observations, these sediments are less generally pebbly than those of periglacial origin, but this conclusion needs testing by systematic study. The pebbly material is normally basal and more or less horizontally bedded: streams which have subsequently been incised into the sediments tend to run on these basal gravels. Aggradation of this type is characteristic of the drier southeastern quadrant of Tasmania, in country still mainly covered by open sclerophyll woodland that often approximates to savanna woodland. The Clarence Hills, rising to just over 300 m to the east of Hobart, provide a good example of this sort of landscape. The hills are relatively finely dissected by short valleys which frequently carry no discernible stream channel but which are floored with substantial deposits of gravels derived mainly from shaly siltstone and sandstone and extensively excavated for commercial purposes. This gravel is clearly fossil.

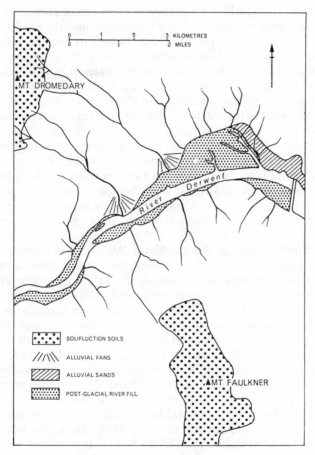

1.10 *Superficial deposits of the Derwent valley near*
Bridgewater (based on Dimmock 1957)

There seem to be three possible explanations for valley fills such as those in the Clarence Hills. The first is that periglacial limits in the Pleistocene were lower than is now thought, and that much, if not all, of them are in fact due to frost climates. On present evidence this remains possible, but unlikely for reasons that have been mentioned and others that will be mentioned. The second is that they are due to deforestation and agricultural exploitation of the land during the 150 years of European colonisation. There undoubtedly has been small-scale alluviation as a result of European occupation, but relatively little of the surface of Tasmania has in fact been cleared by Europeans (Davies 1964) and this cannot explain the bulky and widespread valley fills. The Clarence Hills are still wooded, and where there has been clearing there is plenty of evidence to show that it took place after and not before the period of aggradation. Thus many of the fill terraces in southeastern Tasmania were covered with dense scrub when European settlement first occurred.

The third possibility, which by process of elimination may seem most likely, is that at some time between the end of the Pleistocene and the coming of Europeans there occurred a rather drier period when changes in the character of the vegetation on the hill slopes led to accelerated mass movement and a consequent spread into the valleys of sheets of colluvial material which the streams were incompetent to evacuate. The occurrence of a mid-Recent period of greater aridity in Australia has been widely postulated in the past (for instance, Crocker 1941), but little indubitable evidence for it has been found in Tasmania. We could expect its effects to be most noticeable in the drier section of the island, where annual rainfalls are below 750 mm, and in places below 500 mm, and it is precisely in these areas that evidence of an apparently post-glacial phase of valley aggradation is so obvious. It is in these areas too that the effect of aboriginal occupation was probably most marked. Even if the aborigines were here before the mid-Recent—and as yet we have no evidence that they were—their modification of the vegetation through fire would inevitably have been most effective under a drier climate.

Work by Goede (1965) in the Buckland Basin of the southeast represents a first step towards a solution of the problem thus posed. The Buckland Basin is surrounded by hills thought to be marginally low for periglaciation. There is evidence on the higher summits for periglacial solifluction (Loveday and Dimmock 1958), but many of the encircling interfluves are thought to have escaped. Within the basin, Goede found clear evidence for two aggradational phases separated by a period of incision, and thus giving rise to two fill terraces. From a number of circumstances, he argued a periglacial origin for the older and a mid-Recent date for the younger, and this has been supported by a radiocarbon age of 4435 ± 110 years B.P. obtained for wood from the base of the younger fill. A worked stone implement was found in the same horizon.

More recently the writer has obtained a radiocarbon date for charcoal from gravels in the Barilla valley in the Clarence Hills. Here also two aggradational phases seem to be identifiable. An older phase is represented by more angular cemented gravels and a younger by more rounded uncemented gravels. The present stream is incised into both. An age of 7900 ± 460 years was obtained for charcoal near the top of the older gravels. Thus the latest aggradational phase again appears to be of mid-Recent age.

The question of post-glacial aggradation may have some relationship to a problem of forest distribution mentioned elsewhere (Davies 1964). This concerns the possibility that much of the vegetation of eastern Tasmania may be largely anthropogenic, and that the hypothesis of cultural interference rather than climatic change, put forward for New Zealand by Cumberland (1962), may also apply to the Australian island. A three-pronged attack on the problem of post-glacial environments along sedimentological, palaeobotanical, and archaeological lines should prove extremely rewarding and should shed light on a number of related questions.

Streams in the subhumid province generally give the impression of being underfit. In many of the smaller valleys cut into siltstone and sandstone, drainage is unchannelled and there is no observable stream. The larger valleys contain streams which look ridiculously small for the landforms and sediments with which they are associated. Such subjective judgments are supported by the evidence of abandoned stream channels with greater widths and longer meander wave lengths than those of modern streams. An example is provided by the 'prior stream' of the Tea Tree Rivulet near Buckland described by Goede (1965). It seems evident therefore that many fluvial landforms, particularly in the southeast, are inherited from times of greater flood discharge when precipitation was higher, or at least when runoff was higher due to such factors as lower temperatures, greater rainfall intensity, and seasonal snowmelt. That such times may be correlated with glacial and periglacial conditions also seems evident, but we are left wondering how swings from high discharge to low discharge relate to swings from braiding to meandering or from aggradation to incision. The evidence obtained by Goede from the Tea Tree Rivulet confirms the expectable association of aggradation and braiding with high ratios of load to discharge, the load being comprised of poorly sorted material supplied by excessive mass movement. The first identifiable period of aggradation is to be correlated with the early stages of periglaciation in which downward movement of the previously weathered mantle would have provided particularly heavy stream loads. Towards the end of the cold period, on the other hand, it is possible to postulate a falling off in the supply of waste material for distribution by periglacial processes, particularly if this was largely a product of previous chemical weathering and was therefore to some extent only slowly renewable. If the stream discharge continued to reach a relatively high level, this should have produced a change from braiding to meandering and, in support of this speculation, it is notable that the large meanders of the prior Tea Tree clearly date from the end stage of deposition of the periglacial fill, after the braided phase and before the phase of incision.

FIXED INLAND DUNES

The last group of features which may be called in evidence in a discussion of landforms and climatic change in Tasmania are the inland dunes which are all now fixed. These seem to comprise three main groups. The first consists of low sand dunes or undulating sand sheets, almost always on the eastern side of rivers and clearly derived from them. These have been described particularly by Nicolls (1958a, b) and have been termed 'valley dunes' in the present discussion. The second consists of lunettes or dunes of clay, silt and sand on the leeward side of shallow lakes or depressions. According to the hypothesis of origin put forward by Stephens and Crocker (1946), they were derived from the associated depression at a time when it was seasonally dry. The third group, which is less extensive and less clearly known, consists of sheets of sand derived by deflation of the sandy A horizon of podsolic soils formed on friable Triassic sandstone. A good example is to be found in the Kingston-Blackmans Bay district south of Hobart. With very few known exceptions these windblown features are confined to the subhumid province and are more or less bounded in distribution by the 30 inch (750 mm) isohyet (Fig. 1.11).

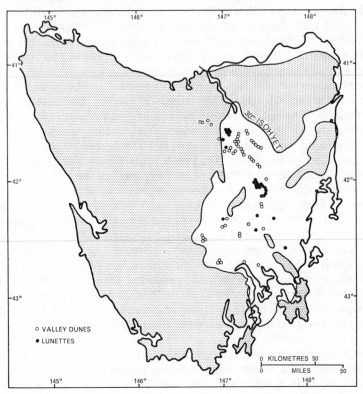

1.11   Occurrence of inland dunes (based mainly on information from CSIRO)

It seems that the valley dunes are associated with a period of stream aggradation and, more especially, a period when braiding was prevalent. However, the particular period of aggradation with which they are associated is not yet known. Nicolls (1958b) compared the evidence for periglacial or semi-arid origins and decided in favour of periglaciation. He noted in particular the absence of evidence for wind erosion on the interfluves, other than the development of lunettes, and concluded that the combination of stable interfluves and braided streams did not favour a hypothesis of semi-arid conditions. Such a conclusion must now be placed against the evidence from the Buckland and Clarence Hills districts of a distinct post-glacial period of aggradation, the evidence of the lunettes which are generally agreed to be the result of drier conditions, and the contention that saltation of the sands over appreciable distances from the river

channels must have required some diminution in vegetative cover. Their distribution too, as far as it is known, supports an origin due to excessive drought
rather than excessive cold, and soil profile development on at least some of the
valley dunes is comparable with that on the lunettes, which seem certain to be
semi-arid in origin. The strongest argument at the moment for a Pleistocene age
for the valley dunes is probably that, along the Brumby valley in the Longford

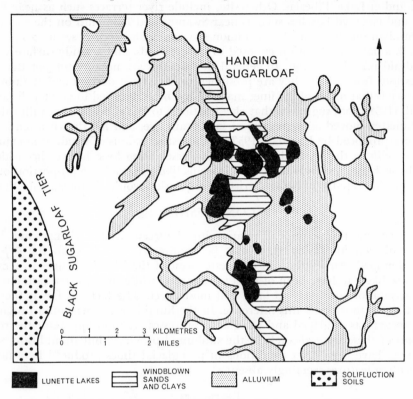

1.12 *Superficial deposits of the Ellenthorpe Plains, near Ross (based on
Leamy 1961)*

area, they have been shown by Nicolls (1958a, 1960) to be overlain in places by the
latest alluvium. If sand sheets at Bridgewater on the Derwent (Fig. 1.10) are in
fact wind-redistributed alluvium, this also would support a Pleistocene (low sea-
level) age, since they border a section of the river now drowned by the sea. At
present the question remains an open one and the real relationship may prove
complex. Nicolls noted some variation in soil profile development on the valley
dunes and, in part at least, this may reflect more than one period of origin.
Although it often appears clear, as at the Ellenthorpe Plains (Fig. 1.12), that the
material is derived from periglacial solifluction deposits, the period of deflation
may have occurred later.

Formation of the lunettes seems to demand an assumption of a semi-arid
climate. Only rarely does a climate such as the present allow the floors of associ-

ated depressions to dry out sufficiently for wind action to take effect, and the dunes show no evidence of recent accretion. The lunettes are particularly numerous on the broad flattish interfluves of the Woodstock surface (Nicolls 1960) in central Tasmania, the soils of which have been strongly podsolised to produce typical sandy A horizons. They are sometimes associated with places where river capture has taken place, for instance at Western Lagoon near Cressy (Nicolls 1960) and at Lake Tiberias. Other sites include river terraces such as near Buckland, and emerged beaches such as near Swansea and Falmouth on the east coast and Strahan on the west. The common environmental factors seem to be a low rainfall, a flat open location exposed to strong winds, and a sandy surface which would aid initial deflation. In general the lunettes are notably smaller than the depressions from which they are presumed to have been derived and the obvious inference is that much of the finer material has been removed to greater distances. Nicolls (1958b) has suggested that clay fractions, to be found in both valley dunes and lunettes, moved as aggregates of sand-grain size, and has drawn attention to evidence produced by Loveday (1957) to suggest accessions of windborne material to some soils in the Sorell district. Nothing resembling loess has yet been identified. In such a relatively small island it seems likely that a large proportion of the finer particles capable of being carried in suspension would disappear into the sea.

CONCLUSION

In summarising this account of relationships between climatic changes and landform evolution in Tasmania, it may be appropriate to advert to the *a priori* deduction made earlier that, in the wetter west of the island, changes in temperature are likely to have been of most significance, while in the drier east, changes in precipitation are likely to have had most effect. The facts, as far as they are known, seem to support this inference. In the humid and superhumid provinces, the direct effects of glacial and periglacial processes are most apparent; the repercussions of these were also felt in the subhumid province, but in addition, what appear to have been drier conditions in post-glacial times produced here fluvial and aeolian features seemingly absent elsewhere.

REFERENCES

Cailleux, A. and Taylor, G. (1954). *Cryopédologie: Études des sols gelés*. Paris.
Costin, A. B. *et al.* (1964). Snow action on Mount Twynam, Snowy Mountains, Australia. *J. Glaciol.* 5: 219-28.
Crocker, R. L. (1941). Notes on the geology and physiography of south-east South Australia with reference to late climatic history. *Trans. R. Soc. S. Aust.* 65: 103-7.
Cumberland, K. B. (1962). 'Climatic change' or cultural interference? New Zealand in Moahunter times, pp. 88-142 in *Land and Livelihood: Geographical essays in honour of George Jobberns*. Ed. M. McCaskill. Christchurch.
Davies, J. L. (1958). The cryoplanation of Mt Wellington. *Pap. Proc. R. Soc. Tasm.* 92: 151-4.
——— (1964). A vegetation map of Tasmania. *Geogrl Rev.* 54: 249-53.
Derbyshire, E. (1963). Glaciation of the Lake St. Clair district, west-central Tasmania. *Aust. Geogr.* 9: 97-110.
Dimmock, G. M. (1957). Reconnaissance Soil Map of Tasmania. Sheet 75, Brighton. CSIRO Aust. Div. Soils. Div. Rept 2/57.

Gentilli, J. (1947). Map No. 25, Climatic regions, in *Regional Planning Atlas*. Hobart.

Gill, E. D. (1956). Radiocarbon dating for glacial varves in Tasmania. *Aust. J. Sci.* **19**: 80.

Goede, A. (1965). The geomorphology of the Buckland basin. *Pap. Proc. R. Soc. Tasm.* **99**: 133-54.

Hale, G. E. (1958). Some aspects of jointing and decomposition in Tasmanian dolerites, pp. 184-96, in *Dolerite: a Symposium*. Hobart.

Jennings, J. N. (1956). A note on periglacial morphology in Australia. *Biul. peryglac.* **4**: 163-8.

—— and Ahmad, N. (1957). The legacy of an ice cap. *Aust. Geogr.* **7**: 62-75.

—— and Banks, M. R. (1958). The Pleistocene glacial history of Tasmania. *J. Glaciol.* **3**: 298-303.

Leamy, M. L. (1961). Reconnaissance Soil Map of Tasmania. Sheet 61, Interlaken. CSIRO Aust. Div. Soils, Div. Rept 6/61.

Lewis, A. N. (1922). A preliminary sketch of the glacial remains preserved in the National Park of Tasmania. *Pap. Proc. R. Soc. Tasm.* 1921: 16-36.

—— (1923). A further note on the topography of Lake Fenton and district, National Park of Tasmania. *Pap. Proc. R. Soc. Tasm.* 1922: 32-9.

—— (1924). Notes on a geological reconnaissance of Mt Anne and the Weld River Valley, south-western Tasmania. *Pap. Proc. R. Soc. Tasm.* 1923: 9-42.

—— (1925). Notes on a geological reconnaissance of the Mt La Perouse Range. *Pap. Proc. R. Soc. Tasm.* 1924: 10-44.

—— (1933). Note on the origin of the Great Lake and other lakes on the Central Plateau. *Pap. Proc. R. Soc. Tasm.* 1932: 15-38.

—— (1945). Pleistocene glaciation in Tasmania. *Pap. Proc. R. Soc. Tasm.* 1944: 41-56.

Linton, D. L. (1955). The problem of tors. *Geogrl J.* **121**: 470-81.

Loveday, J. (1957). *Soils of the Sorell-Carlton-Copping Area, Tasmania.* CSIRO Aust. Soil Publ. No. 8.

—— and Dimmock, G. M. (1958). Reconnaissance Soil Map of Tasmania. Sheet 76, Buckland. CSIRO Aust. Div. Soils, Div. Rept 13/57.

McKellar, J. B. A. (1957). *Geology of the Western Tiers near the Great Lake, Tasmania.* Rec. Queen Vict. Mus. (N.S.) No. 7.

Nicolls, K. D. (1958a). Reconnaissance Soil Map of Tasmania. Sheet 47, Longford. CSIRO Aust. Div. Soils, Div. Rept 14/57.

—— (1958b). Aeolian deposits in river valleys in Tasmania. *Aust. J. Sci.* **21**: 50-1.

—— (1958c). Soil formation on dolerite in Tasmania, pp. 204-9, in *Dolerite: a Symposium*. Hobart.

—— (1960). Erosion surfaces, river terraces and river capture in the Launceston Tertiary Basin. *Pap. Proc. R. Soc. Tasm.* **94**: 1-12.

Palmer, J. and Radley, J. (1961). Gritstone tors of the English Pennines. *Z. Geomorph.* **5**: 37-52.

Spry, A. and Banks, M. R. (eds.) (1962). Geology of Tasmania. *J. geol. Soc. Aust.* **9**: 107-362.

Stephens, C. G. and Crocker, R. L. (1946). Composition and genesis of lunettes. *Trans. R. Soc. S. Aust.* **70**: 302-12.

2

Structural Geomorphology and Morphoclimatic Zonation in the Central Highlands, Australian New Guinea

M. J. J. BIK

INTRODUCTION

Attention has recently been drawn to the lack of information on morphoclimatic zonation on mountain chains in low latitudes (Tricart *et al.* 1962). This essay is intended to reduce this gap, but since it is based on reconnaissance survey* the subject has of necessity been treated qualitatively; much field and laboratory work needs to be done before there can be a quantitative approach.

The study area (Fig. 2.1) is part of the central cordillera of New Guinea and extends between 5°20'S. and 6°30'S. It is characteristically an area of ranges and high basins, with generally very rugged topography. Most of it lies between 1500 and 3000 m, with mountain ranges, mainly of sedimentary rocks, attaining 3700 m, although declining in altitude towards the south; above these, the extinct volcano, Mt Giluwe, rises to 4100 m. The lowest part of the area is in the southwest, where Lake Kutubu is at an altitude of only 800 m.

STRUCTURAL GEOMORPHOLOGY

(a) *The Geological Record*

'Bismarck Granodiorite', of presumed pre-Permian age, is exposed in a small area between the Lai and Tsak Rivers (Rickwood 1955), where it shows a non-intrusive contact with Cretaceous deposits. A considerable period of erosion apparently occurred prior to Mesozoic deposition (Rickwood 1955; A.P.C. 1961), but the stratigraphic discontinuity is not recorded in the geomorphological development of the area.

The pattern of sedimentation during the Jurassic and Lower Cretaceous was controlled by the presence of two troughs and an intermediate 'high'. The 'high', known as the Erave-Wana Swell (A.P.C. 1961), extended NNW from the southeast corner of the area. On its northeast side Jurassic and Lower Cretaceous sedimentation occurred in a belt 'considered to represent the first stage of development

The Director, Bureau of Mineral Resources, Canberra, kindly permitted the author to use unpublished information collected by Mr Ward and Mr Dow.

* This essay is based on data gathered in the course of a survey by the Division of Land Research, CSIRO, in parts of the Western and Southern Highlands Districts of Australian New Guinea in 1960 and 1961.

26

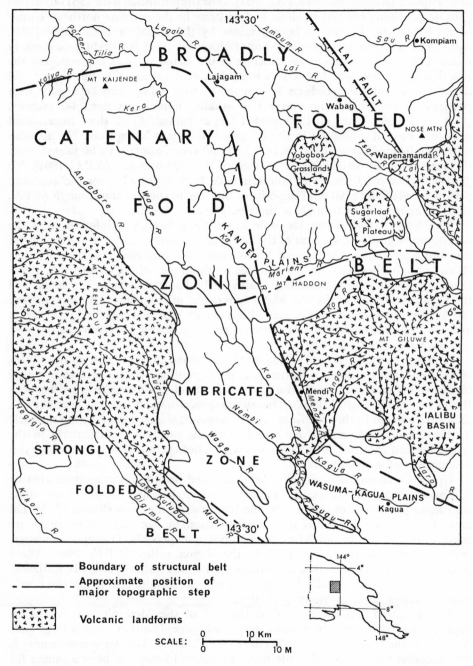

2.1 *Structural zones in part of the Western and Southern Highlands Districts, Australian New Guinea*

of a "Papuan Geosyncline" ' (A.P.C. 1961). Dow (unpublished data 1961) describes
Jurassic sandstone covered by shale and siltstone in the extreme northeast corner
of the area. The Jurassic is here overlain by the Labalam Beds (Dow 1961),
equivalent to Cretaceous Kondaku Tuffs (Rickwood 1955) but slightly different in
facies. The basaltic lava and agglomerate of the Labalam Beds exposed near the
junction of the Sau and Lai Rivers were deposited sub-aerially, but since rapid
deposition of volcanic products is thought to have more than kept pace with
geosynclinal subsidence, no reversal of sinking movements need be assumed
(Rickwood 1955). Ward (1949) reported Upper Jurassic black shale intercalated
with thin beds of sandstone in the Porgera valley near Mongurebi. No mention
was made here of Lower Cretaceous, which, however, appears to be present over
the Jurassic in the Strickland gorge, west of the area of study (A.P.C. 1961). No
Jurassic or Lower Cretaceous outcrops have been reported from the southern
part of the area, the 3700 m of deposits of that age in the Kutubu Trough (A.P.C.
1961) being masked by younger sediments.

The NNW trend of the Mesozoic Erave-Wana Swell was inferred from the
occurrence of granodiorite west of the Lai valley; if extrapolated to the northwest
it would separate the northeastern Jurassic outcrops from others in the northwest
(Ward, unpublished data 1949) and in the southern part of the area (A.P.C. 1961).
It would also separate the drainage basins of the Lai, tributary to the Sepik, and
the Lagaip, tributary to the Strickland River, and offer a convenient explanation
for the survival of an extensive area of less deeply dissected highland, ranging in
altitude from 2750 m to 3350 m, between the Lagaip and Ka Rivers in the west
and the Lai River in the east.

A change in the pattern of sedimentation occurred in this area with the advent
of the Cenomanian, but was initiated at the beginning of the Cretaceous period
further to the southeast, where the Erave-Wana Swell became submerged between
Bwata and Ialibu (A.P.C. 1961). This submergence marked the development of a
shelf environment in the southwest, which, however, was emergent during the early
Tertiary, and a geosynclinal environment in the northeast, particularly in the
Oligocene and Miocene. The distribution of relief types is closely related to this
new pattern of sedimentation.

Upper Cretaceous deposits have been reported from the northeastern area by
Rickwood (1955), where about 1200 m of calcareous shale and tuffaceous sandstone
with more pyroclastic elements near the base rest on the granodiorite of the Lai
anticline. Soft Mango Marls of tentative Senonian age (Rickwood 1955) are
exposed west of the Mendi River near Mendi, and possible Turonian sandstone
and (?) Mango Marls are exposed in the Kagua valley (A.P.C. 1961). Ward
reports Upper Cretaceous limestone from the Porgera valley below Mt Kaijende,
and tuffaceous sandstone with Upper Cretaceous foraminifera from further north,
from the Kaiya River in the Porgera area.

Sedimentation was interrupted at the end of the Mesozoic era in western
Papua, where minor warping, emergence, and 'peneplanation' over a large part
occurred at the beginning of the Tertiary (A.P.C. 1961). Angular unconformity is
the exception rather than the rule here. The same history has been assumed for
that part of the study area located in the Territory of New Guinea (Perry in Perry
et al. 1965), but Ward (1949), Rickwood (1955), and Dow (1961) give no evi-

IIa   Core boulders in the lower part of a weathering profile in calcareous greywacke sandstone in the Ambun valley at 2300 m

IIb   Buried soil profiles in a road cut in the Ambun valley, reflecting alternating stability and instability in weathering waste on steep slopes

IIIa   Pleistocene glacial landforms on the summit plateau of Mt Giluwe, where catenary valleys with conspicuous lateral moraines extend below 3000 m

IIIb   The northern sector of the Kandep Plain, at 2300 m, is typical of intramontane basins in the Western Highlands of Australian New Guinea. Footslopes are covered by volcanic-ash, whilst the central portion has alluvium and peat of unknown thickness.

dence to support this assumption. Though a similar emergence appears to have occurred in southern West Irian, where Palaeocene and Eocene are absent from the 'South New Guinea Province' (Visser and Hermes 1962), there is ample evidence that sedimentation was continuous into the Tertiary in the 'Central New Guinea Province'.

The pattern of Tertiary sedimentation in this area was one of limestone in the south and southwest, with occasional argillaceous and arenaceous intercalations, and ending with the deposition of mudstone of Muruan (Upper Miocene) age, and of largely arenaceous and argillaceous deposits, dominantly of volcanic or marine-pyroclastic* origin in the north and east. In the southwestern sector of the area, as much as 1700 m of limestone was deposited chiefly during the Eocene and the Miocene; however, the Kutubu region formed part of the emergent area of southwest Papua during the Lower Tertiary, and transgression did not occur here until the Miocene. In the north and east, Dow (1961) reports a total thickness of approximately 7500 m of sediments, comprising the non-volcanic, fine-grained Eocene (with 210 m of calcarenite), the largely volcanic and arenaceous marine-pyroclastic Oligocene-Miocene sequence of the Kompiam Beds (5500 m) and the shallow-water shale, sandstone, mudstone and conglomerate of the Birip Beds (750 m). Rickwood (1955) described a similar sequence from the Lai gorge.

The two depositional environments contrasted above appear to have alternated in an intervening belt. Between the Lai and Ka Rivers, north of the Ko River, in the headwaters of the Maramuni River, and locally to the west of the Kandep Plain, thick deposits of greywacke sandstone and tuffaceous sandstone are intercalated with shale and mudstone. Limestone beds are also found locally, generally increasing in thickness towards the west. These limestones have been assigned a tentative Upper Cretaceous to Eocene age;† they seem to underlie thick arenaceous deposits which apparently represent a westward extension of the Kompiam Beds and perhaps of the Birip Beds. Ward (1949) reported Eocene limestone along the upper Lai valley and in the Sirunki Grasslands. The 900 m of limestone forming the north face of Mt Kaijende, in the Porgera valley, range in age from Upper Cretaceous to Lower and Middle Miocene. Eocene and Miocene limestones, intercalated with sandstone and siltstone and underlain by mudstone and shale, were found along the upper Wage River. These limestone beds become increasingly argillaceous northwards beyond the Tilia River. In the Mendi-Kagua area Tertiary limestone is intercalated with greywacke sandstone and mudstone, but such intercalations become thinner and perhaps less frequent southwestwards towards Lake Kutubu.

The area of limestone deposition apparently reached at least as far north-eastwards as the Tilia River, Laiagam, and the Lai valley, and was perhaps continuous with the Linganas Beds of the Kompiam area (Rickwood 1955). During the Oligocene and Miocene the eastern limit of this area shifted westwards and

---

* Marine-pyroclastic: fragmental volcanics cooled in the atmosphere but deposited in a marine environment shortly after emission from vents, or supplied to the area of sub-aqueous deposition through the erosion of unweathered ash and agglomerate deposits.

† Samples of limestones collected during 1960 between the Lai and Andabare Rivers were analysed for their microfauna by G. R. J. Terpstra, Bureau of Mineral Resources, Canberra.

D

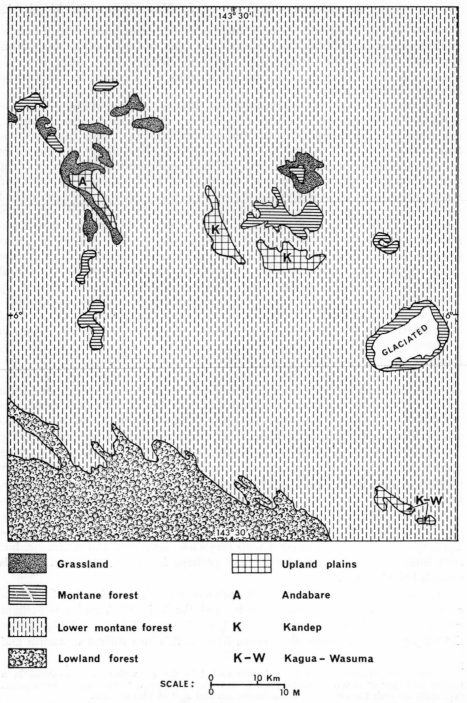

SCALE:

0	10 Km
0	10 M

Legend:

- Grassland
- Montane forest
- Lower montane forest
- Lowland forest
- Upland plains
- **A** Andabare
- **K** Kandep
- **K-W** Kagua – Wasuma

2.2 Main vegetation types in part of the Western and Southern Highlands districts, Australian New Guinea

southwards, while north of the line Laiagam, Ka River, Mt Haddon, Ialibu the dominant deposits were arenaceous and argillaceous.

Sedimentation ceased in the area towards the end of the Miocene and the orogenesis forming the present structure and topography occurred during the Pliocene (A.P.C. 1961; Dow 1961; Rickwood 1955; Visser and Hermes 1962). Intermittent movement has continued up to the present, as indicated by frequent earth tremors.

(b) *Relief as Related to Structural Zones*

The relief of this part of the central cordillera reflects the pattern of tectonic movements. The structural zones are to some extent related to the lithology of at least the Tertiary rocks, and they may also reflect variations in tectonic competence of deeper horizons. The four zones outlined below represent more or less uniform types of terrain (Fig. 2.2).

(i) *Strongly Folded Belt*

A strongly folded belt has been distinguished in the southwest (A.P.C. 1961). The highest points are chiefly along anticlines. Some thrusting along SE-NW longitudinal faults has created a few homoclinal ridges, with southwest-facing escarpments generally and northeastern dipslopes. The mountain crests usually attain 1500 m and crest altitudes increase in a northeasterly direction. Local relief is about 750 m. The belt largely coincides with the area of dominant limestone deposited during the Tertiary.

(ii) *Imbricate Zone*

Strike-faulting becomes very important to the north of the Strongly Folded Belt, and virtually all valleys are bounded on the north by fault scarps. The A.P.C. named this area 'Imbricate Zone' (A.P.C. 1961). The longitudinal faults are generally located on the axes of the anticlines or on their southern limbs. Relief inversion occurs frequently in this zone. Mountain crests generally attain 2150 m and local relief is about 750 m. The zone largely coincides with the area where substantial argillaceous and arenaceous beds are intercalated with limestone.

(iii) *Catenary Fold Zone*

A somewhat different structural type occurs in the central and western sector, in northwesterly continuation of the Imbricate Zone. Catenary folds,* separated by longitudinal faults mainly along anticlinal axes, and occasionally offset along transverse faults, dominate the relief of the area. The mountain crests in this zone generally attain 3050-3350 m, and local relief is about 750 m. The Catenary Fold Zone contains most of the intramontane plains such as Andabare Plain (2600 m) and Kandep Plain (2300 m). The lithological basis resembles that of the Imbricate Zone.

The Catenary Fold Zone is separated from the Imbricate Zone by a topographic step of 1000 m, the drop in average altitude of the mountain summits

---

* Catenary folds: well developed synclinal troughs separated from each other by longitudinal shear-faults.

occurring over a strike distance of only a few kilometres. This step is continued eastwards to the north of Mt Giluwe, and is believed to be located on a major fault or fault zone. Its western extension disappears under the volcanic cover of Mt Rentoul. South of the Porgera valley the boundary of the Catenary Fold Zone swings towards a western trend.

(iv) Broadly Folded Belt

This zone is characterised by large folds such as the broad anticline exposing Mesozoic shale and sandstone in the Porgera valley (Ward 1949). There are fewer strike faults than in the other zones, but these, nevertheless, have a very clear topographic expression. The belt contains the very wide Lai Syncline and the less wide Lai Anticline (Rickwood 1955; Dow 1961), but more closely spaced synclinal and anticlinal axes are found between the Ka and Tsak Rivers. A major fault zone is thought to mark the eastern side of the Lai valley, which is perhaps a rift valley comparable with the fault-controlled, north-trending alluvial plain of the upper Ka River, nearby in the Catenary Fold Zone.

This belt contains the greatest local relief in the area. The Lai River, at 1525 m near Wapenamanda and at 1200 m in its gorge downstream, is adjacent to Nose Mountain which attains 3200 m, and Mt Kaijende rises to over 3350 m on the southern margin of the valley of the Porgera River, which is at 1200 m nearby at its junction with the Tilia River. However, there remains an area of relatively undissected upland between the Lagaip and the Lai Rivers.

(c) Regional Strike of Structure and Topography

The pattern of major valleys in the area is accordant with the regional strike, which trends SE-NW in the south of the area, curves towards a north-south trend in its centre, and returns to an ESE-WNW direction in the northwest. The S-bend in the regional strike occurs in the Imbricate and Catenary Fold Zones, but the north-south trend is also apparent near the western margin of the Broadly Folded Belt, between Mt Giluwe and the Sirunki Grasslands.

Transverse valleys occur in all the structural zones. In part these are located along transverse faults, as are the Lai gorge between Mt Hagen and Nose Mountain and many transverse valleys in the Catenary Fold Zone.

However, karst processes also appear to have led to the formation of a number of transverse drainage sectors, particularly where the Andabare River flows underground through a limestone strike ridge north of Mt Rentoul, and possibly in narrow transverse valley reaches along the lower Wage and Erave Rivers.

(d) Volcanic Landforms

Although volcanic activity is now extinct, volcanic landforms dominate much of the landscape and three major and many minor eruption centres are recognised.

Mt Hagen, in the east, rises to about 3650 m. Its centre is strongly incised, but constructional slopes have survived intact in the south and east. Volcanic deposits rest on Tertiary greywacke sandstones at 1300 m in the Lai gorge, indicating that a deep depression existed here prior to the extrusion of basaltic and andesitic lava flows, in part scoriaceous, which filled it up to a level of 1700 m.

Mt Giluwe, a shield volcano hardly touched by erosion, rises 2300 m above its footslopes at 1800 m. Basaltic and andesitic lava flows here extend up to 80 km from the eruption centre along the valleys of the Mendi, Erave, Sugu, and Iaro Rivers. These strike valleys were also in existence before the extrusion of the lava tongues, which are now traversed by gorges 60-300 m deep.

Mt Rentoul, west of the Wage River, consists of several foci; the centres of activity have been destroyed by explosive eruptions and erosion, but the constructional slopes have survived intact on the flanks, except for the incision of canyons locally over 300 m deep. The slopes reach as far as 50 km towards the southeast where part of the north shore of Lake Kutubu is developed in volcanic material. Fault-scarps traverse the body of Mt Rentoul on its southern and eastern side, and movement has occurred here along the Augu Fault, as named by A.P.C. (1961), since the formation of the constructional slopes, with positive vertical displacement of the eastern block of up to 300 m locally. Backtilting of volcanic slopes has been noted north of Lake Kutubu.

Whether volcanic activity started in the Pliocene, as suggested by the volcanic origin of part of the Pliocene deposits of the Strickland Basin (A.P.C. 1961), or whether it is Pleistocene is not clear, and so it is not known for certain how old the buried relief is.

Mt Giluwe, and to a lesser extent Mt Hagen, carry fossil glacial landforms* which have been neither damaged by volcanic activity, nor covered by volcanic products. It seems that the activity of both volcanoes, and by inference—on the evidence of fluviatile erosion—of Mt Rentoul, ceased towards the end of the Pleistocene at the latest. Minor centres of eruption were active until a later date. Timber found in a fighting ditch west of Kaimbia, and covered by 1 m of partly weathered volcanic ash attributed to nearby ash cones to the north and southwest, was dated by radiocarbon as 1580 ± 50 A.D. or 1450 ± 50 A.D. (GRN 3229), indicating that ash deposition persisted into very recent times.

Three horizons of volcanic ash, each several centimetres thick, were in several localities noted in the uppermost metre of the peat in the Ialibu Basin, southeast of Mt Giluwe. These layers, ascribed to a line of foci marked by ash cones and lava domes in the north of the basin (Rickwood 1955), suggest that deposition of ash recurred into the Recent period.

Lava flows cover the central portion of two high intramontane basins northwest of Mt Giluwe. The Sugarloaf Plateau, with a basin altitude of 3050-3350 m, received this cover from many domes, the highest of which, situated in the volcanic cone of Mt Sugarloaf, attains 3800 m. The Yobobos Grasslands, NNW of Mt Sugarloaf, received their lava cover from an ellipse-shaped depression in which Lake Lauo is located. The surface of the volcanic fill here attains 2900 m in the south and 2500 m in the north.

Virtually the entire area was covered by a blanket of volcanic ash. More than 12 m were noted in the Tsak valley, and up to 6 m occur locally in the Sirunki Grasslands. The cover thins west of the Lagaip River, and none was noted in the Porgera area. The Andabare Plain has an ash cover along its margin, and the

---

* A paper dealing with the subject was read to the ANZAAS Symposium on glaciation and periglaciation in the southwest Pacific, Canberra, January 1964. Since it is being prepared for publication, little attention will be paid in this essay to these landforms.

limestone topography in the south has a patchy, but sometimes appreciable ash cover, part of it redeposited after removal from the predominantly steep bounding slopes. Thick ash deposits also occur on the piedmont slopes of the volcanoes. Such an extensive ash cover must belong to the major centres of eruption. Its survival on crests and on the steeper slopes, where it is generally in transit, would indicate a rather sluggish rate of slope destruction, given the tentative date of cessation of activity of the major volcanic centres.

FACTORS AND PROCESSES IN ZONAL GEOMORPHOLOGY

It has been shown above that the distribution of major landscape types is determined by the stratigraphic and tectonic history, to which volcanic activity must be added. The detail of landscape sculpture, however, is related to the past and present dominance of characteristic climatic types at certain altitudes.

(a) *Climate*

Studies of the vegetation, landforms, and soils (Perry *et al.* 1965) have indicated considerable differences between climates at different altitudes. The dearth of weather stations in the area, as well as the short length of records, makes it difficult to assess these differences in quantitative terms.

(i) *Rainfall*

Mean annual rainfall at nine stations for the period 1954-60 ranged between 2167 mm at Laiagam and 4513 mm at Lake Kutubu. 'In general, the mean annual rainfall within the area is of the order of 100 in., but lesser amounts occur in sheltered localities and much higher amounts—probably up to 200 in. in some local areas—can be expected in the more exposed situations' (Fitzpatrick in Perry *et al.* 1965). Lesser monthly falls during the season of southeast winds (June-September) in the north of the area (Wabag, Laiagam) indicate some seasonality. Very little seasonal contrast occurs in the south.

Monthly averages of days with rain are high, 70-90 per cent of all days in the south, still as much as 50 per cent during the southeast season in the north. Periods of consecutive rainless days are short, and in the north a rainless period of ten days is uncommon. The high annual rainfall is 'not so much the result of any abnormal propensity for very heavy falls of limited duration as of the very frequent occurrence of falls up to 1·00 in. per day' (Fitzpatrick in Perry *et al.* 1965).

Some areal differentiation in seasonality is evident from the frequency of daily falls exceeding 50 mm, as well as from the monthly averages. At Wabag and Laiagam there is a marked concentration of days receiving totals greater than 50 mm into the October-May period, with only light daily falls during the low sun period or so-called southeast season. Also in the south, at Lake Kutubu, falls greater than 50 mm are more frequent during the so-called northwest season. At Mendi, on the other hand, daily totals greater than 50 mm occur more commonly during the southeast season.

During the admittedly short period of observation, no rainfalls have been noted of amounts which might be catastrophic for the development of lushly vegetated slopes. Only the lowest station, Lake Kutubu, has recorded daily rain-falls between 100 and 150 mm and none of the higher stations has recorded over 100 mm (contrast with Ruxton, Ch. 5. p. 86).

Stanley (1923) assumed that the decrease in rainfall with altitude, known from other equatorial regions (Tricart *et al.* 1962), applied to New Guinea. However, even today, quantitative information is lacking on changes in the amount of precipitation with altitude above 2150 m, that is, at the levels at which any decrease is to be expected, and there remains no basis whatever for Stanley's assumption. Indeed, Reiner (1960) doubted whether there was such a decrease on Mt Wilhelm, 160 km east of Mt Giluwe. However, if precipitation does in fact decrease with increasing altitude, this is offset by the greater effectiveness of precipitation due to lower air temperature. The morphogenetic system at higher altitudes is decidely moister than the one active at the present time at lower levels.

(ii) Temperature

TABLE 1

Temperature data in degrees Centigrade

Station	Lake Kutubu	Tari	Mendi	Wabag
Altitude	810 m	1600 m	1675 m	2000 m
Annual mean	23·0	18·7	18·0	16·7
Annual mean maximum	28·0	24·0	23·5	22·5
Annual mean minimum	18·0	13·3	12·8	11·0
Highest monthly mean	23·5	19·0	18·5	17·5
	(Oct.)	(Apr.)	(July)	(Mar.)
Lowest monthly mean	21·8	18·0	17·3	16·0
	(Aug.)	(July)	(July)	(July)
Lowest monthly mean minimum		12·5	12·0	10·0
		(Oct.)	(Oct.)	(July)
Highest maximum on record	37·0	33·7	34·5	29·0
(1954-60)	(Mar.)	(Dec.)	(Nov.)	(Sept.)
Lowest minimum on record	5·0	1·8	3·0	2·5
(1954-60)	(July)	(Sept.)	(Sept.)	(Sept.)

Temperature data for four stations are given in Table 1.

All the stations are in valleys or basins, though sited on locally higher ground. Frost damage to native crops has been noted in the vicinity of all stations with the exception of Lake Kutubu, though no temperatures below freezing point have been recorded at screen level. Occasional night frosts may occur at ground level in cold air pockets down to at least 1500 m.

Extrapolation of the recorded temperatures would suggest that no mountain top in this area reaches into 'periglacial' levels, and not even the highest mountain peak, Mt Giluwe, displays periglacial activity. Calculation of temperature on the basis of lapse rates entails some risk, especially in the case of maximum and minimum temperatures, but for want of observations above 2500 m such extra-polation has been employed here.

Fitzpatrick (in Perry *et al.* 1965) calculated an average lapse rate of approxi-mately 0·55° C. per 100 m on the basis of mean annual temperatures of all stations in or near the area in relation to their elevation. Extrapolation from the mean annual temperature of Wabag (16·7° C.) indicates that mean annual temperature would be at the freezing point at approximately 5000 m. The range from monthly mean temperatures to monthly mean minimum temperatures increases at higher altitudes as shown in Table 2.

The environmental lapse rate calculated on the basis of annual mean minimum temperatures is approximately 0·60° C. per 100 m. Extrapolation of annual mean minimum temperature indicates that night frosts would occur regularly at the screen level at approximately 3800 m.

However, the environmental lapse rates computed on the basis of mean monthly minimum temperatures for the period June to October, when the mean monthly temperatures are below the annual means of the stations, are of the order of 0·61-0·65° C. per 100 m. Using this rate, calculation suggests that night frosts may occur regularly at screen level at 3500 to 3600 m in this period.

TABLE 2

Range between monthly mean and monthly mean minimum temperature in degrees Centigrade

Station	Altitude	Range for the year	Mean	Range June-Oct.	Mean
Wabag	2000 m	5·4-6·4	5·8	5·7-6·2	5·9
Mendi	1675 m	4·8-5·8	5·4	4·8-5·7	5·2
Tari	1600 m	4·8-5·9	5·3	4·8-5·9	5·3
Lake Kutubu	810 m	4·1-5·8	5·1	4·1-5·6	4·8

Cook (1958) has questioned the validity of the assumption that daily frost cycles are an important morphogenetic agent in the periglacial environment. The absence of active frost-shattering on the highest mountain in the area tends to support Cook's hypothesis that annual frost cycles are the responsible agent. The annual range of mean daily temperatures is much smaller than the daily temperature range at any altitude in the low latitudes. Annual frost cycles of sufficient duration to permit penetration of frost into rock and soil can occur only at much higher altitudes. Monthly mean temperatures, rather than monthly mean minimum temperatures, need to approach the freezing point. This would happen at about 4500 m during October. During this month environmental lapse rates calculated from monthly mean temperatures are larger than those found for any other month of the June-October period.

The values calculated for this area are consistent with the estimated altitude of 4500 m for the present snowline at Juliana Peak, in the Star Mountains (Verstappen 1960), and with the calculated altitude of 4700 m for the theoretical snowline above Mt Wilhelm (Reiner 1960).

With the small annual temperature ranges of low latitudes, the altitude at which an annual frost cycle can be established will lie only little below that at which mean monthly minima of all months are below freezing point, and hence permanent frost conditions will prevail. For this reason it can be inferred that the periglacial zone on high mountains of low latitudes will be of lesser vertical extent than on mountains in the temperate zone.

Though true periglacial conditions do not occur in the area at the present time, occasional night frosts at low elevations nevertheless have important effects on the vegetation; in particular they induce alpine grasslands, with important morphogenetic consequences through slope instability.

(b) *Weathering*

Chemical and associated biological processes are the most important weathering agents throughout the area between 800 m at Lake Kutubu and 4100 m on Mt Giluwe. Observed depths of weathering penetration are less than those reported from other humid tropical areas, but it was impossible to arrive at maximum depths for want of exposures. Depths of not less than 24 m were noted in ash-covered andesitic lavas exposed in the Anga gorge southeast of Mendi at approximately 1500 m; not less than 18 m in volcanic ash and tuffs at about 1850 m in the Tsak valley; not less than 9 m in tuffaceous sandstones at 2300 m east of Wabag; not less than 8 m in volcanic ash at 2600 m in the Sirunki Grasslands; a similar depth in andesitic lava under thin ash cover in the Yobobos Grasslands; not less than 9 m in exposures of tuffaceous sandstones at 3050 m on the Sugar-loaf plateau.

Weathering profiles of the corestone type have been observed on andesitic lava flows, and on tuffaceous and greywacke sandstone, siltstone and mudstone. In resistant rock the corestones are hard and of fresh appearance and are arranged according to joint patterns in the case of sandstone (Plate IIa), and according to irregular cooling-fracture patterns on lava flows. Core outlines were also observed in weak siltstone and mudstone, separated by poorly expressed joints, sometimes parallel and sometimes irregular. The cores are of fresh unweathered appearance, calcareous, and of grey-blue colour, in contrast with the brown tints of the weathered surround, but have little coherence due to the fractured nature of the unweathered rock.

Silt and clay dominate the upper part of the weathering profiles. The lower part is characterised by undigested corestones bedded in a gritty matrix which often shows no disturbance of the original rock texture but which is quite plastic when manipulated. Colour, size, and shape of fragments and matrix may vary with rock type and with altitude, but the general profile appears similar to that commonly described for granite in the tropical zone (Wilhelmy 1958).

In general there is no completely unweathered rock exposed in the area, with the exception of sites of unusually vigorous stream incision, and of outcrops of limestone, presumed Mesozoic quartz-sandstone in the Lagaip valley, and lava above the Pleistocene glacial limit on Mt Giluwe.

Insufficient data are available to designate altitudinal zones of weathering. Exposures of the full profile down to unaltered bedrock are very rare. Profile morphology and chemical composition need to be studied in relation to altitude to evaluate relative rates of weathering with altitude.

Fitzpatrick (in Perry *et al.* 1965) is of the opinion that the high rainfalls and their rather even distribution over the year prevent depletion of soil moisture to the extent of inhibiting plant growth. He concluded, from estimates of evaporation which range from 8·4-14·0 cm per month at Lake Kutubu to 6·8-10·1 cm at Wabag, Mendi, and Tari, that plant growth could have been inhibited at the latter three stations on only a few occasions, and at Lake Kutubu only twice during the period 1954-60. Hence, ample moisture is available for chemical weathering processes.

There is no seasonal change in the weathering conditions at any particular location, but the weathering environment becomes decidedly moister with increasing altitude.

(c) *The Soil Profiles*

The assumed increase in precipitation effectiveness with altitude finds support in the vertical distribution of soil types as described by Rutherford and Haantjens (in Perry *et al.* 1965).

Reddish Clay Soils most commonly occur at altitudes below 1500 m; above this level they are limited to crests and slope convexities; below it they occur on steeper slopes as well. They were found on sedimentary rocks and on lava.

Humic Brown Clay Soils form the most common group and are developed on many kinds of parent rock including volcanic ash, clastic sedimentary rocks, limestone, and alluvium. They are found mainly between 1200 m and 2750 m, preferably on well drained sites.

Humic Olive Ash Soils are of common occurrence on poorly drained sites at lower levels, but are also found on steeper ash slopes in a very wet environment above ± 1500 m (5000 ft), generally between ± 2000 m (6500 ft) and ± 2750 m (9000 ft). These soils 'are considered to be poorly drained counterparts of the Humic Brown Clay Soils on ash' (Rutherford and Haantjens in Perry *et al.* 1965).

Peat soils include 'bog soils of depressions, seepage areas, and extensive swamps throughout the area', and alpine peat soils found on mountain summit areas above 2750 m.

Fine textured sedimentary rocks, such as calcareous shale and mudstone, and marl, show no zonal tendency in soil development. Slopes on such deposits are unstable and mass-wasting is rapid. Gleyed Plastic Heavy Clay Soils occur on these rock types at altitudes up to 3050 m, mainly on colluvial footslopes. These rocks were not encountered at higher altitudes.

(d) *Vegetation*

Lowland Rainforest, with three tree layers, its canopy generally at 30 m, and rather open near the forest floor, occurs generally below 1200 m (Robbins and Pullen in Perry *et al.* 1965) (Fig. 2.2). Lower Montane Rainforest, with two tree layers, canopy at 24 m, and dense vegetation on the forest floor, occupies the zone between 900 m and 3050 m, even on steep slopes. Large areas have been cleared for gardening and extensive man-made grasslands have replaced the forest. Natural Lower Montane Grasslands are found down to 2450 m and are thought to result from accumulation of cold air in valleys and basins with floors at this and higher levels. They overlap in altitude the Lower Montane Forest, man-made *Miscanthus* and *Imperata* Grasslands, and Montane Rainforest. The latter, with one tree layer, canopy at 9-12 m, and a forest floor covered with sprawling roots and a carpet of mosses, is found between 3050 m and 3800 m. Above this level Alpine Grasslands prevail.

(e) *Mechanisms of Weathering-Waste Removal*

Ground cover and rooting structure of the vegetation types have a large measure of control over slope processes and the resulting slope morphology.

Tree roots do not penetrate to great depths in the weathering profiles of the area, but generally spread parallel to the surface because of the generally saturated conditions of the weathering profiles. The greater depth of intense weathering penetration in comparison with regions exposed to temperate conditions and the destruction of the coherence of the rock substratum weaken the attachment of the weathered layer to the underlying rock. Roots give a measure of coherence to the upper part of the weathering debris, and it seems that the stronger roots under forest bind and stabilize the layer of weathered waste more effectively than under grassland, where individual roots are less strong and where root penetration may be less.

Slope failure appears to occur more readily under grassland than under forest at altitudes above 2450 m, where the boundary between Lower Montane Forest and Natural Lower Montane Grasslands in basins and valleys forms a most important morphogenetic boundary as well. At lower altitudes, where man-made grasslands are widely distributed, variation in slope stability is not apparent.

Slopes under forest are well protected against the direct erosive effects of high rainfalls, more particularly at higher altitudes, where in contrast to the less developed, but apparently adequately protective ground layer of herbs, vines, and shrubs of the Lowland Rainforest, a layer of roots, forest litter, dead trees and branches, covered by mosses and interspersed with herbs, shrubs and ferns, often completely masks the surface of the soil. The latter was noted even on slopes up to 40°. A carpet of mosses often covers the ground surface completely in the Montane Rainforest.

Clearly, erosion of the soil surface by rainsplash and sheetflow does not operate in this environment. The dense vegetation on the forest floor minimises runoff concentration and gullying and promotes infiltration. Morphogenetic effects of high rainfall on these slopes are limited to chemical weathering, removal in solution, and lubrication of mass movement. Grass vegetation appears to give similarly adequate protection. Below 3050 m it covers the ground with a dense carpet. Above that level one perceives the surface of the soil between hummocks, but no gullying or sheet-erosion is apparent and it seems that the peat carpet on the soil adequately protects it against both.

Weathering waste is removed by slumps, rotational slips, mudflows, and perhaps by creep from forested sites and from sites under man-made grasslands below 2450 m. The steeper slopes undergo cycles of weathering preparation and waste removal, and various stages of such cycles may be active concurrently, even on a small slope segment (Tricart *et al.* 1962). Weathered debris is deposited either on the slopes themselves, wherever more firmly rooted vegetation may inhibit downslope progress of slump lobes and mudflows, or on footslopes or floodplains, or in the stream bed itself when the previous two are missing. Mass movement, though most conspicuous on the steep ridge and mountain slopes, also occurs on footslopes down to slope angles of 3-5°. It is not clear how evacuation is achieved from footslope sectors of lesser declivity in the forested zone, but pronounced creep and perhaps flow occur on equivalent slopes under natural grasslands.

Mountain and ridge slopes are generally hummocky, with slump alcoves and niches alternating with debris lobes. Successions of buried soil profiles, seen often where roadcuts traverse slope re-entrants (Plate IIb), bear witness to the alternation of stability and instability of the weathering waste at such sites. It is thought that this alternation is characteristic of present conditions. The normal ranges of meteorological conditions and perhaps earth tremors are thought to trigger movement of weathering waste. Downward progression of the weathering front (Mabbutt 1961) seems to increase instability at any one site. It eventually overcomes the cohesive effects of vegetation roots on the weathering waste, and slope failure ensues.

Slope failure generally involves the removal of the upper, finely comminuted horizons of the weathering profile on steep mountain and ridge slopes, but also reaches down into the zone where corestones or angular rock fragments are found. If, on removal from the weathering site, such waste masses are placed directly into the stream channels a supply of coarse, undigested debris is added to them, together with the silt and clay that dominate the upper part of the weathering profile.

MORPHOCLIMATIC ZONES

(a) *Lower Montane Forest Zone*

This zone extends from 800 m or less to 3000 m. The general landscape model on the tuffaceous sandstone, siltstone and Tertiary volcanic agglomerate is one of intense dissection, usually with narrow-crested mountain and hill ridges, and of varying local relief (90-900 m). Ridge slopes are steep (25-35°) and, though generally hummocky in detail, nearly straight (Plate IVa). The steepest ridge slopes occur in re-entrants, where slopes above 40° are commonly found. Valley heads are often of a concave embayment type. Footslopes are concave, usually 3-17°. Though less hummocky than the slopes above, they are seldom smooth in their upper sectors; the lower sectors, however, are generally more even. Narrow floodplains occur along the stream channels of higher order, but often the stream channel is located at the intersection of the steep valley slopes, and concave footslopes are then only developed in slope re-entrants. The V-shaped valley is widely distributed in this humid tropical area (cf. Louis (1961) in conflict with the view expressed by Büdel (1957)).

The model is found on either side of the Lai valley and in the Sau valley. Subtle adjustment of first-order valley and spur patterns to structure was often noted, such as the chevron spurs frequently found in areas where thin beds of varying resistance are intercalated. This adjustment is a reflection of different rates of weathering penetration as much as of drainage incision, in that first-order valleys may develop from slump alcoves and niches.

In the Kagua valley and somewhat to the north of it, this landscape model occurs next to landscapes of hill and low mountain ridges on tuffaceous sandstone in which colluvial footslopes and embayments occupy larger areas than the steep ridge slopes.

The gently sloping constructional surfaces surrounding Mt Hagen, Mt Giluwe, and Mt Rentoul have a somewhat different arrangement of elements. Parallel dissection has carved elongate segments from these slopes, leaving smooth ridge crests and shallow valleys with bounding slopes generally lined with slump alcoves. Concave footslopes below directly lead to the stream channels.

Between the deep gorges, the piedmont surfaces of the volcanoes, usually sloping less than 4°, have thick ash covers over lava flows. They are generally traversed by widely spaced stream channels, usually not incised more than 60 m, with valley sides showing the same sequence of slope segments as described for sandstone. The steep and nearly rectilinear upper slope sectors contain many amphitheatral slump niches and lead via colluvial footslopes to the valley floors, which may be up to 1000 m wide and which usually contain floodplains. The interfluves are dissected by slumping and it seems that depth of weathering controls the depth to which such slumps can 'incise'. Though slumping of the steep valley sides is the dominant process achieving their retreat, few slump lobes are to be found in front of them. The steepness of valley sides apparently does not vary with their width; hence slopes waste back, rather than downwards, both in volcanic terrain and in areas of arenaceous and argillaceous rocks. Bakker's hypothesis (1957a, b) that backwasting and pedimentation are not limited to the more arid parts of the tropical zone appears to find support in the area studied.

Within forested areas on sandstone, siltstone, and volcanic rocks in this morphoclimatic zone the ridge and mountain slopes generally increase in hummockiness upwards. Studies of the soils and forest vegetation indicate that there are strong altitudinal contrasts within the zone, but no morphogenetic subdivision can as yet be made. Accordingly, the whole vertical section is interpreted as one morphoclimatic zone, in which, however, the rate of movement of slope waste increases with altitude.

(b) *A Possible Montane Forest Zone*

Summit areas above 3000 m, when covered with montane rainforest, can be distinguished from the Lower Montane Forest Zone in that dissection is far less advanced or is entirely absent. The central area of the Lai Syncline (Nose Mountain) and the country around Mt Haddon are examples. Both areas are situated on gently inclined strata, and structural rather than climatic factors could explain the absence of strongly incised valleys, since adjacent areas under natural grassland show a similar lack of dissection. This situation resembles that in the Venezuelan Andes (Tricart *et al.* 1962).

On strongly inclined structures, ridge crests above 3000 m in the western part of the area are wider than those at lower altitudes. Under Pleistocene climates a morphogenetic system dominated by mass movement and colluviation is thought to have been established even below 3000 m, and the bevelled crest forms of this zone could have been fashioned at that time. On the basis of reconnaissance data it cannot be determined whether the country above that level, covered by montane forest, owes its different forms to changes of climate with time and with altitude, or to climatic differences with altitude alone, and thus constitutes a morphoclimatic zone, or whether the contrasts are azonal in the sense that the upland levels on these gently inclined strata approximate to primary tectonic relief.

(c) *Natural Grassland Zone*

Clear morphogenetic boundaries exist between areas covered by forest and those covered by natural grassland. The grassland environment is found above 3350 m on convex relief, and extends down to 2450 m in valleys and basins, where it is intermingled with the forest zones, for cold air drainage and frost pockets may depress the treeline as much as 900 m, leaving valley slopes forested.

The removal of weathering waste from steeper slopes under grassland appears to be similar to that described for the forested zones, for the ground is well protected by the grass cover, and neither gullying nor sheet erosion was observed. Slump niches and alcoves formed by rotational slips tend to be concentrated near the base of the slope, whereas those occurring higher up are in valley heads. Niches situated on the sides of slope salients and spurs usually end with an abrupt concave break of slope at the slope foot; in contrast, niches in valley heads pass with smooth concave sectors into the footslopes or connect with them via gently stepped valley floors.

The first-order valleys are embayments in the ridges and generally have wide, level or concave floors, with slopes varying from 3° to 10°. Auger holes here encountered neither fluviatile deposits nor well developed soil, but usually a chaotic mixture of weathering loams and partly decayed organic material. Stream channels are absent and surface drainage is dispersed. Water content is high and peat bogs occur locally on slopes up to 7° (Plate IVb).

Second-order valleys, with similar wide floors, may contain channels, but these are often partly obscured by overhanging banks and vegetation, and are usually less than 1·5 m wide. Fluviatile deposits are not generally found on the valley floor, the entire width being occupied by colluvial aprons sloping up to 5°. Although generally smooth, these surfaces are more hummocky in front of slump alcoves. Auger holes in these aprons generally revealed material with high moisture content similar to that found in first-order valleys.

Floodplains were noted along the higher-order streams in basins and valleys, and fluviatile deposits were here encountered in auger holes close to the channels, with peat occupying the backswamp. Gravel and pebble-size material, if at all present in the stream, is generally well weathered, although limestone debris forms an understandable exception.

The absence of channels in first-order valleys, the apparent difficulty of maintaining proper channels in second-order valleys, and the chaotic mixture of weathering debris and peat in colluvial aprons and valley floors, suggest that waste removed from steeper slopes creeps or flows over the aprons and through the lower-order valleys towards the main drainage lines. The generally high water content of the material appears to maintain near-liquid conditions in it. The meandering higher-order channels, which generally traverse floodplains, locally have their banks in colluvial aprons, and weathering debris is apparently removed from the local landscape through bank erosion by these streams. Roughly circular scour pools on the outer side of angular bends in the channels of the upper Andabare River and some of its tributaries are an example of this process.

This association of forms is widely distributed in the high country of the Broadly Folded Zone between the Lagaip and the Lai Rivers, and in the Catenary Fold Zone, where bevelled spurs frequently carry topogenous bogs on slopes up to 9°, unusually steep in comparison with temperate latitudes. Large tracts of the rolling surfaces of the high southern sector of the Sugarloaf Plateau, above 3350 m, are covered by these bogs. Though valleys up to 30 m deep are present here, there are virtually no stream channels on the floors, which are concave in cross-section in higher as well as in lower-order valleys. Slopes generally do not exceed 15°, and the slump-steepened spurs so typical of basin grasslands are not in evidence. The northeastern part of the Sugarloaf Plateau is traversed by wide valleys up to 90 m deep, and stream channels here occur in second, as well as in higher-order valleys, and slopes on spurs over-steepened by stream trimming may attain over 40°. This part of the plateau is on average 300 m lower than the southern one, and contrast between the two would suggest that a solifluction-dominated morphogenetic system was established in existing valleys in the northern sector.

(d) *Pleistocene Glacial Zone*

Above 3000 m, the gently sloping summit plateau of Mt Giluwe, though covered by natural grassland, has solifluction forms only in a narrow belt just above the treeline; deep weathering of the volcanic deposits (more than 6 m) is still found here, and the valleys, generally not more than 30 m deep, are lined with colluvial aprons and bounded by slopes over-steepened through slumping. However, in contrast to the Sugarloaf Plateau, Mt Giluwe was generally glaciated down to 3000 m and weathering waste was swept from the summit area (Plate IIIa).

All slopes less than 45° are covered with a dense carpet of grass, up to the level of the highest peak, and the constructional glacial landforms have been beautifully preserved. Streams have not incised themselves into the glacial topography, with the exception of regressive incision in catenary valley floors near the lower margin of the glaciated summit area. Screes occur commonly above 3600 m and locally below that level, but well developed peat soils up to 30 cm thick indicate that these are now stabilized. 'Macro-gelifraction' (Tricart *et al.* 1962) does not now occur below 4100 m, the height of the western peak of Mt Giluwe; 'micro-geli-fraction', if it occurs, is restricted to levels above 3800 m. Chemical weathering is the sole rock-destroying process active below 3800 m and perhaps for some distance above it, but it has made little progress, for the alpine peat soils which cover all country sloping less than 45° rest directly on polished glacial rock, glacial and glacifluvial deposits, and periglacial scree. Studies of these soils (Rutherford 1964) reveal that chemical alteration is less advanced than in other areas of comparable altitude which were not glaciated, for instance the content of feldspars was found to be high except in the clay fraction of the surface soil. Glacial deposits, usually found within 30 cm of the surface if present, also have high content of unaltered feldspars.

Lack of weathering penetration inhibits slumping on steeper slopes and solifluction on gently inclined surfaces. Absence of stream incision, ascribed to lack of debris through stabilization of the slopes by the vegetation and peat carpet, has further favoured preservation of the glacial and periglacial landforms. The binding effect of root systems seems sufficient to stabilize the steeper slopes of depositional glacial forms. Slumping and solifluction will not begin until weathering has gone on for a much longer time than has elapsed since deglaciation.

This distinctive morphoclimatic zone produced by Pleistocene glaciation is also found on Mt Hagen, where it extends down to 3350 m only, because of somewhat less favourable morphology for glaciation.

(e) *Zonal Forms on Limestone*

Vertical zonation of karst landforms has been discussed for Australian New Guinea (Jennings and Bik 1962) and two of the three levels distinguished appertain to this area, although their altitudinal limits have not been precisely defined. Mapping of the limestone terrain has shown that, in addition to altitudinal climatic gradients, variations in structure and lithology cause important differences in landforms. Verstappen (1964) concluded from studies of the Star Mountains that the physical characteristics of limestones are an important determinant in karst morphology.

PROBLEMS OF THE INTRAMONTANE PLAINS

Intramontane plains are found adjacent to deeply incised V-shaped valleys in this part of the New Guinea Highlands (Plate IIIb). These plains are generally strike-aligned and the most conspicuous of them, the Andabare Plain (2525 m), the Kandep Plain (2225 m), and the Wasuma-Kagua Plain (1500 m), contain wide central alluvial flats and rather short footslopes, with concave surfaces sloping between 1° and 3°, abutting against steep valley sides between 25° and 35°. They are generally less than 3 km wide but locally attain 8 km. Superficially they resemble the 'hill-bordered saucer-shaped valleys' *(Flachmuldentäler mit Rahmenhöhen)* described by Louis (1964). The diagnostic features of such landforms are held by Louis (1961) and Büdel (1957, 1963) to be their essentially erosional nature on weathered bedrock, although fine-textured alluviation may occur along larger rivers, and their concave cross-profiles with marginal 'ramp-slopes' eroded by sheetwash.

Whether the plains are mainly erosional could not be determined. In the central alluvial portions augering was only carried out to 2 m and encountered alluvium solely. In the Kandep Plain the ubiquitous volcanic ash made it difficult to determine whether the gentle footslope zone was a degradation surface in a weathering profile. Auger holes in the footslopes of the Wasuma-Kagua Plain north of Kagua indicated the presence of weathered country rock, but it could not be determined whether this was *in situ*.

Sizeable levees accompany some river channels in the Wasuma-Kagua Plain, where fluviatile deposition prevails in the centre, with peat growth occurring but not dominating in the backswamps. In the alluvial flats of the Ka River in the Kandep Plain, clastic deposition is found close to the river channels but peat accumulation prevails elsewhere and clearly more than keeps pace with alluvial deposition in that the surface of the plain rises gently away from the river (Jennings 1963).

In the Andabare Plain, and in particular its extensions along tributary strike

IVa *V-shaped valleys of the Ambun River and its tributaries. Valley floors here are at approximately 2300 m and ridge crests at 2900 m.*

IVb *Slump-steepened spur margins alternate with short footslopes on which creep and solifluction are active in a tributary embayment of the upper Andabare valley at about 2750 m. In the flat valley floor are the levee-fringed tributary channel and extensive peaty back-plains.*

valleys, where the footslopes often abut against the stream channels, the former are certainly slopes of transport of weathering waste. However, sheetwash, postulated by Louis as the transporting agent, does not operate on the well vegetated slopes in the area of study. In fact the mechanism of waste transport across gentle footslopes at these altitudes is not at all clear, and the subject deserves detailed research, especially to determine whether transport occurs at all at present. If it does occur, as it is known to do above 2500 m, these footslopes are active surfaces of 'ramp-slope' nature. If transport does not now occur below this level, could such surfaces be inherited features resulting from Pleistocene lowering of the morphoclimatic zones? In any event it seems that these intramontane plains, although resembling 'hill-bordered saucer-shaped valleys', have formed outside the climatic range of 500-1000 mm of rainfall postulated by Louis (1964).

The three larger plains described, as well as many smaller ones, are separated by stream sections with rapids and falls from plain sections at lower altitudes, or from sections in which more graded stream conditions prevail. The Wasuma-Kagua Plain itself consists of several plain sections at different altitudes, separated by sandstone strike ridges which are traversed with increased gradients by the stream. Movement along faults, and to some extent volcanic extrusions, have caused the majority of the steeper gradient sectors. The reconnaissance data do not indicate how far other stream profiles result from staged uplift or from zonal differentiation of landscape on a primary tectonic relief raised in a single movement shortly after sedimentation ceased. Gorge sections of very limited length incise these plains and the streams are generally only well equipped with abrasive tools in these gorge sectors, a condition which should favour the maintenance of a *Dauerjügendstadium* (permanent stage of youth) (Bakker and Müller 1957) in the longitudinal profiles.

The occurrence side by side of the V-shaped valley *(Kerbtal)* and the saucer-shaped valley *(Flachmuldental)* poses the question whether the dichotomy between temperate and tropical landscape models proposed by Büdel (1957) is indeed valid for the whole of the humid tropical zone, or whether it is limited to the lowland. Louis (1961) acknowledges this dichotomy only between the temperate zone and the seasonally humid tropical zone. Citing Behrmann (1917, 1924, 1927) for New Guinea, and Sapper (1935) for Guatemala, he excludes the fully humid tropical environment from Büdel's generalisation. Louis (1964) limits *'Rumpfflächen-bildung'*, as in the formation of his saucer-shaped valleys, to areas of the tropical zone with precipitation ranging between 500 and 1000 mm.

It has been stated above that slumps, rotational slips, and mudflows could supply undigested debris to stream channels (Tricart *et al.* 1962). Deposition of weathering waste below the niches on a mountain slope, on a gentle footslope, or in a slope re-entrant would permit further weathering. Material derived from the lower horizons of the weathering profile could thus be comminuted on the site of temporary deposition, and the supply of abrasive tools to stream channels would then be further restricted, depending on rock type. This prompts the hypothesis that vertical incision of streams in such an environment might be inhibited once footslopes have developed in originally V-shaped valleys in climatic conditions such as prevail in the New Guinea Highlands. Landslides, valley damming by volcanic extrusions, warping, and faulting, could all lead to inhibi-

E

tion of stream incision and to the alluviation of valley floors. Chemical weathering of waste carried out on to the alluvial plains, as well as of the stream deposits themselves, could still further deprive the stream of abrasive tools.

Climatic change, through its effect on the protective vegetation on the steep mountain slopes, could also have promoted valley alluviation in the New Guinea Highlands by modulating the supply of weathering waste.

Bedrock type, climatic variation with time, and tectonically or volcanically induced valley alluviation, deserve to be considered as well as the variations in annual precipitation proposed by Louis (1964) as the dominant control of '*Flachmuldentalbildung*'. Detailed study of weathering profiles and superficial deposits could provide answers to many of the questions posed in this essay.

REFERENCES

Australasian Petroleum Company Pty (A.P.C.) (1961). Geological results of petroleum exploration in Western Papua, 1937-1961. *J. geol. Soc. Aust.* 8: 1-13.

Bakker, J. P. (1957a). Quelques aspects du problème des sédiments corrélatifs en climat tropical humide. *Z. Geomorph.* (N.F.) 1: 1-43.

—— (1957b). Zür Granitverwitterung und Methodik der Inselbergforschung in Surinam. *Tag. Abh. dt. Geogr. Würzburg*: 122-31.

—— and Müller, H. J. (1957). Zweiphäsige Flussablagerungen und Zweiphäsenverwitterung in den Tropen unter besonderer Berücksichtigung von Surinam. *Lautensach Festschrift. Stuttg. geogr. Stud.* 69: 365-97.

Behrmann, W. (1917). *Der Sepik (Kaiserin-Augusta-Fluss) und sein Strömgebiet*. Mitt. dt. Schützgeb. Erghft 12.

—— (1924). *Das westliche Kaiser Wilhelms Land in Neuguinea*. Z. Ges. Erdk. Berl. Erghft 1.

—— (1927). Die Oberflächenformen in den feuchtwarmen Tropen. *Düsseldorfer geogr. Vortr. u. Erört.*, 3Teil., Morphol.d.Klimazonen, 4-9.

Büdel, J. (1957). Die Flächenbildung in den feuchten Tropen und die Rolle fossiler solcher Flächen in anderen Klimazonen. *Tag. Abh. dt. Geogr. Würzburg*: 89-121.

—— (1963). Klima-genetische Geomorphologie. *Geogr. Rdsch.* 15: 269-85.

Cook, F. A. (1958). Temperatures in permafrost at Resolute, N.W.T. *Geogrl Bull.* 12: 5-18.

Dow, D. B. (1961). The geology of the Sau River and environs, New Guinea. Aust. Bur. Min. Res. Geol. Geophys. Unpub. Rec. 1961/73.

Jennings, J. N. (1963). Floodplain lakes in the Ka Valley, Australian New Guinea. *Geogrl J.* 29: 187-90.

—— and Bik, M. J. (1962). Karst morphology in Australian New Guinea. *Nature, Lond.* 194: 1036-8.

Louis, H. (1961). *Allgemeine Geomorphologie*. Berlin.

—— (1964). Über Rumpflächen und Talbildung in den wechselfeuchten Tropen besonders nach Studien in Tanganyika. *Z. Geomorph.* 8: 43-70.

Mabbutt, J. A. (1961). 'Basal surface' or 'weathering front'. *Proc. Geol. Ass.* 72: 357-8.

Perry, R. A. *et al.* (1965). *General Report on Lands of the Wabag-Tari Area, Territory of Papua and New Guinea, 1960-1961*. CSIRO Aust. Land Res. Ser. No. 15.

Reiner, E. (1960). The glaciation of Mount Wilhelm, Australian New Guinea. *Geogrl Rev.* 50: 491-503.

Rickwood, F. K. (1954). The geology of the Western Highlands of New Guinea. *J. geol. Soc. Aust.* 2: 63-82.

Rutherford, G. K. (1964). The tropical alpine soils of Mt Giluwe, Australian New Guinea. *Can. Geogr.* 8: 27-33.

Sapper, K. (1935). *Geomorphologie der feuchten Tropen.* Geogr. Schr. 7. Leipzig.

Stanley, E. R. (1923). The salient geological features and natural resources of the New Guinea Territory. App. B. of *Report on Territory of New Guinea 1921-22,* Parliamentary Paper No. 18 of 1923, Commonwealth of Australia.

Tricart, J., Cailleux, A., and Raynal, R. (1962). *Les particularités de la morphogénèse dans les régions de montagnes.* Paris.

Verstappen, H. Th. (1960). Preliminary geomorphological results of the Star Mountains Expedition 1959, Central Netherlands New Guinea. *Tijdschr. Konk. ned. aardrijksk. Genoot.* 77: 305-11.

———— (1964). Karst morphology of the Star Mountains (Central New Guinea) and its relation to lithology and climate. *Z. Geomorph.* 8: 40-9.

Visser, W. A. and Hermes, J. J. (1962). *Geological results of the exploration for oil in Netherlands New Guinea.* Verh. K.N.G.M.G. Geol. Ser. 20.

Ward, H. J. (1949). A geological reconnaissance of the country between Mt Hagen and Mongureba, Central Highlands District, Mandated Territory of New Guinea. Aust. Bur. Min. Res. Geol. Geophys. Unpub. Rec. 1949/79.

Wilhelmy, H. (1958). *Klimamorphologie der Massengesteine.* Braunschweig.

3

Spectral Analysis of Meanders of some Australasian Rivers

J. G. SPEIGHT

INTRODUCTION

The channel pattern of a river may be analysed for various parameters, such as meander wavelength, that have been correlated with magnitude of flow. This raises the possibility that in future important data on water resources may be derivable directly from air photos instead of depending on long periods of careful hydrologic recording. As yet, however, the correlations have been insufficiently refined to have much practical value, being based on unsatisfactory methods of measurement.

This essay is concerned with an elementary application of the technique of power spectral analysis to the problem of meander wavelength, and presents the results of some pilot studies of relationships between spectrally-determined meander wavelengths and other geomorphological and hydrological parameters.

MEANDER WAVELENGTH

Interest in the apparent orderliness of the phenomenon of stream meandering has, during the past three decades, prompted several attempts to derive quantitative relations between meander form and either channel form or streamflow. Inglis (1949) first pointed out that the wavelength of a meander, as well as the width of the stream, tends to be proportional to the square root of the 'dominant discharge', that is, the discharge or flow that is most effective in modifying the stream channel. Leopold and Wolman (1957) collected more evidence pointing to a similar conclusion, namely that meander wavelength, λ, expressed in feet, was related to bank-full discharge, Q, in cubic feet per second, (widely held to provide an estimate of 'dominant discharge') by the relation:

$$\lambda = 36 \ Q^{0.5} \tag{1}$$

They also claimed that the relation between meander wavelength and bank-full width (w) in feet:

$$\lambda = 6.5 \ w^{1.1} \tag{2}$$

was even more consistent, leading them to postulate that in terms of mechanical

The author wishes to acknowledge the generous help of Professor E. J. Hannan of the Department of Statistics, Australian National University, who was responsible both for the initial suggestion of the spectral method and for the mathematics involved. After preliminary testing on the IBM 1620 of the A.N.U., analyses were computed at first on the IBM 7090 of the Weapons Research Establishment, Salisbury, South Australia, and later on the CSIRO C.D.C. 3600 at Canberra. A fortran programme for the C.D.C. 3600 was kindly written by Jane Speight, and is available on request from the Division of Land Research, CSIRO.

principles wavelength is more directly dependent on width than on discharge. The same authors (Leopold and Wolman 1960) later amended the wavelength-width relation to

$$\lambda = 10 \cdot 9 \ w^{1 \cdot 01} \tag{3}$$

and Dury (1963) assessed the relation of meander wavelength to bank-full discharge as

$$\lambda = 30 \ Q^{0 \cdot 5} \tag{4}$$

It is important to note, however, that the (logarithmic) standard deviation of data about the regression of equation (3) exceeds $0 \cdot 17$, that is to say, one-third of the estimates from the regression line would be in error by a factor equal to or greater than $1 \cdot 5$ (the antilog of $0 \cdot 17$). The scatter of data about regression lines for equations (1) and (4) is even worse.

Relations (3) and (4) have already been used by Dury in a number of studies on the problem of misfit streams (see particularly Dury 1958, 1964), in which he demonstrates that both the wavelength of present-day stream meanders and the much greater wavelength of meandering valleys are consistently related to catchment area on a regional scale. More utilitarian application of the equations, however, such as the prediction of flow from wavelength or vice versa, is precluded by their unreliability.

Current methods of measurement of meander wavelength are probably the most serious obstacle to progress in this field. Standard methods are (i) to choose a well developed sinusoidal meander and find twice the straight-line distance between successive points of inflection or (ii) to choose a meandering reach, measure all the straight-line distances between successive points of inflection and calculate the mean wavelength for the reach. As well as being unduly subjective, each method involves a dubious assumption: in the first case the well developed meander is assumed to be the dominant oscillation, in the second the variation between individual meander wavelengths is taken to be merely the expression of variability about a single modal value. The use of a straight-line measure is also suspect, for the water particles must move along the line of the channel, so that the cross-country distance between two points on the channel can have little physical relevance. In practice wavelengths measured along the channel correlate with width and discharge at least as well as straight-line wavelengths do (L. B. Leopold, personal communication), and the local presence of narrow meander necks does not then produce anomalously short meander wavelengths as it does with the straight-line method.

Precise and reliable analysis of meander wavelength demands consideration of the total oscillatory behaviour of a river reach. The technique used here consists of (i) measurement of direction of flow of the stream at closely spaced equal intervals along the channel, (ii) analysis of the resulting series for auto-correlation, and (iii) estimation of a spectrum of 'meander intensity' versus frequency of oscillation per unit of distance.

SPECTRAL ANALYSIS

On a map or air photograph of a river reach that is to be analysed a line is drawn to follow the estimated line of maximum flow of the stream, and points are marked on it at equal increments of distance $\triangle d$, of the order of twice the channel width. With the protractor of a drawing machine the direction of flow between every pair of adjacent points is measured in degrees relative to some arbitrary datum direction chosen to make all angles positive. This angle is x_d where $d = 1, 2, \ldots n$.

It is first necessary to find the average degree of agreement, or auto-correlation, between all pairs of angles spaced l increments apart for $l = 0, 1, 2, \ldots m - 1$, the value of m being limited in practice to less than one-fifth of that of n. Coefficients of auto-correlation $C_x(l)$ are calculated by:

$$C_x(l) = \frac{1}{n}\left[\left\{\sum_{s=1}^{n-l} x_s x_{s+l}\right\} - (n - l)\,\bar{x}^2\right] \tag{5}$$

On a correlogram, a graph of $C_x(l)$ versus l, a periodic oscillation tends to produce a regular ripple in the curve. This is likely, however, to be masked by non-periodic components and by random oscillations. To assess objectively the contributions to the total variance of flow-direction made by oscillations of specific wavelengths a type of Fourier transformation may be employed. This transformation does not produce results in terms of wavelengths directly, but in terms of equal-width bands of frequency of oscillation per unit distance. The 'meander intensity' $X(k)$ associated with each band of frequency k, where $k = 0, 1, 2, \ldots, m$ is estimated by:

$$X(k) = C_x(O) + \sum_{l=1}^{m-1}\left\{ C_x(l)\left(1 + \cos\frac{\pi l}{m}\right)\cos\frac{\pi k l}{m}\right\} \tag{6}$$

and the spectrum of $X(k)$ versus k constructed (cf. Blackman and Tukey 1958). The frequency band values k can be simply converted into frequencies ν, in the convenient unit of cycles per (ft $\times 10^5$) by the relation

$$\nu = \frac{k \times 10^5}{m \times 2 \triangle d} \text{ cycles/(ft} \times 10^5) \tag{7}$$

and into wavelengths in feet by

$$\lambda = \frac{10^5}{\nu}\text{ ft} \tag{8}$$

Examples of meander spectra are shown in Figure 3.1.

The spectral envelopes are characteristically multi-peaked, and to quantify the spectral peaks each peak has been assumed to have an approximately Gaussian form. This assumption has resulted in the 'explanation' of each spectrum by quite a small number of peaks with relatively little accompanying 'noise'. Each peak may be evaluated in terms of its peak intensity $X(p)$ in arbitrary units, and its peak frequency ν_p or wavelength λ_p.

THE ANGABUNGA STUDY

This technique was first applied (Speight 1965a) to a study of the Angabunga River, in central Papua, which has a long, unobstructed, rapidly changing, meandering course over broad alluvial plains (Figure 3.2). Although discharge information was minimal, a triple cover of air photos (1938, 1957, 1963) allowed investigation of the changes in meander behaviour with distance downstream and with time, not only during the period of record but also as indicated by ancient abandoned river courses.

Analyses were carried out on overlapping reaches of the river of length $d =$ 126,000 ft spaced at intervals of 31,500 ft downstream using a point spacing $\triangle d$ of 600 ft. The value of n ($n = d/\triangle d$) thus became 210 and the number of frequency-bands m was set at 40, giving a probable error of estimate of meander intensity of the order of $\pm$ 30 per cent. An independent set of analyses was made of the course from the mountain front to the sea on each of the three dates, and analyses were also carried out on several prior channels and on the course immediately upstream from the mountain front, where the river was clearly confined to a narrow gorge in bedrock.

The changes in the parameters of spectral peaks with distance downstream on a given date may be conveniently represented on the diagram shown in Figure

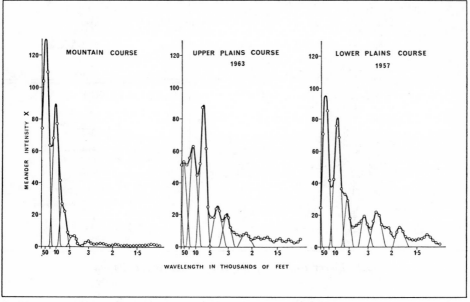

3.1   Typical meander spectra from the Angabunga River

3.3. The horizontal scale represents the distance from the mountain front, measured along the talweg, of the mid-point of any reach. Spectral peaks are shown at the appropriate wavelength λ by a symbol representing the peak intensity $X(p)$. Wavelengths of well formed individual meanders are also plotted on the figure for comparison. Similar diagrams were constructed for the several dates, allowing a number of important conclusions to be drawn:

(i) Most peaks were very stable in successive spectra, allowing considerable confidence in the reality of the peaks, some of which might otherwise have been classed as fortuitous oscillations or 'noise'.

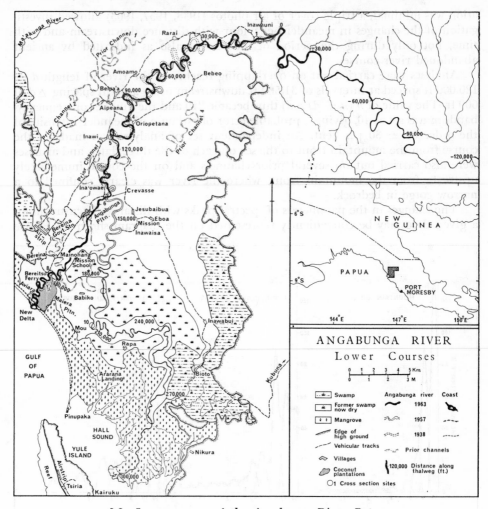

3.2 *Lower courses of the Angabunga River, Papua*

(ii) In general, there were three important long wavelength (or low-frequency) peaks dominating each spectrum. These were labelled A, B, and C, C being the shortest. Peak B was the most stable and most consistently intense of the three, whilst peak C commonly represented a wavelength likely to be chosen as 'typical' by subjective assessment. (Peak A was seldom properly resolved by the analysis.)

(iii) There was usually a sharp drop in meander intensity at wavelengths shorter than that of peak C. However, especially in deep, narrow sections of the river channel, minor peaks of short wavelength did occur, invariably influencing the subjective judgment of 'typical' meander wavelength.

(iv) The mountain course, which seemed devoid of meanders, appeared to have a meander spectrum very similar to those of reaches on the alluvial plain, indicating that the tendency to orderly, multiple-wavelength periodicity in the direction of flow of the stream was by no means suppressed by incision into bedrock.

(v) Peak wavelengths were more stable in the downstream direction than was channel width, and there was no simple relationship between the two.

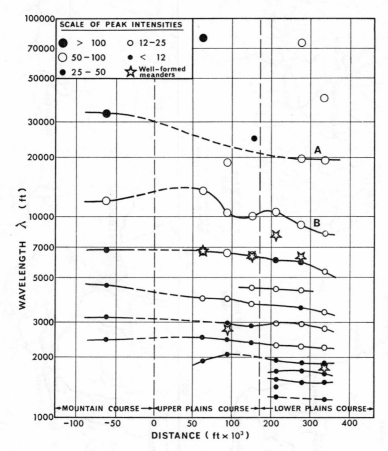

3.3 *Relation of spectral peaks of meander wavelength to downstream distance for the Angabunga River in 1938*

AUSTRALIAN RIVERS

In order to explore the general range of types of meander spectrum and to study the relation of spectrally determined meander wavelengths to measures of dominant discharge, analyses have been carried out on gauged reaches of a number of rivers in New South Wales and Victoria as shown on the map, Figure 3.4. Availability of flow records and of maps or air photos, and freedom from large tributaries were the only criteria used in choosing the reaches, which include a wide

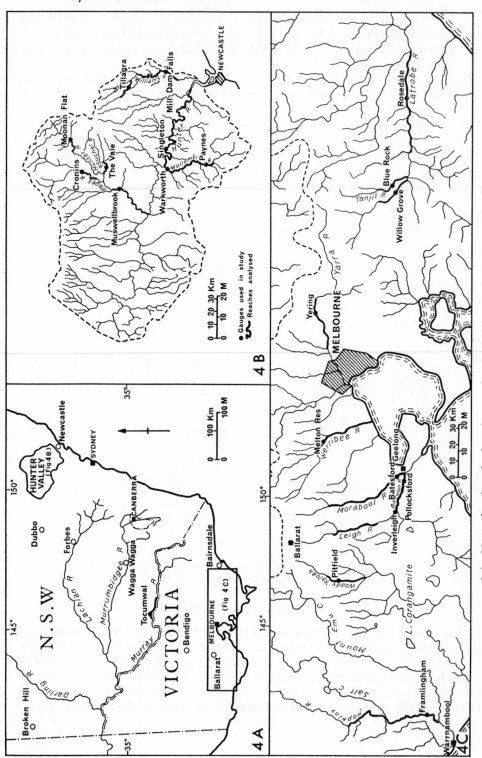

3.4 *Maps showing the location of the Australian river reaches analysed*

range of channel morphology from serpentine meanders to angular reaches deeply incised in bedrock.

In the spectral analysis programme provision was made for considering angles of a given sequence at intervals of p, where $p = 1, 2, \ldots 9$, to allow a broad range of wavelengths to be investigated. Shorter wavelengths analysed using every angle of the sequence can be referred to short reaches of the river, yielding detailed information on changes with distance downstream. Selection of angles representing flow direction between more widely spaced points by the use of higher values of p allows resolution of longer wavelengths, but these refer to longer reaches and yield less specific information. From the spectra obtained by the analysis the characteristics of dominant wavelength-peaks were abstracted as in the preceding study, and the peak parameters were plotted against downstream distance for each stream. Two of the conclusions of the Angabunga study were immediately confirmed, namely that peaks are relatively stable in successive spectra, and that 'non-meandering' reaches have orderly spectra that resemble those of contiguous freely meandering reaches.

From the plots of wavelength versus distance downstream the probable meander spectrum in the neighbourhood of the river gauge was estimated for comparison with measures of discharge.

RELATIONS OF WAVELENGTH TO DISCHARGE

For comparison of streamflow magnitude between different streams it is desirable to find a flow that approximates to the channel-forming dominant discharge. This discharge has been held to be closely related to bank-full flow (Wolman and Miller 1960) which has, in turn, been correlated with the most probable annual flood (Dury, Hails, and Robbie 1963), (i.e. a flow of recurrence interval of $1 \cdot 00$ years on the partial duration series or $1 \cdot 60$ years on the annual flood series) or with flows of recurrence of that order (Wolman and Leopold 1957; Dury 1961).

Published monthly maximum flows (Bibra and Mason 1964; N.S.W. Water Conservation and Irrigation Commission 1962) provided data for the estimation of partial-duration flood-frequency curves from which the discharge of the most probable annual flood may be read. Considerable adjustment and extrapolation was necessary to reduce the effects of non-coincidence of period of record (see Table 1). The adjusted figures, Q_{MPAF}, represent an estimate of the discharge of the most probable annual flood for the period 1912-50 based on the long-term records of a few of the streams. The relation of meander wavelength to most probable annual flood discharge Q_{MPAF} is shown in Figure 3.5. It is at once apparent that the simple regression

$$\lambda = A \, Q^B \tag{9}$$

suggested by previous workers to explain a single dominant meander wavelength need not be rejected as inapplicable to the multiple-wavelength case, but may be replaced by a series of relations

$$\lambda_1 = A_1 \, Q^{B1}$$
$$\lambda_2 = A_2 \, Q^{B2} \tag{10}$$
$$\lambda_3 = \text{etc}$$

where λ_1, λ_2, . . . constitute a series of preferred wavelengths dependent on a single meander-forming dominant discharge. The scatter of points about any such regression lines is considerable, however, and two considerations point to the desirability of a second approach. Firstly, as the author has previously suggested (Speight 1965b) the flows that modify a stream channel may be considerably more frequent than those that are responsible for maintaining the channel-floodplain boundary (bank-full flows). Secondly, much more reliable stage-discharge relations may be expected at ordinary flows than at the flood flows used in the analysis. The

TABLE 1

River Reach	Catchment sq. miles	Record	$Q_{10(M)}$* (ft³/sec)	Varia-bility $LVI_{(M)}$	Q_{MPAF}* (ft³/sec)
Hunter Valley					
Hunter River at Moonan Flat	290	1912-50	290	0·48	4000
Pages River at Cronins	400	1941-47	350	0·68	4500
Rouchel Brook at The Vale	155	1941-47	420	0·91	4900
Hunter River at Muswellbrook	1630	1912-50	1000	0·67	6400
Wollombi Brook at Paynes Crossing	375	1941-47	700	1·13	6500
Williams River at Tillagra	75	1941-47	420	0·70	6600
Hunter River at Singleton	6170	1912-50	2500	0·82	14700
Williams River at Mill Dam Falls	374	1941-47	1500	0·82	15000
Victoria					
Woady Yaloak River at Pitfield	125	1958-60 1918-33	38	0·67	1350
Moorabool River at Morrisons	225	1949-60	149	0·88	1350
Latrobe River at Willowgrove	224	1924-60	430	0·24	1350
Moorabool River at Batesford	430	1908-21 1946-48	224	1·10	1750
Werribee River at Melton Resr.	446	1917-60	207	0·59	2000
Hopkins River at Framlingham	2050	1956-60	215	0·95	2400
Tanjil River at Blue Rock	140	1925-55	375	0·27	2700
Leigh River at Inverleigh	340	1946-60	132	0·61	2800
Barwon River at Pollocksford	1200	1906-21	273	0·82	2800
Yarra River at Yering	825	1947-60	1590	0·38	3900
Latrobe River at Rosedale	1600	1936-60	1920	0·37	5100
Murray River at Tocumwal	10200	1908-60	16000	0·37	29000
Papua					
Angabunga River at Iaifa	840	1958-63	7500	0·27	13000

* Extrapolated to the period 1912-50.

use of monthly maximum figures precluded the possibility of using recurrence intervals appreciably shorter than one year on the flood frequency curves, so attention was turned to flow-duration analysis of monthly mean flows. Here the highest flows that could be assessed with any confidence were those equalled or exceeded as a monthly mean in 10 per cent of the months, $Q_{10(M)}$, adjusted to represent long-term values as in the case of Q_{MPAF}. The flow-duration curves also yielded values of Lane's variability index (Lane and Lei 1950) which, although limited by being based on monthly rather than daily flows, were adequate to indicate the relative variability of the streams considered.

The relations of meander wavelength to $Q_{10(M)}$ are indicated in Figure 3.6 which displays a pattern very similar to that of Figure 3.5. One may now note, however, that the alignment of points along postulated regression lines would be greatly improved by moving the points of streams of low variability (e.g. Latrobe,

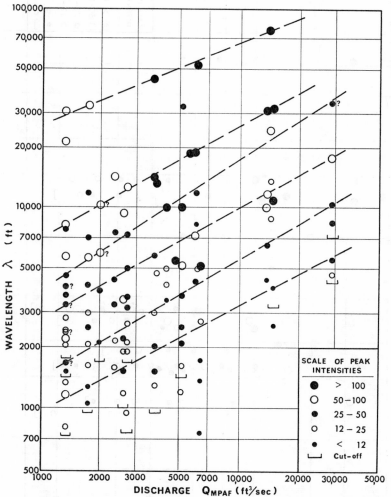

3.5 *Relation of spectral peaks of meander wavelength to estimated discharge of the most probable annual flood* (Q_{MPAF}) *of 21 Australasian river reaches. Cutoffs mark sharp drops in meander intensity.*

Yarra, Angabunga) to the left and those of high variability streams (e.g. Williams (M.D.F.), Wollombi, Barwon) to the right. Relative adjustments in these directions would follow from the selection of a less frequent flow on the flow-duration curve, so there is at least an indication that some flow less frequent than $Q_{10(M)}$ may control the meander pattern. Re-examination of Figure 3.5 yields sufficient evidence of the opposite tendency (streams of low variability plotting too far to the

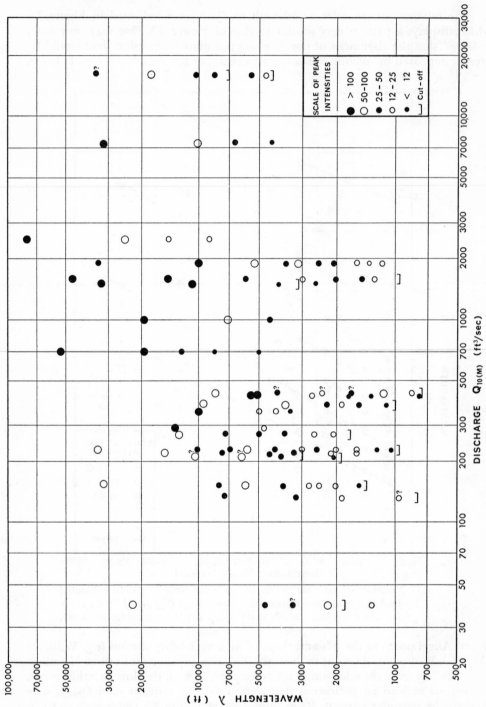

3.6   *Relation of spectral peaks of meander wavelength to* $Q_{10(M)}$, *the discharge equalled or exceeded as a monthly mean in 10% of the months*

left) to indicate that the frequency of meander forming dominant discharge may lie between $Q_{10(M)}$ and Q_{MPAF}. For the purpose of obtaining numerical relations until more precise data are analysed it has been arbitrarily assumed to fall in the neighbourhood of $\sqrt{Q_{10(M)}\,Q_{MPAF}}$.

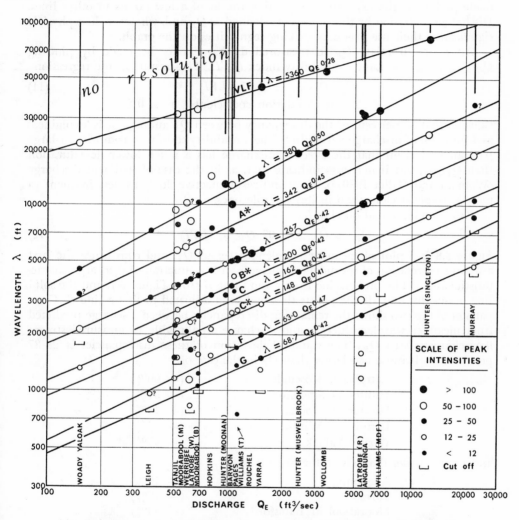

3.7   *Relation of spectral peaks of meander wavelength to a discharge* Q_E *approximating to the geometric mean of* $Q_{10(M)}$ *and* Q_{MPAF} *and adjusted to give the best fit of possible regression lines. Solid vertical lines indicate wavelengths not resolvable.*

In view of the gross uncertainties in the discharge figures above, compounded from errors in measurement in the field up to the use of the final geometric mean, there can be little quarrel with an experimental adjustment to either side of values of $\sqrt{Q_{10(M)} \, Q_{MPAF}}$ to investigate the best fit of the wavelength figures to possible multiple regression lines. The result of this exercise is displayed in Figure 3.7, in which the fit of points to the line *B*, which appeared to be the most consistent regression of all (being represented by a peak in every spectrum), has been made perfect at the expense of worsening the fit of a few points to other lines. Discharges arrived at by this process are defined as Q_E and, whatever their physical significance, their use produces striking regularities on the graph.

An effort to relate Q_E to measured discharge may be made by plotting $Q_E/Q_{10(M)}$ against Lane's variability index (*LVI*). This results in the regression

$$Q_E/Q_{10(M)} = 4\cdot07 \ (LVI)^{\,0\cdot826} \tag{11}$$
$$\text{with correlation coefficient} \quad r = 0\cdot8$$

showing that 65 per cent of the discrepancy between Q_E and $Q_{10(M)}$ is 'explained' as a function of discharge variability. The variability term may comprise in large part an indication that the effective discharge has a much lower flow-duration than $Q_{10(M)}$, but it may also indicate that, as in the case of sediment discharge (Wolman and Miller 1960, p. 56-60 and refs.) effective flows are less frequent in more variable streams than in less variable ones.

Re-arranging equation (11), let

$$Q_F = \hat{Q}_E = 4\cdot07 \ Q_{10(M)} \ (LVI)^{\,0\cdot826} \tag{12}$$

Figure 3.8 is a plot of meander wavelength versus Q_F, and constitutes the best available correlation of meander wavelength with a function of discharge characteristics alone. The broken line is regression line *B* from Figure 3.7, and the solid line passes through all the points that had been adjusted to lie on line *B*. Comparison of the two shows the remaining discrepancies between discharge predicted from meander wavelength, Q_E, and discharge attributable to measured stream flow characteristics Q_F. The standard deviation of these discrepancies is $\pm$ 27 per cent, Q_E being much larger than Q_F in the case of:

Latrobe at Rosedale	(+ 60%)
Hunter at Singleton	(+ 51%)
Hunter at Moonan Flat	(+ 48%)
Latrobe at Willowgrove	(+ 46%)
Woady Yaloak	(+ 35%)

and much smaller than Q_F in the case of:

Angabunga	(− 46%)
Yarra	(− 46%)
Moorabool at Batesford	(− 30%)

Although the nature of the relationships on Figure 3.7 allows some alternative plotting positions along the horizontal axis for a given river reach (Q_E = 13,200 ft ^{3}/sec for the Yarra, for instance), the above discrepancies could in no case be reduced by shifting the plot to an alternative position.

Since the discharge estimates may well include errors sufficiently large to account for the discrepancies, no attempt to account for them by factors other than discharge is likely to be profitable. Errors in estimation of meander wavelength probably do not exceed $\pm$ 5 per cent except in cases where the evidence

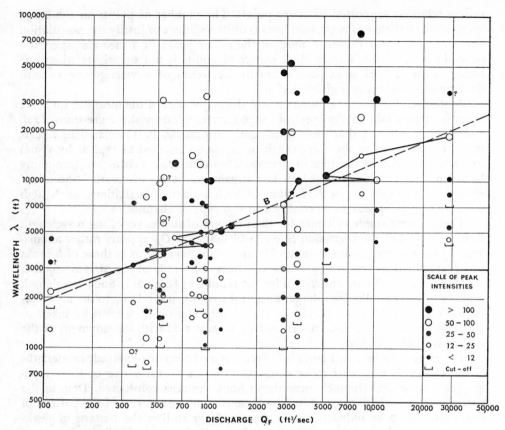

3.8 Relation of spectral peaks of meander wavelength to Q_F, an estimate of Q_E derived from a function of discharge characteristics alone

for an individual spectral peak has been obscure or conflicting.

To return to the examination of Figure 3.7, bearing in mind that numerical relationships are unlikely to stand in the light of more precise data, the following regression lines may be established by eye:

$$\lambda_{VLF} = 5360 \quad Q_E{}^{0.28} \qquad (VLF)$$
$$\lambda_A = 380 \quad Q_E{}^{0.50} \qquad (A)$$
$$\lambda_A{}^* = 342 \quad Q_E{}^{0.45} \qquad (A^*)$$
$$\lambda_B = 267 \quad Q_E{}^{0.42} \qquad (B)$$
$$\lambda_B{}^* = 200 \quad Q_E{}^{0.42} \qquad (B^*)$$
$$\lambda_C = 162 \quad Q_E{}^{0.42} \qquad (C)$$
$$\lambda_C{}^* = 148 \quad Q_E{}^{0.41} \qquad (C^*)$$
$$\lambda_F = 63 \cdot 0 \quad Q_E{}^{0.47} \qquad (F)$$
$$\lambda_H = 68 \cdot 7 \quad Q_E{}^{0.42} \qquad (H)$$

The designations *VLF* (Very Low Frequency), *A, B, C,* etc are those used in a previous paper (Speight 1965a), those with an asterisk being less consistent sub-

F

sidiary relations supported by fewer points. The number of points on the figure 'explained' by these few regression lines is quite sufficient to justify the postulation that the wavelength values of most of the major peaks of a meander spectrum depend on Q_E alone. The residual scatter of points is not surprising when one considers the lack of strict parallelism in the trends of wavelength peaks with distance downstream in a given stream.

As suggested by the Angabunga study, the major part of the meander intensity of most streams falls in the spectral range characterised by the regressions *A, B,* and *C,* peak *B* being that most consistently appearing. Peaks related to line *C* tend to correspond to the wavelength of meanders selected as typical by visual inspection, except in the case of narrow, deep channels, such as are commonly bounded by levees and related to low stream gradients, where the 'meanders' correspond to peaks in the *F-H* range of high-frequency oscillations. Such high frequency peaks appear to be confined to this type of channel.

There is now ample evidence for the presence of stable, very long wavelength oscillations (*VLF*) the regression line of which against Q_E appears rather anomalous. Their wavelengths are between five and ten times as great as those of *B*-peaks and represent distances several hundred times the width of the stream channel (e.g. 14 km for the Yarra, and 24 km for the Hunter at Singleton). Such wavelength peaks may well be relict from larger ancestral streams, and related to the meandering valleys of G. H. Dury (1964). In their interpretation, care must be taken to allow for a possible increase in stream length associated with development of the shorter wavelength peaks.

The regression lines of Figure 3.7 represent a pattern of preferred wavelengths of oscillation that appears to be common to streams irrespective of their topographic setting and channel form throughout the area considered. Despite the great range of variability exhibited by these streams, the spread of the pattern of peaks appears to be independent of degree of variability: the pattern of peaks moves as a whole as a function of dominant discharge. It is likely that some distortion of the general pattern results from rock structures that impress an angular pattern on the stream course resulting in a tendency towards the series:

$$\lambda, \frac{\lambda}{3}, \frac{\lambda}{5}, \frac{\lambda}{7}, \ldots$$

The meander pattern of a stream depends not only on the wavelengths, but also on the relative intensities of spectral peaks, and there is as yet no hint of an explanation of why, in a given stream, certain preferred wavelengths are especially prominent while others are completely elided. Until the factors influencing relative intensity of preferred peaks are isolated one cannot even identify which peak of the spectrum is which without an independent estimate of dominant discharge, so that the goal of predicting discharge from wavelength is still not attained.

CONCLUSION

The use of the technique of power spectral analysis in the study of river meandering has revealed that, rather than having a single ill-defined dominant meander wavelengh, each stream is characterised by multiple wavelengths of lateral oscillation, related to each other and to stream flow in a remarkably orderly fashion. The precise relationships between wavelength on the one hand and flow, channel shape, gradient, and bed and bank material on the other have yet to be investigated, but it is clear that the new data should be carefully assessed in relation to theories of meander formation and probably also to the principles of fluid flow in open channels.

REFERENCES

Bibra, E. E., and Mason, R. G. (1964). *Victorian River Gauging to 1960.* State Rivers and Water Supply Commission of Victoria, Melbourne.

Blackman, R. B., and Tukey, J. W. (1958). *The Measurement of Power Spectra,* New York.

Dury, G. H. (1958). Tests of a General Theory of Misfit Streams. *Inst. Brit. Geographers Publ. No.* 25, pp. 105-18.

——— (1961). Bankfull discharge: an example of its statistical relationships. *Int. Assoc. scient. Hydrol. Publ.* 6 (3) : 48-55.

——— (1963). Prior stream deposition. *Aust. J. Sci.* 25 (7) : 315-16.

——— (1964). *Principles of Underfit Streams.* U.S. Geol. Surv. Prof. Pap. 452-A.

———, Hails, J. R., and Robbie, M. B. (1963). Bankfull discharge and the magnitude-frequency series. *Aust. J. Sci.* 26 (4) : 123-4.

Inglis, C. C. (1949). *The Behaviour and Control of Rivers and Canals.* Central Water-power Irrigation and Navigation Research Station, Poona, India.

Lane, E. W., and Lei, Kai (1950). Stream flow variability. *Trans. Am. Soc. civ. Engrs.* 115: 1084-134.

Leopold, L. B. and Wolman, M. G. (1957). *River Channel Patterns: Braided, Meandering and Straight.* U.S. Geol. Surv. Prof. Pap. 282-B.

——— and ——— (1960). River meanders. *Bull. Geol. Soc. Am.* 71: 769-94.

N.S.W. Water Conservation and Irrigation Commission (1962). *Surface Water Supply of New South Wales: Stream Flow Records.* Vol. 3, Sydney.

Speight, J. G. (1965a). Meander spectra of the Angabunga River. *J. Hydrol.* 3: 1-15.

——— (1965b). Flow and channel characteristics of the Angabunga River, Papua. *J. Hydrol.* 3: 16-36.

Wolman, M. G., and Leopold, L. B. (1957). *River Flood Plains: Some Observations on their Formation.* U.S. Geol. Surv. Prof. Pap. 282-C.

——— and Miller, J. P. (1960). Magnitude and frequency of forces in geomorphic processes. *J. Geol.* 68 (1) : 54-74.

4

Landslide Distribution and Earthquakes in the Bewani and Torricelli Mountains, New Guinea

A Statistical Analysis

DAVID S. SIMONETT

INTRODUCTION

All observers have been impressed by the frequency of landslides in the mountainous high rainfall tropics. So much so, indeed, that most geomorphologists accept without question the view that rapid movements such as slumping, landslides, and avalanches of saturated soil masses combine significantly with *Tiefenerosion*, or vertical erosion downward, in fashioning the characteristically steep, and often uniform slopes of the mountainous humid tropics.

Evidence for this view was given most convincingly by Sapper (1935) in his *Geomorphologie der feuchten Tropen*. Yet, curiously enough, Sapper did not consider in detail the different types of earth movement operating on weathered mantles of various thicknesses or on different parent rocks and structures. Nor did he examine the role that these forms of earth movement might play in slope-modelling. Soil avalanches on the basalts of the Honolulu watershed were studied in some detail by Wentworth (1943), who concluded that avalanching was the key factor in the maintenance of slopes of 42° to 48°. Some 200 slides occurred in a 39 km² area in 8 years and Wentworth was able to estimate an average rate of lowering of the whole surface of 10 cm in 130 years by avalanching.

With the exception of Wentworth's work, I am aware of no quantitative study

This study forms a portion of the results of Research Contract No. 583(11), 387-133 with the Geography Branch, Office of Naval Research, United States Navy. It is a pleasure to acknowledge the substantial financial and other assistance provided by the Office of Naval Research. The aerial photographs, geologic and base maps and diapositives of the Aitape-Vanimo area were made available through the courtesy of the Australasian Petroleum Company. Military maps and diapositives were also provided by the Royal Australian Army Survey Corps, and the Royal Australian Air Force provided air photographs for field studies. Paper positives and multiplex set-ups used in height determinations were made by Adastra Airways, Mascot, Sydney. The help of Mr G. A. Taylor of Port Moresby in obtaining data on earthquakes in New Guinea, and in valuable discussion is appreciated. Father Valentine Brown and Mr C. A. Trollope, Assistant District Officer, Lumi, provided information on the 20 September 1935 earthquakes. Mr Eric Morgan, Commonwealth Bureau of Mineral Resources, Canberra. Mr L. A. Morris, and Mr R. T. Ernst, Australasian Petroleum Company, Port Moresby, assisted with problems in production of diapositives, and Dr George Jenks gave much valuable cartographic advice. I am especially indebted to Dr Duane Knos for advice on statistical design. Professor James S. Peoples criticised the sections dealing with seismic data. Especial acknowledgment is due to Mr R. L. Schuman, formerly of the University of Kansas, who worked in the field with me and carried out much of the early plotting of landslides on to base maps.

of the landslide family in the selva since the general and descriptive account by Sapper. As far as New Guinea is concerned, Sapper's conclusions were based substantially upon the travels at the turn of the century by Behrmann.

Among the many questions concerning the significance of landslides in the humid tropics for which answers are needed are the following:

1. Are there major differences in the frequency and type of landslides on different parent rocks?

2. What are the relations between type, size, and frequency of occurrence of landslide, and slope angle, length of slope, degree of cohesion of the weathered mantle, stream gradient at the base of the slope, vegetation cover, and other factors?

3. What is the critical minimal angle for the initiation of landslides on a variety of parent rocks and under a range of annual rainfall?

4. What estimates may one make of the amount of surface lowering as a result of landslide activity on various parent rocks?

It was in the search for answers to these questions that detailed field and air photo studies of several areas in New Guinea were initiated under contract with the Office of Naval Research, United States Navy, in the expectation that the results from New Guinea would be likely to be of general application in other parts of the humid tropics. These studies are still in progress at the time of writing (February 1964), and this essay is an interim report.

This chapter briefly introduces the methods used in the field and air photo study which constitute the bases of quantification. The results of field study were extrapolated by air photo analysis to the Bewani and Torricelli Mountains and associated hill lands in the Aitape-Vanimo area of the Sepik District, New Guinea (Fig. 4.1). For this area, a map of volumes of landslides (Plate V) was produced, and multiple correlation analysis was carried out to unravel the contributions of several variables to landsliding in the area.

METHOD IN QUANTIFICATION

The method used is given in the following steps. The rationalisations and justifications of this procedure will be published elsewhere; the working method is here presented simply as background to the later portion of this essay.

1. Field-work was carried out primarily in the Bismarck, Finisterre, Adelbert, and Prince Alexander Mountains. Some 400 or more slides were studied and 201 were recorded in sufficient detail to enable areas and volumes to be estimated. The sample of 201 contains a wide variety of landslide type and size, parent rock, slope angle, length of slope, vegetation cover, and altitude.

2. Photo interpretation of landslide size, type, and age, was checked in the field in relation to photo scale and quality, vegetation, native agriculture, and other factors.

3. A statistical study of the relationship between field estimates of slide surface area and volume was next made with reference to variance between observers over a range of lithologies and slopes. Figure 4.2 shows there are negligible differences in the relation between area and volume as estimated by two observers.

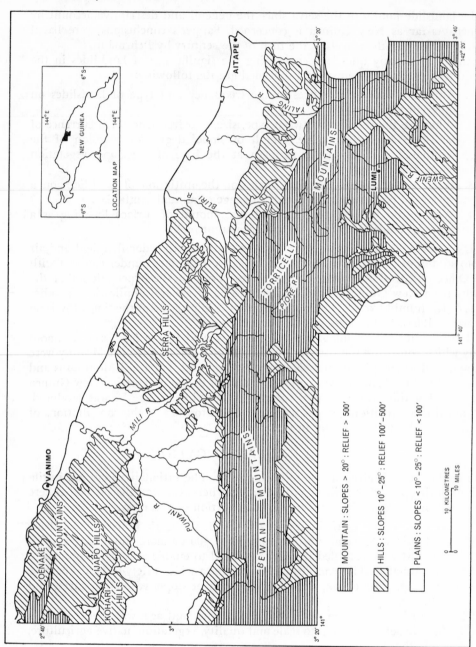

4.1   *Mountains, hills, and plains in the Aitape-Vanimo region of New Guinea. Places shown are mentioned in the text*

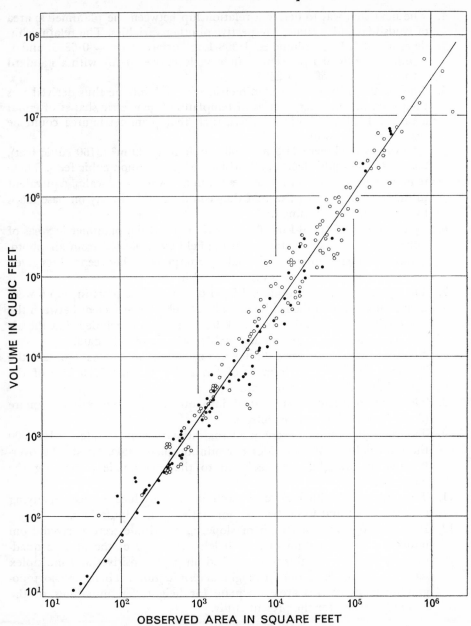

4.2 *Relationship between field-estimated areas and volumes of landslides in New Guinea. Note the absence of any significant difference between estimates by Simonett (open circles) and Schuman (closed circles)*

4. The next step was to derive a relationship between the planimetric area of landslides and volume, irrespective of other variables. The relationship determined is Log Volume $= 1 \cdot 368$ Log Surface Area $- 0 \cdot 6885$, and is significant at the $0 \cdot 1$ per cent confidence level ($r = 0 \cdot 98$), with a standard error of estimate of $\pm 0 \cdot 2857$.

5. The relationship between planimetric area and volume thus derived was then used to construct a series of templates of geometric shapes of equal areas, in 1/2-logarithmic intervals, such that planimetric area could be read directly as volume.

   The values used were $28 \cdot 3$ m³ (1000 cubic feet), 89 m³ (3160 cubic feet), 283 m³ (10,000 cubic feet) . . . 2,831,600 m³ (100 million cubic feet). These templates were made on transparent film at a variety of scales, equivalent to the base maps in use, so that they could be laid directly on base maps to read equivalent volumes.

6. By the use of a Radial-Line Planimetric Plotter, the planimetric areas of some seventy landslides studied in the field were plotted from air photographs and their volumes estimated by interpolation between values given on the transparent templates constructed in step 5.

7. The estimated volumes obtained from the radial-line plots in step 6 were then compared with the field data. The correlation coefficient between the two methods was found to be $r = 0 \cdot 92$, and it was concluded that the air photo measurements gave an acceptable estimate of field data.

8. A Radial-Line Planimetric Plotter was used with air photos to obtain the locations and planimetric areas of landslides in some 7770 km² of the Bewani and Torricelli Mountains.

9. The area so treated was divided into quadrangles one minute square ($3 \cdot 413$ km² or 1847 square metres).

10. Transparent templates were used for estimating at a scale of 1:40,000 the total volume of landslides per minute quadrangle. Landslides overlapping quadrangles were assigned to the quadrangle containing the larger part.

11. The raw data obtained in step 10 were used to produce the accompanying map (Plate V), and form the basis for statistical manipulations.

12. Data on slope angles, length of slope, and altitude were derived from multiplex determination of spot heights for most of the minute quadrangles. The spot heights were marked on paper positives and multiplex set-ups were made to obtain height determinations. There are no topographic maps of this area adequate for height determinations of the accuracy needed for the present study.

LANDSLIDES IN THE BEWANI AND TORRICELLI MOUNTAINS

Landslides in the Bewani, Torricelli, and Oenake Mountains and associated hill lands were plotted on base maps at a scale of 1:40,000 using the procedures discussed above. The base maps were prepared by the Australasian Petroleum Company for geological surveys in this region in the late 1930s and early 1940s.

The volumes of earth moved per minute quadrangle were then estimated using the template procedure as noted.

Since the base map scale was 1:40,000 and the reproduction scale in this essay (Plate V) is approximately 1:1,900,000, and since as many as 52 landslides were counted per quadrangle, it has not been possible to show individual landslides.

The solution adopted for these problems was to use point symbols:

1. Circles, such that the largest volume class just filled a minute quadrangle.
2. Five size classes were adopted:

very large	$100\text{-}316 \times 10^6$ ft³	$(2\cdot83\text{-}8\cdot95 \times 10^6$ m³)
large	$31\cdot6\text{-}100 \times 10^6$ ft³	$(0\cdot90\text{-}2\cdot83 \times 10^6$ m³)
medium	$10\text{-}31\cdot6 \times 10^6$ ft³	$(0\cdot28\text{-}0\cdot90 \times 10^6$ m³)
small	$3\cdot16\text{-}10 \times 10^6$ ft³	$(0\cdot09\text{-}0\cdot28 \times 10^6$ m³)
very small	$0\cdot316\text{-}3\cdot16 \times 10^6$ ft³	$(0\cdot009\text{-}0\cdot09 \times 10^6$ m³)

3. The symbols were placed as near the 'weighted' centre of gravity of occurrence of landslides within the quadrangle as possible.

The distribution of landslides was then viewed successively against backgrounds of topography (mountains, hills, plains), vegetation (virgin rainforest, and cleared, regrowth, and cultivated areas), and against geology based on data from the Australasian Petroleum Company. Of these the geological base was selected as the most significant background to the volumes of landslides as shown in Plate V. Comparison may also be made with the distribution of mountain and hill lands (Fig. 4.1).

The pattern of landslide occurrence shown in Plate V deserves some general comment.

First, there is a complete absence of landslides from the plains, which virtually coincide with the alluvial lands. An exception to the general absence of landslides from alluvium is in the hilly area southwest of Lumi, where there is a moderate occurrence on Pleistocene alluvia, which have been sharply elevated and dissected.

Comparison of Figure 4.1 and Plate V shows that the hill lands can be differentiated into two groups on the basis of landslide occurrence: an area south of Lumi with very large volumes of earth moved (and also, although the maps do not so indicate, by many more landslides) per minute quadrangle; a series of other areas, including the Ijapo Hills east and south of the Oenake Mountains, the Serra Hills west of the Bliri River, and the hills north of the Torricelli Mountains, drained by the Yalingi River. In this series of areas relatively few landslides are shown, especially so in the Ijapo Hills. These differences appear to be related mainly to the following facts of relief and geology. The area south of Lumi has a striking cuesta topography in which limestone and sandstone cap the scarps. Dip slopes lie mostly in the range 10° to 25°, but scarp slopes range from 35° to 55°. Landslides are very largely either of debris avalanche type (Sharpe 1938; Varnes 1958) on the scarp slope or of rotational slump type along the scarp foot, the latter involving failure of incompetent plastic strata (mudstone, siltstone, shale) beneath the cuesta-forming beds. Relative relief in this region is in the range of 90 to 300 m and scarps may be as much as 150 m high.

In contrast, the remaining hill areas either lack cuesta topography, or have it in much less marked degree; slopes are notably shorter (Ijapo Hills 125-150 m) and gentler (15-30°), and relative relief lies in the range 30 to 90 m.

However, it will be seen from Figure 4.3 that there is a westward decline in volume and frequency of landslides along the southern flank of the Torricelli and Bewani Mountains which is not adequately accounted for by differences in cuesta topography as described above. It will be argued later that this appears largely to be related to intense earthquake activity in the Torricelli Mountains a few years prior to the 1938-9 aerial photography.

Within the main mountain mass of the Bewani and Torricelli Mountains there appears to be some relation between rock type and the volume of earth moved in that the number, type, and size of landslides in the granites forming the spine of the mountain system contrast with those in the adjoining sedimentaries, which are predominantly mudstone and siltstone.

Granitic areas have both single debris avalanche movements and complexes of deep and shallow avalanches coupled with extensive gullying of deeply weathered bedrock, once landsliding breaches the subsoils. In some areas where debris avalanche slides coalesced, giant mud and debris flows have surged down valleys. Also in the years following the earthquake, stream valleys have become choked with alluvial fill, derived from continued gullying of weathered granite. I have seen this feature repeatedly in many areas of New Guinea, and photo-interpretation strongly suggests gullying in the Torricellis. The major movements on the sedimentary rock, however, are massive rotational slumps, except on steep scarp slopes where shallow debris avalanche movements also take place.

TABLE 1

Comparison of volumes of earth lost by rock class in the eastern and western Bewani Mountains and the Torricelli Mountains

	Bewani West	Mountains East	Torricelli Mountains
GRANITE			
Area*	417	430	238
Volume†	0·0383	0·1310	2·5267
Depth lost‡	0·0061	0·021	0·40557
WEAK SEDIMENTARY			
Area	326	383	290
Volume	0·0178	0·0343	0·7412
Depth lost	0·00286	0·0055	0·11893
MIXED SEDIMENTARY			
Area	85	536	1134
Volume	0·0028	0·0653	0·4628
Depth lost	0·00046	0·01043	0·07431

* Total area of each region in square kilometres.

† Volume of earth moved by detectable landslides in millions of cubic metres per square kilometre.

‡ Average depth lost for each region as given by detectable landslides shown on the 1938-9 aerial photographs. Depths in metres.

The volumes of earth moved for three rock types are compared in Table 1, for the Torricelli, eastern Bewani, and western Bewani Mountains respectively. It is clear that there are very substantial differences within each type in the western, central, and eastern areas. Also, within each region, there are marked differences between the volumes of landslides by rock type. In short, the rock types are important but partial controls of landslide occurrence.

The reasons for the differences along the line of the Bewani and Torricelli Mountains may now be explored further, confining our attention to granite, which we can reasonably assume to be uniform, and in which slopes are both symmetrically disposed and remarkably uniform in all valleys. In all three respects the granite is to be contrasted with the sedimentaries in which complex interbedding and facies change are the rule, with asymmetry of slopes on dipping beds, and with typically irregular and concave slump-moulded profiles.

STATISTICAL ANALYSES

In the granite areas data for 68 minute quadrangles were left for analysis after eliminating all quadrangles with no detectable landslides, those not exclusively on granite, and those for which no slope measurements were available.

Two major questions may be raised:

What variables contribute to differences in volume of earth moved per minute quadrangle?

What variables influence the number of landslides per minute quadrangle?

(a) *Choice of Variables*

We may set up the problem as essentially one of multiple correlation, involving the contribution of the following variables to the two dependent variables, volume of earth moved per minute quadrangle, and number of landslides per quadrangle: number of landslides, slope angle in degrees, tangent of slope angle, length of slope from crest to valley floor, stream gradient, distance from an inferred earthquake epicentre in the Torricelli Mountains, the logarithm of the distance from the inferred epicentre, and finally a 'dummy' variable and the necessary interaction variables (Suits 1957) expressing the seismicity of the Torricelli Mountains and the aseismicity of the Bewani Mountains.*

Each variable will now be considered in turn.

X_1 — Volume of earth moved per minute
quadrangle in millions of cubic metres

The dependent variable was obtained simply by summing for each minute quadrangle the volumes of earth moved as determined from the planimetric areas using the templates described earlier.

X_2 — Number of landslides per minute quadrangle

The number of landslides per minute quadrangle was obtained directly from the 1:40,000 landslide compilation maps. This variable was included as an inde-

---

* No portion of New Guinea is, in a strict sense, aseismic. For our purposes here, however, we may distinguish those regions which are subject to relatively mild earthquake activity as 'aseismic'.

the more landslides per minute quadrangle, the larger the volume of earth moved, at least for moderate to large landslides. It is recognised, of course, that a few massive landslides can account for much greater volumes moved than many smaller ones.

X_3 — Representative slope angle per minute quadrangle*

The choice of slope angle as a variable rests on the following argument: all other factors being equal, the steeper the slope the greater the number of slides and hence, to the degree that number and volume are related, the greater the volume of material in movement. It is thus to be anticipated that much of the effect of slope angle will be exerted via the effect on number of slides. It was decided, however, that it should be included in the analysis, if only to unravel this effect. Also, there remains the possibility that steepness of slope may influence volumes independently of the effect on number of slides.

Spot heights of hill-crest sites and valley-floor sites directly downslope were plotted on base maps prepared on dimensionally stable plastic at scales of 1:15,840 and 1:12,672. The distance between spot heights was measured, accurate to ± 0.04 mm. Slope angles were then derived from a nomogram of slope angle for difference in elevation against distance.

X_4 — Tangent of representative slope angle per minute quadrangle

This variable was included as a possible alternative to slope angle in degrees, in the possibility that an exponential relationship might appear as a linear relationship.

X_5 — Representative length of slope in metres per minute quadrangle

Inclusion of length of slope as a variable derives from the expectation that the longer slopes would be more likely to have larger landslides, and hence larger volumes of earth moved per minute quadrangle. Also, the longer the slope above a prescribed minimum length, the greater the likelihood of landslides, as the critical height for instability is approached (Scheidegger 1961).

Differences of height and sines of slope angle values obtained earlier were used to work out the lengths of slopes.

X_6 — Representative gradient of stream bed per minute quadrangle

This variable was included in the analysis primarily on the grounds that many valleys showed triangular landslides widening to the valley floor, a type which is produced substantially by stream undercutting at the base of a slope. It was thought desirable to test if there was any relation between stream gradient and

---

* The 'representative' slope angle (variable X_3), length of slope (X_4), and stream-bed gradient (X_5) values were based on inspection under a 3-power stereoscope of air photographs. Where an area was very uniform, one or two slopes per minute quadrangle were selected for slope angle and other determinations. Where a quadrangle was less uniform (in slope length and angle), three sites for determinations were selected. The sites used in the writer's judgment reasonably define the parameters. Cost and time prevented a substantial examination of points for spot-height determination. The number of slopes used in this analysis is 146.

frequency of landslides, holding all other factors constant. Wherever slopes were measured, the streambed gradient in metres per kilometre was determined from multiplex spot heights.

X_7 — Distance in kilometres from an inferred earthquake epicentre

Inspection of the air photographs of the Torricelli Mountains led early to the question as to whether the very large number and volume of landslides in those mountains might be related to one or more severe earthquakes. As can be seen in the stereopair of air photos of a portion of the Torricellis (Plate VIa), the number of landslides and the surface area they cover, and presumably the volumes involved, are so large that some catastrophic event seems necessary to explain them. Indeed, the area involved in sliding is so large (approximately 40 per cent of the surface in some valleys of more than a square kilometre) and its apparent contemporaneity so evident (almost all the slides are fresh and lack vegetative cover) that no random distribution of minor events could be responsible. Only minor differences exist in slope angle and length of slope between the relatively slide-free

TABLE 2

A comparison of selected parameters related to landslides in the granite areas of the Bewani and Torricelli Mountains

Mean Values Per Minute Quadrangle

Mountains	No. of cases	Volume millions cubic metres	Slope degrees	Length metres	No. of slides
Bewani	40	0·07731	36·21	434·6	4·32
Torricelli	28	0·91237	35·51	541·0	26·00
TOTAL	68	0·42107	35·92	478·2	13·25

Bewanis and the slide-dominated Torricellis (Table 2) so these must be eliminated as possible contributing factors. Detailed inspection under the stereoscope shows that floors are choked with debris and alluvial fill in valley after valley in the heart of the Torricelli Mountains. All the above features point to some unusual major event, and the only adequate alternative to earthquake activity would seem to be extraordinarily heavy rainfalls. However, experience in New Guinea suggests that within the life of landslide scars, such rainfalls would not be confined to any one area, and could thus not explain the restriction of heavy landsliding to the Torricellis.

Any remaining doubts on the efficacy of earthquakes in this regard vanish on reading the thorough descriptions by Wright and Mella (1963) of the landslides triggered by the 23 May 1960 earthquake in south central Chile, and there is striking similarity between the denuded slopes shown in the stereo model of the Torricellis (Plate VIa) and photographs by Wright and Mella.

The core of the Torricellis is remote from native settlement or administrative posts but Father Valentine Brown of the Franciscan Mission at Karaitem, 13 km north of Lumi, reports that 'many spectacular landslides occurred around the whole Lumi area and these are attributed by the indigini directly to the earthquake of September 1937' (mistake for 1935). After writing to Father Brown, I found the interesting photographs and account by A. J. Marshall (1937), who traversed the Torricellis in December 1935, only four months after the earthquake.

Data on the epicentres for earthquakes of magnitude 6 or greater in New Guinea for the period before the aerial photography were obtained from Gutenberg and Richter (1954). These records show that on 20 September 1935 there were two earthquakes in the vicinity of the Torricelli Mountains.

Magnitude 7·9; 3° 30′ S., 141° 45′ E.
Magnitude 7·0; 3° 15′ S., 142° 30′ E.

Both earthquakes were shallow (less than 60 km deep), and the second earthquake was an aftershock of the first. It is recognised that since the energy released in the magnitude 7·9 earthquake is 20 to 40 times more than that of the lesser tremor (Richter 1958), it would be the prime mover.

In the determination of epicentres, Gutenberg and Richter (1954) note that 'epicentres have in general not been determined more closely than the nearest quarter degree of latitude and longitude'. Other residual errors are present in the determinations, so that the values given could be in error by as much as 25 km. Also, since an instrumentally determined site for an epicentre need not necessarily be the site for maximum surface expression of an earthquake, there is an appreciable margin of uncertainty as to the precise surface sites of the respective maximum intensities of the two earthquakes.

The heart of the zone of maximum number and volumes of landslides in the granite area of the Torricellis lies at 3° 22′ 30″ S., 142° 5′ 30″ E. on the line joining the two epicentres, being 39 km ENE of the magnitude 7·9 epicentre and 45 km WSW from the magnitude 7·0 epicentre, and has been taken as the most likely position for the epicentre of the magnitude 7·9 earthquake in the expectation that the maximum intensity in an area of uniform igneous rock would be the area of greatest number and volumes of landslides. This determination within the granite area applies only for the purpose of statistical analysis for locating an epicentre. However, it is not intended to imply that the energy released has a point source. Reference to Plate V showing the impressive volume (and, inferentially, number) of landslides on the sedimentaries between the derived site for the epicentre in the granite area and the Gutenberg and Richter 'location' for the epicentre for the magnitude 7·9 earthquake to the WSW argues rather for a wide 'zone' of intense shock. In the granite area of the Torricellis, perhaps because of the nature of the rock involved (especially its elasticity) and perhaps also because this area lies near the margins of this zone of maximum intensity, the numbers of landslides per minute quadrangle decrease sharply east and west of the derived epicentre. Neumann (1954) argues that the rate of decline in intensity in basement rock (granite) with distance from an epicentre is much more rapid than in sedimentary rock.

The numbers of landslides per minute quadrangle were plotted for the 68 quadrangles available against distance in miles from the derived epicentre on the granite. It was found that the numbers of slides dropped off very sharply with distance from the derived epicentre, a feature wholly compatible with a shallow earthquake of high intensity in which diminution of intensity and hence numbers of landslides would be expected to follow some exponential function of distance from the centre.

X_8 — Logarithm of the distance in kilometres
from the inferred epicentre

Graphical testing showed that the landslide numbers decreased with logarithm of distance from the inferred epicentre.* Consequently, the logarithm of the distance in kilometres from the inferred epicentre was used as a variable (X_8) in the multiple correlation. At the same time, arithmetic distance was retained as a variable for inclusion with the dummy variable, as will be explained in the following section.

X_9 — A 'dummy' variable expressing the seismicity of the
Torricelli Mountains and the aseismicity of the Bewani Mountains.

In the preceding section it was pointed out that there was a relation between number of landslides per minute quadrangle and the logarithm of the distance from the inferred epicentre. The actual equation is:

Number of slides $= 37 \cdot 09 - 17 \cdot 31$ log. Distance (in kilometres)
$r = 0 \cdot 831$, significant at $0 \cdot 001 \%$

However, it does not follow that the earthquake influences all variables in the same fashion, nor for that matter is it certain that a single logarithmic function defines the relation with number over the entire universe, or indeed that the simple distance may not in some circumstances function better than the logarithm of the distance in 'explaining' the relations.

It may well be, in short, that different relations exist between the variables in the Torricelli Mountains, in the region of intense shock, from those in the Bewani Mountains, where the effect of the earthquake was much less pronounced. To accommodate these differences in a multiple regression we may define two mutually exclusive areas by using a dummy variable (Suits 1957; Knos 1962) such that,

$\triangle$ — a sample minute quadrangle takes the value 1 if it
occurs in the Torricelli Mountains, 0 if it occurs in
the Bewani Mountains.

Now, in order to investigate whether there are differences in the slopes of the regression lines between the seismic zone of the Torricelli Mountains and the aseismic zone of the Bewani Mountains, we introduce into the regression the interaction variables between the dummy variable and all other variables.

The regression for volume as dependent variable then takes the general form,

$$V = a + (b_2 + d_2\triangle)N + (b_3 + d_3\triangle)S + (b_5 + d_5\triangle)L + (b_6 + d_6\triangle)G$$
$$+ (b_7 + d_7\triangle)D + b_9\triangle$$

* A fuller analysis of the relation between numbers of landslides and distance from the epicentre will be published elsewhere, and graphical solutions given. In the present study, in which only those minute quadrangles *with* landslides are used, the regressions with number of landslides as dependent variable are biased by failure to include those quadrangles *without* landslides. The cost of the necessary multiplex set-ups and spot-height determinations was the main deterrent to following a complete procedure. The prime concern here is in relation to volume of earth moved, and for this purpose the failure to include the quadrangles without landslides does not introduce bias.

where:
$V =$ volume of earth moved
$N =$ number of landslides per minute quadrangle
$S =$ slope angle or tangent of slope angle
$L =$ length of slope per minute quadrangle
$G =$ stream gradient per minute quadrangle
$D =$ distance or logarithm of distance
$\triangle =$ dummy variable

A similar regression defines number as the dependent variable.

Given the above model, the matrix of zero-order correlation coefficients was calculated between each variable and all other variables. An IBM 7040 computer was programmed to add step-by-step each variable, in all possible combinations with and without the dummy and the interaction variables, and with two sample populations of 68 and 66 respectively. It is stressed that all possible combinations were explored. Those given here in Tables 2 and 3 represent the addition of each new variable in the order that gives the maximum 'explanation' at each step with the minimum number of variables. In the limited space here all these combinations cannot be given.

The use of dummy variables is not a widely known technique. In an earlier version of this essay I followed the traditional pattern of analysing both areas (the seismic and aseismic regions) together and then of splitting them into two sub-regions. This procedure has only the virtue of familiarity to recommend it. The advantages of the dummy variable procedure are several.

The number of degrees of freedom for the whole population is applicable also to the sub-regions, when analysis of the significance of a variable is made. In the traditional procedure, the population is effectively split in two, by regions, severely reducing the sample size; and as a consequence, several variables now known to be significant following the dummy variable technique are not 'significant' in the split-method.

In addition, the 'seismicity and aseismicity' of the Torricelli and Bewani Mountains are documented as to their quantitative significance using dummy variables. The dummy technique gives a significantly higher per cent 'explanation' than in its absence, thus indicating clearly that the relations between the variables are more sharply defined with this technique than by the normal procedure.

(b) *Size of Samples*

The reasons for the use of the two samples of 68 and 66 cases respectively may now be examined. The two quadrangles omitted from the smaller sample are ones in which extremely large volumes of earth were moved by landslides. These constituted the largest residuals in the multiple regression involving 68 cases.

This problem of undue weight being assigned to one or two aberrant values is a familiar one in multiple regression and arises where some of the samples in a study are drawn from another population not being investigated, or where gratuitous information is present.

The basis for the exclusion here is twofold. First, the two samples represented the largest residuals in the multiple regression with volume of earth moved as the dependent variable. Data screening, censoring or winsorisation is now a well known procedure as discussed by Tukey (1962), and by Scott (1964), and in the

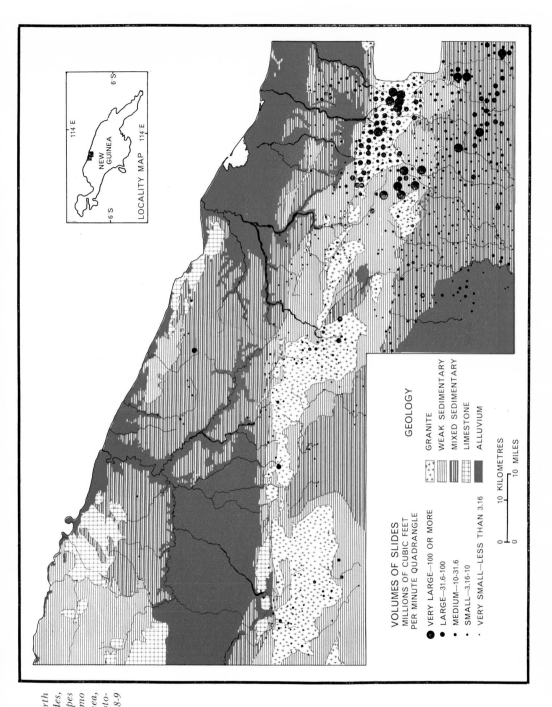

V Volumes of earth moved by landslides, and main rock types in the Aitape-Vanimo region of New Guinea, based on air photographs taken in 1938-9

GEOLOGY

GRANITE
WEAK SEDIMENTARY
MIXED SEDIMENTARY
LIMESTONE
ALLUVIUM

0   10 KILOMETRES
0   10 MILES

VOLUMES OF SLIDES
MILLIONS OF CUBIC FEET
PER MINUTE QUADRANGLE

● VERY LARGE—100 OR MORE
● LARGE—31.6–100
• MEDIUM—10–31.6
· SMALL—3.16–10
· VERY SMALL—LESS THAN 3.16

LOCALITY MAP

NEW
GUINEA

6 S
114 E
6 S
114 E

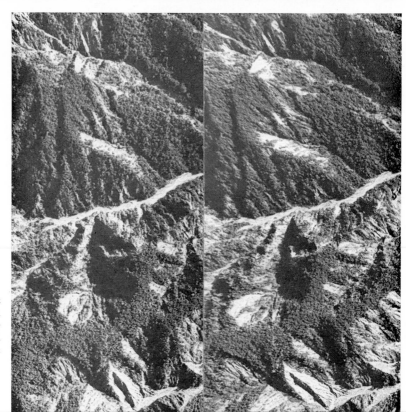

VIa Stereopair of Mau Creek, Torricelli Mountains. Centre of area approximately 3° 20′ 30″ S., 142° 8′ 36″ E. Photographs by Australasian Petroleum Company.

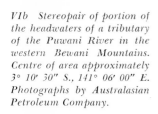

VIb Stereopair of portion of the headwaters of a tributary of the Puwani River in the western Bewani Mountains. Centre of area approximately 3° 10′ 30″ S., 141° 06′ 00″ E. Photographs by Australasian Petroleum Company.

present instance the loss in degrees of freedom is more than compensated for by a substantial improvement in the per cent explanation of the multiple regression.

Second, it has been the writer's experience in the field in New Guinea, that extremely large landslides of the type involved in the two aberrant quadrangles are relatively rare events whether triggered by earthquakes or not, and thus may well represent samples drawn from a potentially very different population from that being investigated here. Both sample populations are consequently given in Tables 3 and 4, and the reader may make his own judgment on the matter.

RESULTS OF THE STATISTICAL ANALYSES

The results of the multiple regressions are given in Table 3 for volume as dependent variable and in Table 4 for number of landslides per minute quadrangle as dependent variable. Each will be taken in turn.

(a) *The Contribution of the Variables to Volume of Earth Moved by Landslides*

We may draw the following conclusions from Table 3:

1. Without the dummy variable, numbers of landslides, arithmetic distance, the logarithm of the distance and length of slope all make a significant contribution to the regression when other variables are held constant. This is true for the 68 and 66 population samples.

2. The dummy variable and interaction variables* very markedly improve the relations over those above, indicating that there are differences between the Torricelli and Bewani Mountains not accounted for by a simple arithmetic or logarithmic function of distance. In brief, our speculation to this effect is borne out.

3. There is little to choose between distance and logarithmic distance in their efficiency as predictors of volume, as indicated by the two columns DR^2 and log DR^2 in Table 3. However, the highest per cent explanation is achieved using logarithm of the distance and the dummy variable, and this is taken to indicate that the different functions in the Torricelli and Bewani Mountains are probably logarithmic rather than arithmetic.

4. Slope angle does not contribute significantly to the regression without the dummy, and is significant with the dummy variable present. We may interpret this as evidence that the relations between slope angle and volume of earth moved, with other variables held constant, are significant, but markedly different in the seismic and aseismic zones. The equations given later show this well.

5. Gradient of the stream bed makes no significant contribution to the regression either with or without the dummy variable.

6. Exclusion of the two most aberrant samples from the 68 sample population results in a 23 per cent improvement in explanation without dummies (from 0·5214 to 0·7511) and a 14 per cent improvement with the dummy (from 0·6610 to 0·8057).

7. The per cent improvement in explanation achieved using the dummy is

---

* Hereafter dummy variable is to be taken as including the interaction variables.

G

surprisingly high and very clearly suggests the important role of the earthquake in influencing volume of earth moved.

8. There is a negligible difference between slope as measured in degrees, and the tangent, as a predictor of volume.

9. The equations for the four cases of sample populations (66 and 68) with and without the dummy are given below, using only significant variables, with log D rather than D as one variable and slope in degrees rather than tangent as another:

68 samples:

$$V = 4 \cdot 290 + 0 \cdot 5419N - 10 \cdot 32 \log D + 0 \cdot 0066L$$
$$r = 0 \cdot 7221 \qquad \mathrm{SEE} = 0 \cdot 400$$
$$(\mathrm{SEE} = \text{standard error of estimate})$$

68 samples:

$$V = -39 \cdot 48 + (0 \cdot 6321 - 0 \cdot 2451 \triangle)N + (7 \cdot 619 + 17 \cdot 40 \triangle) \log D$$
$$+ (0 \cdot 000167 + 0 \cdot 00594 \triangle)L + (0 \cdot 2582 + 0 \cdot 8802 \triangle)S$$
$$- 17 \cdot 01 \triangle$$
$$r = 0 \cdot 8131 \qquad \mathrm{SEE} = 0 \cdot 354$$

66 samples:

$$V = -0 \cdot 923 + 0 \cdot 6527N - 6 \cdot 533 \log D + 0 \cdot 00384L$$
$$r = 0 \cdot 8667 \qquad \mathrm{SEE} = 0 \cdot 219$$

66 samples:

$$V = -19 \cdot 208 + (0 \cdot 5873 - 0 \cdot 0221 \triangle)N + (1 \cdot 066 + 8 \cdot 593 \triangle) \log D$$
$$+ (0 \cdot 0000644 + 0 \cdot 004786 \triangle)L + (0 \cdot 1539 + 0 \cdot 3799 \triangle)S$$
$$- 10 \cdot 87 \triangle$$
$$r = 0 \cdot 8976 \qquad \mathrm{SEE} = 0 \cdot 204$$

(b) *The Relations Between Number of Landslides and Other Variables*

Inspection of Table 4 suggests the following conclusions:

1. The logarithm of the distance is a more efficient predictor of number of landslides per minute quadrangle than is arithmetic distance in all combinations of variables and sample sizes, but excluding the dummy variable. A logarithmic decline in the intensity of the shock with distance appears a rational expectation in a subject dominated by logarithmic relations.

2. With arithmetic distance as a variable, plus the dummy, all variables including the dummy appear to make a 'significant' contribution to the regression, achieving maximum per cent explanations of $0 \cdot 7645$ ($68 \triangle$) and $0 \cdot 7670$ ($66 \triangle$). However, since the logarithm of the distance accounts for 69 per cent of all the variance, and all other variables including the dummy add merely 7 per cent, the statistical 'significance' of all these is distinctly questionable. All the evidence ·· that log D is the more appropriate function, and consequently the ⌐chieved by adding other variables to arithmetic distance (with s, being derived from that portion of the explanation properly D.

ietic distance as a variable, and in the absence of the dummy

TABLE 3

The relationship between volume of earth moved by landslides
per minute quadrangle and five independent variables

(The dependent variable is *volume of earth* moved)

No. of cases used	Independent variables	D R^2	log D R^2
68	Number of landslides	0·4562	0·4562
68△		0·5134*	0·5134*
66		0·7063	0·7063
66△		0·7337*	0·7337*
68	As above + Distance (D)	0·5073†	0·4911†
68△	or log Distance (log D)	0·6107*†	0·5885*†
66	from Inferred Epicentre	0·7355†	0·7304†
66△		0·7620*†	0·7691*†
68	As above + Length of	0·5354†	0·5214†
68△	Slope	0·6161*	0·6094*†
66		0·7527†	0·7483†
66△		0·7813*†	0·7869*†
68	As above + Slope Angle in	0·5415	0·5300
68△	Degrees	0·6454*†	0·6610*†
66		0·7544	0·7511
66△		0·7979*†	0·8057*†
68	As above + Stream	0·5439	0·5352
68△	Gradient	0·6540	0·6660
66		0·7547	0·7511
66△		0·7985	0·8059
68	Number + Distance or	0·5413	0·5321
68△	log Distance + Length	0·6509	0·6421
66	of slope + Tangent of	0·7542	0·7504
66△	slope + Gradient	0·8014	0·8028

△ With dummy variable and interaction variables.
R^2 The coefficient of determination, giving per cent explanation.

* Indicates that the R^2 including the dummy variable is a significant improvement (at at least the 5 per cent level) over the equivalent number of variables using the raw data only.

† Indicates that the additional variable added results in a significant improvement (at at least the 5 per cent level of confidence) over the previous group of variables. The test of significance is based on adjusting the R^2 according to the following formula:

$$\text{Adjusted } R^2 = 1 - \left(1 - R^2 \cdot \frac{n-1}{n-m}\right)$$

For the raw data the 't' test also indicates that number, distance, and length of slope make a significant contribution to the regression.

variable, no other variable significantly improves the prediction of number of landslides over the simple correlation between number and arithmetic distance.

4. With log D as a variable there is no significant improvement in explanation by adding any other variable including the dummy, except for the addition of stream gradient in the presence of the dummy. From this we may conclude that

the same logarithmic slope exists in the regressions in the Torricelli and Bewani Mountains, except for stream gradient. In this regard it is interesting that separate multiple regressions run on the 28 and 26 samples lying in the Torricelli Mountains both indicate that log *D* and stream gradient are significant at the 5 per cent

TABLE 4

The relationship between number of landslides per minute quadrangle and four independent variables

(The dependent variable is *number of landslides*)

No. of cases used	Independent variables	D R^2	log D R^2
68	Distance or log Distance	0·5439	0·6902
68△	(log D) from Inferred	0·6240*	0·6911
66	Epicentre	0·5453	0·6891
66△		0·6226*	0·6819
68	As above + Slope Angle in	0·5451	0·6936
68△	Degrees	0·7005*†	0·7045
66		0·5465	0·6927
66△		0·7007*†	0·7060
68	As above + Length of	0·5537	0·6991
68△	Slope	0·7321*†	0·7172
66		0·5573	0·6994
66△		0·7316*†	0·7192
68	As above + Stream	0·5567	0·7095
68△	Gradient	0·7645*†	0·7535*†
66		0·5610	0·7109
66△		0·7670*†	0·7579*†
68	Distance (D) or log Dis-	0·5553	
68△	tance (log D) + Tan Slope	0·7219	
66	Angle + Length of Slope +	0·5593	
66△	Stream Gradient	0·7217	

△ With dummy variable and interaction variables.
R^2 The coefficient of determination, giving per cent explanation.

* Indicates that the R^2 including the dummy variable is a significant improvement (at at least the 5 per cent level) over the equivalent number of variables using the raw data only.

† Indicates that the additional variable added results in a significant improvement (at at least the 5 per cent level of confidence) over the previous group of variables. The test of significance is based on adjusting the R^2 according to the following formula:

$$\text{Adjusted } R^2 = 1 - \left(1 - R^2 \cdot \frac{n-1}{n-m}\right)$$

level, and that no other variable is significant. It is tentatively suggested that a significant number of landslides in the Torricelli Mountains resulted as a secondary effect from pronounced undercutting of slopes as masses of material surged downvalley following the earthquake, and that this effect was more pronounced in steeper and narrower valley floors.

(c) *The Relation Between Distance from the Derived Epicentre and Number of Landslides*

This relation, as already noted, is a semi-logarithmic function, with the severe effects of the earthquake not extending beyond 80 km, as judged by the numbers of landslides.

The rate at which the severe effects of this earthquake apparently diminished with distance agrees with data from other regions. Hodgson (1964), after noting the relation between distance and damage for a number of North American earthquakes, concludes

> it appears that major damage will not extend more than fifty miles from an epicenter of the magnitude likely to be encountered in North America, and that minor damage may extend to distances of 200 miles.

A quantitative expression of this relationship of particular relevance to this study was given by Neumann (1954) in a valuable contribution on earthquake intensity and related ground motion. He derived a relationship for minimum intensities on granitic rock or equivalent as a function of distance from the epicentre of the 13 April 1949 Puget Sound earthquake. The relation was semi-logarithmic with a rapid decline in intensity with distance from the epicentre, comparable to that noted in this study. The relation derived was:

$$I = a - b \log D$$

where

$I =$ Modified Mercalli Scale intensity at an epicentral distance D

$a, b =$ constants

$D =$ Distance from the epicentre in miles

This equation is of identical form to that derived in this paper relating number of landslides to the logarithm of distance from the epicentre, and suggests that the number of landslides reflects intensity with a high degree of faithfulness, and that in fact there is a function

$$\log N = aI - b \text{ (using previous nomenclature)}$$

Terzaghi (1950) has analysed the components of motion of earthquakes in connection with landslides and demonstrated the importance of horizontal accelerations in exceeding the critical values for slope failure and triggering landslides. Both Neumann (1954) and Richter (1958) derive a logarithmic relation between intensity and horizontal accelerations. Richter observed the relation

$$\log A = 0.33\,I - 0.5 \text{ where } A = \text{acceleration in cm/sec}^2 \text{ and}$$
$$I = \text{intensity on the Modified Mercalli Scale.}$$

From these and the earlier equations it seems not unreasonable to anticipate that number of landslides as obtained in this study may be a measure of the horizontal accelerations involved.

If the above analysis is correct, then a practical consequence of value to seismology emerges: in remote regions of granitic type rocks, air photo analysis of ancient landslides revealing a logarithmic relation of numbers from a central point would be strongly suggestive of ancient earthquakes, perhaps older than recorded earthquakes.

All the foregoing lead to the further conclusion that in evaluating the distribution of present-day slides (i.e. those formed in the last thirty years or so) it becomes a matter of some importance to know the distribution, frequency, intensity, and magnitude of earthquakes of earlier times. Areas where a severe earthquake has taken place, once revegetated, should remain substantially slide-free from other causes for extended periods of time, at least of the order of a half century or so, since so much of the weathered mantle will have been brought to a stable position. However, renewed seismic activity could trigger many additional slides.

In the Torricelli Mountains, air photos show a large number of older, partially revegetated debris avalanches which appear to be some 20 to 25 years old. These could perhaps be related to the magnitude 7·5 shallow earthquake on 3 July 1918, with its epicentre in the general area of 3° 30′ S., 142° 30′ E. (Gutenberg and Richter 1954). A number of avalanches in the eastern Bewani Mountains appear to be of the same age and may also be related to this earthquake. However, in the western Bewani Mountains landslides are notably few, and there is no evidence of landslides of similar age, in spite of the record of a magnitude 7·6 earthquake on 29 July 1917 (epicentre 3° 30′ S., 141° E.) a mere 32 km away, which might fairly have been expected to trigger avalanches. A typical stereoscopic view of the western Bewanis is given in Plate VIb. The uniformity of tree height characteristic of the whole area argues strongly against a major earthquake in the vicinity for some time before the aerial photography.

The most likely explanation of this discrepancy would seem to be that the fix for the epicentre is near the limit of probable error in determination (Gutenberg and Richter 1954) and that the epicentre for this shock lay some 55 km from the western Bewanis.

Field experience in granite areas in the same altitude range as the Torricellis indicates that large isolated debris avalanche or composite gully slides as in the Torricellis are usually revegetated and become undetectable within forty years.* Very large areas, comparable to the extensive skinned areas of a large earthquake, are commonly detectable after fifty years and may even be detectable after sixty years.

In the western Bewani Mountains, then, it seems reasonable to conclude that no major shock could have occurred later than, say, 1870.

THE CONTRIBUTION OF LANDSLIDES AND EARTHQUAKES TO DENUDATION

For the purposes of estimating the volumes of earth moved we may divide the granitic areas into those given in Table 1, namely the western Bewani Mountains, virtually unaffected by the earthquake, the eastern Bewani Mountains, affected only slightly, and the Torricelli Mountains, very profoundly affected. As may be seen, the effects of this one shock in the Torricellis exceed the 'normal' rate of landsliding as represented in the western Bewani Mountains some 66-fold, and the eastern Bewanis exceed the western Bewanis by 3·4-fold. This calculation is

* This conclusion on revegetation time represents my judgment based on analysis of air photos of 1938-9 and World War II vintage compared with post-World War II photographs of particular landslides, coupled with intensive questioning of New Guineans.

based on the fact that slope angles and length of slope are not markedly different in each region (Table 2), and assumes further that the sample areas (238, 417, and 430 km²) are all larger than the critical minimal area to obtain a 'true' mean value of equivalent depth lost, and that the sample of landslides drawn for 1938-9 in the western Bewanis is a 'true' random sample except for the exclusion of major seismic effects. As noted earlier, there is every reason to believe that no large earthquake occurred after 1870 in the western fringes of the area.

If the sample drawn from the western Bewani Mountains does represent a random sample drawn from a time and space random distribution, then the only additional factors needed to estimate denudation loss from landslides in that area through time are:

1. The mean period for revegetation of non-contiguous landslides and for a new set of landslides to replace them.
2. The error terms arising from air photo interpreters failing to detect all slides observable in the field.

Rough approximations to these values based on field study would be thirty years and 20 per cent.

Taking these values leads then to a crude estimate of the rate of surface lowering in the western Bewani Mountains as 10 cm every 440 years.

The contribution of the 1935 macroseism to denudation in the Torricellis as given in Table 1 is truly impressive. In the granite region, the loss is equivalent to a layer 40 cm thick from the planimetric area (238 km²). In the weak sedimentaries the loss equals a layer of almost 12 cm, and for the mixed sedimentaries the loss is 7·4 cm.

We have no knowledge of the frequency of large earthquakes in the Torricelli Mountains over a long period, though in a recent unpublished report (of the Commonwealth Bureau of Mineral Resources, Canberra) J. Brooks has estimated from 1930-59 data, that the Torricelli and eastern Bewani Mountains would experience between ten and twenty shocks of magnitude 6 or greater per square degree per century.

A spectacular event such as that described in this paper would accomplish as much denudation as a host of lesser shocks. A larger earthquake of this magnitude every 500 years, and surely this is very conservative, plus the lesser shocks and rainfall-triggered landslides, would lead to rates of denudation by landslides of the order of 10 cm every 70 to 100 years in the seismic granite area of the Torricelli Mountains.

REFERENCES

Gutenberg, B. and Richter, C. F. (1954). *Seismicity of the Earth and Associated Phenomena*. 2nd ed. Princeton.
Hodgson, J. H. (1964). *Earthquakes and Earth Structure*. Englewood Cliffs.
Knos, D. S. (1962). *Distribution of Land Values in Topeka, Kansas*. Lawrence.
Marshall, A. J. (1937). Northern New Guinea. *Geogrl J.* 89: 489-504.
Neumann, F. (1954). *Earthquake Intensity and Related Ground Motion*. Seattle.
Richter, C. F. (1958). *Elementary Seismology*. San Francisco.
Sapper, K. (1935). *Geomorphologie der feuchten Tropen*. Geogr. Schr. 7. Leipzig.
Scheidegger, A. E. (1961). *Theoretical Geomorphology*. Berlin.

Scott, A. J. (1964). Optimising statistical analysis: data screening and preconditioning. Tech. Rept No. 7 of O.N.R. Task No. 389-135, Contract Nonr 1228 (26), Geography Branch, Office of Naval Research, Northwestern University.

Sharpe, C. F. S. (1938). *Landslides and Related Phenomena*. New York.

Suits, D. B. (1957). Use of dummy variables in regression equations. *J. Am. statist. Ass.* **52**: 548-51.

Terzaghi, K. (1950). Mechanism of landslides. *Geol. Soc. Am.* (Berkey Vol.): 83-123.

Tukey, J. W. (1962). The future of data analysis. *Ann. math. Statist.* **33**: 1-67.

Varnes, D. J. (1958). Landslide types and processes, in *Landslides and Engineering Practice* (ed. E. B. Eckel). Highway Research Board U.S.A., Special Rept No. 29, N.A.S.-N.R.C. Pub. 544.

Wentworth, C. K. (1943). Soil avalanches on Oahu, Hawaii. *Bull. geol. Soc. Am.* **54**: 53-64.

Wright, C. and Mella, A. (1963). Modification to the soil pattern of south-central Chile resulting from seismic and associated phenomena during the period May to August 1960. *Bull. seism. Soc. Am.* **54**: 1367-402.

5

Slopewash under Mature Primary Rainforest in Northern Papua

BRYAN P. RUXTON

INTRODUCTION

High temperatures and abundant, evenly distributed rainfall in the humid tropics provide optimum conditions for plant growth. The dense, luxuriant vegetation has conventionally been considered adequate to protect the ground from mechanical erosion (Tricart and Cailleux 1955; Krynine 1936), thereby permitting deep penetration of chemical weathering itself accentuated by the climate. Thorough weathering of deep, fine-textured regoliths is considered to leave few tools for stream corrasion (Birot 1960) and to lead to strong mass movement on steep slopes (Sapper 1935; White 1949). Thus a distinct selva (humid tropical) 'morphogenetic region' has been formulated (Peltier 1950) in which chemical denudation and mass action are strong and pluvial erosion is minimal.

In the absence of data, the protective effect of a rainforest cover has been deduced from observations in the better known humid temperate forests. In temperate regions, mechanical erosion under natural forest is much slower than under grassland (Walker 1963). Forest canopies intercept a considerable proportion of the rainfall, breaking the force of raindrop impact and increasing immediate loss by evaporation, and raindrops and waterdrops which reach the ground strike an absorbent layer of leaf litter and duff. The soil surface is protected in this way, and the soil structure preserved; hence a steady rate of infiltration is maintained during rainstorms (Lowdermilk 1930). Surface runoff is relatively small and most of the water reaching the streams travels by subsurface and groundwater flow.

However, early descriptions of rainforest exaggerated the denseness of the vegetation, suggesting closed canopies, impenetrable undergrowth, and a thick layer of vegetable debris on the ground. Whilst such conditions often obtain in regrowth, they are not typical of mature primary rainforest, where in fact canopy openings commonly occur, where the shrub layer is often sparse, owing to the lack of light, and where leaf litter is thin, averaging only between 1 and 3 cm (Richards 1952), due to the more rapid vegetative decay in the higher prevailing temperatures and to an absence of seasonal leaf drop. These factors, combined with much higher and often much more intense rainfall (Krynine 1936; Birot 1960), lead to much greater runoff under tropical rainforest than under temperate forest cover.

The author is grateful to Mr K. Paijmans, plant ecologist on the Safia-Pongani survey, for criticising the manuscript, and to Mr J. Wolfe for guidance in flash photography.

Thus a high rate of denudation and shallow, immature weathering mantles are to be expected in the mountains of the humid tropics as in New Guinea. Mountainous selva in fact often has a fine-textured relief with sharp ridge crests and deep narrow ravines, implying vigorous dissection in progress. In this respect there is resemblance to some humid temperate mountain regions such as New Zealand (Cotton 1962), illustrating that differences between morphogenetic systems are commonly less marked in the mobile mountain belts. Cotton (1958, after Krynine 1936) claimed that such dissection is by vertical corrasion and that rain-drop erosion and rainwash are of little importance, whilst Krynine himself emphasised the presence of strongly weathered deep regoliths on steep mountain slopes as evidence of the prevalence of vertical corrasion over slope erosion. However, other authors have noted the occurrence of shallow, immature soils and the incidence of rainwash on such slopes (see Richards 1952).

These conflicting views point to the need for more observations of slope processes in the selva morphogenetic régime. Slopewash and its effects were observed at many sites under mature primary rainforest during a land resources survey of the Safia-Pongani area in northern Papua in 1963.* The northern part of the area was revisited in 1964, and further observations were made, mostly around Numba and Dareki (Fig. 5.1).

THE ENVIRONMENT

Annual rainfall ranges from between 1500 and 2000 mm in a relatively dry area about the Musa Basin near Safia, through intermediate values mainly in the coastal plain, to over 3000 mm at higher altitudes. It is distinctly seasonal, with a maximum in December and January and a minimum in June or July, but the degree of seasonality decreases with increasing rainfall. Sudden heavy downpours are frequent, and falls of 250 mm and above may occur in a single day (R.A.A.F. 1942). The mean annual temperature ranges from about 28°C. at sea level to 16°C. at 2000 m, and there is little seasonal variation.

The wettest areas are characterised by lower montane and *Castanopsis* forests, which prevail above about 1000 m (Fig. 5.1). These evergreen hill forests have fairly even dense canopies between 25 and 35 m high, which become lower and more open at higher altitudes. Evergreen lowland forests cover most of the areas of intermediate rainfall; hill forests here have irregular canopies, between 30 and 40 m, with numerous emergent trees and with large gaps. The dry areas have extensive grasslands, eucalypt savannah, and mixed deciduous-evergreen forests, the latter with an irregular canopy, usually between 30 and 35 m, with numerous gaps.

Mountains and hills make up most of the area (Fig. 5.2) and are predominantly of the erosionally graded ridge-and-ravine type, with sharp crests, steep straight slopes, mainly between 35° and 40°, and narrow valley bottoms. Soils are generally shallow to very shallow acid loams, often with some gravel. Most of the observations were made in this kind of terrain, mainly in the high rainfall area.

Volcanic landforms were visited only south of Dareki in the area of inter-

---

* The results of this survey are to be published under the title 'Lands of the Safia-Pongani area, Territory of Papua and New Guinea' in the Land Research Series, CSIRO, Melbourne.

mediate rainfall. Here Recent flows of andesitic basalt lava have been shallowly dissected to form a gently undulating plateau surface between 600 and 800 m adjacent to the Pongani River. Slopes are mainly between 3° and 15°, and areas of poorly permeable dark brown acid clay soils alternate with minor stony ground.

The uplands contrast sharply with low-angle fans and nearly flat alluvial plains in lowland areas. These are rapidly aggrading surfaces with immature shallow soils.

RAINFOREST FEATURES RELEVANT TO SLOPE PROCESSES

(a) *Canopy Gaps*

Although closed forest canopies were recorded on well drained alluvial slopes, on some ridge crests, and on some footslopes, open forest canopies predominate. Canopy openings may occur either because trees have never grown in certain sites, or because trees or branches have fallen. Tree growth is inhibited by stony land

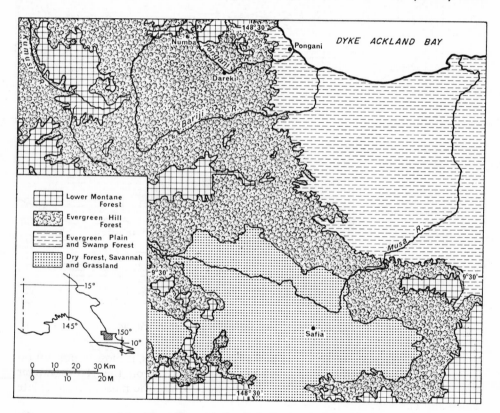

5.1 Vegetation of the Safia-Pongani area, Papua

and poorly drained soils; thus some blocky lava cascades have thin-stemmed, low open forest, whilst poorly drained alluvial slopes typically have poor forests with open canopy. In such instances the lower tree storey and/or the shrub layer is usually very dense where the upper canopy is lacking.

Most of the rainforest, however, is hill forest with an irregular canopy and abundant gaps due to treefall (Plate VIIa). Treefall is facilitated by the general shallow root anchorage of rainforest trees and appears to be caused by three main agents—erosion, mass movement, and wind. Catastrophic treefall, namely destruction by large rapid mass movements, earthquakes, or heavy airborne ash falls, is not considered here.

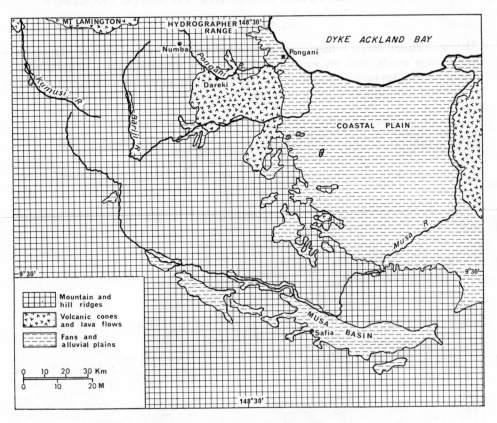

5.2   *Landforms of the Safia-Pongani area, Papua*

Treefall by erosion, though common along stream banks, is most important on steep slopes where easily erodible friable soils occur, as on the Hydrographer Range. Small trees with very shallow rooting systems are the most affected (Plate VIIIb and c).

Treefall by mass movement is clearly displayed in linear gaps torn in the forest canopy by small-scale rapid avalanches, slides, and slips (Plate VIIa). However, slow mass movement, though less obvious, may in aggregate create more canopy gaps. On very steep slopes many tree bases are bent, large trees often lean over at angles, and owing to the creep of the soil and weathered rock the trees usually fall down before reaching maturity.

Wind-caused fall of trees and branches is common amongst old emergent trees in exposed situations, such as high ridge crests and gaps in the mountains through which the wind is funnelled. Winds of up to 60-70 km per hour have been estimated during squalls on exposed coastal sites. Monsoonal gales may last several days (R.A.A.F. 1942), and with the high accompanying precipitation will be the most likely to cause treefall.

Falling trees often tear large gaps in the canopy, particularly where climbers are abundant, for neighbouring trees are pulled down too. Thus near Dareki, in a tall evergreen hill forest with abundant rattans and high emergent trees, the fall of large strangling figs has created canopy gaps of over 1000 m² on gentle slopes.

(b) *The Forest Floor*

Leaf litter and duff average about 20 mm thick under closed canopy forest on gentle slopes, and on ridge crests may be exceptionally thick, attaining 250 mm at 2000 m (Plate VIIIa). On hill and mountain slopes they are thin (Plate VIIb), averaging less than 3 mm, and on many steep slopes the ground typically has only a scattering of recently fallen leaves.

In forests with canopy gaps due to treefall, trunks, branches, and twigs are scattered over the forest floor in various stages of decomposition. Owing to the rapid rate of decay, such debris is never very abundant, and it is unlikely that it has a significant effect on the processes of erosion described below.

SLOPEWASH PROCESSES

The general term slopewash is here taken to include the action of raindrops and unconcentrated wash.

(a) *Raindrop Erosion*

The erosive action of pelting rain, described by Bradley (1940), has been analysed in some detail by Ellison (1944, 1950), who termed the process splash erosion by rainbeat. When rain falls on a bare soil the initial raindrops break down the soil aggregates by impact, detaching soil particles and forming muddy suspensions. Further raindrops may cause splashing, which tends to displace the muddy suspensions preferentially downslope. Where the soil surface includes resistant portions, differential raindrop erosion forms small earth pillars.

In rainforest only a small proportion of the raindrops fall directly to the ground except at canopy openings. Most of them are intercepted by the leaves in the canopy, and either re-form as waterdrops which fall from the drip tips of the leaves, or trickle down twigs and branches to reach the ground by the tree trunks. Freise (1936) estimated that in Brazilian rainforest about two-thirds of the total rainfall reaches the ground, one third as raindrops and waterdrops, and one third by streaming down the tree trunks.

In the study area, the effects of raindrop and waterdrop erosion are seen mostly in small earth pillars on the bare incoherent subsoil brought up by treefall, and on slopes where leaf litter and duff are sparse or absent (Plate VIIId). Most areas with a pronounced development of earth pillars are found beneath canopy openings and are therefore the product of raindrop erosion. In some instances the areas covered by earth pillars extend beyond the canopy openings, and this is attributed to the penetration of driving rain at varying angles. Waterdrop erosion produces smaller earth pillars scattered over bare soil patches beneath closed canopies. Although less obvious, it may be a more important agent of erosion than raindrop erosion because it operates over much larger areas.

Many of the waterdrops in rainforest will have a free fall of over 8 m and will be close to their terminal velocities when they strike the ground (Laws 1941; Mihara 1951). Waterdrop erosion is thus more important under rainforest than under temperate forest because of the higher upper storey, the greater rainfall, and the less abundant leaf litter. Small raindrops in light rainfall will re-form in the rainforest canopy into waterdrops which may be of large size. This may explain why the effects of slopewash are pronounced on steep slopes at 1800 m, where the precipitation is mainly from light rain and drizzle, for the observer experiences a constant dripping in the lower montane forest at high altitudes, even in mist.

(b) *Unconcentrated Wash*

Unconcentrated wash includes rainwater flow and braided rills (Fenneman 1908) and may be defined as the 'water from rain after it has fallen on the surface of the ground and before it has been concentrated into definite streams' (Bryan 1922). Unconcentrated wash in rainforest in this part of northern Papua performs three functions—removal of leaf litter and duff, removal of muddy suspensions formed by raindrop and waterdrop erosion, and erosion of the soil surface.

During prolonged and intense storms rainwater flow sweeps away the loose leaf litter and duff by direct hydraulic action involving flotation and fluviraption (Malott 1928). Further, the buoyant effect of the water on debris of such low density reduces friction considerably and allows transport by traction, even with thinner water films. Near Dareki, leaf litter has been removed on a large scale on slopes as low as 5°, and deposited downslope.

Muddy suspensions formed by raindrop and waterdrop erosion have been observed moving away from areas of earth pillars during rainstorms. It is to be expected that unconcentrated wash at such sites will be loaded to capacity from the start (Lawson 1932), and it may even grade into minute mudflows (Bradley 1940). The material so transported is often deposited at root barriers to form a series of steps which hinder further erosion immediately upslope until the roots are undermined or rot away.

Scoured surfaces and accumulations of lag gravel (Plate VIIId) indicate that unconcentrated wash frequently has sufficient depth and energy to transport detached soil particles. Initially the water films derived from litter-covered surfaces are clear, but as they gather into braided rills and travel over patches of bare soil, erosion commences and the water becomes turbid. Much of this erosion will involve only the sweeping away of loose particles on the soil surface, but if rain and waterdrops fall on to the moving water the motion of water threads into the soil locally is often sufficiently enhanced to detach soil particles (Ekern 1950).

There is evidence in many places of irregular downcutting into the soil on slopes as gentle as 10°.

Rainwater streaming down tree trunks sometimes has sufficient energy to effect erosion at the tree base (Birot 1960). Leaf litter and duff are often removed preferentially from the lower side of trees, and it has been observed locally that severe scouring has undermined lateral surface roots downslope. In no instance, however, was a rill seen to head at a large tree, and it seems that the water concentrated by trunk trickle is rapidly dispersed. Tree-base scouring is often followed by caving of the risers at root steps (Plate VIIIb), and so may lead to treefall. Caving is apparently assisted by seepage and backtrickle (Ireland *et al.* 1939; Ireland 1955).

SLOPE EROSION

The rapid rise of the streams and their muddy nature after heavy rains indicate considerable runoff from and erosion of the slopes. Little of this erosion, however, results from concentrated linear flow, as gullies are infrequent; nor is mass movement thought to be the dominant agent, as slope scars and terracettes are common only on the minority of slopes steeper than 40°. Erosion appears to act uniformly over the whole slope and any irregularities are rapidly smoothed out. Thus, although a mound and trench microrelief due to treefall may persist on gentle slopes, particularly on ridge crests, only very fresh mounds and trenches are seen on the steeper slopes, where trenches have often been filled by crudely stratified soil. It appears that slopewash, combined with mass movement which does not cause surface irregularities, is responsible for the fashioning of these smooth, straight profiles.

The removal of leaf litter and duff is probably largely due to runoff derived from trunk trickle, through which a large proportion of the total rainfall reaches the ground. In this way water is commonly supplied to the soil at the tree base faster than it can infiltrate, and runoff may therefore occur after only moderate rainfalls. The author has witnessed runoff downslope from tree bases on steep slopes in the Hydrographer Range after only 40 mm in five hours. The downslope removal of vegetable debris is an important part of total erosion (Lovering 1959), since leaves contain a high proportion of mineral matter.

The detachment of the soil on the other hand is mainly by raindrop and waterdrop action, as in other climates (Baver 1959; Ellison 1945; Mihara 1951). This is apparent in that there is no tendency for soils to become finer downslope, as should result from unconcentrated wash, which usually selectively transports only the fine soil particles, leaving coarser-textured soils upslope (Birot 1949). Raindrop and waterdrop erosion involves a very wide range of soil-particle sizes, and intermediate (fine sand) grade is often preferred (Ekern 1950). Drops of large size and high impact velocity can move particles of up to 10 mm diameter (Ellison 1944); hence these processes are capable of transporting the whole range of soil material.

Some authors have stated that slopewash operates only when soil is saturated after heavy and prolonged rain (Baulig 1940), but runoff can occur whenever water is supplied to the soil surface faster than it can infiltrate, as at tree bases. Moreover, raindrop and waterdrop erosion are effective from the beginning of a rainstorm, and runoff starts as soon as the soil surface is sealed by the fine particles released by drop impact. Further, the occurrence of tree-base scour indicates that runoff can locally erode without an initial phase of overland flow (Horton 1945).

To the effects of slopewash must be added those of superficial mass movement, including soil creep, local soil flow, and downslope eluviation of subsoil material. These movements are augmented by treefall, which tends to bring coarser-textured subsoil to the surface.

As the forests evolve, and as canopy gaps produced by treefall are followed by regrowth, with resulting changes in the distribution of leaf litter, the whole slope surface, including both coarse and fine soil particles, will be evenly worked over by the processes described above.

The effects of slopewash under mature primary rainforest were observed on nearly all slopes above 5° in the Safia-Pongani area, between sea level and 2000 m, and under rainfalls ranging from 1750 to over 3000 mm. The effects were most pronounced on steep slopes where the hill forest canopies are very irregular with abundant gaps, and where leaf litter and duff are thin; however, severe slopewash can occur on gentle slopes. Thus near Dareki, clayey silt soils developed on basalt have been considerably redistributed by slopewash on declivities of 3° to 15° where treefall is common on this exposed plateau. On very steep slopes, between 40° and 50°, the effects of soil flow and soil slips are apparent in terracettes, whilst soil avalanches are common in the wetter areas, particularly on the more clayey soils.

Deforestation in the drier areas, as in the Musa Basin, has formed large areas of savannah and grassland in which slopewash has been accelerated. In contrast, deforestation in the wetter areas has resulted in large areas of regrowth with a dense cover of shrubs and low trees which provide almost complete protection of the ground. In such areas slopewash has been slowed down, but it gradually regains its importance as regrowth develops into secondary forest.

SLOPE BUDGET AND LANDFORMS

The straight slopes, between 35° and 40°, which predominate in the mountain areas, are mantled with shallow, loamy soils containing a high proportion of unstable minerals from the parent rock, and there is no change in depth of weathering or coarseness of soil up and down the slope; neither is there a tendency for leaf litter and soil material to accumulate at the base. Weathering is therefore balanced by erosion, and the material eroded is transported from the area by the rivers as fast as it is fed to them. On these smooth slopes gully corrasion produces only a minor part of the rock debris, and because of the dominance of slopewash in erosion most of the detritus is derived from the shallow, immaturely weathered soil layers. Hence correlative sediments in aggrading fans and alluvial plains consist mainly of fresh, unstable rock and mineral particles of sand and coarse silt grade.

Characteristically straight profiles indicate that erosion acts uniformly over the whole slope. This may be an expression of the fact that slopewash is more effective in moving than in detaching material, and that processes of transport are competent to handle the load supplied, despite a possible downslope increase

VIIa *Evergreen hill forest in northern Papua shows an irregular canopy with numerous openings mostly caused by treefall and gaps caused by rapid mass movements*

VIIb *Differential erosion at tree roots forms steps with risers facing downslope. Note the sparsity of leaf litter.*

VIIIa Thick leaf litter occurs only on ridge crests where slopewash is absent

VIIIb Undermining of small trees by caving beneath the root mat assisted by seepage and back-trickle

VIIIc Shallow-rooted trees heave up a thin wall of soil on falling

VIIId Rainbeat forms small earth pillars, whilst raindrop erosion and unconcentrated wash leave lag gravel

resulting from progressive accession of material from above. Another factor may be the shifts of localised erosion beneath irregular forest canopies.

Such is the balance that basal slope concavity is generally absent, and it is noteworthy that exceptional development of concave lower slopes is only found where deforestation in the drier Musa Basin has resulted in accelerated rillwash and even in gullying. Erosion shows no tendency to diminish near the crests, and slopewash would appear capable of maintaining narrow ridge crests. Davis (1892) and Schumm (1956) have both claimed, in other morphoclimatic settings, that dominant rainwash erosion produces steep, straight slopes and narrow divides.

True knife-edge ridges occur in the Safia-Pongani area only where relict weathering profiles are present on the ridge crests and where resultant rapid mass movement on upper slopes has led to over-steepening. Similarly in Hawaii, Wentworth (1928, 1943) claimed that very straight, steep slopes, between 40° and 50°, are maintained by soil flow and that soil avalanching during exceptionally heavy rains produces knife-edge ridges.

A combination of uniform slope erosion and competent removal of eroded material by rivers results in 'ridge-and-ravine' landforms which predominate in the area. Since in unit time an equal thickness of material is eroded from all parts of the straight slopes, parallel slope retreat results (cf. Twidale 1960). Where straight slopes meet in narrow ridge crests, parallel slope retreat constitutes a vertical lowering of the whole land surface, including ridge crests and ravine bottoms, at a uniform rate; in other words there is a state of dynamic equilibrium (Hack 1960).

REFERENCES

Baulig, H. (1940). Le profil d'équilibre des versants. *Annls Géogr.* **49**: 81-97.

Baver, L. D. (1959). *Soil Physics.* New York.

Birot, P. (1949). *Essais sur quelques problèmes de morphologie générale.* Lisbon.

—— (1960). *Le cycle d'érosion sous les différents climats.* Rio de Janeiro.

Bradley, W. H. (1940). Pediments and pedestals in miniature. *J. Geomorph.* **2**: 244-55.

Bryan, K. (1922). *Erosion and Sedimentation in the Papago Country, Arizona.* U.S. Geol. Surv. Bull. No. 730.

Cotton, C. A. (1958). Dissection and redissection of the Wellington landscape. *Trans. R. Soc. N.Z.* **85**: 409-25.

—— (1962). The origin of feral (fine-textured) relief. *N.Z. Jl Geol. Geophys.* **5**: 269-70.

Davis, W. M. (1892). The convex profile of badland divides. *Science* **20**: 245.

Ekern, P. C. (1950). Raindrop impact as the force initiating soil erosion. *Proc. Soil Sci. Soc. Am.* **15**: 7-10.

Ellison, W. D. (1944). Studies of raindrop erosion. *Agric. Engng, St Joseph, Mich.* **25**: 131-6, 181-2.

—— (1945). Some effects of raindrops and surface flow in soil erosion and infiltration. *Trans. 26th Ann. Meeting Am. Geophys. Union.* Pt III: 415-29.

—— (1950). Soil erosion by rainstorms. *Science* **111**: 245-9.

Fenneman, N. M. (1908). Some features of erosion by unconcentrated wash. *J. Geol.* **16**: 746-54.

Freise, F. (1936). Das Binnenklima von Urwäldern in subtropischen Brasilien. *Petermanns Mitt.* **82**: 301-7.

Hack, J. T. (1960). Interpretation of erosional topography in humid temperate regions. *Am. J. Sci.* **258-A**: 80-97.

H

Horton, R. E. (1945). Erosional development of streams and their drainage basins; hydrophysical approach to quantitative morphology. *Bull. geol. Soc. Am.* **56**: 275-370.

Ireland, H. A. (1955). Surface tension as a factor in gradation. *Am. J. Sci.* **253**: 162-72.

———, Sharpe, C. F. S., and Eargle, D. H. (1939). *Principles of Gully Erosion in the Piedmont of South Carolina.* U.S. Dept Agric. Tech. Bull. No. 633.

Krynine, P. D. (1936). Geomorphology and sedimentation in the humid tropics. *Am. J. Sci.* **232**: 297-306.

Laws, J. O. (1941). Measurements of the fall-velocity of water-drops and raindrops. *Trans. Am. geophys. Un.* **22**: 709-21.

Lawson, A. C. (1932). Rain wash erosion in humid regions. *Bull. geol. Soc. Am.* **43**: 703-24.

Lovering, T. S. (1959). Significance of accumulator plants in rock weathering. *Bull. geol. Soc. Am.* **70**: 781-800.

Lowdermilk, W. C. (1930). Influence of forest litter on run-off percolation and erosion. *J. For.* **28**: 474-91.

Malott, C. A. (1928). An analysis of erosion. *Proc. Indiana Acad. Sci.* **37**: 153-63.

Mihara, Y. (1951). Raindrop and soil erosion. *Bull. natn. Inst. agric. Sci.*, Tokyo (Ser. A) **1**: 48-51.

Peltier, L. (1950). The geographic cycle in periglacial regions as it is related to climatic geomorphology. *Ann. Ass. Am. Geogr.* **40**: 214-36.

R.A.A.F. (1942). *Weather on the Australia Station. Part I. Bismarck Archipelago.* Publ. No. 252, Vol. II, Air Force H.Q., Melbourne.

Richards, P. W. (1952). *The Tropical Rain Forest.* London.

Sapper, K. (1935). *Geomorphologie der feuchten Tropen.* Geogr. Schr. 7. Leipzig.

Schumm, S. A. (1956). The role of creep and rainwash on the retreat of badland slopes. *Am. J. Sci.* **254**: 693-706.

Tricart, J., and Cailleux, A. (1955). *Introduction à la géomorphologie climatique.* Paris.

Twidale, C. R., (1960). Some problems of slope development. *J. geol. Soc. Aust.* **6**: 131-48.

Walker, E. H. (1963). Relative rates of erosion under grass and forest in a valley of western Wyoming. *NW. Sci.* **37**: 104-11.

Wentworth, C. K. (1928). Principles of stream erosion in Hawaii. *J. Geol.* **36**: 385-410.

——— (1943). Soil avalanches on Oahu, Hawaii. *Bull. geol. Soc. Am.* **54**: 53-64.

White, S. E. (1949). Processes of erosion on steep slopes of Oahu, Hawaii. *Am. J. Sci.* **247**: 168-86.

6

Hillslopes and Pediments in the Flinders Ranges, South Australia

C. R. TWIDALE

INTRODUCTION

In many parts of the Flinders Ranges the landscape is dominated by precipitous quartzite bluffs which tower abruptly and majestically over the plains. Scarps formed of other rocks are lower and less dramatic than these, but they too rise sharply from the adjacent lowlands. The nature and evolution of these escarpments and plains, and especially of their junction in the piedmont zone, are examined in this essay.

The observations recorded here derive principally from the Flinders Ranges in South Australia (Fig. 6.1). The area investigated is part of a great geosynclinal belt extending 800 km from the Lake Eyre depression to the Southern Ocean. Sediments of Precambrian and Cambrian age were deposited in the geosyncline. They include several massive beds of quartzite, though three, in ascending stratigraphic order the Emeroo Range, A.B.C. Range, and Pound Quartzite Formations, are especially important in the study area. Wherever they are exposed they dominate the landscape, rising to 300 m above the adjacent plains and valleys. The sediments were folded and faulted during the Palaeozoic; subsequently there has been further considerable faulting and some slight compression. The contorted strata have been subjected to several cycles of erosion, during which structures in resistant strata have been etched out, leaving the erosional history clearly expressed in the present landscape. High in the relief there are remnants of an undulating surface which truncates the structure of the underlying rocks. Its age range is not precisely known, but it is post-Triassic, for it cuts across lacustrine sediments of that age in both the northern and southern Flinders Ranges. Below this high surface are remnants of a system of old valley floors and piedmont plains eroded across the less resistant argillaceous sediments between the upstanding quartzites. These ancient valley floors, which are younger than the high level surface and probably of mid-Tertiary age, have been dissected and in many districts all but eliminated; new plains of erosion have developed in many valleys and basins, while the lower areas have been buried by alluvium. Thus three separate erosional surfaces are represented in the landscape. The present plains and the bench, plateau, and mesa remnants of old valley floors and piedmont plains form part of this study, while the oldest surface, high in the relief, sets a limit to the range of processes discussed later.

The pattern of relief imposed by structure has persisted at least since the Mesozoic. There is evidence of some relief inversion, but many valleys have long been valleys, and relief amplitude has increased throughout later geological time.

95

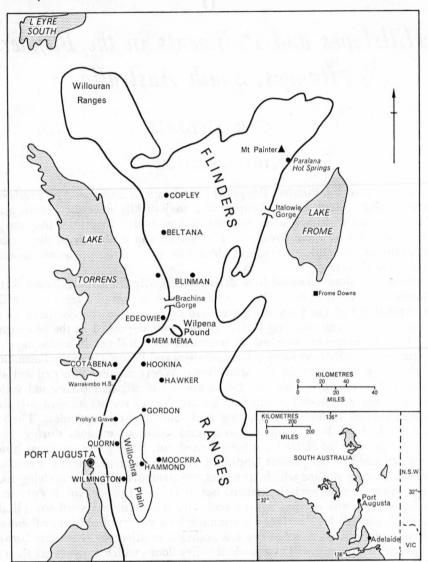

6.1 *The Flinders Ranges and adjacent plains. The upland boundary is marked by a solid line. For* Mem Mema *read* Mern Merna

The Flinders Ranges are semi-arid and arid, and are bounded on the east, north, and west by arid plains traversed by sand dunes and including some notably large salinas. Within the uplands the average annual rainfall decreases from south to north and from west to east (Table 1; Fig. 6.1).

In this typical desert upland rivers are ephemeral. Nevertheless, during floods they transport large volumes of debris, including incredibly large blocks, and achieve much erosion and deposition. Considerable damage is caused by river red gums *(Eucalyptus camaldulensis)* being uprooted and hurled downstream on the flood. Heavy rains also cause serious sheetwash and gullying. Rainfall in this desert area is no more intense than in many humid regions (cf. Russell 1936), but it is particularly effective in erosion for a number of reasons. Runoff is more rapid because of the presence of crusts and other indurated, impermeable soil layers which are common in arid zones. The sparse vegetation, especially in late summer, leaves the soil surface unprotected and the topsoil unbound, thus facilitating erosion, and raindrop impact (Ellison 1945, 1950) is a highly effective erosive force in such conditions. For all these reasons the short-lived floods of these streams probably accomplish more erosion and deposition than results from years of work by more evenly regulated streams.

TABLE 1

Rainfall at selected stations

Station	Annual average cm	Recorded maximum cm (with year)	Recorded minimum cm (with year)
Wilmington	43	74·44 (1889)	21·03 (1940)
Quorn	33	65·45 (1889)	11·99 (1929)
Hawker	30	67·69 (1920)	8·48 (1940)
Blinman	28	54·68 (1920)	8·36 (1940)
Hammond	28	53·67 (1921)	10·01 (1888)
Port Augusta	24	53·08 (1945)	5·61 (1865)
Edeowie	23	45·11 (1920)	6·63 (1940)
Copley	19	39·72 (1889)	5·41 (1940)
Frome Downs	17	47·11 (1950)	2·11 (1902)

Man has aided erosion in deeply weathered bedrock, and especially in unconsolidated veneers, by land clearance and over-grazing, the use of agricultural machinery, the construction of roads, and the introduction of new plants and animals. There is in train an anthropogenic epicycle of erosion manifested in accelerated sheetwash and gullying.

The effects of gullying are spectacular, but erosion by sheetwash, although not as obvious, is at least as important. After rain, plain surfaces are strewn with lines and patches of mixed vegetational and mineral debris, clear evidence of the effects of wash by thin sheets of water. Wind erosion changes the land surface, particularly in plain areas and in summer; compared with wash and gullying its effects may be minor, but the volume of debris moved by wind is considerable. Overgrazed areas are particularly susceptible, as over wide areas of the Willochra Plain where the nitre bush *(Nitraria schoberi)* is established. Windblown sediment has accumulated about these bushes, whilst between them lowering of the land surface has continued, and dome-like fixed dunes up to 2 m high have formed. In summer the surface of the plain is attacked by wind, and especially by the turbulent eddies known as dust devils or willy-willies: there are few more spectacular and eerie sights than the Willochra Plain on a hot, still, summer's day, with spirals of dust silently marching across the land. Even at night the work of wind continues, for

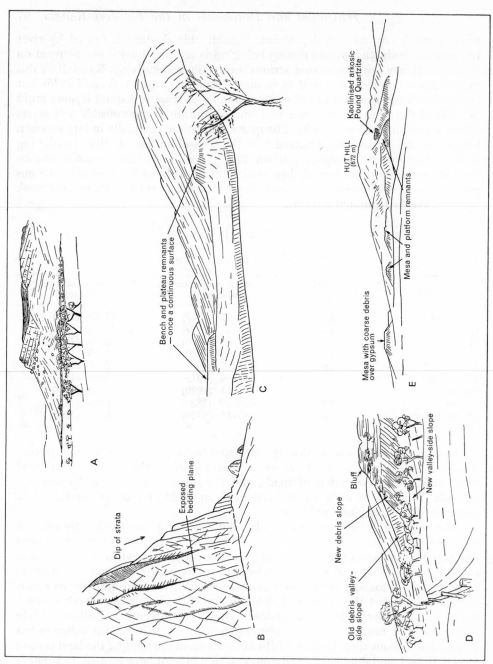

6.2 A. *The Bluff, 15 km NNW of Quorn; a faceted slope with bluff and debris slope units. B. Exposed bedding plane on strike ridge near Buckaringa Gorge. C. Scarp, rock bench, and plateau remnant 1·5 km north of Brachina Gorge. D. Slope adjustments, Pichi Richi Pass. E. Hut Hill, with flanking benches and mesas, including mesa of Fig. 6.6.*

katabatic winds in the vicinity of ridges and ranges move sand and dust in large quantities.

Several agencies collaborate in the weathering, erosion and transportation of detritus, in the scouring of hillslopes, the gullying of unconsolidated debris, and the wash and deflation of all plain surfaces. Both water and wind are important, yet although aeolian activity may be more significant than is generally supposed, the landscape of the Flinders Ranges is one weathered and moulded to an overwhelming extent by water.

THE PIEDMONT ZONE

The piedmont zone comprises four distinct elements: the backing scarp, the present plains, the remnants of former plains and valley floors, and the piedmont angle or junction between hillslope and plain.

(a) *Structural Control of Hillslopes*

Ridges and ranges rise abruptly from the plains whether the latter be depositional or erosional. The uplands are composed of various steep slope units which commonly include bluffs and so-called debris slopes, especially where quartzite crops out. Debris slope, or constant slope (Wood 1942), is the term applied to a rectilinear bedrock slope of moderately steep inclination and commonly possessing a veneer of debris. Several factors influence the forms of steep slopes. Structure exerts a strong control, but the nature and effectiveness of the present weathering and erosional processes, and the history of the region in question, are also important.

Bold bluffs have developed upon resistant quartzite and to a lesser extent upon limestone and tillite. On quartzite they are extremely common and require no exemplification. The western face of the ranges in the neighbourhood of Brachina Gorge (Plate IXa) shows a bluff formed on limestone. Bluffs formed on argillaceous rocks occur in the study area, but smooth graded concave slopes are more characteristically developed on them.

The attitude of strata significantly influences the detailed form of steep slopes, particularly those based upon resistant rocks.

The Bluff and Dutchmans Stern, immediately to the NNW of Quorn (Fig. 6.1), are simple escarpments comprising a single massive bluff of A.B.C. Range Quartzite succeeded below by a smooth rectilinear debris slope (Fig. 6.2A), though close examination shows that the debris slope is interrupted in a few places by low bluffs coincident with outcrops of resistant beds or lenses of quartzite similar to that which forms the main bluff. Nevertheless these are intrinsically simple forms, in contrast with others comprising several bluffs separated by gentler debris slopes. Such compound slopes occur on the east-facing Pound Quartzite escarpment of the Elder Range, north of Hawker, and on the outward-facing bluffs of Wilpena Pound.

Structural planes have greater expression in the bluff than in any other slope unit. Which plane predominates in a given locality depends principally upon the disposition of the strata. On very steep dips as near Buckaringa Gorge, 31 km north of Quorn, where the A.B.C. Range Quartzite dips 70-80° to the east, the prominent bluffs on scarp as well as dip slopes are in fact exposed bedding planes (Fig. 6.2B). More commonly, however, it is joints which effectively control the form of the bluff, either through the weathering of joint blocks *in situ* or through the dislodgment of blocks. Outlines have been softened and rounded by weathering, but only to a minor extent where quartzite crops out.

On more typical, less steeply inclined strata, however, dip slopes are long inclines coincident with bedding planes, separated by short steep reverse slopes which are joint planes. Some of these steeper facets face upslope, others down. Such dip slopes are very common in quartzite terrain, for instance on the inner slopes of Wilpena Pound, adjacent to The Bluff and Dutchmans Stern, and on quartzite-controlled slopes between Copley and Beltana. The influence of structure on slopes is well seen in the Horseshoe Range, north of Moockra, where minor anticlines and synclines occur in a broad synclinal structure affecting the A.B.C. Range Quartzite: here the forms of slopes change abruptly with the attitude of the beds. Between Wilpena Pound and Blinman, where limestones are inter-bedded with softer argillaceous strata, long dip slopes are separated by short but precipitous escarpments coincident with the limestone outcrops; these latter display minor solutional effects and blocky disintegration.

(b) *Weathering and Erosion of Slopes*

In the arkosic Pound Quartzite disintegration is facilitated by the presence of feldspar susceptible to hydration, and the numerous white scars in gullies and landslips in many parts of the Flinders Ranges are exposures of such weathered rocks. Not all the quartzites are arkosic, but even those which are virtually pure and therefore chemically almost inert are nevertheless susceptible to weathering. They disintegrate without apparent alteration or loss of particles into quite coarse fragments, and are eventually broken down to their constituent sand. The quartzites may also be slightly susceptible to solution, for the Pound Quartzite in particular displays superficial granular disintegration resulting in the production of a sugary texture, possibly due to the removal of the siliceous matrix. The insolation hypothesis of rock weathering has been resurrected to explain the blocky disintegration of quartzite in central Australia (Ollier 1963), despite negative results of earlier laboratory experiments carried out to test the mechanism. The intense heat of bushfires causes flaking of rock (Blackwelder 1927; Emery 1944), as is clearly seen on the slopes of Wilpena Pound, which experienced severe fires during November 1960, but the temperatures thus generated are beyond the range of insolation effects. Griggs (1936) suggested, however, that heating and cooling effectively shatter minerals and rocks in the presence of moisture, and there is some indication, in the form of secondary silicification and iron-staining, that water penetrates into the quartzites in the study area.

Many blocks on bluffs are affected by cavernous weathering, in which the interiors are wasted away, leaving an exterior shell largely intact. In some cases these hollows have coalesced to form large shelters or caverns. At several such sites in the Flinders, flaking on inside walls has been noted, though there is no evidence as to whether the process is active or not. In some, successive thin flakes of quartzite (Plate XIIa) exemplify a type of negative exfoliation (Wagner 1912; cf.

Simpson 1964), while in a shelter at Yourumbulla Caves, south of Hawker, a silicified sandstone displays perfect large-scale conchoidal fractures caused by weathering.

Cavernous weathering is of some significance in slope development, for bluffs are maintained and retreat because they are undermined. This undermining results from strong erosion of the debris slope and lower bluff, in part related to differential cavernous weathering. Some rocks are not sufficiently coherent to withstand any undermining, and hence no caverns form, but basal sapping and recession of the bluff nevertheless occur. In the Arkaba Hills, and north of the Chace Range, 8 km southeast of Wilpena Pound, for example, voluminous cones of finely comminuted purple shale at the base of low bluffs in the same material have resulted from their undermining and collapse.

Caverns are initiated by several agencies acting either singly or in combination, and in several sites. They develop where strata of contrasted lithology and resistance to weathering and erosion crop out in a bluff, or by the undermining of the base of the bluff by regressive stream erosion on the debris slope. Examples are common, but are especially fine near Puttapa Gap, between Copley and Beltana. The base of cliffs or bluffs is very susceptible to cavern initiation; accordingly, where a line of caverns occurs within the bluff, and where there is no bedrock control, it is arguable that it developed in relation either to a former plain level or to the upper limit of a debris slope which is no longer present. There is also evidence that some caverns develop because of particularly intense weathering in the zone of oscillating water table, and that caverns may be initiated by lateral stream action, through corrasion, in wet bank slumping, or tunnel development.

Of all the sites for cave initiation, the cliff foot is the most common. It is the area most exposed to wetting and drying and to maximum biological activity, both of which assist in rock weathering. The contact of bedrock and plain mantle is particularly susceptible to solution. The mantle may in places act as an impermeable capping and induce spring-line conditions at the junction, at which there in some evidence of flushing (Twidale 1964).

Weathered debris is evacuated from the bluff by wash and by mass movement. Coarse blocks fall when rendered unstable by the weathering of adjacent blocks, and especially when undermined. Fine debris is washed through cracks and fractures and across rock faces. After very heavy rains torrential mudflows and debris avalanches occur on steep slopes such as the north face of Dutchmans Stern, Mt Aleck (in the Elder Range), and on the western face of the ranges between Parachilna and Port Augusta. This waste material falls or is otherwise transported to the debris slope.

Structural control, and sapping and undermining, together ensure that the bluff maintains a constant inclination within narrow limits as long as it survives. The preservation of the bluff, which principally distinguishes the faceted from the graded slope, is important in that it allows quite steep debris slopes to be maintained. Its survival is aided by the presence of protective cappings such as laterite, silcrete, and dolerite, or other resistant strata (Fair 1947; Pallister 1956); the removal of such a capping permits slopes to decline, in contrast with the parallel retreat that occurs during earlier stages.

In the Flinders Ranges debris slopes range between 10° and 30°, 22-26° being general on quartzite and limestone slopes unaffected by stream attack. Inclinations on argillaceous rock are of a lower order, generally between 10° and 12°, but ranging up to 25°. The calibre of the debris veneer varies according to the nature of the bluff and the debris slope supplying the detritus, but in general it decreases down the slope. In many places, as on the older granites of the Mt Painter complex (Fig. 6.1), and especially on quartzite, the cover is negligible. Elsewhere it forms a uniform veneer, for instance a 30-40 cm layer over most of the slopes of the conical peak known locally as Fuji Yama in the Arkaba Hills (north of Hawker and east of the Elder Range). In some places thick wedges of debris blanket the slopes, for instance in the Pichi Richi Pass between Port Augusta and Quorn, where debris is at least 8 m thick in one locality.

The characteristic smoothness of many debris slopes is due to a combination of weathering, erosion, and the filling of hollows by debris migrating downslope, and most slopes on argillaceous rocks are graded in this manner; however, smoothness is rarely attained on slopes on quartzite or limestone.

The mechanism by which coarse debris fallen from the bluff is set spasmodically in motion is suggested by observation on the debris slope of The Bluff, on the upper sector of which there are numerous blocks of quartzite. On the debris slope some of these crumble to sand *in situ,* but others migrate downslope and may attain the base of the debris slope while still virtually unweathered. Some blocks rest on the surface of the slope, whilst some are being buried by fine debris from upslope. Buried and unburied blocks may be incorporated in slow or rapid mass movement of debris; or some blocks may roll independently downslope. Blocks at rest form obstacles to the downhill migration of fines, which accumulate behind and above them to form terracettes. Below the blocks, however, are depressions presumably caused by the unhampered downslope migration of detritus below. In this way, blocks are gradually undermined and eventually rendered unstable; they roll downslope, possibly breaking as they go; when they come to rest, the whole process recommences.

The lower parts of some debris slopes (e.g. Fuji Yama) have slightly convex longitudinal profiles, through very marked stream dissection, or as a result of general steepening. However, the smooth slope between the bluff and stream channel is most commonly slightly concave (Fig. 6.2A), largely, and almost wholly in its lower part, due to water erosion.

Where debris is efficiently evacuated, and there is therefore no significant accumulation, debris slopes on any given rock type have remarkably uniform inclination. This is the inclination just sufficient to permit the available debris to maintain progress downslope, and is an equilibrium slope. It is not the maximum slope, for there are all gradations between this range of gradients and the bluff. But wherever the debris slope, as identified by a veneer of transient debris, is steeper than the equilibrium slope, the obvious cause is intense basal attack and steepening by streams.

The intensity of attack at the base of slopes is an important factor determining slope form in many parts of the Flinders Ranges. Many of the quartzite ridges are broken by river gaps, and in the vicinity of these, where stream attack is locally strong and where evacuation of debris is readily accomplished, debris slopes are of lesser extent and bluffs are consistently higher than between the gaps, and there is basal steepening with the development of slightly convex profiles.

In the winding Brachina Gorge, which is cut into the west-facing escarpment of the Flinders Ranges, there is a consistent relationship between the proportions of the slope units and the effectiveness of debris evacuation as indicated by the position of the stream in relation to a particular slope profile. In places the stream impinges directly against the base of the bluff; here no debris slope exists. Where, however, the channel has migrated from the base of the bluff, a debris slope has developed between stream and bluff. This is in part a slipoff slope formed by the lateral migration of the stream during incision, but it developed also through upward retreat of the bluff under basal attack, especially through cavernous weathering and the corresponding growth of the debris slope.

(c) *Present Plains*

The sinking of bores and the erosion of deep gullies have revealed that many of the plains of the Flinders Ranges are of depositional origin and are underlain by considerable thicknesses of unconsolidated sediment which masks the form of the underlying bedrock surface. The plains surfaces are remarkably flat in general and some in detail also, although others display minor irregularities.

The most extensive area of deposition lying wholly within the study region is the Willochra Plain, some 100 km long from north to south, averaging 17 km in width, and underlain by up to 180 m of unconsolidated basin sediments. Debris continues to accumulate at the margins of the plain, where streams debouch and divide into a number of distributary channels. Many of them fail to reach Willochra Creek, the main drainage line, and in consequence deposit their sediment over the plain surface. In the vicinity of Willochra Creek, however, deep gullying is in progress, whereas the rest of the plain is affected by sheetwash and by aeolian erosion.

There are many other essentially depositional surfaces throughout the area investigated. The interior of Wilpena Pound, for example, is floored by an unknown thickness of unconsolidated debris of mixed alluvial-colluvial origin (Fig. 6.3), and there are numerous local constructional plains along stream valleys. At the foot of Fuji Yama for instance there is a perfect plain which is morphologically indistinguishable from many others in the region, but which, as demonstrated in river and gully sections, is underlain by 6-7 m of red clays and gravels resting upon an irregular rock floor.

Although there are no extensive plains where bedrock is everywhere at the surface, the area does contain plains with a blanket of unstratified detritus no more than 3 m thick, which does not significantly modify the form of the bedrock floor. Erosional surfaces of this type occur as valley floors and narrow piedmont plains, and more extensively as areas of subdued relief, as east of the Willochra Plain. The latter area, however, is suffering incision, and evidence suggests it is cyclically equivalent to the residual plateaux and mesas described below. The erosional surfaces are smooth, characteristically rectilinear or slightly concave, possess few concentrated lines of drainage, and have very little relief save near major channels. They slope gently away at 2-3° from adjacent scarps or hills.

They meet the uplands in a zone of marked concavity rather than angular discontinuity; this is, however, narrow, and the transition from plain to upland is more abrupt than in many landscapes.

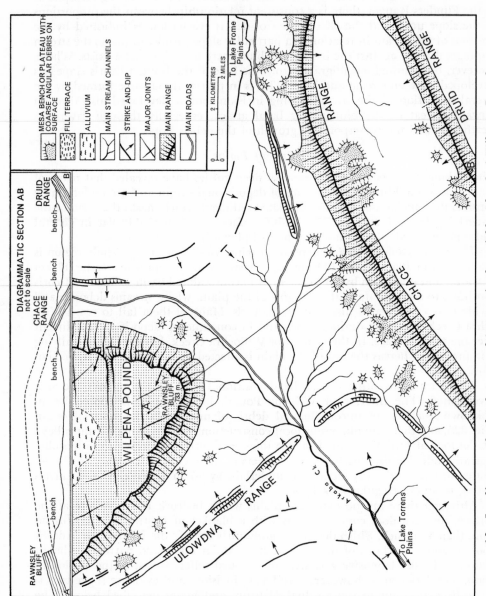

6.3   *Landforms and related structural features in the neighbourhood of Wilpena Pound, Chace Range, and Druid Range*

The thin debris cover consists predominantly of fines, in contrast with that of the old valley-floor remnants described below. Rills and sheetwash are occasionally active and keep the superficial fine debris, though not of course the whole accumulation, in intermittent motion.

(d) *Residual Plateaux and Mesas*

Throughout the Flinders Ranges, remnants of former valley floors and piedmont plains stand above the present plains. They once were comparable with present-day erosional plains in the area, but they have suffered dissection such that only plateaux, mesas, and even-crested spurs remain. These remnants are nowhere extensive, but are much better and more commonly preserved in the north of the area. For example, numerous residuals up to 1·25 km² in area front the ranges on the western side between Hookina and Beltana, a distance of some 110 km.

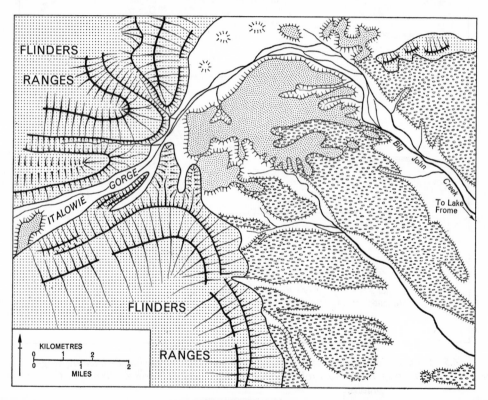

6.4   *Landforms east of Italowie Gorge*

Similar well preserved and comparatively large remnants occur on the eastern flank of the uplands, to the east of the Italowie Gorge, and in the Paralana region (Fig. 6.4).

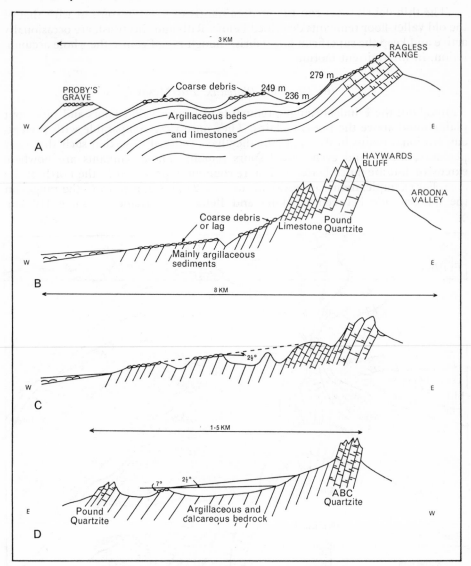

6.5 *Cross-sections of lag-capped mesas and benches in relation to backing ridges.*
A Ragless Range to Probys Grave. B. and C. Just north of Brachina Gorge.
D. At Argadells.

between 1° and 4°, though an inclination of 7° occurs near Argadells, some 27
km north of Quorn, where a hill-plain junction is preserved (Fig. 6.5D). All the
residuals possess a mantle of coarse debris.

In both the Brachina and Italowie Gorge areas there are several former plain
levels. The large number of mesa and plateau remnants in the Brachina area
especially do not fit into a small number of height ranges, even allowing for

The residuals stand between 10 and 50 m above local baselevels, the deepest dissection observed being east of the Italowie Gorge. The upper surfaces of the mesas and plateaux slope smoothly down from the nearby uplands at angles of variation with distance from the escarpment. Some individual spurs and mesas, certainly, can reasonably be correlated on the basis of elevation and projected profiles, but some cannot.

(e) *The Hill-Plain Junction*

In most areas the former plain remnants are separated from the backing scarp by subsequent valleys. In some few areas, however, the former hill-plain junction is preserved, as near Brachina Gorge (Fig. 6.2C; Plate IXb), and on the western slope of the Ragless Range (Fig. 6.5A). The most abrupt junction near Brachina Gorge is a narrow, steeply curved zone in which a 2-2½° slope increases to 22½° in a distance of about 100 m (Figs. 6.5B, 6.5C). The zone of transition is formed in bedrock, and there is no question of a more abrupt rock junction masked by alluvial-colluvial fans. This steeply curved but not truly angular piedmont junction is typical.

THE DEBRIS MANTLE

(a) *Description*

Remnants of the former valley floors and present plains are strewn with angular to subangular debris (Plate XIIb) derived overwhelmingly from local outcrop of quartzite. Though only thin, the debris completely masks the structural trends of the underlying bedrock (Plate X). In gully sections and landslips it appears between 1 m and 3 m thick. The average size of fragments varies considerably from place to place. At Brachina, fragments of 20 cm maximum diameter are characteristic, though they are coarser closer to the bluff. In the Wilpena Pound area, fragments up to 1 m maximum diameter are commonplace, and on the Argadells mesa there is one massive block of 3 m diameter. Although the mantle overlying modern erosional plains is of the same order of thickness as that upon the ancient remnants, the concentration of coarse debris is usually much less. The cappings of the residuals consist of masses of coarse debris set in a matrix of fines, but the veneers found on modern erosional plains commonly consist of fines through which and upon the surface of which there is a scattering of coarse cobbles and gravels. However, the valley floor between Wilpena Pound and the Chace Range has a virtually continuous mantle of cobbles and boulders (Plate IXc).

The mesas are mainly underlain by strata which comprise intensely weathered argillaceous sediments which contribute to the fines but which could not have produced the coarse debris; nowhere are they underlain by massive quartzite. Local bedrock, where resistant, constitutes a significant part of the superficial debris, but even here quartzite is most abundant. Thin underlying limestones contribute to the veneer northwest of Brachina Gorge, thin quartzites elsewhere, but the bulk of the material has been brought in from outside. Perhaps the most convincing demonstration of the alien nature of the coarse superficial deposits occurs in the Hut Hill area northwest of Gordon, where a veneer up to 2·5 m thick overlies wedges of gypsum up to 3 m thick, regarded as salina deposits

(Fig. 6.6). In some few areas, for instance near Probys Grave and Mern Merna, and in the Quorn area, fragments of the siliceous duricrust known in Australia as billy, are an important component of the debris veneer. Around Probys Grave, at one site at Kanyaka 5 km northwest of Gordon, and on the eastern side of the Willochra Plain, the veneer is ferruginised in patches.

The coarse debris is set in a matrix of sand and clay, which becomes quite hard when dry. It is characteristically angular or subangular, and would not appear to have travelled far from its source on backing slopes.

Around Probys Grave and on the dissected Italowie plateau there is much more rounded material than average, but in the latter area some of the rounded boulders and cobbles have been split. Many are of quartzite, and the cause of the

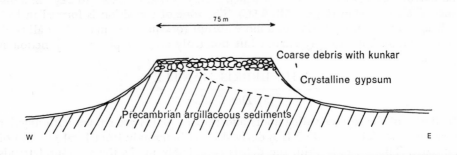

6.6   Mesa with lag capping gypsum, southwest of Hut Hill

disintegration is not known; but one may speculate on the relationship between angularity of debris and duration of exposure. Most of the debris on residuals, however, shows no signs of having been rounded, and there is, moreover, no possibility of its having travelled far along stream beds; only short rills and streamlets could have contributed to most of the plateau mantles.

The coarse debris, both on former and on present plains, is most abundant on residuals located within denuded anticlines, for example between Wilpena Pound and the Chace Range; in synclinal situations, as in the Horseshoe Range, there is less.

(b) *Origin of the Debris Veneer*

(i) *Transportation from Backing Scarps*

Much of the debris found on modern plain surfaces is in course of transport across the slope. In an area in which water flows intermittently, debris is stranded when flow ceases, and some of the next runoff percolates into this debris and causes more to be deposited: the process is thus cumulative. This debris, and particularly coarse debris, exerts a protective influence on the surface.

The debris originating on the bluff and debris slope is carried to the plains by rills, wash, gullying, and by mass movements. Observations suggest that some coarse debris may survive intact the journey down the debris slope and become

IXa Dissected mantled pediments below the western escarpment of the Flinders Ranges north of Brachina Gorge. The lower ridges are of limestone, the higher one behind of Pound Quartzite.

IXb Bench on steeply dipping limestone south of Brachina Gorge, accordant with plateau surface at extreme right

IXc Plateau remnants and gibber-strewn valley floor northwest of quartzitic Chace Range

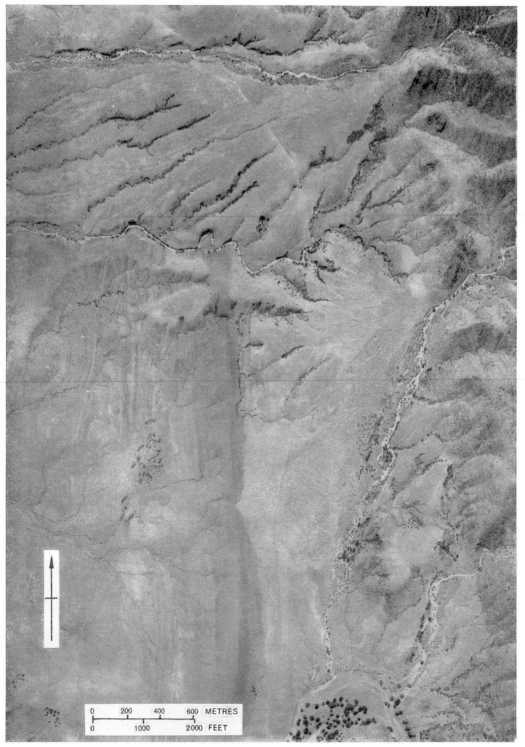

X   *Vertical photograph north of Brachina Gorge showing obliteration of structure on debris-mantled plateau. Photograph by Department of Lands, S. Australia.*

0   200   400   600   METRES

0   1000   2000   FEET

XI   Kaolinised arkosic Pound Quartzite exposed by gullyhead slumping on lower debris slope on west flank of Ragless Range. Note quartzite bluff on crest.

XIIa (right) Details of negative exfoliation on quartzite, Wilpena Pound

XIIb (centre) Coarse debris mantle on plateau near Brachina Gorge

XIIc (below) Bedrock surface beneath debris mantle, smoothly truncating geological structure, 8 km north of Upalinna homestead

immobile once on the plains. Fines, however, continue across the plain surfaces under the influence of wash and streamflow. The coarse debris that remains at or near the scarp foot eventually disintegrates into fines which follow the same path.

It is difficult to conceive of such coarse blocky material as constitutes the debris of the plains moving down slopes of less than 3°, which are prevalent on present and former plains in this area. The matrix of fines could assist mass movement, but even so it is difficult to visualise mobility of debris on such low gradients under the present climate. On steeper slopes, however, local slips and avalanches are initiated during heavy rains, and it is reasonable to enquire whether the debris could have reached its present position by mass movement on slopes of steeper gradient than those obtaining at present, and whether there is any evidence of such steeper slopes in former times.

Debris slides and avalanches have been noted on several steep slopes within the area, and mass movements of a slower type on the debris slope of The Bluff. The limiting slope below which no appreciable mass movement takes place is not known: in areas subject to frost action, movement of material on slopes as gentle as 1° has been recorded, and Balk (1932; see Sharpe 1960) has reported the movement of blocks on inclines of less than 5°. The sparse vegetation and the spasmodically heavy rainfall doubtless favour mass movement in the semi-arid Flinders Ranges and surrounding arid plains, and it is conceivable that there is slow downhill movement of waste saturated with water. Many exposures of slope debris, with rudimentary stratification and consisting of gravel and occasional cobbles set in a matrix of fines, have been observed in the study area, especially in the Pichi Richi Pass, and the lowest inclination of bedrock surface over which such deposits have moved appears to be 3°.

On slopes only slightly steeper than those prevalent on the piedmont plain at present (the evidence suggests that in the Ragless Range/Probys Grave district (Fig. 6.5A) the former concave slope was 4°, steepening upslope to 10° and 20°) coarse debris set in a matrix of fines could be transported a considerable distance from bluffs in intermittent mass movements. Not all the coarse veneer may have been transported in this manner, but it is suggested that this process has played some part. The coarse debris may then have been concentrated by wash and wind. Surfaces with such a debris mantle extending from base of bluff to drainage channel are preserved in the narrow valley known as the Pichi Richi Pass (Fig. 6.2D) and in a few other localities, but most such surfaces have suffered intense erosion in the upper and middle sectors. The lower segments of such slopes are often well preserved: they are the plateau and mesa remnants described in this essay.

In a few areas such as Wilpena Pound, Brachina Gorge (Fig. 6.2C) and adjacent to the Ragless Range (Fig. 6.5A) there are smooth gently inclined benches which could be regarded as remnants of the high plain, but which more probably once connected in gentle concave profiles with the mesa and plateau remnants of the mid-Tertiary plains, from which they have been separated by intense dissection in the scarp foot zone.

White scars of exposed weathered rock are common throughout the Flinders Ranges on lower steep slopes at higher levels than the mesa and plateau remnants. They result from slumping and gullying of bedrock intensely weathered to a

J

depth of at least 12 m. In places, argillaceous sediments have been wholly kaolinised, but most commonly it is the kaolinised feldspars of arkosic sandstone, such
as the Pound Quartzite, which provide the stark white splashes. Such scars are
found below Hut Hill (Fig. 6.2E), on the flanks of Ragless Range (Plate XI), in
the Wilson and Mern Merna areas, and especially in the Angepena-Nepabuna
area of the northern Flinders, west of the Italowie Gorge.

It is unlikely that chemical alteration of this degree could have occurred on
such bare, steeply inclined slopes, and it is more credible that it took place
beneath a gently inclined land surface. As the scars occur consistently lower than
the high-level benches, which may be presumed once to have been more extensive,
the deep and intense weathering may have occurred beneath this former level,
and have facilitated dissection of the surface and exposure of the weathered rock.

The surface of high-level benches and mesas in several areas can be joined by
extrapolation to form gently concave profiles comparable with those of the debris-
mantled slopes of today. This is not conclusive proof of their former connection,
as in some instances the isolated sectors can be fitted to a number of possible
profiles, but it is a contributory line of evidence.

The isolation of the mesas has resulted from differential erosion at the scarp
foot. As rejuvenation migrates upstream, a bluff develops at the base of the
debris slope, erosion and the growth of subsequent tributaries are progressively
more pronounced in the scarp foot zone of deeper weathering, and the lower
parts of the debris slopes are isolated as mesa remnants in a manner recently
suggested for the development of flat-irons in Cyprus (Everard 1963).

(ii) Derivation of Mantles from Superincumbent Strata

Where quartzite beds dip away from the remnants, in anticlinal situations as
between Wilpena Pound and the Chace Range, the coarse fragments may have
been deposited on or close to the escarpment when the latter was in fact adjacent
to the present position of the mesas; the coarse debris has survived weathering
and has been concentrated as a lag due to the evacuation of fines. This origin is
possible in the structural circumstances indicated, but cannot apply in synclinal or
basin structures unless quartzites occurred in formerly superincumbent strata.

At Argadells, for instance (Fig. 6.5D), the quartzite bluff can never have been
in proximity to the mesa, and here the quartzite probably derives from lenses in
the *Archaeocyatha* limestone sequence above the Pound Quartzite: it is suggested
that here too the mantle is in large measure composed of the most resistant part
of once superincumbent strata which have been mostly removed by erosion, the
coarse fraction of which has gradually been concentrated. Such a hypothesis
accounts for many of the characteristics of the coarse superficial debris. Its abundance in areas where quartzites have been folded into anticlinal structures is
readily understood. The contrasted calibre of debris on old surfaces as compared
with modern valley floors is also comprehensible in that the coarse debris
deposited on modern valley floors continues to be inundated in fines washed
from higher levels and spread over the plain surface. Only at the surface of some
modern valley floors has a mantle of coarse debris formed, primarily due to the
winnowing of fines by wind and water, although vertical sorting of debris also

plays a part—in summer, when the soil cracks, fine debris can fall down the crevices, but pebbles and cobbles cannot, and so the coarse tends to be concentrated at the surface.

Much of the coarse debris in the Flinders is considered to have been derived from superincumbent strata. Nevertheless there are areas where this explanation may not hold. In some areas where there is coarse quartzitic debris there is no indication that they were ever overlain by quartzitic strata, for instance north of Brachina Gorge (Fig. 6.5B, 6.5C) the Pound Quartzite to the east of the plateau dips to the west, and cannot have contributed debris to its surface, and though lenses of quartzite may have occurred in the beds formerly overlying the *Archaeocyatha* limestone it is unlikely to have been sufficiently abundant to supply the observed volume of debris.

(iii) Mantles of Fluvial and Lacustrine Origin

In a few areas the coarse debris was emplaced by streams. As noted earlier, some of the coarse debris on the Italowie plateau (Fig. 6.4) is rounded or subrounded and was transported and distributed by Big John Creek, flowing at a higher level than at present, as it emerged from the ranges through the Italowie Gorge. Some of the rounded debris at the north end of the Horseshoe Range could probably have been carried by short streams flowing to Bellaratta Creek, which drains the synclinal basin. The pronounced roundness of the coarse superficial debris between Ragless Range and Probys Grave is less easily explained. The debris may here have been rounded by several streams which converge upon the area, but since lakes are known to have existed in such situations, the rounded debris may be beach shingle.

One of the outstanding features of the western margin of the Flinders Ranges is the distribution of alluvial fans. North of Warrakimbo homestead in the Lake Torrens catchment, there are no alluvial fans, only mantled plains such as those described for the Brachina region. South of Warrakimbo, however, there are magnificent coalesced alluvial fans which continue virtually unbroken to Sellicks Hill, some 55 km south of Adelaide. The explanation of this distribution may lie in the Quaternary history of Lake Torrens, which is now a dry salina lying 34 m above sea level, but which in the fairly recent past contained a considerable body of water. In the Cotabena area lacustrine clays containing mammalian remains suggest a higher stand of the former lake, probably in late Pleistocene or early Recent times. The fossils include diprotodonts which in this region appear to be of late Pleistocene or early Recent age.[*] It can thus be argued that the dissection of the alluvial fans and concentration of coarse debris could date from the shrinkage and eventual elimination of the lake and consequent lowering of base-level. Such an argument would explain why well formed alluvial fans survive outside the catchment of Lake Torrens and why they are absent or present in only a degraded form within the lake basin, and is consistent with the concentration,

---

[*] On the east side of the Willochra Plain the fossil jawbone and teeth of *Nototherium* have been dated at 14,000 ± 225 years B.P. Further to the southeast in the Orroroo district, *Diprotodon* remains have been dated at 11,000 ± 130 years B.P. (Daily 1960). It is unlikely that these giant marsupials could have survived on the modern vegetation of the area, and they probably indicate a former more lush vegetation related to a pluvial climate.

nature, and form of the debris of the mantle. A similar situation obtains in the piedmont zone of the Flinders Ranges in the Lake Frome Basin.

The weakness of this argument rests in the completeness of degradation of the alleged alluvial fans: surely, somewhere, the original thickness of deposits would have survived in this arid climate?

ORIGIN OF THE BEDROCK SURFACES

The problem of the genesis of the bedrock surfaces, the erosional surfaces beneath the thin mantles, remains. They resemble pediments as generally described. It has been suggested that some pediments are exhumed forms, (Yi-fu Tuan 1959), but there is no evidence of this in the Flinders, and in any case the mode of development of the remarkably smooth bedrock surfaces is not thereby explained. Observations on plains where rock is at or near the surface suggest that the rillwash, distributary streams, weathering, and sheetwash presently responsible for moulding the erosional plains also developed the older plains and valley floors, either before or during the deposition of debris. Subsurface erosion by solution (Trendall 1962) and by subsurface drainage and flushing (Ruxton 1958) may also have played a part.

Wherever it has been observed, the bedrock surface below the transported debris is smooth, with no evidence of buried soils or alluvium between it and the slope debris (Plate XIIc). This type of section is well exposed 1 km north of Upalinna homestead, some 8 km northeast of Wilpena Pound, and there are similar sections in the Pichi Richi Pass, but slopes are somewhat steeper there. The form of contact suggests that the incorporation of weathered bedrock into a static or slowly moving debris veneer may have been an important further cause of subsurface bedrock smoothing. That mass movement of unconsolidated debris can erode underlying bedrock is shown by the so-called 'shaved surfaces' of the Wellington region of New Zealand (Cotton and Te Punga 1955), and there seems no reason why slower flows on the more gentle slopes of this area could not have eroded the surfaces over which they passed, particularly if the bedrock were weathered.

THE PIEDMONT ANGLE

Both past and present plains meet the backing scarps in sharp transition. This abrupt break of slope is not truly angular, as is the case elsewhere (Howard 1942), but falls into the category of piedmont angle. The feature is a critical one in that the distinction between pediments and Davisian mature valley-floor side strips (Davis 1930) rests largely upon the sharp break of slope between the pediment and the escarpment. Otherwise, as Hills (1955) has implied, there is no essential difference between the two forms. The origin of the piedmont angle is therefore significant.

In the study area, several factors contribute to the development of a piedmont angle. One is the burial of lower bedrock slopes by alluvium, colluvium, and wind-blown debris. As the surface of such accumulations is commonly very gently inclined, compared with the lower bedrock slopes, the junction of hill and plain is inevitably made more abrupt. This is the case where there are valley fills of considerable thickness, for example Fuji Yama which rises abruptly from an alluvial plain. But this is not a general explanation, for most junctions are etched in bedrock.

Another factor contributing to the comparatively rapid change of gradient is structure. The piedmont angle is generally related to a change in lithology, though it is not suggested that it everywhere coincides with a lithological boundary. Escarpments consist of or are capped by resistant strata—commonly quartzite, though limestone also acts in this way—which shed coarse veneers over the steep lower slopes excavated in weathered or unconsolidated rocks. Such cappings defend the slope and prevent its decline. They are removed principally by undermining, and in this way generate the steepest possible escarpments. Further, it is the protection afforded plain surfaces by gibber and similar accumulations which accounts for the prevalence of plateau and mesa forms in the plains.

The abrupt change of slope in the piedmont zone is caused principally, however, by differential weathering at the foot of the scarp. Northwest of Brachina Gorge, for example, the bedrock 1·5 km from the scarp is weathered only to a moderate degree: structural features such as bedding remain distinct and the rock retains its strength and cohesion. Close under the scarp, however, similar strata are much more intensely altered. Kaolin is abundant, bedding only vaguely discernible, and the rock has lost much of its strength and is easily crumbled in the hand. A similar zone of deep and intense weathering occurs around the southern and southwestern scarp of Wilpena Pound. Runoff from the often bare hillslopes percolates into the rock strata where it reaches the plain, causing intense weathering (cf. Clayton 1956; Twidale 1962). Where pervious quartzites or limestones form the scarp the effect of differential weathering may be even more pronounced on account of subsurface seepage into the hill foot zone.

Once consequent streams regress to the scarp foot, tributaries rapidly develop in this weakened zone, causing most remnants to be separated from the scarp. Furthermore, the etching out of deep valleys in the scarp foot zone and the development of tributaries on the lower slopes of the escarpments ensure that the latter are constantly regraded. Resistant cappings are in this way undermined. Thus a fairly abrupt transition from plain to hill is inevitable. Moreover, the dissection of the scarp-foot zone and regrading of escarpments cause the removal of all but a few remnants—the high-level benches mentioned earlier—of former, more gentle slopes.

This hypothesis is summarised in Figure 6.7, where a sequence of forms is shown. Considering an anticlinal structure in which there is a massive quartzite stratum, the early valley is narrow, the streams short and swift, and the debris weathered and eroded from the valley sides is readily evacuated. The coarse debris is, however, distributed on the debris slope and especially on the upper part of that element. The bluff is undermined and retreats, maintaining a constant inclination.

Erosion of the bedrock surface of the debris slope is effected by rills, streams, and wash. Evacuation of coarse debris becomes progressively more difficult and the coarse fraction is concentrated to form a debris mantle on lower slopes. Erosion of the bedrock by surface water diminishes but may be continued by subsurface agencies. At inclinations of 2-3° evacuation of debris is so slow as to be negligible. The mantled slope is immune from wash and rill action, but streams that have

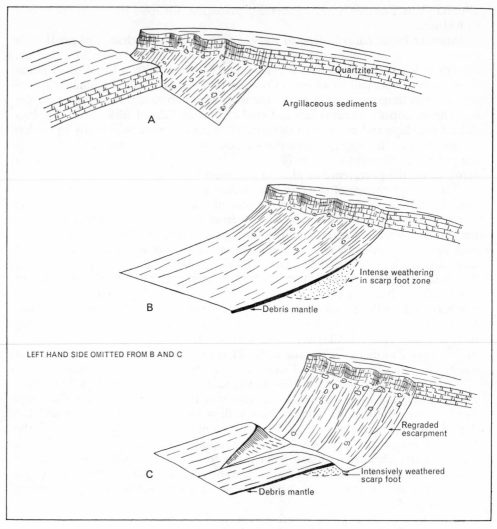

6.7   Scheme of development of hillslopes and mantled pediments

penetrated through the debris veneer extend and develop rapidly laterally; once they reach the zone of bedrock that has been deeply weathered they incise rapidly, and quickly develop tributaries; the bluff at the base of the erstwhile debris slope recedes under this intensive erosion and eventually merges with the bluff above to form the steepest possible slope. The lower slopes are dissected and isolated, and the new plain level extends headwards.

Such an evolution of the piedmont zone is consistent with the suggested modes of origin of the debris veneers which mantle both present plains and former plain remnants. The three suggested origins of the debris veneer are not of course mutually exclusive: on the contrary it is certain that all have operated and still operate, though each assumes especial significance locally. The wash of debris from slopes and its transportation by streams clearly proceed in step. Subsurface percolation on lower debris slopes evidenced in this area and elsewhere, not only causes intense weathering of bedrock in the zone, but also causes debris to be deposited there through loss of surface water. The debris absorbs subsequent runoff, and thus sediment accumulation is self-promoting.

The subsurface decay of bedrock permits scarp foot erosion and stream incision, which in turn isolate the debris; the latter is then subject to degradation, though it is no longer added to. There is, within the area investigated, no evidence concerning the rate of surface lowering of the debris surfaces, but Kedar (1957) and Sharon (1962) have claimed that hamada surfaces in Israel with 100 mm rainfall are lowered at an average rate of 3-4 mm per annum by the evacuation of fines.

The explanation of the coarse debris mantles as being derived from hill slope-wash and from alluvial fans is in accord with the suggested evolution of the piedmont angle, but it would be unwise to discard a possible origin from super-incumbent strata where structure allows. If this explanation is valid, however, the inheritance of some debris originally accumulated on the high or summit surface is involved; as the latter is very old, a remarkable capacity for survival of debris would be thereby indicated.

DISCUSSION

It remains to classify the present and former erosional plains described here. Despite various interpretations placed upon the term 'pediment', there is no doubt that the features would be considered pediments by many workers. They occur in arid and semi-arid lands, in which many workers consider all erosional plains to be *ipso facto* pediments, and correspond to those pediments recorded and illustrated in the literature (see Tator 1952-3). The plains and plain remnants are, or were, bedrock surfaces displaying few lines of concentrated drainage and possessing a discontinuous veneer of debris of alluvial-colluvial origin. Most are rectilinear or concave, though the toes of some older surfaces have been rendered gently convex by later erosion. Near Brachina Gorge, for instance, there are plain remnants (Plate IXa) which correspond in every detail with dissected pediments described and figured by Koschmann and Loughlin (1934) and by Blackwelder (1954).

The thickness and calibre of the superficial debris are similar to those reported from other areas (see Bryan 1922). Though several metres thick in places, the mantles do not intrinsically modify the form of the bedrock surface. Some workers consider that the debris veneer on pediments should be transient; others consider that the veneer plays a part in the formation of the surface yet is not essential to its form, since the pediment is essentially a bedrock surface. In this respect, the debris mantles in this arid area pose problems, for in conditions of intermittent rainfall and runoff such as obtain here debris inevitably accumulates on plain surfaces, and it is impossible to determine what portion of the debris is immobile and what portion will be evacuated during the next decade or century. Some of the debris of the mantles described is stable, and has exerted an important protective and preserving influence on the surface on which it lies. If the remnants described here are to be labelled pediments by virtue of the form of the bedrock floor and the nature of the transition between this and the backing escarpment, cognisance must be taken of an essential characteristic and the adjective 'mantled' added in qualification.

Many writers consider that pedimentation and parallel scarp retreat go hand-in-hand; however, it may be argued from the calibre and source of the debris mantle, the landforms observed in the area, and the distribution of weathering, that there has been slope steepening and plain extension in the piedmont zone, rather than parallel slope retreat: the hill-plain junction has become more abrupt.

The mantled pediments and remnants thereof described here are surfaces similar to many of the gibber plains of the northern part of South Australia.

The reason for the marked development of the mantled pediment in arid lands may be related to the climatic and weathering régimes, for the formation of indurated crusts and soil horizons and the concentration of coarse debris by wind and water lead to the protection and preservation of plain surfaces which are susceptible to reduction and elimination by incision and undercutting. Paradoxically, water is important in weathering in arid as in humid lands; its effects are concentrated in the lows, and lead in turn to more marked erosion there. Valleys beget deeper valleys. The excavation of valleys and especially of the scarp-foot zone causes the regrading of escarpments and the development of an abrupt transition from plain to hills.

It seems theoretically possible for such regradation to be initiated merely by the change in time of the nature of the bedrock due to weathering. Thus it may be that discontinuous forms develop within a cycle, during a continuous sequence of events. In the Flinders Ranges, however, there have been changes of baselevel due to a combination of tectonism and climatic changes, and thus the features described here are of cyclic character.

REFERENCES

Balk, R. (1932). Geology of Newcomb Quadrangle. *Bull. N.Y. St. Mus.* **290**: 78.

Blackwelder, E. (1927). Fire as an agent in rock weathering. *J. Geol.* **35**: 134-40.

———— (1954). Geomorphic processes in the desert, pp. 11-20 in *Geology of southern California*. Ed. R. H. Jahns, Calif. Dept Nat. Res. Div. Mines Bull. No. 170.

Bryan, K. (1922). *Erosion and Sedimentation in the Papago Country, Arizona*. U.S. Geol. Surv. Bull. No. 730.

Clayton, R. W. (1956). Linear depressions (*Bergfussniederungen*) in savannah landscapes. *Geogrl Stud.* **3**: 102-26.

Cotton, C. A. and Te Punga, M. T. (1955). Solifluxion and periglacially modified landforms at Wellington, New Zealand. *Trans. R. Soc. N.Z.* **82**: 1001-31.

Daily, B. (1960). *Report of the Museum Board*, 1958/59, p. 12. Adelaide.

Davis, W. M. (1930). Rock floors in arid and in humid climates, II. *J. Geol.* **38**: 136-58.

Ellison, W. D. (1945). Some effects of raindrops and surface-flow on soil erosion and infiltration. *Trans. Am. geophys. Un.* **26**: 415-29.

———— (1950). Soil erosion by rainstorms. *Science* **111**: 245-9.

Emery, K. O. (1944). Brush fires and rock exfoliation. *Am. J. Sci.* **242**: 506-8.

Everard, C. E. (1963). Contrasts in the form and evolution of hillslopes in central Cyprus. *Trans. Inst. Br. Geogr.* **32**: 31-47.

Fair, T. J. D. (1947). Slope form and development in the interior of Natal. *Trans. geol. Soc. S. Afr.* **50**: 105-19.

Griggs, D. T. (1936). The factor of fatigue in rock exfoliation. *J. Geol.* **44**: 783-96.

Hills, E. S. (1955). Die Landoberfläche Australiens. *Erde, Berl.* 1955: 195-205.

Howard, A. D. (1942). Pediment passes and the pediment problem. *J. Geomorph.* **5**: 95-136.

Kedar, Y. (1957). Water and soil from the desert: some ancient agricultural achievements in the central Negev. *Geogrl J.* **123**: 179-87.

Koschmann, A. H. and Loughlin, G. F. (1934). Dissected pediments in the Magdalena District, New Mexico. *Bull. geol. Soc. Am.* **45**: 463-78.

Ollier, C. D. (1963). Insolation weathering: examples from central Australia. *Am. J. Sci.* **261**: 376-81.

Pallister, J. W. (1956). Slope development in Buganda. *Geogrl J.* **122**: 80-7.

Russell, R. J. (1936). The desert-rainfall factor in denudation. *Rept 16th Int. geol. Cong.* Pt 2: 337-72.

Ruxton, B. P. (1958). Weathering and subsurface erosion in granite at the piedmont angle, Balos, Sudan. *Geol. Mag.* **95**: 353-77.

Sharon, D. (1962). On the nature of hamadas in Israel. *Z. Geomorph.* **6**: 129-47.

Sharpe, C. F. S. (1960). *Landslides and Related Phenomena.* New Jersey.

Simpson, D. R. (1964). Exfoliation in the Upper Pocahontas Sandstone, Mercer County, West Virginia. *Am. J. Sci.* **262**: 545-51.

Tator, B. A. (1952-3). Pediment characteristics and terminology. *Ann. Ass. Am. Geogr.* **42**: 295-317; **43**: 47-53.

Trendall, A. F. (1962). The formation of 'apparent peneplains' by a process of combined lateritisation and surface wash. *Z. Geomorph.* **6**: 183-97.

Twidale, C. R. (1962). Steepened margins of inselbergs from north-western Eyre Peninsula, South Australia. *Z. Geomorph.* **6**: 51-69.

—— (1964). Effect of variations in the rate of sediment accumulation on a bedrock slope at Fromm's Landing. *Z. Geomorph.* Suppbd 5: 177-91.

Wagner, P. (1912). Negative spheroidal weathering and jointing in a granite of Southern Rhodesia. *Trans. geol. Soc. S. Afr.* **15**: 155-64.

Wood, A. (1942). The development of hillside slopes. *Proc. geol. Ass., Lond.* **53**: 128-40.

Yi-fu Tuan, (1959). *Pediments in Southeastern Arizona.* Univ. Calif. Publ. Geogr. No. 13.

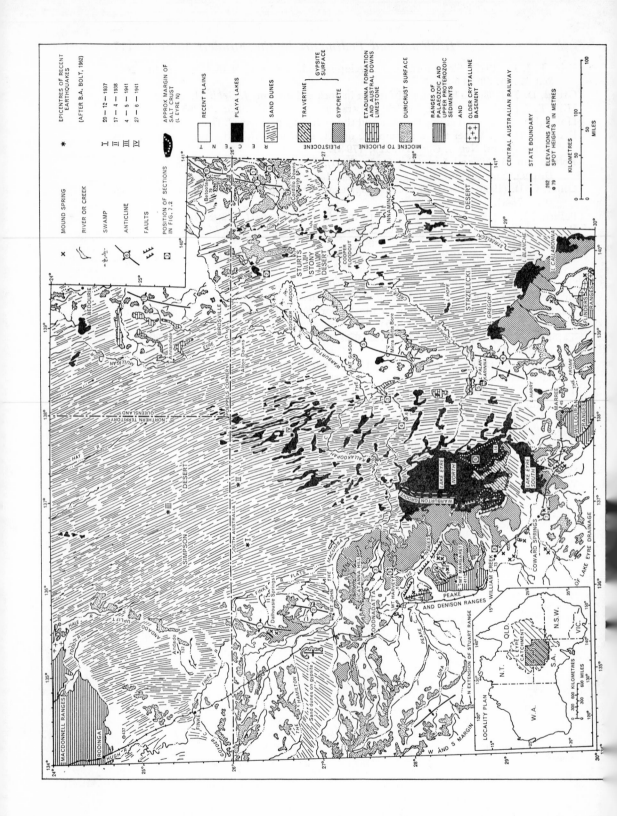

7

Geomorphological History of the Lake Eyre Basin

H. WOPFNER AND C. R. TWIDALE

INTRODUCTION

The area discussed in this essay lies in the west of the Lake Eyre drainage area and is referred to as the Lake Eyre Basin. This basin includes Lake Eyre, which at a maximum depression of 14 m below sea level, is the lowest point on the Australian continent.

The Lake Eyre Basin is an intracratonic basin and is defined as the area immediately affected by, and structurally related to the Lake Eyre depression. Thus the margins of the basin are demarcated by various positive structures as shown in Figure 7.1. The west and northwest boundary is formed by the Protero-zoic-Archean inlier of the Peake and Denison Ranges, and by a chain of Mesozoic-Tertiary structures comprising the Ucatanna upwarp, the Mt John anticline, the Dalhousie anticline and the Andado upwarp. To the south the basin is bounded by the Upper Proterozoic structures of the Willouran and Flinders Ranges. The Dulkaninna, Mt Gason, Cordillo and Birdsville upwarps delineate the basin to the east and northeast, whilst ranges of Archean, Proterozoic and Palaeozoic rocks form a natural boundary to the north.

The tectonic origin of the Lake Eyre Basin as a late Cainozoic unit is well documented by numerous faults along the west shore of Lake Eyre, collectively referred to as the Lake Eyre lineament. It is further evidenced by the fact that the basin has been the scene of considerable contemporary seismicity, as demonstrated by Bolt (1958, and personal communication 1962).

The area is the driest in Australia, averaging less than 127 mm annual rain-fall, but the river systems which run into and towards Lake Eyre serve a catch-ment in excess of 1,300,000 km², including some areas of north and central Queensland which enjoy comparatively heavy and regular rainfall. The Lake Eyre depression, which forms the focus of this large endoreic system, is asymmetrically placed in the far southwest corner of the drainage area.

The study area is in no sense a distinct physiographic entity, for it includes elements of several landform assemblages which extend beyond its confines; yet contained within its borders are several features characteristic of much of arid

---

7.1 *Major landforms of Lake Eyre Basin. Positive tectonic structures delimiting the basin: (1) Dalhousie Anticline. (2) Mt John Anticline. (3) Ucatanna Uplift. (4) Dulkaninna Uplift. (5) Mt Gason Uplift. (6) Innamincka Anticline. (7) Nappamilkie Anticline. (8) Mt Howie Anticline (7 & 8) comprising Cordillo Uplift. (9) Betoota Anticline. (10) Birdsville Uplift.*

119

Australia, while others either in type or degree of development are unique to the area. Monotonous plains, unbroken in their regularity and evenness over large distances, and dissected plateaux and escarpments are the main morphological features of the area.

The plains include several distinctive landform assemblages. For the most part they are sandy, here organised into well defined longitudinal dunes and corridors, there with less distinct pattern of corridor and dune, elsewhere consisting of disordered sand ridges and mounds displaying no apparent order. Some interdune corridors are stony, and these in some areas, as in Sturts Stony Desert, achieve considerable extent.

Cuestas and plateaux capped by siliceous duricrust protrude some 30 to 50 m above the general plain level, particularly in areas domed or otherwise uplifted by young tectonic movements. Detrital material, derived from the breakdown of the Tertiary duricrust and subsequently winnowed by deflation, forms the well known stone pavements of the 'gibber plains' which cover extensive areas, particularly in the eroded centres and around the margins of domal structures.

Innumerable playas, some saline, others clayey or gypsiferous, have been formed on or below the general level of the sandy and stony plains; between Lake Eyre and Poeppels Corner for example there are hundreds of salinas and claypans, large and small, many elongated parallel to the dune trend (Fig. 7.1). However, the largest salinas occur adjacent to the northern Flinders Ranges, about which they are strung like beads on a necklace—Lakes Torrens, Eyre, Gregory, Blanche, Callabonna, and Frome, but on closer analysis they are seen to be located along ancient yet frequently reactivated tectonic lineaments.

The Lake Eyre Basin has a long and complex geological and geomorphological history to which it is necessary to refer in order to understand the origin of these several landform assemblages.

PRE-MIOCENE GEOLOGICAL SETTING

The modern Lake Eyre Basin is situated on the western part of the intracratonic Great Artesian Basin which is essentially of Jurassic and Cretaceous age. Thus the area is underlain by varying thicknesses of Cretaceous shale and Jurassic sandstone which rest either disconformably on flat-lying Permian strata or unconformably on moderately to strongly folded Lower Palaeozoic or Proterozoic rocks.

The oldest sediments referable to the Great Artesian Basin are kaolinitic sandstone with thin intercalations of shale and coal of Middle and Upper Jurassic age. These are not exposed here but are widely known from oil exploration wells in the deeper portions of the basin. They are succeeded by a coarse to medium grained sandstone of Upper Jurassic age which underlies the Cretaceous sequence everywhere in the basin, extensively overlapping the preceding Middle Jurassic sediments to the south and west, where it rests unconformably on Lower Permian or older rocks. This sandstone has been termed Algebuckina Sandstone (Sprigg and staff 1958) and its subsurface equivalent is referred to as the Mooga Sandstone.

The base of the Algebuckina Sandstone also represents the oldest ancient land surface the presence of which can be demonstrated within the Lake Eyre Basin. Its occurrence in the present landscape is restricted to stripped surfaces in marginal areas, as in the Peake and Denison Ranges and in the Granite Downs area.

This Upper Jurassic surface is evidenced by deep weathering profiles developed on rocks underlying the Algebuckina Sandstone and further by the presence of residual gravels at the very base of the sandstone, interpreted as lag deposits, (Wopfner 1964a, 1964b).

The Algebuckina Sandstone is the most important aquifer of the Great Artesian Basin. Natural outlets for the artesian water of this aquifer are found in flowing or sometimes pulsating mound springs which are generally associated with marginal faults and 'highs' in the underlying basement. Major areas of mound-spring development are along the Central Australian Railway south and west of Lake Eyre South, along a zone between the Peake and Denison Ranges and Lake Eyre, and at Dalhousie Springs about 120 km north of Oodnadatta (see Fig. 7.1).

The Algebuckina Sandstone is overlain by an Aptian to Albian (Lower Cretaceous) marine shale sequence (Roma and Tambo Formations) which in turn is succeeded by the Albian-Cenomanian Winton Formation. The latter consists of interbedded siltstone and fine-grained sandstone. The Cretaceous sediments, which reach a thickness of about 1400 m in the area immediately north of Lake Eyre, form an uninterrupted blanket from about 134° E. to the Great Divide in Queensland.

The close of Winton deposition also saw the termination of Mesozoic blanket sedimentation. Subsequent Cretaceous deposition was restricted to fluviatile sediments (Wopfner 1963) and to minor accumulations in small and isolated troughs (Johns and Ludbrook 1963). However, a brief recurrence of widespread sedimentation is noted in early Tertiary time when a thin sheet of gravels, sands, and lignitic clays, rarely exceeding 60 m, was spread over the older sediments.

STRATIGRAPHY AND EVOLUTION OF THE LAKE EYRE BASIN

(a) *Stratigraphic and Morphostratigraphic Units*

In the past decade various authors have described and defined younger sedimentary sequences in different parts of the Lake Eyre Basin, (King 1956; Stirton *et al.* 1961; Johns and Ludbrook 1963), but no correlation and stratigraphy of the whole basin has hitherto been attempted. Only such a stratigraphic concept, however, can provide a key to the sequence of events.

The stratigraphy proposed here (Table 1) is by no means complete, and only a broad correlation of stratigraphic and morphostratigraphic units (Frye and Willman 1962) is attempted, based on numerous observations in various parts of the Lake Eyre Basin (Fig. 7.2). Due to lack of fossil evidence, emphasis has to be given to the succession of events rather than to strict time subdivisions.

The mid-Tertiary duricrust is used as a reference horizon for this stratigraphy, and was chosen by reason of its wide distribution and its importance in the present relief. It is also the youngest horizon which was subjected to fold movements which affected the whole of the basin (Wopfner 1960). It will be shown later that these folding movements had a controlling influence on younger events up to the development of the present landforms.

In the following descriptions of these younger stratigraphic and morphostratigraphic units, established formal names will be used where appropriate and will be defined; for the rest, informal names will be used.

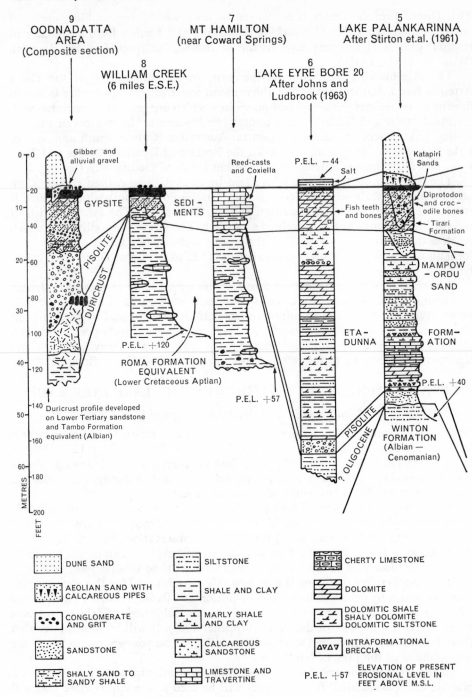

9
OODNADATTA
AREA
(Composite section)

8
WILLIAM CREEK
(6 miles E.S.E.)

7
MT HAMILTON
(near Coward Springs)

6
LAKE EYRE BORE 20
After Johns and
Ludbrook (1963)

5
LAKE PALANKARINNA
After Stirton et.al. (1961)

Gibber and
alluvial gravel

GYPSITE

PISOLITE

DURICRUST

P.E.L. +120

ROMA FORMATION
EQUIVALENT
(Lower Cretaceous Aptian)

Duricrust profile developed
on Lower Tertiary sandstone
and Tambo Formation
equivalent (Albian)

SEDI-
MENTS

Reed-casts
and Coxiella

P.E.L. +57

P.E.L. —44   Salt

Fish teeth
and bones

ETA-
DUNNA

? OLIGOCENE

PISOLITE

Katapiri
Sands

Diprotodon
and croc–
odile bones

Tirari
Formation

MAMPOW
– ORDU
SAND

FORM-
ATION

P.E.L. +40

WINTON
FORMATION
(Albian —
Cenomanian)

METRES
FEET

DUNE SAND

AEOLIAN SAND WITH
CALCAREOUS PIPES

CONGLOMERATE
AND GRIT

SANDSTONE

SHALY SAND TO
SANDY SHALE

SILTSTONE

SHALE AND CLAY

MARLY SHALE
AND CLAY

CALCAREOUS
SANDSTONE

LIMESTONE AND
TRAVERTINE

CHERTY LIMESTONE

DOLOMITE

DOLOMITIC SHALE
SHALY DOLOMITE
DOLOMITIC SILTSTONE

INTRAFORMATIONAL
BRECCIA

P.E.L. +57   ELEVATION OF PRESENT
EROSIONAL LEVEL IN
FEET ABOVE M.S.L.

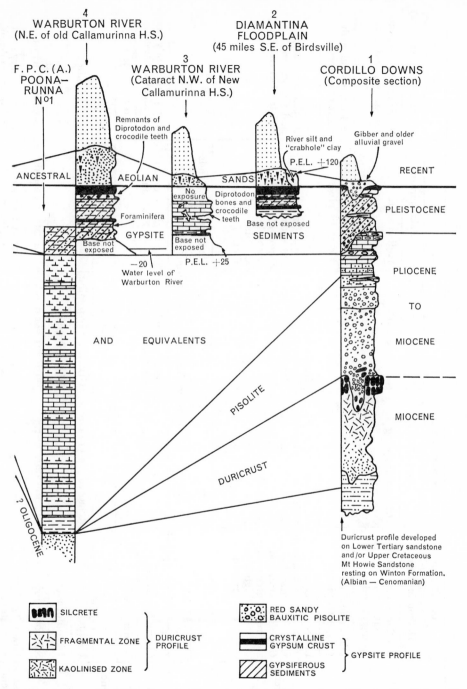

7.2 *Correlation of mid-Tertiary to Recent stratigraphic and morphostratigraphic units in the Lake Eyre Basin*

TABLE 1

Correlation of sediments of Lake Eyre Basin

	West Margin (Oodnadatta-Dalhousie Area)	Southwest Margin (Curdimurka-William Creek Area)	Centre		East Margin (Sturts Stony Desert and Cordillo Area)
			Lake Eyre Bore 20	Lake Palankarinna	
Recent	Aeolian sand; alluvial silt, sand, and gravel; spring deposits	Drift sand; spring deposits	Clay and salt	Aeolian sand	Aeolian sand; interdune clay, alluvial silt, and gravel
	Old dune sand with calcareous pipes			Old dune sand with calcareous pipes	Old dune sand with calcareous pipes
Pleistocene	Limestone with Coxiella and reeds — Gypsite (Gypsiferous gravels, sand and green clay; high-level gravels)	Limestone with Coxiella and Diprotodon — Gypsite (Gypsiferous sand and silt; green and mottled clay)	Crystalline gypsum; clay with fish-teeth	Gypsite (Gypsiferous sand and silt with Diprotodon and crocodile remnants = Katapiri and Tirari Formations)	Gypsite (Gypsiferous clay; sand and gravel; high-level gravels)
				Mampowordu Sands	
		Strong Erosional Disconformity			
Pliocene to Miocene	Cherty limestone	No deposition	Dolomite and dolomitic clay of Etadunna Formation	Dolomite and dolomitic clay of Etadunna Formation	Cherty and sandy limestone; bituminous limestone
	No deposition		*Disconformity*		No deposition
	Pisolite	Removed by erosion	Gritty, sandy pisolite	?	Sandy pisolite
	Disconformity		Disconformity		Unconformity
	Siliceous duricrust	Siliceous duricrust	Duricrust not developed, or later removed	Duricrust not developed, or later removed	Siliceous duricrust
Pre-Miocene Basement	Lower Tertiary sandstone	Lower Cretaceous shale	?Oligocene sand	Winton Formation (ferruginised)	Lower Tertiary sand or Mt Howie Sandstone

XIIIa (left) Silcrete pavement of polygonal columns northeast of Sturts Stony Desert, 86 km northwest of Cordillo Downs homestead. Photograph by A. R. Crawford.

XIIIb Asymmetrical syncline in duricrust at Mt Harvey, southeast of Oodnadatta. The partly mature duricrust dips from 25° to 45° eastwards as indicated and is unconformably overlain by horizontal white shale. Photograph by H. Wopfner.

XIIIc Gypsite-capped tableland rising 35 m above the alluvial plains of the Neales River, 115 km southeast of Oodnadatta. In the foreground is the pebble-covered gypsite surface. Photograph by G. R. Heath.

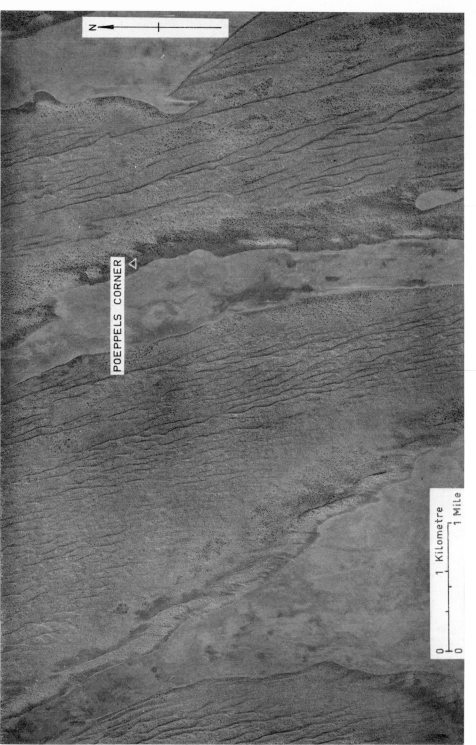

XIV Playas and sand dunes at Poeppels Corner. Closely spaced dendritic dunes branch from higher sand ridges as in the dune belt west of Poeppels Corner. Shallow ground water below the gypsiferous silt surface of the playas maintains a prolific growth of gidgee trees (Acacia cambagei), particularly along the eastern shores. Note fresh sandblows along northeast shore of playa on left. Vertical air photograph by Department of Lands, S. Australia.

(b) *Siliceous Duricrust*

At the onset of the Oligocene, much of the area of the Great Artesian Basin was land.

The only sedimentary record from this time is the thin carbonaceous, silty clay beds of probable Oligocene age from Lake Eyre Bore 20 (Johns and Ludbrook 1963). Due to lack of contemporary tectonic movements, this mid-Tertiary land surface presented itself as a vast, stable sediplain with restricted erosion and deposition. A deep weathering profile formed culminating in the widespread development of a siliceous duricrust, dissected remnants of which now cap prominent plateaux and cuestas (Fig. 7.3). The duricrust profile developed on various strata truncated by this mid-Tertiary land surface, and consequently one finds the duricrust on rocks which range in age from Proterozoic to Lower Tertiary (Wopfner 1964a). The duricrust thus has to be regarded as a morpho-stratigraphic unit.

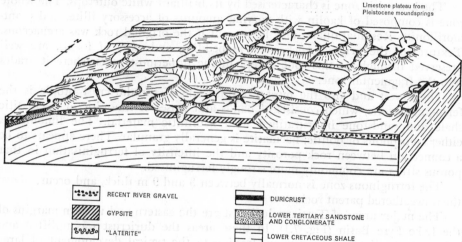

Limestone plateau from Pleistocene moundsprings

RECENT RIVER GRAVEL

GYPSITE

"LATERITE"

DURICRUST

LOWER TERTIARY SANDSTONE AND CONGLOMERATE

LOWER CRETACEOUS SHALE

7.3 Schematic relationship between duricrust and gypsite surfaces on a post-duricrust anticline, based on the Dalhousie Anticline

Regardless of parent rock, a typical duricrust profile consists, from top to bottom, of the following zones:

Kaolinised zone

Ferruginous zone

Silcrete

Fragmental zone

All boundaries, except perhaps the bottom of the silcrete, are gradational.

The silcrete zone varies in thickness from about 0·5 to 3 m and usually exhibits a flat, even surface. This crust is typically composed of polygonal columns, ranging in diameter from 15 cm to 1 m and consisting of light grey to light creamy grey and olive grey, hard and dense silcrete. They give the surface a characteristic pavement appearance (Plate XIIIa). The sides of the columns invariably exhibit distinctive vertical grooves and ridges formed by linear arrangements and agglutinations of nodular to ellipsoidal silica concretions. The formation of the concretions is apparently the first stage of the silicification process.

K

This is indicated by occurrences of silcrete the formation of which was apparently interrupted at an early stage, clearly showing the linear arrangement of the concretions but lacking the interstitial silica cement. It is thought that the silcrete zone represents the B horizon of a fossil soil profile.

Petrological examination shows that the silcrete consists of medium to fine quartz grains embedded in a micro- to cryptocrystalline quartz matrix. Secondary growth on detrital quartz grains is common, and often the secondary growth is found to be in optical continuity with the original grain (McCarthy 1962).

The silcrete cap is underlain by the fragmental zone which varies in thickness from about 5 to 9 m. This zone is generally massive and textureless and forms reddish brown and often vertical outcrops. The fragmental zone consists of angular rock fragments derived by disintegration of the parent rock. The fragments are light grey, kaolinitic and partly siliceous inside, but are generally coated with a film of ferruginous material which also acts as cement.

The kaolinitic zone is characterised by its brilliant white outcrops. The whole zone is composed of kaolin with varying amounts of accessory illite, and montmorillonite. Residual quartz may be present if the original rock was arenaceous. Textures of the original rock, such as bedding and casts of fossils, are well preserved throughout this zone except in the uppermost parts where it grades into the fragmental zone.

The lowest and also the most variable zone of the duricrust profile is the ferruginous zone, which consists of bands and lenses of limonitic or haematitic shale and sandstone interstratified with kaolinitic material. The limonite is either amorphous or oolitic; haematite is generally granular. There appears to be a connection between rock porosity and the intensity of ferruginisation in that porous strata are commonly more strongly ferruginised.

The ferruginous zone is normally between 3 and 9 m thick, and occurs above the unweathered parent rock.

The major areas of Tertiary duricrust are the eastern and western margins of the Lake Eyre Basin (Fig. 7.1). In these areas the duricrust was uplifted and subsequently dissected by erosion, leading to the typical development of large dissected plateaux and cuestas with steep escarpments, or groups of mesas and buttes. This type of relief is widespread near Oodnadatta, in the Cordillo area, near the Innamincka Dome and in the vicinity of Mirra-Mitta-Mt Gason Uplift. Duricrust has been removed by erosion from the large domed area west of Lake Eyre, particularly between the Peake and Denison Ranges and the Stuart Range.

Although in some areas duricrust has been encountered to depths of 60 m beneath younger sediments (Wopfner 1960), it appears to be absent beneath Lake Eyre, where younger pisolite rests directly on older (possibly Oligocene) sediments in Lake Eyre Bore 20 and F.P.C.A. Poonarunna No. 1 Well. The most likely explanation is that the area now occupied by Lake Eyre was already a shallow water body during at least part of the time in which the duricrust formed.

(c) *Pisolite*

This unit previously referred to as laterite (Wopfner 1960) is a dark brick-red, sometimes dark yellow-brown, sandy pisolite, with occasional interbedding of ferruginous sandstone. The constituent pisoliths vary in diameter from 5 to 20 mm, the average being about 12 mm. Although the pisolite has a strong ferruginous appearance, its average content of Fe_2O_3 is only 4 per cent. In contrast, the content of Al_2O_3 averages 12·5 per cent, giving a ratio Fe_2O_3 to Al_2O_3 of 0·32; thus the pisolite is bauxitic. Contrasting with those low values is an average content of silica of 70·2 per cent; this high silica content is largely due to detrital quartz.

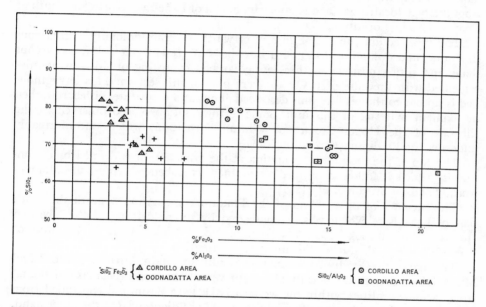

7.4 *Percentages of Fe_2O_3 and Al_2O_3 plotted against SiO_2 for bauxitic pisolites from the Cordillo Downs and Oodnadatta areas. Note that for any given silica content the ratio between Fe_2O_3 and Al_2O_3 remains fairly constant at about 0·3.*

In Figure 7.4 it is shown graphically that the relationships between SiO_2 and Fe_2O_3 and between SiO_2 and Al_2O_3 are both linear. However, with decreasing SiO_2 values, the content of Al_2O_3 increases at a much higher rate than does the content of Fe_2O_3.

The lower portions of the pisolite commonly contain reworked pebbles and cobbles of silcrete, partly water transported and partly derived from disintegration *in situ* of the underlying duricrust.

The pisolitic unit rests disconformably or unconformably on duricrust or kaolinised zone, depending on local structural conditions. It is widely distributed over both the eastern and western marginal areas of the Lake Eyre Basin, where it occurs either in shallow consequent valleys or in structural depressions, as near Cordillo and Innamincka and in the Oodnadatta area, or covers extensive plateaux, as between the Arckaringa and the Neales Rivers, west of Oodnadatta. Generally, the thickness of the pisolite does not exceed 9 m but rare instances up to 35 m were observed.

Very similar sediments consisting of a limonitic gritty pisolite with reworked grains of silcrete were encountered in Lake Eyre Bore 20, beneath the Etadunna Formation (Fig. 7.2). This limonitic pisolite is tentatively correlated with the pisolite of the marginal areas.

(d) *Etadunna Formation and Equivalents*

This stratigraphic unit was first described by Stirton, Tedford and Miller (1961) from the type locality at Lake Palankarinna, east of Lake Eyre North and south of Coopers Creek (Locality 5, Fig. 7.2).

The type section consists of 26·5 m of white to cream dolomite, argillaceous limestone, and dolomitic shale, with inter-beds of grey to green clay, arenaceous shale, and silty sandstone. A thin lenticular bed consisting of siliceous nodules cemented with limonite occurs at the very base of this section. This ferruginous bed is similar to the pisolite unit described above and constitutes either reworked or remnant material of this unit. Some ferruginisation is also observed in the siltstone of the Upper Cretaceous Winton Formation, which unconformably underlies the Etadunna Formation.

The top of the Etadunna Formation at the type section is defined by disconformity which is followed by medium-grained, cross-bedded sands, the Mampowordu Sands of Stirton *et al.* (1961).

The presence of up to 35 m of the Etadunna Formation beneath the south part of Lake Eyre North was demonstrated by recent drilling in the lake bed (Johns and Ludbrook 1963). Poonarunna No. 1 Well, about 65 km west of Cowarie homestead, also cut this important formation.

The age of the Etadunna Formation is still uncertain. Stirton, Tedford and Miller (1961) described a locally abundant vertebrate fauna (Ngapakaldi fauna) from various localities within the western Lake Eyre Basin and concluded from it that the Etadunna Formation might be as old as Oligocene. On the other hand, from foraminifera in the basal unit of the Etadunna Formation in Lake Eyre Bore 20, Ludbrook (1965) suggests a Miocene or younger age, which is tentatively adopted here.

Thin limestone sequences similar to the Etadunna Formation occur over wide areas in northeastern-most South Australia and on the east of the Simpson Desert further north (Fig. 7.1). The sequences consist of pink to red sandy limestone and calcareous shale near the base and of slabby, grey to yellowish grey, cherty, and sometimes dolomitic limestone higher up. Secondary migration of silica often leads to enrichment in chalcedony near the top. These limestones rarely exceed 9 m in thickness and generally rest disconformably on the pisolite.

So far no diagnostic fossils have been found in these limestone deposits, but the stratigraphic position suggests an Upper Tertiary age, and they are tentatively correlated with the uppermost part of the Etadunna Formation (Table 1). Limestones of similar appearance in southwestern Queensland, generally referred to as Austral Downs Limestone (Paten 1960), are thought to be late Tertiary in age.

(e) *Gypsite and Equivalent Fresh Water Limestones*

Gypsite is proposed as a morphostratigraphic term to identify a weathering profile associated with an extensive Pleistocene land surface.

The gypsite profile is characterised by a massive gypsum crust at the top, an intermediate, sometimes mottled, gypsiferous zone, and a thin ferruginous zone at the base. The thickness of the profile varies between 6 and 12 m.

The gypsum crust is composed of coarsely crystalline butterfly twins, but also incorporates clastic material, ranging from silt to boulders. Analogous to such terms as silcrete and calcrete, the term 'gypcrete' is proposed for this type of crystalline gypsum crust. On the average it is between 0·6 and 1·5 m thick. As a rule only one crust is present (Fig. 7.2 and Plate XIIIc), but in areas where the gypsite has not been affected by later erosion, as for instance in Sturts Stony Desert and to the northeast of Lake Eyre, up to three separate gypsum crusts have been observed.

The zone underlying the gypsum crust consists of clastic sediments ranging from clay to pebbles. Its main feature is a high content of gypsum which is dispersed within the original sediment. The gypsum is finely crystalline, but large gypsum prisms often form a tightly intergrown matrix, giving a lustrous mottling.

The colour of this zone appears to depend on the grain size of the original sediment. Coarse clastics and sands vary from cream to yellow-brown whilst finer clastics, particularly clays and clayey silts, are mostly red and green mottled in the upper parts but olive green lower down. Minor bleaching has also been observed.

The basal ferruginous zone is generally quite thin and is variable in appearance and distribution. Most commonly it consists of dark brown, generally spherical limonite concretions 8-25 mm in diameter, locally referred to as 'iron-stone'. These concretions are most prominently displayed in areas where the gypsite profile has been stripped, leaving the limonite concretions in large, very dark brown patches at the base of receding escarpments. Less commonly, ferruginisation takes the form of boxwork in which joints and fissures have been filled with limonite.

An interesting feature of the ferruginous zone can be observed where the gypsite profile has developed in previously unaltered Lower Cretaceous sediments. Limestone concretions, which are widely intercalated in the Lower Cretaceous shale, were partly or wholly altered into goethite, limonite, and in minor degree to haematite. Sheets of selenite and less common bands of satin spar are often associated with these altered concretions. As the unaltered limestone concretions are generally rich in pyrite it appears that sulphate-rich groundwaters reacted with the carbonate and pyrite to form gypsum and hydrous iron.

In some areas silicification occurred within the gypsite profile. However, the silcretes resulting from this silicification are composed of chalcedony and opaline matrix and are thus distinctly different from the silcretes of the duricrust profile. The formation of precious opal may also be connected with the gypsite surface.

The gypsite profile formed on an aggradational plain, similar to the modern alluvial plains of low gradient formed by Coopers Creek west of Innamincka, by the Diamantina south of Birdsville, and by the Neales River east of Algebuckina (Plate XIIIc). This plain developed after the marginal areas of the Lake Eyre Basin were folded and uplifted and streams had excavated new valleys. Consequently, one observes the gypsite profile and its associated sediments overlying older sediments in the structurally depressed and stable areas, such as Lake Eyre, Simpson Desert and Sturts Stony Desert but abutting against older sediments in areas of uplift (as in the Cordillo, Innamincka, and Mt Gason upwarps and in the Oodnadatta and Dalhousie regions). The relationship of the gypsite surface to older sediments and to the folded and uplifted duricrust surface is demonstrated in Figure 7.3.

Consistent with this history, gypsite profile has developed on many different sediments, ranging from clays, silts and sands in the structurally depressed and stable areas to pebble and cobble conglomerates near duricrust plateaux. The thickness of the sediments associated with the gypsite profile varies from several metres to a mere few centimetres where the erosional surface was not alluviated. For convenience they will be referred to as 'gypsite sediments'.

The Pleistocene age of these sediments is demonstrated by their fossil content. *Diprotodon* bones, sometimes with crocodile remnants, are known from Lake Palankarinna (Stirton *et al.* 1961) (Locality 5, Fig. 7.2), the lower Macumba River, the Warburton River near the new Kalamurina Station (Locality 3, Fig. 7.2), and near old Kalamurina ruins (Locality 4, Fig. 7.2). A sample of green clay from the last mentioned locality, about 6 m below the *Diprotodon*-bearing stratum, was reported on by Dr N. H. Ludbrook, S.A. Department of Mines, as follows:

A few small pauperate foraminifera are present:

cf. *Bolivina rugosa*	1 specimen
Discorbis sp.	1 specimen
Cibicides cf. *refulgens*	1 specimen
Cibicides sp.	1 specimen
Cassidulina laevigata	2 specimens

This material is of considerable interest as the presence of foraminifera indicates deposition under salt-water conditions during the Pleistocene. However, the presence of foraminifera does not necessarily indicate a marine environment. Ludbrook (1965) has demonstrated that foraminifera, introduced by birds into inland lakes, may survive there for periods of time, 'if the salinity of the water into which they are introduced is favourable'.

In the centre of the Lake Eyre Basin and on its more stable eastern margin the gypsite horizon is situated at or below the present-day erosional surface and is generally overlain by sand dunes. Along the southern and western margin, however, post-Pleistocene uplift has led to strong erosion and removal of much of the profile. In these areas the gypsite forms extensive tablelands which are capped by the gypsum crust and generally sloping gently eastwards (Plate XIIIc). The difference in elevation between the summits of the gypsite tablelands and the present erosion plains varies from 12 to nearly 45 m.

Simultaneously with the deposition of the gypsite sediments extensive freshwater limestones were formed along the southwest and west margin of the Lake Eyre Basin. The distribution of these limestones follows very closely that of active mound springs. However, the travertine mounds of the modern springs rest on a much younger and considerably lower erosional surface than that of the Pleistocene freshwater limestones.

The formation of the Pleistocene limestones took place on or near the same erosional surface on which the gypsite sediments were deposited. Thus, the limestones either overlie clastics from the lower sequence of the gypsite sediments, or they rest disconformably on Aptian shale. Limestones and gypsite sediments commonly interfinger near Dalhousie.

The limestones vary from dark greenish grey, microcrystalline and slightly dolomitic limestone south of Lake Eyre South to yellow-brown, saccharoidal, vuggy, dolomitic limestone near Coward Springs (Locality 7, Fig. 7.2). This second type contains a great abundance of casts of reeds and grass. The freshwater gastropod *Coxiella* is present in all the limestones, and remnants of *Diprotodon* were found in them south of Lake Eyre South.

The lithology, fossil content, and the strong association of the Pleistocene limestones with areas of modern spring activity, clearly indicate that the limestones were formed by precipitation of carbonate from Pleistocene artesian springs.

The same post-Pleistocene movements which uplifted the western and southern margin of the Lake Eyre Basin and led to the dissection of the gypsite surface also affected the area of Pleistocene limestone deposition. Today these hard limestones top isolated mesas or small plateaux between 20 and 40 m high, protecting underlying softer sediments against erosion. It is particularly noteworthy that the present elevation of the Pleistocene spring limestones is considerably higher than the hydrostatic levels of surrounding modern mound springs.

From all the evidence presented, there can be no doubt as to the Pleistocene age of the gypsite profile and the contemporaneous spring limestones. Remnants of *Diprotodon* from Lake Callabonna, approximately 210 km southeast of Lake Eyre, were dated older than 40,000 years B.P. and 6,700 ± 250 years B.P. respectively (Daily 1960; Grant-Taylor and Rafter 1963). Contamination by carbonate-bearing young groundwaters may be responsible for the extremely young date of the second specimen, and therefore the older age is tentatively accepted as real. Specimens of *Coxiella gilesi* from a cliff of gypsiferous sandstone on the south shore of Lake Eyre North were dated at almost 40,000 years B.P. (Johns and Ludbrook 1963).

(f) *Post-Gypsite Deposits*

The gypsite horizon is followed by a great variety of deposits. On the uplifted western margin of the basin, younger sediments are generally found below the level of the gypsite tableland. They include sediments in several discontinuous terraces between the top of the gypsite and the present level of erosion, floodplain deposits and extensive gibber plains of redistributed gypsite sediments.

In the stable and depressed parts of the Lake Eyre Basin, that is in the centre and along the eastern margin, the gypsite is overlain by grey to yellow, medium-grained sandstone, slightly cemented by a clayey matrix and commonly exhibiting cross-bedding with steep, planar foresets of aeolian origin. A particular feature of these sandstones is the abundant, hard calcareous pipes, commonly of conical or vermicular form, generally circular in cross-section, sometimes with an axial canal and ranging between 5 and 60 mm in diameter. They are always vertical or near vertical, and they resemble fillings and incrustations of root cavities.

These sandstones belong to an old dune system, and always underlie modern sand dunes where they are in contact. Furthermore, if the interpretation of the calcareous pipes is correct, a period of heavy vegetation separated the ancestral dunes from the modern sand dunes.

SAND DUNES

Unconsolidated aeolian sands mask very extensive areas of the Lake Eyre Basin (Madigan 1936, 1946). Borelogs, however, suggest that this sand cover nowhere exceeds 35 m and it is considerably thinner towards the margins of the dune fields. The sands are underlain by alluvial sands, gibber, gypsite, and older formations. Although earlier dune formations have been observed, the modern dune fields are essentially of middle to late Recent age.

The distribution of the dune fields is strongly influenced by patterns of structural deformation of the duricrust (Fig. 7.1). As shown on the map, all major dune fields, including the Simpson Desert, Sturts Stony Desert, and the Strzelecki Desert, occur in structural lows. The reason for this relationship is probably twofold: firstly, all important sources of sand, such as playas and large flood-outs, are restricted to them, and secondly these areas provide even surfaces favourable to aeolian sand movements.

The sands of the dunes are composed overwhelmingly of quartz grains. Heavy minerals (magnetite, titano-magnetite, zircon, garnet, epidote, tourmaline) constitute only 0·5-1·5 per cent.

The quartz grains are generally subangular to subrounded, and their sizes range from 0·05 mm to 1·2 mm (Fig. 7.5). The median grain size is about 0·5 mm on the crest of dunes and 0·3 to 0·26 mm on slip faces (Fig. 7.5). All sands of active dunes show excellent sorting, with a Trask sorting coefficient in the vicinity of 1·4, whereas the sands of the interdunal areas are less sorted, with a coefficient of about 2·0.

Clay may constitute up to 5 per cent of the dunes, and as a result of illuviation is far more abundant in the dune cores than at the surface. Semi-consolidated cores, in which clay particles fill the interstitial spaces between the sand grains, are not specific to the dunes of the Lake Eyre Basin, as clay illuviation into lower parts of dunes has also been described from the Channel Country of southwest Queensland (Whitehouse 1948). Tabular pellets of clay are blown on to the dunes from adjoining claypans where they are derived from dried up, cracked and curled clay films formed after rains.

Most dunes are brownish pink or brick red but some are yellow-brown or grey-brown, and others are white. To the north of source areas such as Lake Eyre and the Warburton River, the sands are light coloured, but they become redder to the north. Where sands have been blown from recent floodplains, for instance along Eyres Creek and Goyders Lagoon, they are white or light yellow; the further the sand grains are blown, the redder they become, acquiring a pellicule of iron oxide in the absence of water. The iron oxide, probably derived from the small clay fraction within the dune sands, gives the red colour so characteristic of the Simpson Desert dunes and other well established dune fields of the Lake Eyre Basin and its surroundings.

The longitudinal dunes are asymmetrical in cross-section and generally the eastern side is the slip face, its inclination approaching the angle of rest of the

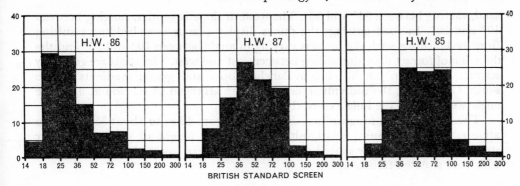

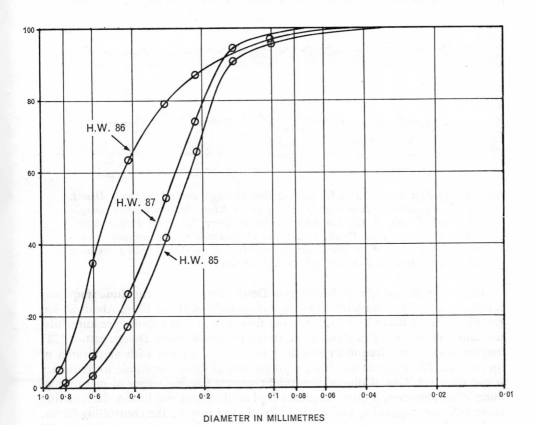

DIAMETER IN MILLIMETRES

7.5 *Grading of modern dune sands from the Strzelecki Desert shown by histograms and cumulative curves. Sample 86 from a dune crest near Fortville is coarser than sample 87 from the slip face of the same dune and sample 85 is from an avalanching slip face on a dune 150 km to the west near Lake Blanche.*

sand, varying between 34° and 38°. The western slope is gentler, ranging between 10° and 20°. In road cuttings the dunes display planar cross-bedding resulting from avalanching, with the foresets varying in angle between 10° and 30° and the direction of foreset dips alternating between east and west. The crests are generally serrate, with steep north-facing avalanche slopes and gentle gradients to the south. Commonly, the individual 'saw-teeth' are arranged in echelon at an acute angle westward to the long axis of the dune.

The height of the longitudinal dunes varies from 10 m to about 35 m. There appears to be a definite relationship between the height of dunes and their spacing (Fig. 7.6); closely spaced dunes are generally of lower altitude than those which are situated farther apart.

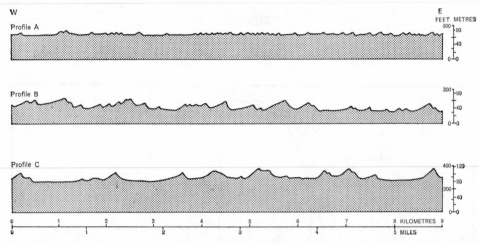

7.6 *Dune-profiles along F.P.C.A.'s seismic line through central Simpson Desert. Profile A is situated immediately east of Finke River flats on western margin of desert, Profile B 110 km ENE of Finke River flats, and Profile C immediately east of Eyre Creek, 18 km SSE of Annandale. The profiles demonstrate the increase of spacing as dunes grow higher. Published with permission of French Petroleum Company (Australia) Pty Ltd.*

In the western margin of the Simpson Desert, for instance, the dune frequency is between 5 to 6 per km with an average amplitude of about 15 m. About 80 km east of the Finke River flats the frequency decreases to 3 to 4 dunes per km whilst the amplitude increases to about 25 m. In the eastern Simpson Desert, east of 138° longitude, the dune frequency is only 1 to 2 dunes per km with amplitudes of up to 38 m. The cause of this inverse proportion of dune amplitude to frequency is not clear yet. Casual observation might suggest varying stages of maturity of dune fields. However, if dune frequency is plotted against amplitude, the resulting curve is linear, suggesting that availability of sand may be the controlling factor.

Individual dunes extend unbroken for scores of kilometres, with NNW-SSE trend. The dunes commonly display Y-junctions as a result of the gradual convergence of adjacent sand ridges. Although north-convergence is most common, it is not invariable, as claimed by King (1960), and Y-junctions with south-convergence are quite common (Plate XVa). A somewhat special case of sand accumulation is found in the vicinity of the playa lakes around Poeppels Corner, where the dune frequency is about 1 to 2 per km with an amplitude of approximately 35 m. However, superimposed on this large 'wave pattern' are closely spaced 'auxiliary' dunes at a frequency of up to 8 per km and with an amplitude of about 10 to 15 m (see Plate XIV). Similar conditions can be observed in the vicinity of large playa lakes in Sturts Stony Desert and Strzelecki Desert also. Thus it appears to be typical of dune fields in the immediate vicinity of source areas. In areas of episodic flooding, reticulate dune patterns have developed, with the longitudinal elements joined by cross or transverse members which meet them obtusely, forming a linked-chain effect. Claypans are commonly found in the centre of such links. Average height of these reticulate dunes rarely exceeds 20 m.

In each of the three patterns so far described—parallel ridges, forked dunes, and reticulate dunes—dune and corridor are quite separate; but sometimes the distinction between individual dunes is less clear and there are no interdune flats, as in the lee of some playas and floodplains where the sand has been moulded into a disordered mass of ridges and hollows.

In most of the dune areas of the Lake Eyre Basin, active migration of sand is restricted to the crests of the dunes. The dune flanks are to some extent stabilized by sparse vegetation, particularly of cane grass (*Zygochloa paradoxa*) and spinifex (*Triodia basedowii*), but in many areas where sand supply is inadequate the flanks are being eroded by wind, especially on the western sides. Wind erosion is also particularly marked on the south ends of dunes which rim the north shores of playas and claypans, where dunes have commonly been eroded to their semi-consolidated cores (Plate XVb). However, erosion does not take place where the adjacent playas or floodplains contain abundant sand. In such areas there are actively migrating dunes, for instance, north of Goyders Lagoon and north of Lake Blanche. Thus, the shapes of dunes vary with place and time depending on factors such as sand supply and the balance of erosion and deposition.

Dunes near the south shore of Lake Eyre have been described as a kind of wind-rift dune (King 1960) in that they have cores and plinths of lacustrine deposits, which have been wind-gouged leaving longitudinal dune corridors. There is no doubt, however, that these are not characteristic of the desert as a whole. Roads bulldozed through the sand ridges have provided numerous deep sections; seismic shot holes have been drilled over considerable areas of the Simpson Desert, and in none of these cases has a core of distinctly different material been brought to light. The dunes of the Simpson Desert are built throughout of aeolian quartz sand varied only by higher clay content within the core.

The evidence above shows clearly that the dunes have been built up and are still being moulded by the wind to the leeward of source areas. Accordingly they have to be classified as longitudinal dunes as defined by Bagnold (1941). Furthermore, the dunes are shaped under bi-directional wind régimes, their northward migration being largely the resultant of more than one wind component. This is demonstrated by alternation of foreset dips between east and west and also by the forms of the dunes themselves. For instance, the effect of alternating cross winds is adequately demonstrated in Plates XVIa and b, where a barchan forming part of a longitudinal dune crest and adjusted to WSW winds has been completely reversed within three weeks by winds from the southeast sector.

The longitudinal dunes of the Simpson Desert, Sturts Stony Desert and other South Australian dune fields resemble both in shape and internal structure the seif dunes of the Libyan Desert which were shown by McKee and Tibbitts (1964) to have been formed under bi-directional wind régimes.

Observations indicate that the most important winds are from the southeast and southwest. These winds appear to determine the local and ephemeral asymmetry of the ridges and play an important part in shaping the dunes in detail. The pronounced northward drift is a resultant of the two cross winds but is also assisted by southerly winds. North winds, although causing spectacular dust storms during the summer months, appear to have little part in shaping the dunes.

It is unfortunate that no long term and systematic observations of wind strength and direction have so far been made in the deserts as observations over a long period are necessary for a statistical analysis of these important parameters. Perforce, reliance has to be placed on the wind records of meteorological stations which lie outside the sandy desert, and upon incidental short-term records of travellers and surveyors. In detail, there are suggestions of a recent slight change in wind régime; for example, east of Strzelecki Creek, formerly north-trending dunes now display offshoots trending NNW-SSE, which indicate a backing of the wind. Similarly, Wopfner and Heath (1963) have described northeast-trending seif dunes with superimposed north-trending chains of fuljes and barchans which they have attributed to a shift in the resultant wind direction west of Lake Eyre. Nevertheless, it is clear that the general pattern of winds has not changed markedly over the past few thousand years.

The dune sands are derived mainly from alluvium deposited in this, the lowest part of Australia, in late Pleistocene and Recent times. The alluvium was deposited by various rivers on floodplains, flood-outs and playas, and subsequently picked up by the wind and carried in suspension and by saltation to the north of the source areas.

PLAYAS

(a) *Origin of Basins*

The numerous playas of the study area are deflation hollows. Clays and sands deposited in topographic lows have been picked up by the wind and either exported from the region or redeposited locally and eventually moulded into dunes.

The major playas, however, also owe their location and, in part, their shape to ancient structural lineaments. Lake Eyre, for example, occurs at the intersection of two major lineaments, one trending NW-SE through Lake Callabonna, Lake Blanche, and Lake Eyre North, the other trending NNW-SSE through the western shores of Lake Torrens, Lake Eyre South, and Lake Eyre North. Tectonism has been active in the recent past here, and is indeed still active. Mound springs and the foci of earth tremors are located on these lineaments; for instance on the west side of Lake Eyre North, late Pleistocene movement along this line is suggested by the detailed subsurface stratigraphy of Lake Eyre. Shells of *Coxiella gilesi*, dated at about 40,000 years B.P., occur on gypseous lacustrine clays in the coastal cliffs of Lake Eyre, while organic remains found in the sediments of the present lake bed have been dated as almost 20,000 years old. These facts could be interpreted as indicating a phase of marked deflation between 40,000 and 20,000 years ago, when the lake bed was lowered by some 12 m (King 1956).

Deflation is and certainly has been an important agent in the removal of recent sediments, producing the intricate southern shore of Lake Eyre North, for example. However, the primary cause for the existence of Lake Eyre and other marginal playas such as Lake Gregory, Lake Blanche, and Lake Callabonna is young tectonic movements. Such young tectonism is evident along the western shore of Lake Eyre where faults can be observed displacing the gypsite surface. It is further indicated by the presence of active mound springs in the western portions of Lake Eyre North and by the presence of the Warburton Groove and the rejuvenated channels of the major feeders in the immediate vicinity of Lake Eyre. The occurrence of gypsite in the high cliffs west of the Lake Eyre lineament and also beneath the surface of Lake Eyre as shown in the stratigraphy corroborates a tectonic origin of the lake.

Last but not least, the very fact that the Lake Eyre depression embraces a vast drainage area of more than 1 million km² can only be explained by tectonism and not by incidental deflation of a few metres of recent sediments. Tectonism is the cause, deflation the result.

(b) *Hydrology*

The playas fill with water infrequently and for short periods, and only one filling, that of Lake Eyre in 1949-50, has been studied in detail.

During the second half of the nineteenth century several travellers reported seeing water in Lake Eyre, and in 1857 Captain Freeling was despatched by the South Australian government with a boat to investigate and if possible to cross a large fresh-water lake extending as far as the eye could see and enclosing the northern Flinders Ranges on three sides. This lake had been reported to a startled Adelaide by W. G. Goyder, then Assistant Surveyor-General and newly arrived from England. Goyder mistook a flooding from one of the ephemeral streams to be permanent standing water and was totally deceived by the mirage which seemingly extended the sheet of water beyond the horizon. However, it now appears likely that reported sightings of water in Lake Eyre by such as Ross in 1869 were correct.

The great flooding of Lake Eyre in 1949-50 is the first to have been closely analysed (Bonython *et al.* 1955; Bonython 1960) and provides a valuable measure by which to judge the probability of floods in terms of meteorological events. It is evident that water reaches the lake bed only after prolonged and unusually heavy rainfall both in interior Queensland and in the South Australian Channel Country. Although water from the 1949 rains breached the sand dunes across the Cooper and reached the lake, filling did not take place until the following year. Yet the events of 1950 cannot be understood without reference to 1949.

In February and March 1949, cyclonic disturbances brought heavy rains to inland Queensland, and many stations received record March rains. Thargomindah, for instance, with a March average of 20 mm, reported 394 mm. The northeast of South Australia was also soaked. In the spring further heavy rains fell, and early the next year the Queensland part of the Lake Eyre catchment received such heavy falls that the headwaters of the Thompson, Barcoo, and Diamantina flooded. Three tropical cyclones in succession moved inland during March 1950, bringing exceptionally heavy falls to the already soaked inland. Urandangi recorded 374 mm in March alone, compared with an annual of 245 mm, and similarly Windorah (average annual 255 mm) received 498 mm in one month. All the rivers were in flood, and the Barcoo was 50-80 km wide. The next four months saw average rains, and though August and September were dry, Lake Eyre had filled by early September. Further rains in the last three months of 1950 helped maintain a water cover in the lake.

Although the lake was not full until late 1950, the rains of the previous year had prepared the way. The wetting of the Channel Country in South Australia in particular meant that the floodwaters from central Queensland were not lost by infiltration and so continued to the lake.

Waters from the western and southern streams flowing to the lake, such as the Macumba and Neales, undoubtedly reach the bed occasionally, but are only of minor importance in the hydrology of the area: the vital flow comes from Queensland.

Examination of rainfall records suggests that the lake may fill perhaps twice in a century. On the other hand, a study of the stratigraphy of the Lake Eyre Basin shows that permanent lacustrine conditions obtained at several times in the area in the geological past.

(c) Origin of Salts

The origin of the salt, gypsum and silcrete which occur in such abundance in the Lake Eyre Basin has given rise to some controversy (Bonython 1956). The salt has been variously explained as having been left by a former arm of the sea, as of cyclic origin in that it was carried in atmospherically from the sea, or as connate salt derived from adjacent rocks. There is no evidence of the sea having penetrated to the interior of the continent since the Mesozoic, and in the Lake Torrens corridor for instance, the Cainozoic sediments are fresh-water throughout. Suggestions that the salt, as well as gypsum and lime, could have been blown in from the oceans, and in the case of lime from the Nullarbor, are discounted by observations from Victoria which suggest that the influence of salt blown from the sea is limited to the immediate coastal zone (Cole 1959; Hutton and Leslie 1958). The salt has undoubtedly been derived from the rocks which crop out in the catchment area and, carried dominantly by shallow groundwater to a hot arid region of interior drainage, has then been concentrated at various times during the Quaternary. Groundwaters flow in the same direction as the intermittent surface drainage, that is, it is centripetal to Lake Eyre, but the main contributions come from the north, from the Simpson Desert region. Shallow groundwaters immediately north of Lake Eyre are saturated brines, and the chemical composition of the salt crusts is consistent with such an origin.

Gypsum and silcrete which accumulated in earlier times could also have formed as concentrates with interior drainage, although in both cases there is also strong evidence for vertical movements of solutions within the fossil soil profiles and the underlying rocks.

HISTORY OF THE LANDFORMS

The history of landform development commenced in Oligocene times, when crustal stability and shrinking areas of deposition led to the formation of a mid-Tertiary plain. This plain remained stable till at least the early and possibly the mid-Miocene. The Lake Eyre Basin was probably an area of internal drainage at this time, and shallow sedimentation occurred at least through parts of this period in a more limited basin, occupying about the same area as the present Lake Eyre North. In this area the mid-Tertiary surface was a sediplain, the remaining portion, however, was an erosional surface, although erosion and transport across it were exceedingly small. Thus prolonged deep weathering and bleaching of the near-surface strata took place, forming the duricrust profile with its characteristic kaolinised zone and its hard silcrete horizon (Whitehouse 1940; Woolnough 1930).

At about the middle of the Miocene the Lake Eyre Basin was affected by widespread epeirogenic movements which led to the development of upwarps, including large domes, on the margins of the basin (Fig. 7.1), namely along a line from the Peake and Denison Ranges to Dalhousie Springs on the west side and in the area now travelled by the Birdsville track and further east around Cordillo Downs on the eastern margin (Wopfner 1960).

Positive movements along the marginal areas were compensated by negative movements near Lake Eyre, thus accommodating further sedimentation in late Miocene to Pliocene time. These epeirogenic movements, which also included both normal and transcurrent faulting, did not occur in one episode but intermittently throughout part of the Miocene.

This is indicated by superimposed layers of duricrust-silcrete whereby a steeply tilted duricrust horizon is unconformably capped by flat-lying sediments on which a later duricrust profile has developed (Plate XIIIb). Significantly the two superimposed duricrust profiles show varying degrees of maturity, indicating the time of deformation in relation to the period of duricrust formation. Thus, a case where a deformed embryonic profile is capped by a mature profile would indicate folding during an early stage of the silicification period and a case of immature profiles capping fully mature profiles indicates deformation towards the end of the period during which duricrust was formed.

These and like tectonic movements in southern central Australia at this period resulted in a dome and basin topography in which the Lake Eyre Basin was the largest depression. With the beginning of erosion on the uplifted areas and deposition in the intervening depressions the equilibrium under which the duricrust profile formed came to an end.

The gradients between the structural highs and lows were generally small, however, and ensuing erosion developed only broad, shallow consequent valley systems which rarely cut more than 15 m into the duricrust profile. Soon the structural depressions and then their tributary valleys became partly filled with alluvium eroded from the domes. Subsequent deep weathering, apparently restricted to such filled channels and depressions, formed the bauxitic pisolites. Reworked older laterites may have been incorporated in these pisolites, but this is still uncertain.

Remnants of the old consequent drainage systems, together with the pisolites, have commonly been preserved as perched valleys on the upper flanks of domal structures and on the plateaux. Along the northeastern margin of the Lake Eyre Basin, mainly near Birdsville and Cordillo Downs, later erosion has exposed the pisolite unit in some of the synclinal basin areas. These exposures are particularly significant as the pisolites are here overlain by pink and grey cherty limestones which are correlated with the carbonate sequence of the Etadunna Formation nearer Lake Eyre.

The above observations demonstrate that the deposition of the Etadunna Formation clearly postdated the regional tectonic movements and, at least in the marginal areas of the Lake Eyre Basin, the formation of the bauxitic pisolites. Further evidence to that effect is the presence of pisolitic grit below the Etadunna Formation in Lake Eyre Bore 20, although it is still debatable whether these represent pisolite formed *in situ* or whether they are detrital.

The cause of renewed sedimentation has to be sought in a general subsidence which began at a fault along the NNW-trending western lineament of Lake Eyre and gradually extended eastwards. Hence, by virtue of the same lineament, a similar marked asymmetry characterised the basin in which the Etadunna Formation was deposited as in the Cretaceous basin of deposition. This asymmetry is evidenced by the fact that the Etadunna Formation attains its greatest thickness near Lake Eyre and thins out gradually eastwards against the Mt Gason and Cordillo upwarps. Only perhaps at the later stage of sedimentation did the Etadunna Formation transgress the lineament to the west.

The fossil content of the Etadunna Formation indicates that it was deposited in an inland lake under brackish-water conditions. The intake of detrital material from the surrounding land was, however, generally restricted to clay and fine sand. The small proportion of coarse, terrigenous sediments in a depositional area surrounded by land can only be attributed to an extremely low gradient on the land itself.

In late Pliocene times, deposition of the Etadunna Formation and its equivalents was terminated by the renewal of uplift which affected the Lake Eyre Basin as a whole, but particularly the areas which had been domed in previous epeirogenic movements. The post-Etadunna uplift introduced a more marked erosional phase in the Lake Eyre Basin and led to extensive dissection and removal of the duricrust. Areas affected most by erosion were the domal structures and the large uplifted area west of the Peake and Denison Ranges. The domal structures were breached, leaving only a rim of cuestas on the outward-dipping structure, whilst the area between the Stuart Range and the Peake and Denison Ranges was completely stripped of its duricrust cover. Within these areas erosion cut at least 30 to 50 m deep before a new equilibrium was obtained. The final product of this erosion was broad fluviatile plains with extremely low watersheds separating one plain from another.

Despite the large amount of material known to have been removed there is practically no correlative sedimentary record within the Lake Eyre Basin and we must therefore assume the existence of an external drainage, most likely via Lake Torrens and Lake Frome, which carried the debris out to sea. In this case the low sea levels of the Pleistocene may also have induced these erosional processes; however, on the evidence this remains speculative.

XVa Dunefield northeast of Lake Eyre, with Warburton River in background; looking north-ward and showing some north-facing as well as south-facing Y-junctions of longitudinal dunes. The playa has been invaded by dunes from the south. Photograph from 15,000 feet by H. Wopfner.

XVb Wind erosion on the north margin of a large claypan has exposed the clay-indurated core at the south end of a dune in Sturts Stony Desert SSE of Birdsville. Photograph by H. Wopfner.

XVIa and b   Changes at the northern, growing end of a longitudinal dune on Eyre Creek flats, 24 km southeast of Alton Downs homestead. In XVIa the crest is a small barchan, 3 m high, transverse to strong westerly winds; three weeks later the slip face has been reversed by easterly winds and the height of the dune increased by 50 cm. Photographs by H. Wopfner.

The erosional period prevailed through most of the Pleistocene, resulting in broad plains separated by very low watersheds. As large parts of the Lake Eyre Basin were eroded close to baselevel, clastic sediments began to accumulate on the broad fluviatile plains. This backfilling ultimately led to the deposition of the gypsite sediments. The pauperate foraminifera near the base of the gypsite sediments also indicates the existence of large brackish waterbodies at the beginning of this sedimentary cycle. This indicates reversion to internal drainage or at least to a drainage with restricted outlet. The cause of this change is unknown.

The time at which deposition of the gypsite sediments began can be estimated only within wide limits. The two carbon dates of 40,000 years B.P. relate to the upper third of the gypsite sequence. It is suggested that this sedimentary cycle may have begun about 80,000 years ago allowing about 40,000 years for the deposition of the gypsite sediments. The geomorphological setting must have been rather similar to the present, with alluvial plains of low gradient, but with somewhat higher rainfall and lower evaporation, permitting the existence of large fresh-water and brackish swamps. These accommodated most of the fine-grained clastics, whilst the coarser fractions were deposited near the flanking pediments.

Simultaneously with the deposition of the gypsite sediments, the eastern rim of the Great Artesian Basin was uplifted, causing a marked increase in the piezometric gradient of the artesian aquifers which, together with the liberal charge of the aquifers during the wetter Pleistocene, resulted in the expulsion of artesian water in springs along the west and southwest margin of the Great Artesian Basin, that is west and southwest of Lake Eyre. In the shallow pools surrounding these springs the fresh-water limestones and travertines were formed.

The final product of the Pleistocene events was the gypsite surface, a vast and stable depositional plain extending from the Stuart Range to Cordillo Downs and beyond, and from Marree into the northern Simpson Desert.

It is of interest that at this time only the highest portions of the Peake and Denison Ranges extended above the gypsite surface as is evidenced by several remnants of gypsite sediments on these ranges near Mt Anna and Mt Margaret. During the later stage of this quiescent period, erosion and deposition had reached a low level, thus permitting the development of the gypsite profile.

The final stage in the development of the Lake Eyre Basin probably commenced about 30,000 years ago when tectonic movements along the western lineament depressed Lake Eyre. Simultaneously the area to the west and northwest underwent considerable uplift. These events resulted in rejuvenation of drainage and extensive dissection of the gypsite surface through into the Cretaceous sediments. In places, as on the north bank of the Neales River, escarpments and mesas capped by the gypsum crust stand up to 30 m above the level of the present river plains (Plate XIIIc). Widespread further dissection of remaining duricrust on structural 'highs' also occurred at this time. The area east of Lake Eyre generally remained stable, although some further uplift was experienced by most of the structural domes, as indicated by the rejuvenation of drainage on them. However, the major streams such as the Diamantina and Coopers Creek, with their networks of interwoven channels, achieve little erosion until they leave Goyders Lagoon and the large alluvial flats west of Innamincka respectively. West of these points,

L

deep and well defined channels have been developed up to 20 m deep and cut into the gypsite sediments.

The post-gypsite erosion was not a single large event. Intensive erosion alternated with periods of quiescence and even aggradation, as demonstrated by numerous terraces between the gypsite surface and the present erosional plains.

The detritus derived from post-gypsite erosion was sorted during water transport, and the finer fractions were deposited in Lake Eyre and in other depositional basins such as the chain of lakes north of the Flinders Ranges.

As the climate became more arid (Crocker 1946) these sediments were deflated and transported northwards by the wind and accumulated into dunes. The general northward transport of the sand is indicated by the changes in colour from white or fawn immediately north of the source to deepening hues of red with increasing distance from it.

This sequence of erosion, transport, and deposition by water, and aeolian deflation, transport, and deposition, has dominated until the present, although the balance has changed with climate. During periods of increased rainfall, the balance was in favour of lacustrine deposition and the dunes were fixed by a closer vegetation as indicated by calcareous root pipes in the sands of the older dunes. With the onset of an arid period the depositional areas were deflated and wind deposition was the dominant feature.

Deflation, however, becomes ineffective once the groundwater level has been reached. With arid conditions prevailing, sediment intake is restricted to the small amount delivered by intermittent flooding. During such periods wind erosion attacks the southern portions of the dune fields, particularly along the northern rims of source areas (see Fig. 7.1) and redistributes the material further north.

This is the situation as it prevails today.

REFERENCES

Bagnold, R. A. (1941). *The Physics of Blown Sand and Desert Dunes*. London.

Bolt, B. A. (1958). Seismic travel-times in Australia. *J. Proc. R. Soc. N.S.W.* 92: 64-72.

Bonython, C. W. et al. (1955). *Lake Eyre, South Australia: The Great Flooding of 1949-50. Report of Lake Eyre Committee*. Adelaide.

———— (1956). The salt of Lake Eyre—its occurrence in Madigan Gulf and its possible origin. *Trans. R. Soc. S. Aust.* 79: 66-92.

———— (1960). A decade of watching for water in Lake Eyre. *Proc. S. Aust. Brch R. geogr. Soc. Aust.*, 61: 1-8.

Cole, W. F. (1959). Some aspects of the weathering of terracotta roofing tiles. *Aust. J. appl. Sci.* 10 (3): 346-63.

Crocker, R. L. (1946). *Post-Miocene Climatic and Geologic History and its Significance in Relation to the Genesis of the Major Soil Types of South Australia*. CSIR Aust. Bull. No. 193.

Daily, B. (1960). Report of the Curator of Fossils and Minerals, in *Report of the Museum Board 1958/59*, p. 12. Adelaide.

Frye, J. C. and Willman, H. B. (1962). Morphostratigraphic units in Pleistocene stratigraphy. *Bull. Am. Ass. Petrol. Geol.* 46: 112-13.

Grant-Taylor, T. L. and Rafter, T. A. (1962). New Zealand radiocarbon age measurements—5. *N.Z. Jl Geol. Geophys.* 5: (2): 331-59.

Hutton, J. T. and Leslie, T. I. (1958). Accession of non-nitrogenous ions dissolved in rainwater to soils in Victoria. *Aust. J. agric. Res.* 9: 492-507.

Johns, R. K. and Ludbrook, N. H. (1963). *Investigation of Lake Eyre.* Geol. Surv. S. Aust. Rept Invest. No. 24.

King, D. (1956). The Quaternary stratigraphic record at Lake Eyre North and the evolution of existing topographic forms. *Trans. R. Soc. S. Aust.* **79**: 93-103.

—— (1960). The sand ridge deserts of South Australia and related aeolian landforms of the Quaternary arid cycles. *Trans. R. Soc. S. Aust.* **83**: 93-108.

Ludbrook, N. H. (1965). Occurrence of foraminifera in salt lakes. *Geol. Surv. S. Aust. Quart. Geol. Notes* No. 14: 6-7.

Madigan, C. T. (1936). The Australian sand-ridge deserts. *Geogrl Rev.* **26**: 205-27.

—— (1946). The Simpson Desert Expedition 1939, Scientific Reports: No. 6, Geology— The Sand Formations. *Trans. R. Soc. S. Aust.* **70**: 45-63.

McCarthy, W. R. (1962). Report on petrographic investigations of silcrete-samples. Aust. Min. Dev. Lab. Unpub. Rept MP 1.2.0/1571-4.

McKee, E. D. and Tibbitts, G. C. (1964). Primary structures of a seif dune and associated deposits in Libya. *J. sedim. Petrol.* **34**: 5-17.

Paten, R. J. (1960). Lacustrine sandstones and limestones and spring sinters of far western Queensland. *J. geol. Soc. Aust.* **7**: 391-3.

Sprigg, R. C. and staff (1957). The Great Artesian Basin in South Australia. *J. geol. Soc. Aust.* **5** (Pt 2): 88-101.

Stirton, R. A., Tedford, R. H., and Miller, A. H. (1961). Cenozoic stratigraphy and vertebrate palaeontology of the Tirari Desert, South Australia. *Rec. S. Aust. Mus.* **14** (1): 19-61.

Whitehouse, F. W. (1940). *Studies in the Late Geological History of Queensland.* Univ. Qld Pap. Geol. Vol. 2 (N.S.), No. 1.

—— (1948). The geology of the channel country of south-western Queensland. *Qld Bur. Inv. Tech. Bull.* No. 1: 10-28.

Woolnough, W. G. (1930). The influence of climate and topography in the formation and distribution of products of weathering. *Geol. Mag.* **67**: 123-32.

Wopfner, H. (1960). On some structural development in the central part of the Great Australian Artesian Basin. *Trans. R. Soc. S. Aust.* **83**: 179-93.

—— (1963). Post-Winton sediments of probable Upper Cretaceous Age in the Central Great Artesian Basin. *Trans. R. Soc. S. Aust.* **86**: 247-53.

—— (1964a). Tertiary duricrust profile on Upper Proterozoic sediments, Granite Downs area. *Geol. Surv. S. Aust. Quart. Geol. Notes* No. 12: 1-3.

—— (1964b). Permian-Jurassic history of the Western Great Artesian Basin. *Trans. R. Soc. S. Aust.* **87**: 117-28.

—— and Heath, G. R. (1963). Modified seif dunes west of Lake Eyre. *Geol. Surv. S. Aust. Quart. Geol. Notes,* No. 6.

8

Denudation Chronology in Central Australia Structure, Climate, and Landform Inheritance in the Alice Springs Area

J. A. MABBUTT

"Une conclusion générale s'impose: l'évolution du modelé aride a été très rarement continue; d'où la variété des combinaisons de formes, augmentée par les conditions différentes qu'offrent les climats et les grands traits de la structure"—(de Martonne 1925).

INTRODUCTION

(a) Climate and Landforms in the Australian Arid Zone

Two related factors combine to invalidate the interpretation of landforms solely in terms of the prevailing climate and of a single resultant morphogenesis, namely control by major structure and the persistence of forms moulded under earlier, contrasted climates. The quotation above shows this to have been recognised for desert areas by earlier writers as well as by later proponents of climatic geomorphology, and its truth is well borne out in arid Australia, where present-day contrasts in climate certainly find no simple geomorphological expression. Even such accepted morphoclimatic indicators as the distribution of sand deserts or variations in the status of surface drainage show no obvious relationship to climatic zones (Hills 1953a).

Prescott (1936) superimposed isopleths of evaporation excess on a map of the Australian sand-ridge deserts, purporting to show that their distribution was related to maximum aridity, but apart from a general climatic control in that they are largely contained within the arid zone, the inland dunes mainly reflect patterns of prior deposition of coarse-textured alluvia derived principally from sandstone (Hills 1953a).

A zonal relationship between degree of aridity and the extent of riverless areas (areic) and areas of internal drainage (endoreic) was postulated by de Martonne (1925). The map trace of the index of aridity which he postulated to express the limits of internal drainage follows closely the agreed boundary of the Australian

Many of the maps are based on a CSIRO regional survey, and acknowledgment is made to Messrs R. A. Perry, W. H. Litchfield, and T. Quinlan on this account. Mr Litchfield kindly allowed extensive reference to his unpublished work on soil layers, and Mr M. O. Woodhouse to his preliminary observations on the Alcoota 'beds'. Messrs Litchfield and Quinlan and Dr R. W. Galloway helpfully criticised an original draft.

144

arid zone (Marshall 1948), but large areas in the west of the zone are in fact drained to the sea. De Martonne's mapping of areic and endoreic areas in Australia is complex and certainly not climatically based, and much of the area shown as areic is by no means lacking in surface drainage.

Hills (1953a; 1953b) has stressed the importance of structure and prior relief in the present-day drainage of arid Australia. He distinguishes riverless areas and areas of unco-ordinated and co-ordinated internal drainage. The riverless areas merely express the permeability of aeolian sand surfaces where prior drainage patterns have been obliterated by moving sand. All upland areas are centres of localised drainage dispersal, but lowland drainage is of two types. On the Australian shield, gentle gradients and limited upland catchments have allowed an advanced disarticulation of drainage, whereas the centripetal slopes and extensive fringing uplands of the sedimentary basins have enabled fairly co-ordinated internal drainage systems to persist.

In arid Australia there is no extreme desert, either as defined by Meigs (1953)* or in the sense of the *Kernwüste* of German geomorphologists (Meckelein 1959). The Australian arid areas correspond to the '*déserts attenués*' of de Martonne (1925), in which stream action predominates on all appreciable slopes. Such aeolian surfaces as occur are mainly stabilized by vegetation and are fossil. Land-forming processes active in such 'moderate deserts' do not differ greatly in kind from those of tropical semi-arid or subhumid areas, and landform contrasts within such zones are more expressive of structural differences than of climatic gradients. For instance, Dresch (1962) has defined a group of 'shield deserts' characterised by extensive erosional plains often controlled by duricrusts, with valley terraces related to past pluvial phases, and with extensive sand-ridge deserts in lower parts. Much of arid Australia falls into this category.

The survival of palaeoforms is facilitated in ancient, fairly stable landscapes such as characterise arid Australia. The fossil nature of sandplain and sand dunes has already been noted; older survivals, formed under earlier, wetter climates, include rounded or smoothed upland surfaces and relict duricrusts. Less spectacular are extensive alluvial plains with leached soils indicative of weathering under a more humid climate in the past (Litchfield 1962).

The theme of this regional essay, therefore, is the complex inheritance of an arid landscape and the necessity to understand it in terms of a long history of changing climate. Within the area, the geomorphological expression of the play of past climates has mainly varied with gross structure, meaning major tectonic and lithologic contrasts. Further, and more tentatively, some evidence will be brought that the present climatic gradients also obtained during part of this history, with some effect in the landscape.

The area studied is that part of central Australia surveyed as the 'Alice Springs area' by the CSIRO Division of Land Research in 1956-7 (Perry *et al.* 1962). Covering 375,000 km², it extends southwards from lat. 20°S. to the South Australian border in lat. 26° and is bounded by the meridians 130°30'E. and 136°30'E. (Fig. 8.1).

* 'One in which in a given locality at least 12 consecutive months without rainfall have been recorded, and in which there is not a regular seasonal rhythm of rainfall.'

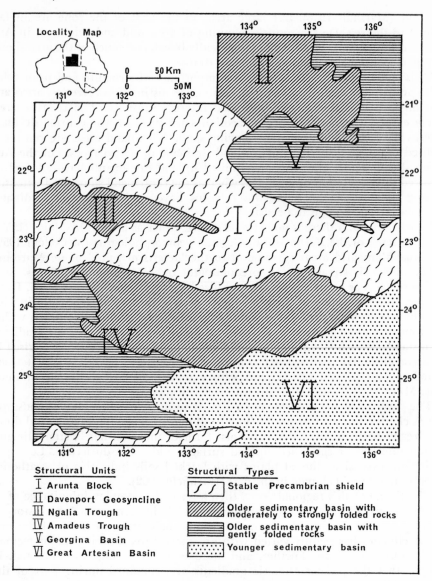

Locality Map

Structural Units
I Arunta Block
II Davenport Geosyncline
III Ngalia Trough
IV Amadeus Trough
V Georgina Basin
VI Great Artesian Basin

Structural Types
Stable Precambrian shield
Older sedimentary basin with moderately to strongly folded rocks
Older sedimentary basin with gently folded rocks
Younger sedimentary basin

8.1   Structural divisions of the Alice Springs area (based on Quinlan 1962)

(b) *Structural Divisions*

Six main structural units recognised in the Alice Springs area (Quinlan 1962) are shown in Figure 8.1. For an understanding of the geomorphological division of the area and in order to explain recurrent regional contrasts in the denudation history, four major structural types must be distinguished:

(i) The stable Precambrian shield of metamorphic and igneous rocks, here referred to as the Arunta Block, which is extensively exposed in the north and west of the area.

(ii) Older sedimentary basins with moderately to strongly folded resistant strata of Upper Proterozoic and Palaeozoic age, giving rise to strike ranges, e.g. the Davenport Geosyncline (Davenport-Murchison Ranges).

(iii) Older sedimentary basins with gently folded Palaeozoic strata of moderate to high resistance, generally forming plateaux and plains, e.g., the Georgina Basin and the southern part of the Amadeus Trough.

(iv) The younger sedimentary basin of subsidence with less indurated sub-horizontal rocks of Mesozoic age—part of the Great Artesian Basin—in the south-east of the area.

(c) *Geomorphological Divisions*

The Alice Springs area is situated in the centre of Australia and extends across the Tropic of Capricorn. It includes three contrasted major relief provinces—the southern desert basins tributary to Lake Eyre, the east-west central ranges which form a major drainage divide, and the northern plains and uplands with a north-ward regional descent. In more detail, and as mapped in Figure 8.2, divisions are as follows:

(i) *Northern Plains*

The landscape north of the central ranges contains extensive plains which comprise a number of basins with partially disorganised drainage. On this basis one can distinguish between

1. Frew River Plains in the northeast
2. Hanson-Lander Plains in the northwest
3. Sandover-Elkedra Plains in the east
4. Sandover-Plenty Plains in the southeast
5. Burt Plain in the southwest.

With the exception of 4, which is more dissected, each comprises a peripheral erosional plain, stable alluvial plains downslope, and a lower part consisting mainly of sandplain. Of the above divisions, 2, 4, and 5 accord largely with the Arunta Block and 1 and 3 form part of the Georgina Basin structure. There is an overall decrease in altitude northwards, from 700 m to less than 250 m above sea level.

(ii) *Northern Uplands*

These islands of strong relief in the northern plains are mainly bevelled and plateau-like, lacking the ruggedness of the central ranges, and relief does not generally exceed 150 m. Three divisions can be made:

1. Mt Doreen-Reynolds Ranges. Granite uplands with quartzite ranges promi-nent in the east and in the extreme west bound the Burt Plain on the north.

2. Northeastern Plateaux. An arc of disconnected plateaux marks the south-western rim of the Georgina Basin. The Barrow Creek uplands and the Dulcie Range are formed of sandstone and the lower Lucy Creek plateau in the extreme

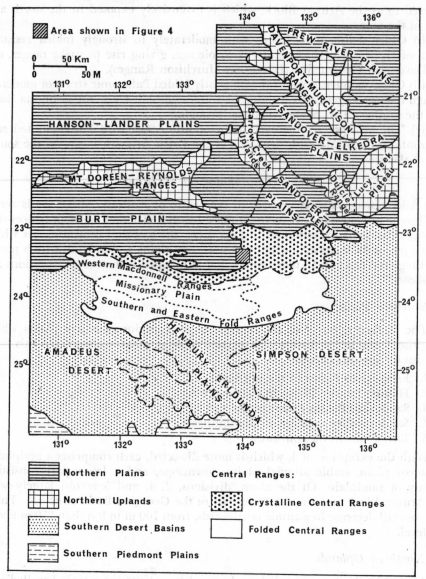

8.2   Geomorphological divisions of the Alice Springs area

east consists largely of limestone. The more rugged Mopunga and Jervois Ranges, which limit the Lucy Creek plateau on the south, are included in this division.

3. Davenport-Murchison Ranges. These are northwest-trending strike ranges of sandstone folded in the Davenport Geosyncline.

(iii) Central Ranges

These form an almost unbroken east-west belt more than 400 km long and at its maximum 160 km from north to south. They fall into two structurally-based geomorphological divisions.

1. Crystalline Central Ranges. Rugged uplands of gneiss and schist mark the south fringe of the Arunta Block. They include the northern part of the Macdonnells and extend northeastwards into the Harts Range. Local relief commonly exceeds 300 m and Mt Zeil (1510 m) is the highest point in central Australia.

2. Folded Central Ranges. These consist of parallel strike ridges, predominantly of sandstone in the west but including limestone in the east, formed from deposits of the Amadeus Trough. There are two belts of ridges—a broader southern and eastern area, in part plateau-like, comprising the Krichauff, James, and eastern Macdonnell Ranges, and a narrower northwestern arm consisting of the more strongly folded western Macdonnell Ranges. The two areas enclose a sandy synclinal lowland—the Missionary Plain. Summits rarely exceed 750 m in the southern and eastern ranges and local relief is generally less than 250 m, but the western Macdonnells have summits mainly between 850 and 900 m, with up to 300 m of relief.

(iv) Southern Desert Basins

These comprise the southern third of the area and contain the main dune fields. There are three subdivisions.

1. Simpson Desert. This tract of longitudinal sand dunes is mainly less than 300 m above sea level. It is part of the Great Artesian Basin and subhorizontal Mesozoic sandstone and shale form stony plains and tablelands and occasional higher plateaux within the dune fields. In the northwest are the flood-outs of such large channels as the Hale and Plenty Rivers and extensive marginal sandplain.

2. Amadeus Desert. This term is proposed for the dune fields in the southwest of the area, occupying the southern part of the Amadeus Trough. The east-west axis is marked by Lake Amadeus, a large salina, and by a line of smaller salt lakes leading eastwards to Karinga Creek, clear evidence of disrupted former drainage. The eastern pans are entrenched into extensive plains of terrestrial and lacustrine limestone between 430 and 490 m above sea level. The tributary slopes are mainly dune-covered; those on the north are interrupted by many strike ridges and on the southern slopes are the spectacular inselbergs, Mt Olga, Ayers Rock, and Mt Conner.

3. Henbury-Erldunda Plains. This area of dissected plains and tablelands interspersed with smaller dune fields separates the main sand deserts and extends between the Finke-Hugh line in the east and the main road from Adelaide to Alice Springs in the west. Structurally, it is transitional between the Amadeus Trough and the Great Artesian Basin; the main relief in its northern part is formed by duricrusted mesas of Palaeozoic rocks, whilst in the south are plateaux built of Mesozoic strata.

(v) Southern Piedmont Plains

These form the piedmont of the Musgrave Ranges, which lie to the south of the area. Precambrian granites of the Arunta Block here build sandy plains which descend eastwards from 650 to 540 m, with scattered hills up to 150 m high.

(d) *Climate and Vegetation of the Alice Springs Area*

Mean annual rainfall ranges from 125 mm in the southeast of the area to 355 mm along the northern margin (Slatyer 1962). This pattern results from increasing summer rainfall northwards, reinforced by the effects of higher altitude in the central ranges and in the country to the north, for a slight rain shadow is expressed in an abrupt if small decrease in annual rainfall immediately south of the central ranges. The number of rainy days also increases northwards, but not in proportion to the increase in rainfall; hence there is a northward increase in rain per rainy day, from 5 to 10 mm.

The temperature régime reflects the continental situation, moderately low latitude, low humidity, and fairly high altitude. In summer, maximum temperatures above 38°C. are the rule and ground temperatures above 50°C. have been recorded. Only in the north of the area are summer temperatures notably depressed by increased humidity and cloudiness. Diurnal temperature ranges of between 23°C. and 28°C. are common. The south of the area has a frost season of more than 60 days and in the higher ranges near Alice Springs this may exceed 100 days, but frosts are rare in the north. Dew is unimportant because of generally low relative humidity, being restricted to a few days during or shortly after rainy periods.

The area lies entirely within the accepted limits of the Australian arid zone (Marshall 1948). Under some climatic classifications it is designated as fully arid and it is certainly so in the sense that crop production is impossible without irrigation (Meigs 1953); other climatic maps indicate the decreasing aridity towards the north. A map based on Köppen's system, for instance, shows an island of semi-aridity over part of the Macdonnell Ranges in the centre of the area and a general transition to semi-aridity in the northernmost part (see Gentilli 1948). Increasing severity of desert conditions in and beyond the southeast of the area is clearly expressed in maps of water deficiency (cf. Prescott 1936).

The vegetation consists largely of open low *Acacia* woodland and extensive grasslands of spinifex (*Triodia* spp.) (Perry and Lazarides 1962). In this respect the area answers well to the broad definition of the desert setting proposed by climatic geomorphologists:

> Les régions sèches sont celles où, par suite de l'insuffisance des resources en eau, la couverture végétale et les sols sont trop réduits pour assurer une protection efficace de la roche contre les actions atmosphériques (Tricart and Cailleux 1960).

UPLAND LANDSCAPES

(a) *Limits of Cretaceous Transgression*

Correlation of the oldest landscape vestiges over large distances necessitates the establishment of general datum points about which a chronology can be built, and for the Alice Springs area it is important to fix the extent of the Cretaceous marine transgression and so to delimit potentially the oldest sub-aerial landscapes. Marine Cretaceous rocks occur extensively in the Great Artesian Basin in the south and east of the area at elevations below 500 m (Quinlan 1962), but Cretaceous geography further north must be reconstructed on evidence of basin and piedmont sediments of the central ranges. In only one locality are the age and facies of such deposits established, namely marine Lower Cretaceous in the lower part of a valley fill more than 180 m thick (530-710 m above sea level) on the piedmont plains 26 km northwest of Alice Springs (Crespin 1950). Quinlan (1962) has suggested that the Cretaceous sea moved northwards and westwards from the Great Artesian Basin, partly drowning the area of the central ranges and extending across much of the northern plains; however, a contemporary marine advance into the Burt Plain from the northwest cannot be precluded. The upper limit of Cretaceous deposition is not definitely known, but there is evidence that the central ranges were not completely buried and that older relief persisted there, in that the known Cretaceous remnants occur at relatively low altitudes on the margin of the central ranges and not in the high watershed areas to the north.

Although Quinlan (1962) refers to rocks possibly of Cretaceous age near Barrow Creek and locally in the Hanson-Lander plains, the nearest mapped areas of marine Cretaceous beds in the north are 240 km north of the Alice Springs area at altitudes below 240 m. Accordingly, it seems likely that the Davenport-Murchison Ranges, with summits extensively above 450 m, escaped submergence and that upland surfaces here might also preserve elements of a pre-Cretaceous landscape.

(b) *Pre-Tertiary Levelling*

Both these probable pre-Cretaceous 'islands' contain smooth upland forms which contrast markedly with rugged angular slopes at lower levels and which may be distinguished as 'upland surfaces' (Fig. 8.3).

(i) *Crest Bevels of the Folded Central Ranges*

The upland surface here comprises two stages, the older of which is seen in the smoothing or bevelling of summits and which has been designated the crest-bevel stage (Plate XVIIa). It is preserved as extensive higher plateau summits at between 600 and 730 m on broad synclines in the James and Krichauff Ranges; in the western Macdonnells it is represented by sloping ridge bevels at between 730 and 850 m, overlooked in the north and west by massive monadnocks such as Mt Sonder, whilst in the more dissected eastern Macdonnells it survives only on the highest quartzite ridges. Reconstruction of the former land surface at this stage would show sloping plains in the south, passing northwestwards with increasing altitude into subdued ridges and vales and then into higher rounded ridges and summits.

Dating of the crest-bevel stage rests on the relationship between the ridge bevels and Tertiary deposits in and near the central ranges. These consist of terrestrial, locally derived clay and moderately consolidated sand, grit, and torrent gravel, in strike vales of the western Macdonnells (Prichard and Quinlan 1962), where they attain 730 m above sea level, at depth near river courses in the southern Burt Plain (up to 670 m), and beneath alluvium of the Todd River plains (250-550 m), where they have been dated as Tertiary on the evidence of contained plant remains (P. R. Evans personal communication). The vale deposits in the western Macdonnells have been deeply weathered and have lateritised and silicified caps, so that a mid-Tertiary or greater age is likely there. On the Finke-

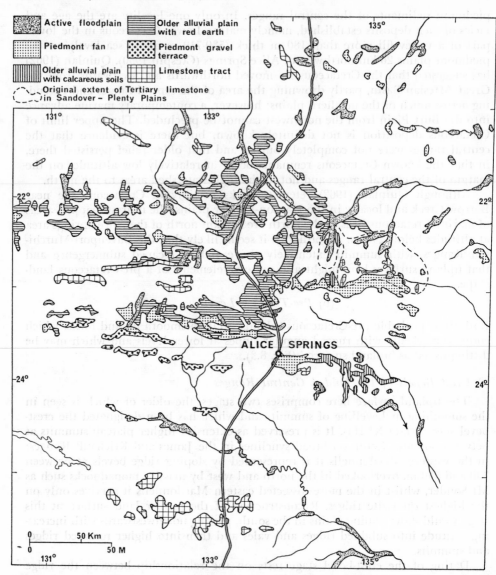

Active floodplain		Older alluvial plain with red earth	
Piedmont fan		Piedmont gravel terrace	
Older alluvial plain with calcareous soils		Limestone tract	
Original extent of Tertiary limestone in Sandover – Plenty Plains			

8.3 Cyclic erosional surfaces in the Alice Springs area

Ellerys Creek divide the deposits terminate upwards in a thick gravel lens which is accordant with the concave upper profile of the fill, such that it is apparent that we are seeing the approximate original upper limit of fill. The crest bevel here stands more than 100 metres higher and is separated from the fill by a phase of deep valley erosion: its fashioning, then, must have been largely pre-Tertiary, and on the evidence of Cretaceous palaeogeography may have extended back into the Palaeozoic.

Linked with the history of the upland surface in this area is that of the transverse drainage as exemplified by the Finke system. This river and its main upper tributaries Hugh River and Ellerys Creek head in the north of the crystalline central ranges and maintain southerly courses, passing in spectacular water gaps through the east-west orographic divide (Chewings Range) and the strike ridges of the western Macdonnells, and in meandering gorges through the plateaux of the James Range. Proffered explanations of this discordant drainage pattern include antecedence (Madigan 1931) and part-superimposition from Cretaceous beds (Ward 1925). Antecedence must be rejected on the evidence that the Devonian (Pertnjara) conglomerates and greywackes deposited along the southern margin of the growing ranges indicate a southwesterly drainage which was progressively obliterated by marine transgression from the west (Prichard and Quinlan 1962). The hypothesis of superimposition from a Cretaceous cover does not accord well with what is known of Cretaceous palaeogeography; in fact the distribution of Mesozoic sediments in the Great Artesian Basin implies a land area in the north and an existing southward drainage. Crest bevels generally descend towards the drainage gaps (Plate XVIIa) indicating that the transverse drainage already existed on, and has been inherited from the pre-Tertiary landscape.

Transverse drainage may be expected to develop in an area such as the western Macdonnells, where relief barriers are fixed by near-vertical dips and where base-level advantage conferred by subsidence further south tends to draw the rivers across the east-west structural grain, but the mechanism remains a problem nevertheless. The water gaps are sufficiently aligned and independent of transverse structure to disqualify the explanation of regressive erosion and capture; on the other hand, crest-bevelling was not so advanced that the rivers could have swung freely across the resistant bands. It is possible, however, that minor, unrecorded depositional phases, such as will be described in the later history of the ranges, may have assisted in carrying the rivers across the low obstacles presented by the quartzite bands at the close of pre-Tertiary levelling and that the drainage may result from a combination of inheritance and limited superimposition (Mabbutt 1966).

The courses of the Todd and Hale Rivers and their tributaries across the relief grain of the eastern Macdonnells suggest that these ranges have shared the geomorphological history of the western Macdonnells, although few traces of the crest-bevel stage of the summit surface now survive.

(ii) Summit Plane of the Davenport-Murchison Ranges

The older element of the upland surface here is a summit plane which truncates in striking fashion the complexly folded sandstone of the Lower Proterozoic Hatches Creek Group (Smith *et al.* 1961), rising southwestwards from between 440 and 460 m in the east and generally attaining 500-520 m in the west of the ranges. Broad culminations superimposed on this gradual ascent carry some summits above 530 m. This plane represents a considerably more advanced erosional achievement than does the crest bevel of the western Macdonnells, a difference which may result from the absence here of the resistant quartzites of the central ranges and in part from an even longer sub-aerial history, this region having been dry land since Cambrian times and having escaped the mid-Palaeozoic orogeny of the Macdonnells.

Since there are no known Cretaceous and Tertiary deposits in these ranges, correlation between the summit plane and ancient surfaces in the central ranges rests on slight geomorphological evidence. Along its western margin the summit plane overlooks and is distinctly separated from the extensively lateritised northern plains, which in turn will be shown to be post-Lower Cretaceous. The summit plane may well be Cretaceous or older, for fine-grained Cretaceous sediments on the northwest margin of the Great Artesian Basin, away to the northeast, indicate advanced planation on its borders by that date.

(c) *Valley Stages of the Upland Surfaces*

In both uplands the subdued higher elements of the upland surface were subsequently isolated by the erosion of deep valleys, giving essentially the present patterns and amplitudes of relief. In the western Macdonnells this erosion preceded and accompanied Tertiary deposition. The distribution and basal altitudes of the Tertiary deposits indicate that erosion was selective and rather localised (Quinlan 1962), proceeding to 180 m and more below present plain level in valleys north of the Macdonnells and in the broader depression below the Todd River plain in the south, reaching the approximate level of the present plain west of the upper Finke, but apparently not achieving the depths of later valley erosion in the heart of the ranges. Everywhere, restriction of Tertiary fill between outcrops of older rock indicates that the unevenness of the sub-Tertiary surface results in part from prior erosion and not wholly from later tectonic deformation, and that strong pre-Tertiary relief existed in the central ranges.

On the quartzite ridges of the western Macdonnells, this erosional episode is expressed as smooth upper slopes which extend down to within 45 m of the present valley floors and which form V-shaped upper profiles in the drainage gaps. The related vale floors survive in a high terrace and locally as duricrusted mesa summits. The high terrace is well preserved on the Finke-Ellerys Creek divide, where it is between 22 and 45 m above present floodplains, and is formed by the Tertiary fill described above. The fill thins valleywards from 15 m to 5 m, but masks an irregular bedrock surface, such that thin quartzite bands may approach to within 2 m of the terrace surface. The lower part of the fill is a grit and the upper part an unbedded conglomerate with sub-rounded cobbles and boulders of Heavitree Quartzite. Mesas with laterite cappings over weathered siltstone and claystone survive west of the upper Finke River, and other mesa groups with silcrete duricrust flank the quartzite ranges southeast of Heavitree Gap. The high terrace surfaces and duricrusts slope up towards and are locally connected with a hillslope bench which terminates the smooth upper slopes, by which token they belong to the valley stage of the upland surface.

Because of the relative thinness of softer beds in the Davenport-Murchison Ranges, the valley stage is here expressed as catenary valleys rather than as broad flat-floored vales. These survive as gently sloping, planed sandstone spurs, commonly with a gravel veneer.

The valleys in the upland surface of the Davenport-Murchison Ranges commonly head near the western margin of the ranges and are occupied by the main east-going drainage, such as Elkedra River. The master valleys are consequent upon the general eastward descent of the summit plane, but there is in addition a considerable strike drainage not foreshadowed in the summit plane contours. Many of the valleys have been formed along belts of slightly folded Cambrian siltstone and conglomerate within the ranges (Smith *et al.* 1961). Near the watershed they are lowered less than 20 m below the summit plane, but the amount of incision increases eastwards to more than 60 m. They grade to lateritised Tertiary plains beyond the ranges in the east, and divides against equivalent plains in the west—as at the head of Elkedra River—are inconspicuous.

Thus, there is a general parallelism between the geomorphological histories of these two upland areas; the valley cycle of the Davenport-Murchison Ranges shows no Tertiary cut-and-fill stage, but it may have an equivalent time-span to that in the central ranges.

(d) *Weathering of Upland Surfaces*

In both these areas the upland surfaces are distinguished from younger slope facets, not only by smooth concavo-convex slopes and catenary valley sections alien to the present morphogenetic régime, but also by associated weathered profiles.

In the recalcitrant sandstones, desilicification in depth is associated with secondary silicification of surficial horizons; there has been overall iron staining and deposition of iron in joint crevices and quartz greywacke has been kaolinised. Many weathered surfaces bear spheroidally weathered boulders which are apparently exhumed corestones, and all the evidence points to stripping of the upper part of a poorly developed weathered profile, probably of silicified lateritic type. In some upland valleys of the Davenport-Murchison Ranges, Cambrian siltstone and conglomerate have been more thoroughly lateritised and remnants of gravelly or sandy laterite above pallid siltstone survive as valleyward sloping benches.

Lowland elements of the upland surfaces were cut in rocks more susceptible to weathering. In strike vales of the western Macdonnells, the Tertiary fill and the underlying rocks have been deeply weathered. There are pallid zones between 15 and 30 m thick, formed in the lower part of the fill and in argillaceous rock below; there is some weathering in the upper conglomerate, and localised development of lateritic gravel cappings. Otherwise, the upper 2-3 m of the terrace deposit is a gravel which appears to have weathered loose from the former duricrust, for the stones are patinated and iron-mottled, and iron pisoliths are common among them. Rock rotting appears to have proceeded to greatest depth at the piedmont junction with the ridge-building quartzites, presumably fostered by pronounced influent seepage. Volcanic rocks in the Davenport-Murchison Ranges have undergone spectacular weathering, with thick laterite crusts above deep pallid zones.

DURICRUSTED PLAINS

The uplands discussed above and others with like history stand prominently in plains which, by their extent and monotony, impress as the characteristic landform of central Australia. The analogy of islands in a broad ocean is pertinent to the facts of Mesozoic geography, for much of the plain areas must have been transgressed by the Cretaceous sea. The chronological marker needed in correlating these post-Cretaceous landscapes is provided by extensive weathered profiles with indurated upper horizons or duricrusts which survive distinctively as mesa cappings or platforms. The significance of the duricrusts as approximate identifiers of former land surfaces was first noted by Woolnough (1927), who recognised that they marked a former reduction of relief such that chemical weathering predominated over corrasion and who claimed that they had formed on a single peneplain.

The Australian duricrusts are continent-wide; in some areas their geomorphological relationships are more complex than Woolnough suggested (cf. Wright 1963), nor can we accept his explanation of them as surface crusts formed by capillarity. In this area their usefulness as stage markers is enhanced, firstly because the duricrusts of central Australia appear to relate to a single erosion cycle and secondly because no younger surface exhibits comparable weathering.

Siliceous duricrust or silcrete and ferruginous duricrust or laterite both occur in the Alice Springs area, but in their characteristic forms they have different distributions as shown in Figure 8.3, belonging to regions which are lithologically distinct. Silcrete is general in the southern desert basins, particularly on Mesozoic argillaceous rocks of the Great Artesian Basin, whilst laterite is typical of the northern plains, more especially on granitic and schistose rocks of the Arunta Block but also extending on to relatively unresistant sandstone in the Georgina Basin. This regional separation is expressed below as 'silcreted southern plains' and 'lateritised northern plains'.

(a) *Silcreted Southern Plains*

The silcrete duricrust is characteristically a capping between 1·5 and 9 m thick, which may be massive, coarsely laminar, nodular, or brecciated. It consists of grey to red-brown amorphous quartz with 'floating' sub-angular quartz grains of coarse-sand grade. In former valleys it may be conglomeratic. Bedrock structure is absent and the duricrust commonly transgresses local dips as it follows faithfully the undulations of an old land surface; its structure and attitude are those of a surface-related illuvial horizon.

The silcrete may be underlain by partly silicified porcellanite or sandstone, but the lowest part of the profile is a typical pallid zone up to 30 m thick with soft kaolinised argillite and arkosic sandstone.

On dissection, the resistant duricrust and soft-weathered rock give rise to characteristic 'flat-top and breakaway' landforms. As mapped in Figure 8.3, the silcrete mainly survives in two strike arcs in the Great Artesian Basin (Simpson Desert), namely on the higher plateaux of the Rumbalara Hills and in a parallel arc of low stony tablelands further southeast, and also on mesa groups in the Henbury-Erldunda Plains, formed in synclinal tracts of Palaeozoic shale and sandstone of the Amadeus Trough. These remnants have been linked in a formline reconstruction of the former land surface (Mabbutt 1965) to show that they formed part of a broadly undulating plain with general descent southeastwards, between 520 and 180 m above sea level. No duricrusted remnants rise above the even skyline of the silcrete cappings (Plate XVIIb) and no surfaces cut below them bear a duricrust, although they may be thickly mantled with derived cobbles and boulders—the 'gibbers' of central Australia. The silcreted plains are clearly post-Lower Cretaceous since they bevel rocks of this age, and as they grade along

XVIIa The smooth upland surface of the western Macdonnells at the entrance to the Finke gorge, showing crest bevels descending towards the drainage gap

XVIIb Remnants of the silcreted plain survive as mesa cappings overlooking the Finke River near Engoordina homestead, with exposures of pallid zone in kaolinised Cretaceous sandstone and claystone

XVIIc The dissected post-duricrust surface east of Erldunda homestead, with characteristic gibber lag

XVIIIa   Ayers Rock, with evidence of three successive phases of formation: the smooth dome, fluting along bedding planes, and cavernous weathering, possibly at a former piedmont junction

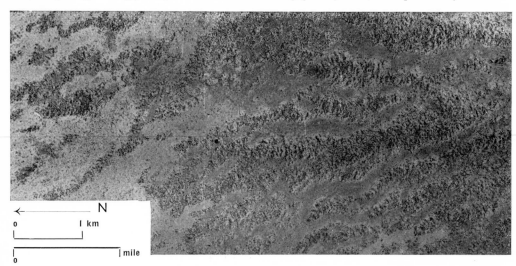

XVIIIb   Anastomosing prior distributaries of Burt Creek (sinuous dark bands), traversing plains with banded tree patterns and tributary to sandplain (light coloured) in the lower part of the Burt Plain. Photograph by R.A.A.F.

XVIIIc   Parallel dune ridges in the northwest of the Simpson Desert. Photograph by C. R. Twidale.

their northern margin into the valley stage of the upland surface of the central ranges, regarded as Tertiary in age, reading of the morphological evidence appears to be consistent in the two areas.

(b) *Lateritised Northern Plains*

Most of the northern plains are young depositional features, with erosional surfaces mainly peripheral to upland masses although becoming more extensive in the north and northeast, particularly in the Frew River Plains (Fig. 8.3). All the erosional northern plains show signs of former lateritic weathering, but the profiles have since been extensively stripped or dissected and the lateritic duricrust has been reduced to remnant cappings on low platforms. The laterite is commonly pisolithic or vesicular, generally between 1·5 and 7·5 m thick, and is associated with typical mottled and pallid zones. It may be residual or be partly developed in superficial sand or gravel. As with the silcrete, contour mapping has shown that the lateritic profiles relate to a single, continuous land surface with a general northward descent from 700 m to 240 m above sea level, albeit sloping towards several separate baselevels. No laterite-capped summits survive above this land surface and no surfaces cut below it are regionally lateritised.

Unlike the siliceous profiles of the south, which vary little in zonation or thickness, lateritic weathering in the northern plains seems to have varied with climate, relief, and lithology.

Climatic control is apparently expressed in a general increase in thickness of the laterite northwards—a trend towards the thicker duricrusts of northern Australia (cf. Wright 1963). From this, one may postulate a northward increase in rainfall at the time of lateritisation, similar to the present climatic gradient. The interrelated factors of lithology and relief seem to have been most effective in the south of the northern plains, precisely in those parts where lateritic duricrusting was less pronounced.

In contrast with climate, the relief factor is expressed in the thickness and zonation of the whole profile. In general, the degree of levelling in the northern plains increases northwards and it may be presumed that the formative physiographic setting was that of today, namely continentally central with peripheral baselevels. Weathering was uniformly deeper below the flatter plains further north, and escarpment sections in the east of the Sandover-Plenty Plains where they are being undercut by head channels of the Plenty River show profiles consistently more than 15 m thick with well developed pallid zones and thin mottled zones. Clearly, these were areas with fairly shallow, steady watertables. On the other hand, local relief-controlled variations in the weathering profile are typical of the piedmont plains further south, which were broadly undulating with up to 15 m of relief. In the southeast of the Burt Plain, for instance, deepest weathering occurred along valleys, where profiles up to 15 m thick include pallid zones. These profiles thin laterally towards the interfluves, where laterite rests on a thin mottled zone above fairly fresh rock. The relief of the former land surface, preserved in slopes on the duricrust, is reflected in exaggerated fashion by the related weathering front (Mabbutt 1961). Another zone of localised deeper weathering lay along the southern margin of the Burt Plain, in the piedmont junction with the crystalline central ranges.

M

Lithological and relief controls are not readily separable; for instance, uniform lateritisation of the Frew River Plains may indicate the uniformity of weatherable Cambrian siltstone and sandstone, or equally the uniform low relief formed on them. In granitic rocks of the Arunta Complex the weathering front was fairly even, although sharply interrupted locally by kernels of resistant rock, whereas in schist it was undulating. These differences stand revealed by later erosion, for extensive etchplains with scattered low tors have been formed on granite and gneiss, as in the Hanson-Lander Plains, whilst schist belts are characterised by flat-topped rises flanked by long, concave slopes in weathered rock.

In the Burt Plain the lateritised surface was levelled across a valley fill with Lower Cretaceous marine fossils and is therefore younger. Consistently, it is overlooked by older pre-Tertiary upland elements of the crystalline central ranges and by the summit plane of the Davenport-Murchison Ranges, where it forms a baselevel for the upland valley stage. A younger age limit is set by the lacustrine deposits which rest disconformably on the laterite in the Sandover-Plenty Plains. These Alcoota 'beds' contain mammalian fossils which, as stated below, may date from around late Miocene to mid-Pliocene, whence a minimal age of mid-Tertiary is indicated for the lateritised plains.

(c) *Relationships Between Laterite and Silcrete*

The relationships between the two types of duricrust and the environmental factors controlling their formation and distribution are very relevant to the history of the Alice Springs area.

Woolnough (1927) stressed the control of parent-rock lithology over the type of duricrust; laterite, he claimed, formed on granitic rocks and silcrete on siliceous rocks. Such control is very apparent along the west border of the Great Artesian Basin in the south of the Alice Springs area, where there is an abrupt passage from silcrete on Mesozoic claystone to laterite on granite, with no break in the associated land surface.

However, silicification and lateritisation seem commonly to have been associated in the Alice Springs area. Many lateritic profiles of the northern plains are silicified, and true silcrete occurs locally in the mottled zone; conversely, the duricrust of the silcreted plains locally includes lenses of lateritic earthy material, it is commonly iron-stained and locally iron-cemented, and the overlying gibber lag typically contains iron pisoliths as if there had formerly existed a cover of lateritic gravel. These relationships, and the occurrence of silcrete in the driest part of the Alice Springs area, recall the claim by Stephens (1961) that the nature of the duricrust is controlled by rainfall, which determines the depth of silica leaching. Hence, independent of lithology, there should be a transition from laterite without silcrete in the wettest parts, through lateritic profiles with silicification at increasingly shallow depth, to silcrete duricrusts with minimal laterite in the driest areas.

There is much still to be learned about these duricrusts and in particular about the conditions under which silica is mobilised and redeposited in the profile, but it is prima facie reasonable that conditions causing surface silicification differ from those giving rise to the deep leached profiles which underlie the silcrete, and hence that siliceous horizons in lateritic profiles are a later modification. Jessup (1960a) claims that this is demonstrated in the southeast of the Australian arid zone, where silcrete truncates the various horizons of a pre-existing lateritic profile and incorporates lateritic debris.

The evidence from central Australia can be read in ways which to some extent reconcile divergent views. Thinning of the laterite southwards within the northern plains may indicate that the climate here was marginally dry for lateritisation, even at the time of deep weathering. Under such conditions lithology might be expected to determine the nature of the duricrust, thus explaining the character-istic association of silcrete with the siliceous rocks of the southern desert basins, although weathered rocks of similar lithology in the more humid north of Aus-tralia bear thick laterite (Wright 1963). At the same time, the predominance of silicification in the south of the area could, as postulated by Stephens, also reflect greater aridity in that direction, in conformity with existing climatic patterns. Under this hypothesis, the siliceous laterites of the northern plains would reflect imperfect leaching of silica under a marginally humid climate.

The weathered profiles of the Alice Springs area are not inconsistent with silicification following lateritisation, and such would be in keeping with the known desiccation of central Australia. Under this hypothesis, silicification should be strongest in the desert areas and should predominate where, for any reason, lateritisation had previously been weakest. On both counts, therefore, silcrete duricrusts are predictable on siliceous rocks in the more arid southeast of the Alice Springs area. Other factors encouraging silcrete formation in the southern plains may have been the subdued topography and generally impermeable rocks, both inhibitive of leaching, and their low-lying position relative to sources of silica such as the lateritised granites of the southern piedmont plains. There is neither sectional nor geomorphological evidence of an erosional unconformity between laterite and silcrete as described elsewhere by Jessup (1960a), but this may reflect the greater tectonic stability of central Australia, where the silcrete is relatively undisturbed, compared with areas further southeast where the silcrete has been strongly deformed (Wopfner 1960).

EROSION OF THE WEATHERED LAND SURFACE

Together, the upland surfaces and duricrusted plains of central Australia consti-tute an older landscape with smooth slopes unrelated to current morphogenesis, and with associated weathered profiles which are at least partly out of keeping with the present aridity and which are generally inconsistent with present water-tables. Although this weathered land surface is cyclically complex, the related profiles do not at this stage demonstrate periodicity of weathering: they vary with lithology, not with age. The oldest landscape elements survive only on the resis-tant sandstones of the uplands, but the truncated profiles of the pre-Tertiary summit surfaces are indistinguishable from those of the weathered-valley stage on similar rocks. There appear to have been no 'levels of weathering'; the whole land surface was attacked in relief as it evolved. Landform evidence concerning 'periods of weathering' must in any case remain ambiguous, since the attainment of a weathered profile does not depend on climate alone, but also on the relative stability of the land surface. Planation and duricrusting may be achieved at successive levels whilst other environmental factors such as climate remain unchanged, and there is no evidence that a climate favourable to thorough weathering did not prevail throughout the earlier sub-aerial history of the Alice Springs area.

Whereas land surfaces younger than the duricrusted plains of central Australia bear laterite in areas further north (Wright 1963), equivalent younger surfaces in this area remain little weathered and it is apparent that the real desiccation of central Australia begins with, and may indeed have been a factor in the erosion of the weathered land surface.

At this stage in the geomorphological history of the Alice Springs area major tectonic and lithological differences come more fully into play, notably the contrast between a relatively stable northern shield and subsiding sedimentary basins in the south and east. This is reflected directly in differences of altitude of marine Cretaceous on either side of the central ranges (up to 650 m above sea level in the northern plains and below 520 m in the south). Within the shield and along its borders there has been broad warping posthumously on ancient structures, affecting the uplands and, in lesser degree, the adjacent plains. Accordingly, it will be convenient to treat separately the later erosional histories of the uplands, northern plains, and southern desert basins.

(a) *Uplift and Erosion of the Uplands*

The main upland belts accord closely with old lineaments recognised in the Australian shield; for instance, the central ranges define the southern margin of the Arunta Block and the Davenport-Murchison Ranges mark the western margin of the 'Sturtian nucleus' (Hills 1961). Such elements 'have repeatedly manifested themselves up to Cainozoic times, and the grain formed in the early pre-Cambrian has continued to influence later structures' (Hills 1945). Tectonically as well as topographically, the uplands are the borderlands of Palaeozoic and Mesozoic basins and have been uplifted relative to such areas of subsidence and sedimentation.

Concerning earth movements youthful enough to have influenced existing land surfaces directly, there is little stratigraphic evidence. Regional dips of Cretaceous strata in the Great Artesian Basin indicate tilting up to the north and west and the known range of altitudes of the marine Cretaceous indicates a broad post-Cretaceous updoming in the area of the central ranges (Quinlan 1962). Geomorphological evidence of greater post-Cretaceous uplift towards the west of the central ranges is provided by increasing vertical separation of crest-bevel and valley stages and by increasing gorge incision below the weathered land surface westwards within the Finke catchment as demonstrated by cross-profiles of drainage gaps in the western Macdonnells (Mabbutt 1966). Resultant rejuvenation of the south-going drainage has led not only to vertical incision but also to regressive erosion and breaching of the orographic divide and former watershed in the crystalline central ranges, as in the Chewings Range which is traversed by the Hugh River and Ellerys Creek in youthful, structurally determined gorges. In the upper Todd catchment, the aggressive south-going drainage, with a baselevel advantage of almost 150 m, has encroached into the southeast corner of the Burt Plain.

Within the Macdonnells, erosion of the weathered land surface has alternated with depositional episodes to be described below. There has been much selective erosion of weathered rock, with the formation of etchplains and tors on crystalline rock, as in the Alice valley, and the exhumation of low sandstone ridges from saprolite in the strike vales further south. The deeply weathered piedmont junction has been particularly vulnerable, as shown in the early isolation of spurs and terrace lobes by strike-channelling along the base of quartzite ridges.

The westward rise of the summit plane of the Davenport-Murchison Ranges and the inception across it of an easterly drainage point to relative uplift in the west of the ranges during the formation of the weathered land surface, probably posthumous on the Palaeozoic Georgina Basin structure, and the increasing incision of the weathered-valley stage below the summit plane eastwards is consistent with further downwarping of the basin to the east of the ranges. Unlike the central ranges, however, erosion of the weathered land surface in the Davenport-Murchison Ranges has been accompanied by little change in regional baselevels and has essentially consisted of landform adjustment towards the morphogenetic régime of an arid climate. Here, as elsewhere, there have been two main changes: the first is an increase in drainage texture, in particular the proliferation of low-order channels, whereby older catenary slopes have been dissected and remain as sloping valley-side benches; the second is the modification of sigmoidal slopes to angular hillslope-pediment profiles, a regrading which has apparently been facilitated by deeper weathering at the piedmont junction.

Earth movements along the southern margin of the former Georgina Basin have affected the arc of plateaux which extend westwards from Lucy Creek plateau to the Barrow Creek uplands. In the three segments of this arc, the plateau summits range in sequence westwards from a stripped plane with remnants of the duricrusted plains surface (Lucy Creek plateau), through a dissected summit surface which represents a moderately extensive survival of that surface (Dulcie Range), to an older, higher summit surface standing separate and above the lateritised northern plains (Barrow Creek uplands). This progressively greater survival of older land surface elements westwards accompanies the transition from the borders of the sedimentary structural basin in the east to the more stable Arunta Block in the west.

Table 1 gives the approximate range of altitudes of land-surface remnants and present baselevels along this plateau arc. To facilitate comparison and to eliminate local relief, the altitudes stated are those of the lower, more planate parts of surfaces. The figures indicate the overall fall of the weathered land surface south-eastwards, although the inherent slope of that land surface and the trend of its drainage is mainly northeastwards. This is suggestive of relative downwarping eastwards within the plateau arc, associated with even stronger deepening of the Georgina Basin and the Great Artesian Basin, such that those areas where the weathered land surface stands lowest are also the areas of its deepest dissection.

The postulated movements, which may be described as a differential peripheral upwarp of the Georgina Basin, run slightly obliquely to older structures, and the plateau arc transgresses a major syncline, with the main relief passing in turn from upper Cambrian limestone (Lucy Creek plateau) to Devonian sandstone (Dulcie Range) and then on to Cambrian sandstone (Barrow Creek uplands).

The Sandover and Bundey Rivers break through the plateau arc to form part of the centripetal drainage of the Georgina Basin and significantly the breaches occur where the highest extant element of the weathered land surface lies closest to present baselevel: further west, the Hanson River is diverted by the higher plateau barrier; further east, in the more dissected area of Lucy Creek plateau, the older northeasterly drainage has since been disrupted and diverted eastwards and southeastwards towards the Great Artesian Basin. The drainage passages of the Sandover and Bundey Rivers through the plateau are narrowly incised below adjacent plateau summits, in contrast to their upper valleys which preserve the broad, shallow forms of the weathered land surface; hence the transverse drainage is antecedent to the upwarp of the plateau arc.

TABLE 1

Levels of land surfaces in the plateau arc
(Heights in metres above sea level)

Locality	Barrow Creek Uplands	Dulcie Range	Lucy Creek Plateau
Higher summit plane	600–900		
Lower element of weathered land surface	520	470	400
Current base level	490	410	320
	(Hanson R.)	(Bundey R.)	(Arthur Ck)
Dissection below weathered land surface	30	60	80

(b) Deformation and Stripping of the Northern Plains

Some evidence of tectonic factors in the history of the northern plains, both during the formation of the lateritised land surface and in its erosion, is afforded by the relationships of uplands and lateritised plains and by patterns of later dissection.

(i) The vertical separation of successive land surfaces in the central ranges increases inwards within the ranges.

(ii) On the Arunta Block, granitic inselbergs are most numerous on the piedmont erosional plains and few rise above the depositional surfaces at greater distance from the uplands.

(iii) Extensions of the summit plane beyond the Davenport-Murchison Ranges, as extrapolated across outlying hills, appear to converge upon the lateritised plains with increasing distance from the ranges, both in the Hanson-Lander Plains and in the Frew River Plains.

(iv) The depth of dissection of the lateritised surface in the southeast of the Burt Plain is greatest near the margin of the central ranges and decreases northwestwards away from the ranges, in which direction the erosional surface becomes progressively more deeply buried beneath younger deposits (Fig. 8.4).

These relationships indicate that the uplands have been broadly warped up relative to the northern plains, the axes of tilting generally lying beyond the upland margins such that the present erosional plains are zones of convergence of land surfaces. For instance, King (1951) referred to the Burt Plain as 'a zone of crossing' of his Gondwana and Australian land surfaces, with which the crest-bevel and duricrusted plain elements of the weathered land surface may locally be identified. Earth movements of this type, recently termed 'cymatogeny' (King 1962), appear to have been characteristic of this shield area of northern central Australia.

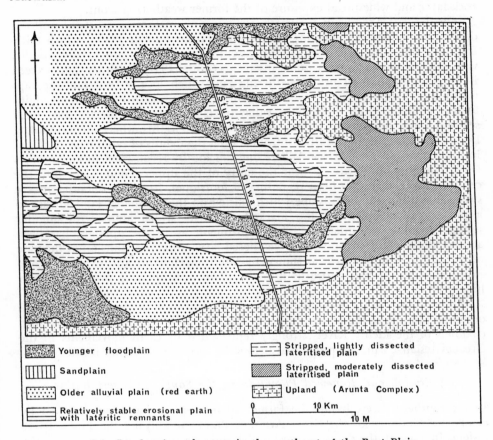

Younger floodplain

Sandplain

Older alluvial plain (red earth)

Relatively stable erosional plain with lateritic remnants

Stripped, lightly dissected lateritised plain

Stripped, moderately dissected lateritised plain

Upland (Arunta Complex)

0   10 Km

0   10 M

8.4   Land-surface elements in the southeast of the Burt Plain

Since the upwarps have been moderate, as indicated by the limited vertical parting of land surfaces and by the gentle dips of Palaeozoic strata in the area, the zones of crossing are broad and the convergence of land surfaces is slight; hence successive planations have occurred within a small vertical ambit, as is shown by the proximity of sub-Cambrian and present-day surfaces (separated by less than 15 m in the Hanson-Lander Plains). The remarkable extent and uniformity of the northern plains may thus be the expression of several closely staged cycles over considerable geological time.

The form of the weathering front at the base of the lateritic profiles has strongly influenced the course of later erosion in these relatively stable northern plains, firstly because, as shown above, the vertical range of rejuvenation has generally not exceeded the depth of prior weathering, secondly because the difference in resistance to erosion offered by fresh and weathered rock is greatest in igneous rocks, and under the prevailing arid climate such lithological contrasts are fully exploited. Accordingly, erosion of the lateritised northern plains has largely involved the shallow dissection and extensive stripping of the weathered rock layer and widespread exposure of the former weathering front.

On the flatter plains in the north, stripping of weathering crusts of uniform depth has resulted in etchplains, such as the Hanson-Lander Plains, which faithfully reproduce the low relief of the parent surface. These are locally studded with granitic tors and domes—zonal inselbergs (Büdel 1957) which nowhere exceed in height the depth of prior weathering and which locally bear lateritic caps which betray their origin as exhumed forms. In the undulating piedmont plains further south, as in the Burt Plain, valley tracts of deeper weathering have been selectively and more deeply etched, and in areas such as this, where the weathering front was itself topographically controlled, even the details of relief have persisted into the younger land surface. Where one can locally reconstruct former profiles from remnants of laterite, as near the entry of the upper Todd River into the central ranges, there has been regrading of footslopes, from the smooth concave sweep into a rectilinear hillslope which existed on the weathered land surface to a present-day pediment of less marked concavity which abuts with angular junction against the hillslope. This adjustment, as in the uplands, has been accomplished by the stripping of a weathered layer which was thickest at the base of the hillslope and which, as shown by lateritic remnants and exhumed corestone mantles, thinned outwards into the plain and upwards over the former hillslope.

An exception to the general shallowness of dissection in the northern plains occurs in the east of the Sandover-Plenty Plains, where vigorous erosion by head channels of the Plenty River, strongly rejuvenated by earth movements in the Great Artesian Basin, has progressed below the former weathering front.

(c) *Erosion and Renewed Planation in the Southern Desert Basins*

In the southern desert basins the former silcreted plain has been dissected by centripetal drainage of the Great Artesian Basin, notably by the Finke River system. In general, the depth of erosion decreases southwestwards away from the Finke River towards the border of the basin, from more than 90 m near Engoordina homestead to less than 20 m along the highway north of Kulgera. Further west, in the Amadeus Trough, higher elements of the weathered land surface survive as bevelled crests of sandstone ridges, but aeolian sand masks much of the evidence at lower levels; however, all the signs are of shallow dissection of the duricrust by drainage tributary to the Finke and ancestral to the sand-choked and disrupted Karinga Creek which now occupies the axial depression of the Amadeus Desert. This general pattern of dissection is consistent with drainage rejuvenation caused by basin subsidence southeast of our area, and significantly the southeastwards fall of the silcrete has been shown to steepen in its eastern part, below the 430 m contour (Mabbutt 1965).

More locally, the Rumbalara Hills mark a NE-SW trending 'high' on the silcrete, across which the Finke River is particularly deeply incised (75-105 m). This may be a secondary upwarp, for there has been post-Cretaceous faulting in the Rumbalara Hills (Sullivan and Opik 1951). Some of the movement, which has carried up a resistant Mesozoic sandstone, may antedate the silcrete however, for mapping has shown that a pronounced valley existed on the duricrusted surface here, along the line of the present Finke River.

In the south of the Amadeus Desert, the three aligned inselbergs, Mt Conner, Ayers Rock, and Mt Olga, presumably stood above the older land surface as prominently as they now rise above the desert plains, but the restricted erosional footslopes yield little evidence of where the weathered land surface lay and what reshaping has occurred with its destruction. Ollier and Tuddenham (1962) have suggested that Ayers Rock and Mt Olga have been reduced in area without slope decline by weathering including spalling, unloading, and caving. It is arguable that their scheme does not allow sufficiently for accompanying changes in climate and baselevel. This is particularly true of Ayers Rock, which seems to have undergone three successive phases of shaping; first the smooth monolith, next deep fluting, and lastly cavernous weathering which truncates both the smooth, older forms (Plate XVIIIa). This succession may well denote decreasing rainfall; uniform chemical weathering being followed by stripping and gullying, and these in turn by localised weathering attack with dominance of physico-chemical processes. Cavernous weathering appears to be particularly pronounced in a zone about 15 m above the present plain level which is further marked by a slight slope break. This zone may mark a former ground surface, the caves having been initiated by groundlevel weathering as demonstrated on inselbergs in arid South Australia (Twidale 1962).

In two main areas, erosion of the weathered land surface was followed by renewed planation at a lower level (Fig. 8.3). The most extensive occurrence of this younger plane is in the catchments of right bank tributaries of the Finke River, from Karinga Creek in the north to Coglin Creek in the south, where the surface was fashioned across soft Mesozoic sandstone and claystone. In a distance of 80 km along Goyder Creek this post-duricrust surface descends from 450 m near Umbeara homestead to about 300 m, where it ends in a dissected terrace overlooking the Finke River. Save for its highest parts and restricted footslopes, it is now mainly covered with aeolian sand.

Little is known of the corresponding level east of the Finke River, but remnant surfaces planed below the duricrust and between 15 and 30 m above the present plains occur in the Rumbalara Hills and about 30 km WSW from Andado homestead. The surface may be considerably more extensive beneath the dune fields further east, but it cannot be regarded as the only 'sub-dune' level, for the dune ridges are seen to extend across still younger erosional plains in both the areas named above.

The surface is identified by its occurrence below the duricrust level (it is commonly cut in the older weathered profile), by its dense, usually uncemented mantle of derived silcrete gibbers, and by extensive calcrete cappings as in the high terrace of the Finke and along Karinga Creek. These features, which are well exemplified in the stony plains east of Erldunda homestead (Plate XVIIc), are very reminiscent of a 'stony tableland' erosion surface described by Jessup (1960b) from the southeast of the Great Artesian Basin, and the post-duricrust surface of the Alice Springs area may be expressive of that general stage in the denudational history of the basin to which the term 'Eyrian' has been applied (King 1951).

Vertical separation between the duricrust and the younger surface decreases westwards from about 60 m near the Finke River at Engoordina homestead to less than 15 m west of the Adelaide highway, indicating that the younger surface was cut after the warping movements described above.

There is a second occurrence of the post-duricrust surface around the east end of the crystalline central ranges (Harts Range). It is here cut across granite and schist, but although not part of the Great Artesian Basin it is topographically and tectonically tributary to it. Near the ranges, the erosion surface was recognised as gravel-capped flattish spur crests up to 15 m high near old Indiana homestead; further east it can be traced into the flat interfluves of a slightly dissected plain which in turn descends eastwards and passes beneath sandplain.

DEPOSITIONAL EPISODES

The weathered land surface was essentially erosional with minor depositional 'facies' in intermont and piedmont sites, and presumably had co-ordinated, outgoing river systems. At some stage after the onset of erosion of the weathered land surface, aggradation began in the lower parts of the landscape and depositional plains now cover more than half of the Alice Springs area (see Figs. 8.5, 8.7). Earth movements may have contributed to this change of régime, but the major cause was undoubtedly climatic, namely the desiccation of central Australia and the dismemberment and disorganisation of its drainage, resulting in the present pattern of interior drainage with disconnected ephemeral river systems.

(a) *Lacustrine and Terrestrial Limestone and Related Deposits*

In much of the Sandover-Plenty Plains the laterite is overlain disconformably by interbedded siltstone and chalcedonic limestone up to 15 m thick (Alcoota 'beds'), with a siliceous capping which also extends beyond the sedimentary basin as a thin layer of chalcedonic limestone above a truncated lateritic profile. This cover has been dissected and much reduced from an original extent of 5200 km² in the valleys of the Sandover and Bundey Rivers and now forms low plateaux and mesa cappings. The Alcoota 'beds' slope northwards from above 610 m to 480 m above sea level with little change in thickness, following the slope of the underlying laterite, and appear to have formed in a series of connected valley lakes. The interbedded chalcedonic horizons probably indicate selective silicification of finer-textured beds, whilst the siliceous capping and its extensions beyond the basin may represent silicified pedogenic limestone.

Somewhat similar limestones, locally with fresh-water gastropods, occur in valleys of the eastern Macdonnells ('Arltungan Beds' of Madigan (1932)), in Phillipsons Pound, along the south margin of the Todd River plain, and in the upper Hale plain within the central ranges, everywhere resting on lateritised rock and commonly including lateritic detritus.

Along the axis of the Amadeus Depression equivalent lacustrine limestones associated with fluviatile clastic sediments have been partly masked by pedogenic limestone, shallowly dissected, and extensively buried by aeolian sand. Because of stronger prior dissection of the weathered land surface in this area, limestone occurs topographically below the silcrete and forms a depositional facies of the post-duricrust plain. Similar deposits mark the lower axis of the Burt Plain.

Madigan (1932) compared the 'Arltungan Beds' with the Eyrian of South Australia, and mammalian fossils recently discovered in the Alcoota 'beds' show affinities with those from Tertiary deposits east of Lake Eyre (Stirton *et al.* 1961; Newsome and Rochow 1964). Preliminary examination of the Alcoota material

suggests it is doubtful that the fauna is as old as Oligocene, although it might date around late Miocene to mid-Pliocene in terms of the sequence of faunas east of Lake Eyre (M. O. Woodburne personal communication).

Hence, an Upper Tertiary age may be attributed to the post-duricrust plain.

In lithology, range of thickness, secondary silicification, lack of obvious tectonic deformation, topographic situation, and relation to the duricrust, these limestones strongly resemble others described from western Queensland (Paten 1960), the Barkly Tableland (Noakes and Traves 1954), and Western Australia (e.g. Maitland 1904). Whether narrowly contemporary or not, they point to a similarity of depositional environment, namely shallow ponding of internal drainage systems with minor, fine-textured clastic sedimentation. Their widespread occurrence requires a general cause, and it is suggested that the onset of semi-aridity may have led to the deterioration of river systems and the accumulation of fresh-water limestone. Earth movements may locally have determined the areas of deposition; for instance, the extensive shallow fills of the upper Sandover and Bundey valleys may have resulted from obstructive backtilting and ponding outside the plateau arc, due to peripheral uplift of the Georgina Basin structure, for it is noted that the lower level of occurrence of the limestones is approximately that of the weathered land surface at the point of drainage traverse through the plateau arc.

A possible fluviatile equivalent of the limestone is constituted by calcreted trains which occupy shallow valleys cut below the laterite in parts of the northern plains (Fig. 8.5). These consist of calcreted alluvia, commonly 9 m or more thick, with chalcedonic horizons resembling those of the lacustrine limestones, and they now appear as tracts up to 6 km wide with elongate limestone platforms generally not more than 2 m high. These trains are overlapped by old alluvium and may still carry secondary drainage, but many of them extend beyond the limits of the present river channels, as in the Hanson-Lander Plains where they may be traced beneath aeolian sand. In this area the valley trains tend NW-SE with the grain of the Arunta Block, oblique to the younger northerly courses of the present river flood-outs.

(b) *Alluvial Deposits and River Action*

The distribution and sedimentary texture of the five categories of alluvial environment mapped in Figure 8.5 are much influenced by major structural contrasts acting directly through prior erosional relief and through lithology of source rock. The widespread red earth plains are associated with the Arunta Block and are derived mainly from igneous and metamorphic rocks; they bury extensive surfaces of little relief eroded on that stable tectonic unit. Piedmont and intermont gravel

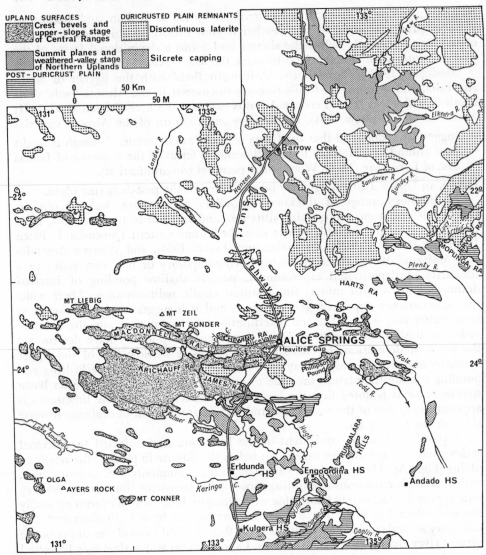

UPLAND SURFACES
Crest bevels and upper-slope stage of Central Ranges

Summit planes and weathered-valley stage of Northern Uplands

POST-DURICRUST PLAIN

DURICRUSTED PLAIN REMNANTS
Discontinuous laterite

Silcrete capping

0   50 Km
0   50 M

8.5   Surfaces of lacustrine and fluvial deposition in the Alice Springs area

terraces are sited mainly in the western Macdonnells, where strong erosion of the upland surface following post-Cretaceous uplift has yielded abundant durable gravels from the ridge-building quartzites and from the Pertnjara conglomerate: such terraces do not survive on weatherable Arunta rocks. The eastern Macdonnells are formed mainly in limestone which has yielded plains of fine-textured, calcreted alluvium with only minor gravel seams. Alluvial fans flank most uplands of the Alice Springs area, but attain mappable extent mainly along the north front of the crystalline central ranges, where coalescent fans have formed about the outlets of the large number of small catchments, due to the abrupt slope break at the upland border. Alluvial textures of fan deposits vary widely with source rock; basic igneous rocks south of the Burt Plain have given rise to extensive clays, but the deposits fronting the Harts Range further east, derived extensively from schist, gneiss, and granite, are predominantly sandy.

With the exception of the upper parts of alluvial fans, the alluvial surfaces described above are mainly stable with mature soils. The active floodplains, which are closely associated with the major river channels, are described in a later section.

Figure 8.5 shows markedly the relative restriction of alluvial surfaces south of the central ranges. In part, this may reflect the continuing competence of the integrated Finke River system in the episode of fluvial deposition; on the other hand, much alluviation by lesser streams was here confined to intermont and piedmont sites, probably because of lower rainfall in the southern part of the Alice Springs area. The main reason, however, has been the widespread obliteration of alluvial surfaces by aeolian reworking, which was considerably more aggressive south of the central ranges.

In detail, the character and disposition of certain alluvial deposits of the Alice Springs area reveal that the trend to aridity responsible for their formation was punctuated by shorter-term fluctuations of climate. The expression of this climatic periodicity in alluvial landforms is most marked in and flanking the ranges, but a confirmatory record also exists on adjacent plains.

(i) Piedmont Gravel Terraces and Floodplains of the Western Macdonnell Ranges

Suites of gravel terraces occur in strike vales of these ranges and also along their south front against the Missionary Plain. The intermont terraces are most extensive where they form the secondary watershed between the Finke and Ellerys Creek. Three terraces are recognised. The highest terrace is that of the Tertiary fill. This fill is a broad multiple fan which rises steeply towards the Heavitree Range, where it links with the hillslope bench, and on this evidence as well as by its weathering status it forms part of the weathered land surface.

The high terrace cycle was by far the most important; it involved fairly complete lowering of the strike vales prior to deposition, and few of the secondary ridges and foothills which now diversify these lowlands showed above its surface. Much of the minor transverse drainage within the western Macdonnells has been superimposed from the high terrace, maintaining itself through ridges as they were excavated from the weathered saprolite.

The middle terrace generally stands between 7 and 22 m above present floodplains, fingering headwards between spurs of the high terrace and broadening downvalley as terrace fans where the high terrace had been previously destroyed. The erosion which preceded its formation was selective only, and the middle terrace is overlooked by much minor relief; consequently it varies in height and gradient from one valley to the next. The middle terrace gravels resemble those of the high terrace but are thinner and unconsolidated and overlie an uneven surface cut partly in fresh rock. Flatter portions of the middle terrace typically bear well developed stony red earth soils.

The low terrace is closely associated with tributary channels and occurs between 1·5 and 4·5 m above present floodplains. It is formed of red-weathered sands with calcreted gravel seams and its rock base is rarely exposed.

There is a similar succession of terraces in the southern piedmont. The gravels are here derived from the Pertnjara conglomerate and are well rounded; they rest on surfaces cut in calcareous greywacke and hence are basally calcreted although they have leached soils. The middle terrace here preserves an original multilobate plan with lobes sited between the main river outlets and was clearly the work of minor streams.

The terraces record a history of recurrent planation and deposition alternating with stream incision. Such cycles date back to the weathered land surface; in the Macdonnell Ranges they are superimposed on progressive downcutting by the Finke drainage, but similar terrace suites adjoin the isolated ranges further west, such as Mt Liebig, which are apparently beyond the effects of continuing rejuvenation. Such a general distribution precludes staged uplift as an explanation of the terrace cycles and favours the hypothesis of climatic change, bringing periodic instability of hillslopes and associated variations in the load/discharge balance of minor streams. Other features of the terraces which are consistent with this hypothesis are the colluvial-alluvial sorting and shape of the gravels, the thinning of the cappings downslope, the fairly steep lobate forms and the association with minor streams, and the general decrease in vertical separation of the terraces with distance from the ranges. A suggested interpretation is that a more humid climate would allow weathering of stable vegetated hillslopes whilst channel incision progressed on lower ground, and that change to a drier climate would lead firstly to erosional planation by loaded, swinging streams and secondly to general instability of hillslope mantles, which would be eroded and spread as stony piedmont fans.

Under this scheme, weathering on the hillslope is a prerequisite for each spread of terrace gravels; it has been estimated, for instance (Mabbutt 1966), that the high terrace capping corresponds to a removal of between 3 and 15 m of mantle from tributary hillslopes, and signs of such truncation of a pre-existing weathered profile on the upland surface of the Macdonnells have been described above. Corroborative evidence of prior hillslope weathering is afforded by scree mantles and short colluvial aprons along the north face of the Heavitree Range. These smooth slopes of red-weathered angular cobbles and small boulders are stable relict forms which are now being gullied locally and which are sparsely and loosely mantled with the larger quartzite blocks produced by present-day weathering.

Climatic fluctuations of this type have been postulated on similar evidence for the borders of dry Australia (cf. Butler 1959), but not previously for the centre of the arid zone. In this area there is much evidence that their commencement dates back to the more humid period of marked weathering and that they are superimposed on the subsequent general trend to desiccation. Successive terraces show not only a decrease in depth of weathering but also a change in weathering type, from lateritisation of the high terrace, through red-earth formation with increasing calcification in the middle and low terraces. Further, successive terraces show decreasing supplies of gravel, indicative of progressive reduction of preparatory weathering on watersheds. Under the present arid régime the hillslopes are but lightly strewn with cobbles and boulders, and this is reflected in the relatively gravel-free character of the youngest alluvia in the ranges.

The floodplains within the ranges are distinguished from the red-weathered terraces by their brownish alluvial soils (Litchfield 1962). Generally, upper and lower floodplains can be distinguished, separated by a step between 1·5 and 3 m high. The upper floodplains, although at or near high flood levels, are apparently stable, but the irregular lower floodplains are clearly subject to rapid change. Rock outcrops are rare along the floodplains and channels, even at traverses through the ranges; for instance, up to 18 m of alluvium overlies the rock floor in Heavitree Gap, south of Alice Springs. Everywhere in the ranges the main drainage now appears to be aggrading following a phase of deep down-cutting either before or after the formation of the low terrace.

(ii) Drainage History and Soil Layers on Piedmont Plains

The alluvial plains of central Australia commonly extend downslope far beyond the flood-outs of the present ephemeral channels and extend laterally into areas from which drainage courses have long since been diverted. Their partly relict character is also indicated by the soils developed on the older alluvia, for these typically have deeply leached acid profiles, showing massive build-up of mixed kaolinitic and illitic clays in lower horizons, expressive of moderate weathering under subhumid conditions and incompatible with an arid climate. The picture is that of a retracting zone of drainage activity on much too general a scale to be due to headward river capture (see Jackson 1962) and explicable only as the result of secular deterioration of climate.

Many prior flow lines are perpetuated in patterns of soils, micro-relief, and vegetation, which to some extent allow this drainage history to be read from air photos. More recently, evidence of soil layering has supported and amplified such reconstructions.

Litchfield (in press) recognises five alluvial episodes in the southeastern Burt Plain following erosion of the lateritised land surface, as revealed by discontinuities between palaeosols. For simplicity, these may be grouped in 3 stages.

1. The two earliest phases of alluviation resulted in broad piedmont sheets which continued downslope in shallow valleys cut between laterite remnants and which opened out extensively in the lower plain. These probably account for most of the depositional surfaces of the area. The alluvia typically rest on truncated lateritic profiles and are weathered into deep red earths (Litchfield 1962). From their weathering status, the younger phase of these oldest alluvial deposits is equated by Litchfield with those of the middle terrace of the western Macdonnells; in the more stable setting of the Burt Plain they now form low interfluves and terraces flanking younger floodplains and also apparently continue beneath the floodplains. They are extensively calcified at a depth of some metres, as is the underlying mottled rock, and the source of this pedogenic lime is to be seen in areas of basic schist on low interfluves upvalley where extensive calcrete crusts survive. Such lime accumulation indicates incomplete leaching following the thorough weathering of the lateritic profiles; and one may speculate that deep calcification of the oldest alluvia is a related continuation of an accumulation

seen in the lacustrine and terrestrial limestones and calcreted valley trains described above.

2. Shallow entrenchment of valleys ensued, followed by two phases of alluviation in which coarse-textured channel deposits are prominent. Alluvium of the

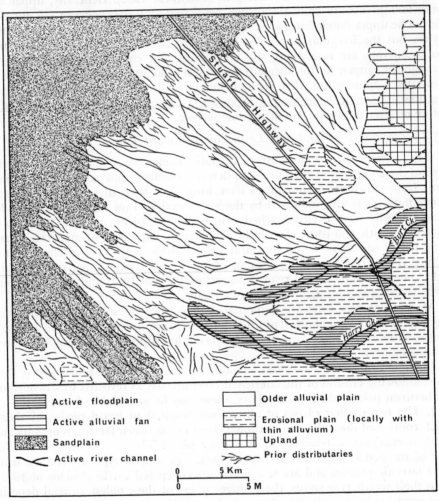

Active floodplain

Active alluvial fan

Sandplain

Active river channel

Older alluvial plain

Erosional plain (locally with thin alluvium)

Upland

Prior distributaries

0   5 Km

0   5 M

8.6 Prior distributaries in the Burt Plain

later phase forms most of the present floodplains in this area, but can also be traced far beyond them in a network of anastomosing prior distributaries which traverse the stable alluvial plains downslope (Fig. 8.6; Plate XVIIIb). These are trains of coarse sand with gravelly cores and they cluster into a number of narrow lobes in general prolongation of the present main channels, indicating a former system of multiple or shifting fan-like terminals of a vigorous if episodic drainage. There is much evidence of modification by wind in the lowest tracts, partly subsequent to the alluvial episode, as shown by the occurrence of elongate rises of wind-sorted sands up to 1·5 m high and 140 m wide on the north (lee) side of westerly trains, but partly a contemporaneous conflict between fluvial and aeolian processes. For instance, it can be seen from Figure 8.6 that the prior distributaries trend NW and WNW, slewed from the more westerly trend of the regional drainage towards the prevalent wind direction, probably as a result of displacement by sand encroaching from the south. Further, each cluster of prior distributaries occupies an alluvial salient into the sandplain, indicating a dynamic boundary. This second group of alluvia and the derived aeolian deposits have red earth soils of lower weathering status than the older alluvia and appear to relate to the low terrace of the Macdonnells.

3. The latest episode is of fine-textured alluviation restricted to the margins of active channels. The deposits are very youthful with immature soils, and indicate the much reduced erosion and fluvial transport of the present régime.

Litchfield (in press) has also investigated the alluvia of the Todd River plains south of Heavitree Gap. This is an area of almost continuous deposition with only minor intervening scour; hence the surface occurrence of older alluvia is mainly related to shifts of the Todd and its distributaries. It is a piedmont fan rather than a floodplain and is therefore of interest for its relevance to the history of the other extensive piedmont fans of central Australia. On soils evidence, only the two younger groups of alluvial deposits of the Burt Plain are represented here. Again, the older of these consists of extensive accretionary channel deposits of sand and gravel which, as in the Burt Plain, have been partly wind-piled. Mapping of alluvial deposits of this general age further downvalley has shown that the Todd and some of its present tributaries may at this stage have pursued more southerly courses into the Simpson Desert, through gaps in the ranges now floored with aeolian sand (Jackson 1962).

Deposits of the youngest phase are more closely associated with the present river and flood-out channels and are generally relatively more extensive towards the head of the fan, where they consist predominantly of fine-textured alluvia. In this history of retraction of drainage may lie an explanation of the apparent reversal of natural textural zonation which characterises many piedmont fans of central Australia; for the lowest, outermost parts commonly consist of sandier alluvia, generally abandoned by present drainage and wind-modified, whilst finer-textured deposits are found in terminal areas of present stream activity upslope.

The ages of the terraces and of the presumed related alluvial layers are not known, but their weathering status and situation indicate that they extend from Recent back into Pleistocene time, linking as they do the wetter period of greater weathering with arid phases of sand movement. It seems likely that this alternation of drier and wetter climates superimposed on a general desiccation may correspond to Pleistocene pluvial-interpluvial rhythms elsewhere.

FORMATION OF DUNE FIELDS AND SANDPLAIN

(a) *Extent and Distribution of Aeolian Sand Surfaces*

Aeolian sand, with an approximate extent of 200,000 km², covers rather more than half the Alice Springs area. Discussion of formative mechanisms has no

N

place in a denudation chronology; on the other hand it is insufficient merely to place the aeolian episode in chronological sequence, and the geomorphological and palaeoclimatic significance of the distribution of aeolian landforms must also be considered.

As stated in the introduction, the Australian sand deserts are mainly a legacy of earlier widespread alluviation, and the aeolian sands of the Alice Springs area exemplify this clearly. They lie towards the centres of basins, commonly beyond the present terminals of perimeter drainage which can still be identified as truncated feeder systems. In this way, alluvial origins are clearly indicated, both for sandplain, as in the Burt Plain, and also for dune fields, as on the margin of the Simpson Desert where the dune ridges gradually decline northwestwards and pass progressively into undulating, then flat sandplain and finally into sandy alluvial plains with little wind modification near the points of entry of present drainage. Heavy minerals in the sands of the Simpson Desert indicate an original southeasterly travel (Carroll 1944) despite northwesterly aeolian displacement involved in dune growth.

There was no simple, overall replacement of fluvial action by aeolian processes; the signs are rather of overlapping and interaction in space and time. Wind-slewing of distributary drainage in the Burt Plain has already been noted and similar conflict is evidenced by the angular turn SSE, into the dune trend, of rivers entering the Simpson Desert in the east of the Alice Springs area.

Sandplain and dune fields are of approximately equal extent but have a contrasted distribution, with sandplain mainly north of the central ranges and dunes mainly to the south (Fig. 8.7). This largely coincides with differences of bedrock, sandplain being associated with igneous and metamorphic rocks of the Arunta Complex and dunes with areas of sedimentary rocks. Exceptions to the general distribution support this association, such as the sandplain on granite near the South Australian border and the dunes north of the central ranges in the far west, where the ranges consist wholly of sedimentary rocks. Crocker (1946a) suggested that this bedrock factor acted through the grading of the derived sands, the primary sands yielded by igneous and metamorphic rocks being of wide grading, unsuited to dune growth, in contrast to the well sorted sands from sedimentary rocks. This explanation is apparently supported by the occurrence through the sandplains in the northeast of the area of linear rises only a metre or so high and more broadly undulating than dune ridges, but trending northwestwards with the continental dune pattern and showing analogous, although subdued cross-profiles with steeper flanks to the northeast. These are clear evidence of arrested dune development. However, the grading of sandplain and that of dune sands do not show great differences (Fig. 8.8), neither can the slightly greater amount of grit in the sandplain have served as effective protection against sand-piling. The difference in surface form is probably due to the much higher content of binding clay and silt in the sandplain sands, whereby the depth and degree of aeolian reworking have been reduced, for it is noteworthy that alluvial features such as bedded grit and fine gravel commonly occur at depths less than 2 m. The higher clay content of the sandplain sands is consistent with their derivation from granitic and metamorphic rocks but may also result from increased weathering under higher rainfall in the north of the area. Heavier rain-

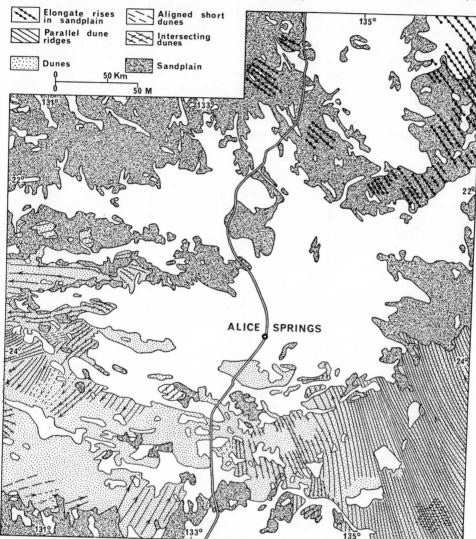

Elongate rises in sandplain

Parallel dune ridges

Dunes

Aligned short dunes

Intersecting dunes

Sandplain

0   50 Km
0   50 M

8.7   Aeolian sand surfaces in the Alice Springs area

fall in the north may also have resulted in more effective anchorage by denser vegetation. A climatic factor is suggested in that sands derived from sandstone of the Davenport Range in the far north of the area have also not been formed into dunes.

Dune trends as generalised in Figure 7 form part of a continent-wide swirl (Madigan 1936; King 1960), and evidence from dune encroachment, wind shadows, and dune convergences confirms that the dunes grew mainly northwards and westwards in response to an anticlockwise wind system. This circulation conforms to the present anticyclonic pressure system and the trend of dune ridges accords closely with prevalent winds (Madigan 1936). Other features of the dune patterns also accord with wind régimes to be expected in an anticyclonic cell with its east-west axis near the southern limit of the Alice Springs area. For instance, the most regular parallel ridges (Plate XVIIIc) lie towards the eastern margin of the anticyclone, where the strongest and most regular winds should occur; inside these are fields of reticulate and irregular dunes, apparently expressive of more variable winds near the anticyclonic centre. Further, the steeper faces of dune ridges are invariably on the east and north, that is outwards with respect to the dune swirl and consistent with a divergent anticyclonic airflow.

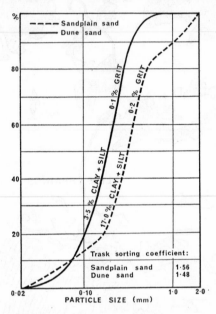

8.8 *Grading curves of dune sands from the northwest of the Simpson Desert and of sandplain sands from the Burt Plain. Means of 4 samples from 15-20 cm depth*

(b) *Age of the Aeolian Sand Formations and their Palaeoclimatic Implications*

The main extension of aeolian sands is generally held to signify one or more arid episodes marking the culmination of the secular trend towards a drier climate shown in the geomorphological record of central Australia from the Tertiary onwards. Increased windiness alone might have produced this effect, but when the sand extension is seen in chronological context as the replacement of a fluvial by an aeolian régime, and seen also in its broadest geographical context (for dunes extend into areas of northwestern Australia presently receiving 500 mm rainfall), the argument for aridity appears overwhelming. Whitehouse (1940) placed this arid phase in the late Pleistocene, contrasting it with earlier Pleistocene 'pluvials', but on evidence from southern and southeastern Australia the concept of a period of maximum aridity in the early to mid-Recent has gained ground (Crocker

1946b; Crocker and Wood 1947) and by bold extrapolation it has been suggested that all the major dune systems of Australia belong to one such period of climatic stress (Crocker 1941; Browne 1945). This 'great Australian Arid Period' has been identified with the post-glacial climatic optimum or 'thermal maximum' (Gill 1955). However, to cite Gentilli (1961),

> Too often now the Great Aridity ... is invoked as the *deus ex machina* .... A re-valuation of Pleistocene climates is needed; more than one 'Great Aridity' certainly occurred in some part of Australia during the interglacials, and there is no need to crowd every biogeographical change into the 2000 years or so of the Recent Great Aridity ....

This is equally pertinent to the problem of the age of the aeolian sand formations.

Conclusive evidence for the age or ages of the aeolian sands is not yet forthcoming from the Alice Springs area; except in the sense of *ante quam non,* a land surface or alluvial deposit does not date overlying or derived aeolian layers. It is apparent that the dunes are of no single, precise age; indeed, it would be remarkable if such extensive features were not diachronous or if the episodic record of the drainage systems were not paralleled in the history of dune formation. However, buried soil layers as identified in southeastern Australia (Churchward 1963) have not yet been discovered in the aeolian sands of the Alice Springs area. Madigan (1946) remarked that the dune ridges in the centre of the Simpson Desert are more regular than those on its borders, an indication of a core of older, more evolved dunes. Signs of lateral growth of the dune fields exist along the western margin of the Simpson Desert, where up to three dune belts may intervene between the parallel dune ridges and the Finke River, showing decreasing organisation of pattern westwards and marking successive replacements of the floodplain by dunes.

For this reason, the incursion of dunes over youthful soils south of the Macdonnell Ranges (Jackson 1962) does not place all the dunes of central Australia as of this age, nor does windblowing of the second group of alluvia in the Burt Plain (Litchfield in press) necessarily mean that all the sandplains are contemporary.

The area apparently showing most erosion since the emplacement of sand dunes is in the southeast, where the post-duricrust plain and the associated calcareous terrace have been narrowly incised by the Finke and its right-bank tributaries, probably as a result of further localised upwarping on the axis through the Rumbalara Hills. At Engoordina homestead, parallel dune ridges survive on spurs of the calcareous terrace, here dissected almost 30 m, whilst younger riverine surfaces bear less organised dune systems which are further differentiated by their paler colours from the red older dunes. Similarly, sandplain and dunes have been isolated and their margins eroded by the incision of Goyder and Lilla Creeks into the post-duricrust plain. However, it must not be overlooked that the Finke terrace margin may have retreated laterally into an area of dune ridges, nor that sandplain and dunes may have formed from alluvia previously isolated on the Goyder-Lilla divide.

Prima facie evidence, however, suggests that the aeolian sands of central Australia are Pleistocene, at least in part. This evidence includes the enormous extent of the sand surfaces and the amount of movement involved in the establishment of regular dune patterns over such an area, erosional achievement, locally, after some of the dunes had formed, and the known occurrence of dunes of different ages, supported by established episodicity in the alluvial record. Some corroborative evidence for a Pleistocene age for the dunes is forthcoming from Lake Eyre, where radiocarbon dates indicate that the deflation of the lake basin occurred between 20,000 and 40,000 years B.P. (Johns 1962), and from the existence of dunes in the intertidal areas near Broome, Western Australia (Fairbridge 1961), whereby a glacial (low sea-level) date is possible.

If the dune systems are partly Pleistocene, they indicate a persistence of present-day pressure and wind patterns through part of that period, with an extension of dry conditions to carry dune formation into the north of the Alice Springs area, and into even higher rainfall areas beyond. The picture is that of a stable, anticyclonic desert core, subject to periodic strengthening and expansion and also to weakening, as indicated by the fluvial episodes, but not to major latitudinal shifts.

RECOVERY FROM THE ARID PHASE

Throughout the Alice Springs area the main tracts of sandplain and dunes appear fossilised, their forms anchored by vegetation. Sandblowing in these environments is now limited to minor movement on the crests of dune ridges. Live dunes are physiographically rather than climatically sited, and are growing only in areas of fresh sand supply such as dry lakes and river flats; wind erosion in other areas—floodplains and plains with calcareous soils—primarily results from land use.

Madigan (1946) suggested that no climatic change need be invoked to explain the stabilization of aeolian sands, which could result merely from successful colonisation by psammophytes; but most authors have cautiously accepted the idea of climatic amelioration following maximum aridity (cf. Crocker and Wood 1947). Whitehouse (1940) contrasted the 'dead' sandhills east of Coopers Creek with the 'living' sandhills to the west, implying a retreat of the desert margin, and some shrinkage of a desert core is indicated in that mobile ridge crests in the northwest of the Simpson Desert are less pronounced than those depicted by Madigan (1946) from the west-central part of the desert. In support of climatic amelioration one may cite the development of soil profiles on aeolian surfaces (involving considerable clay movement in sandplain soils) and the extension of flood-out channels and alluvial tracts into dune swales, as in the northwest of the Simpson Desert.

The influences of major structure and regional climatic gradients are still apparent in this latest and continuing episode. Active floodplains are three times as extensive in the north of the area as in the south (Fig. 8.5). This may reflect greater rainfall in the north; partly, it may result from more widespread persistence of old drainage lines, since erosional and alluvial surfaces in the north of the area escaped the general invasion and obliteration by aeolian sand which occurred in the south. In the sedimentary basins, upper and lower sections of coarser- and finer-textured alluvium can be distinguished; on the Arunta Block, fine-textured alluviation is general, in contrast to the preceding alluvial episode.

These latest changes may combine the effects of a lowering of temperature following the 'thermal maximum' (Gill 1955) with those of increased rainfall.

Amelioration has in any case been slight, and the balance between mobility and stability of sand surfaces remains a delicate one as shown by the active growth of dunes in many areas disturbed by land use. As shown by Litchfield (in press), the latest stage of alluviation is of restricted extent and predominantly of fine-textured sediment, pointing to slow morphogenesis.

Thus the Alice Springs area currently demonstrates a general principle that deserts are regions of conservation rather than of destruction of landforms, where the record of earlier geomorphological events and of their formative climatic setting tends to be preserved (Peel 1960). In central Australia this record is a long one, complicated by a variety of past climates and by structural contrasts, and the denudational history gives strong support for de Martonne's general conclusion cited at the head of this essay. Faced with this inheritance of landforms which have outlasted the systems of erosion under which they were originally shaped, one may well doubt the usefulness of the concept of the arid cycle.

REFERENCES

Browne, W. R. (1945). An attempted post-Tertiary chronology for Australia. *Proc. Linn. Soc. N.S.W.* **70**: v-xxiv.

Büdel, J. (1957). Die 'doppelten Einebnungsflächen' in den feuchten Tropen. *Z. Geomorph.* **1**: 201-25.

Butler, B. E. (1959). *Periodic Phenomena in Landscapes as a Basis for Soil Studies.* CSIRO Aust. Soil Publ. No. 14.

Carroll, D. (1944). The Simpson Desert Expedition, 1939. Scientific Reports: No. 2. Geology—Desert Sands. *Trans. R. Soc. S. Aust.* **68**: 49-59.

Churchward, H. M. (1963). Soil studies at Swan Hill, Victoria. IV. Ground-surface history and its expression in the array of soils. *Aust. J. Soil Res.* **1**: 242-55.

Crespin, I. (1950). Report of micropalaeontological examination of samples from the 16 Mile Government Bore, west of Alice Springs, Northern Territory. Aust. Bur. Min. Res. Unpub. Rec. No. 1950/48.

Crocker, R. L. (1941). Notes on the geology of southeast South Australia with reference to late climatic history. *Trans. R. Soc. S. Aust.* **65**: 103-7.

—— (1946a). The Simpson Desert Expedition, 1939. Scientific Reports: No. 8. The soils and vegetation of the Simpson Desert and its borders. *Trans. R. Soc. S. Aust.* **70**: 235-58.

—— (1946b). *Post-Miocene Climatic and Geologic History and its Significance in Relation to the Genesis of Major Soil Types of South Australia.* CSIR Aust. Bull. No. 193.

—— and Wood, J. G. (1947). Some historical influences on the development of the South Australian vegetation communities and their bearing on concepts and classification in ecology. *Trans. R. Soc. S. Aust.* **71**: 91-136.

Dresch, J. (1962). Remarques sur une division géomorphologique des régions arides et les caractères originaux des régions arides mediterranéennes. I.G.U. Arid Zone Colloquium, Greece.

Fairbridge, R. W. (1961). Eustatic changes in sea level. *Physics Chem. Earth* **4**: 99-185.

Gentilli, J. (1948). Two climatic systems applied to Australia. *Aust. J. Sci.* **11**: 13-16.

—— (1961). Quaternary climates of the Australian region. *Ann. N.Y. Acad. Sci.* **95**: 465-501.

Gill, E. D. (1955). The Australian 'arid period'. *Aust. J. Sci.* **17**: 204-6.

Hills, E. S. (1945). Some aspects of the tectonics of Australia. *J. Proc. R. Soc. N.S.W.* **79**: 67-91.

——— (1953a). The hydrology of arid and sub-arid Australia with special reference to underground water. *Reviews of Research on Arid Zone Hydrology*, pp. 179-202, UNESCO, Paris.

——— (1953b). Regional geomorphic patterns in relation to climatic types in dry areas of Australia. Desert Research Proc., Jerusalem, 1952. *Res. Counc. Israel Spec. Publ.* No. 2: 355-63.

——— (1961). Morphotectonics and the geological sciences with special reference to Australia. *Quart. J. geol. Soc. Lond.* 117: 77-89.

Jackson, E. A. (1962). *Soil Studies in Central Australia.* CSIRO Aust. Soil Publ. No. 19.

Jessup, R. W. (1960a). The lateritic soils of the southeastern portion of the Australian arid zone. *J. Soil Sci.* 11: 106-13.

——— (1960b). The stony tableland soils of the southeast portion of the Australian arid zone and their evolutionary history. *J. Soil Sci.* 11: 187-96.

Johns, R. K. (1962). The sediments of the Lake Eyre basin, evaporites and brines, their constitution and age. *Geol. Surv. S. Aust. Rept Invest.* No. 24, Pt I, pp. 1-69.

King, D. (1960). The sand ridge deserts of Australia and related aeolian landforms of the Quaternary arid cycles. *Trans. R. Soc. S. Aust.* 83: 99-108.

King, L. C. (1951). The cyclic land-surfaces of Australia. *Proc. R. Soc. Vict.* 62: 79-95.

——— (1962). *The Morphology of the Earth.* Edinburgh.

Litchfield, W. H. (1962). *Soils of the Alice Springs area.* CSIRO Aust. Land Res. Ser. No. 6, pp. 185-207.

——— (in press). *Soil Surfaces and Sedimentary History near the Macdonnell Ranges, Northern Territory.* CSIRO Aust. Soil Publ.

Mabbutt, J. A. (1961). 'Basal surface' or 'Weathering front'. *Proc. Geol. Ass.* 72: 357-8.

——— (1966). Landforms of the western Macdonnell Ranges, in *Essays in Geomorphology* (ed. G. Dury). London.

——— (1965). The weathered land surface in central Australia. *Z. Geomorph.* 9: 82-114.

Madigan, C. T. (1931). The physiography of the western Macdonnell Ranges. *Geogrl J.* 78: 417-31.

——— (1932). The geology of the eastern Macdonnell Ranges, central Australia. *Trans. R. Soc. S. Aust.* 56: 71-117.

——— (1936). The Australian sand-ridge deserts. *Geogrl Rev.* 26: 205-27.

——— (1946). The Simpson Desert Expedition, 1939. Scientific Reports: No. 6. Geology —The sand formations. *Trans. R. Soc. S. Aust.* 70: 45-63.

Maitland, A. G. (1904). *Preliminary Report on the Geological and Mineral Resources of the Pilbara Goldfield.* Geol. Surv. W. Aust. Bull. No. 106.

Marshall, A. (1948). The size of the Australian Desert. *Aust. Geogr.* 5: 168-75.

Martonne, E. de (1925). *Traité de géographie physique, Tome II: Le Relief du sol.* Paris.

Meckelein, W. (1959). *Forschungen in der zentralen Sahara I. Klimamorphologie.* Braunschweig.

Meigs, P. (1953). World distribution of arid and semi-arid homoclimates. *Reviews of Research on Arid Zone Hydrology*, pp. 203-10, UNESCO, Paris.

Newsome, A. E. and Rochow, K. A. (1964). Vertebrate fossils from Tertiary sediments in central Australia. *Aust. J. Sci.* 26: 352.

Noakes, L. C. and Traves, D. M. (1954). *Outline of the Geology of the Barkly Region.* CSIRO Aust. Land Res. Ser. No. 3, pp. 34-41.

Ollier, C. D. and Tuddenham, W. G. (1962). Inselbergs of central Australia. *Z. Geomorph.* 5: 257-76.

Paten, R. J. (1960). Lacustrine sandstones and limestones and spring sinters of far western Queensland, in The Geology of Queensland. *J. geol. Soc. Aust.* 7: 391-403.

Peel, R. F. (1960). Some aspects of desert geomorphology. *Geography* 45: 241-62.

Perry, R. A. *et al.* (1962). *Lands of the Alice Springs Area, Northern Territory, 1956-7.*

CSIRO Aust. Land Res. Ser. No. 6.

———— and Lazarides, M. (1962). *Vegetation of the Alice Springs Area.* CSIRO Aust. Land Res. Ser. No. 6, pp. 208-36.

Prescott, J. A. (1936). The climatic control of the Australian deserts. *Trans. R. Soc. S. Aust.* 60: 93-5.

Prichard, C. E. and Quinlan, T. (1962). *The Geology of the Southern Half of the Hermannsburg,* 1: 250,000 Geological Series, Aust. Bur. Min. Res. Rept No. 61.

Quinlan, T. (1962). *An Outline of the Geology of the Alice Springs Area.* CSIRO Aust. Land Res. Ser. No. 6, pp. 129-46.

Slatyer, R. O. (1962). Climate of the Alice Springs Area. CSIRO Aust. Land Res. Ser. No. 6, pp. 109-28.

Smith, K. G., Stewart, J. R., and Smith, J. W. (1961). *The Regional Geology of the Davenport and Murchison Ranges, Northern Territory.* Aust. Bur. Min. Res. Rept No. 58.

Stephens, C. G. (1961). *The Soil Landscapes of Australia.* CSIRO Aust. Soil Publ. No. 18.

Stirton, R. A., Tedford, R. H., and Miller, A. H. (1961). Cenozoic stratigraphy and vertebrate palaeontology of the Tirari Desert, South Australia. *Rec. S. Aust. Mus.* 14: 19-61.

Sullivan, C. J. and Opik, A. A. (1951). *Ochre Deposits, Rumbalara, Northern Territory.* Aust. Bur. Min. Res. Bull. No. 8.

Tricart, J. and Cailleux, A. (1960). Le modelé des régions sèches: Fasc. I. *Le milieu morphoclimatique. Les mécanismes morphogénétiques des régions sèches.* Paris.

Twidale, C. R. (1962). Steepened margins of inselbergs from north-western Eyre peninsula, South Australia. *Z. Geomorph.* 6: 51-69.

Ward, L. K. (1925). Notes on the geological structure of central Australia. *Trans. R. Soc. S. Aust.* 49: 61-84.

Whitehouse, F. W. (1940). *Studies in the Late Geological History of Queensland.* Univ. Qld Pap. Geol., Vol. 2 (N.S.), No. 1.

Woolnough, W. G. (1927). The duricrust of Australia. *J. Proc. R. Soc. N.S.W.* 61: 24-53.

Wopfner, H. (1960). On some structural development in the central part of the Great Australian Artesian Basin. *Trans. R. Soc. S. Aust.* 83: 179-93.

Wright, R. L. (1963). Deep weathering and erosion surfaces in the Daly River basin, Northern Territory. *J. geol. Soc. Aust.* 10: 151-64.

9

Land Surfaces and Laterites in the North of the Northern Territory

JOHN HAYS

INTRODUCTION

The close connection between laterite and land surfaces in the Northern Territory has been stressed by many authors, notably Woolnough (1927), who introduced the term 'duricrust', Christian and Stewart (1953, 1954), Ivanac (1954), Owen (1954), and Gardner (1957). These earlier authors considered that the northern part of the Northern Territory had resulted from warping and dissection of a single peneplain formed in a cycle of erosion that started late in the Cretaceous and ended with a period of extensive lateritisation by the middle of the Tertiary. However, King (1950) had suggested, although without supporting evidence, that Arnhem Land might be a residual of an even older land surface.

Under this earlier view the presence of duricrust was accepted as the criterion of this mid-Tertiary peneplain, and the flat-topped accordant hills, capped with duricrust, in the southern part of the area were accordingly regarded as residuals of that same peneplain. There was no evidence to the contrary until a complete lateritic profile was observed by the author in 1958 in a well on the plains surrounding the hills near Tennant Creek. This fortuitous exposure prompted a study of laterite in relation to regional geomorphology. The work was at first restricted to the Tennant Creek area, but was eventually extended to most of the Northern Territory north of the 22nd parallel (Fig. 9.1). The area reviewed covers almost 600,000 km². Less than 2,500 km² was mapped in detail, and about 12,000 km² was covered by traverses at intervals of 5 km or less. The remaining area was covered by reconnaissance traverses along roads and tracks supplemented by helicopter and light plane reconnaissance, and by examination of bore data. All traverses started at or passed through areas of detailed work, and all such areas were linked by traverses. The only parts not visited are the Sandover River area, the environs of Lake Mackay, parts of Arnhem Land, and the Gulf of Carpentaria.

Detailed studies of laterite were made in many localities, but, because of the vastness of the area, this account of the relations between regional geomorphology and lateritisation remains a simplified general outline.

Lateritisation here refers to all weathering processes which result in the concentration of iron oxides in a subsurface layer which hardens on exposure. If the resultant profile can be subdivided into an upper, ferruginous zone, a mottled

Acknowledgment is due to the many colleagues and friends who have since 1957 contributed by helpful discussion to the development of the views expressed here, but who are at the same time absolved of any responsibility for them.

zone, and a lower, pallid zone (Whitehouse 1940), it is termed the standard lateritic profile. Where the ferruginous zone is recognised as a separate sedentary horizon of vesicular or concretionary ironstone, the term laterite is used. Bauxite is regarded as the aluminous equivalent of laterite. Conglomeratic ironstone consisting of fragments of reworked laterite is referred to as detrital laterite.

The factors which control the development of a lateritic profile with time include temperature, rainfall, level of watertable, and soil micro-organisms. All contribute to the weathering of felspars to clay minerals and of ferromagnesian minerals to iron oxides, but there is no general agreement on their relative importance, chiefly because of the difficulty of identifying their separate effects in the field. This study is concerned with the other factors controlling lateritisation, namely relief and lithology, the effect of which can readily be observed in the field.

GEOLOGY

The rocks in the area exhibit a wide range of age and lithology, but may be classed into a limited number of groups based on age, structure, and lithology (Fig. 9.1).

Possible Archaean and Proterozoic rocks have been intensely folded and regionally metamorphosed in two hilly areas. A northwest-trending belt comprising the Warramunga-Davenport Geosyncline, about 500 km long and between 60 and 120 km wide, passing through Tennant Creek, consists of pelitic and psammitic rocks which crop out abundantly in the numerous ranges. Structural and relief trends are generally northwesterly in the north, becoming more westerly in the south of the belt. The Pine Creek Geosyncline is a large, irregular area of phyllite and slate southeast of Darwin, with a maximum width of 240 km. Trends are here dominantly northerly, but a branch about 50 km wide, extending southwest from Darwin to the Western Australian border, has dominant northeasterly trends. Acid and basic igneous rocks are common in both geosynclinal areas.

Upper Proterozoic sediments, gently folded and generally unmetamorphosed, occur in two main areas. Around the Gulf of Carpentaria, sandstone is prominent, particularly in the Arnhem Land plateau. In the west, inter-bedded sandstone, limestone, and shale give rise to lowlands in the Victoria River Basin, with ridges and plateaux of moderate relief.

Flat-lying Lower Palaeozoic sedimentary and volcanic rocks occur between the Proterozoic areas. Limestone and dolomite predominate, and form extensive lowlands as in the Daly River Basin and in the Georgina Basin in the southeast. Volcanic rocks of the Antrim Plateau, resting disconformably upon Upper Proterozoic sediments, overlook the Daly River lowland on the west.

Middle and Upper Palaeozoic sedimentary rocks border Joseph Bonaparte Gulf in a lowland belt about 45 km wide. They comprise fresh-water and marine sediments, including limestone and thin coal seams.

On the mainland, Mesozoic marine sandstone and shale, and lacustrine sandstone and fine conglomerate occur in patches, reaching their greatest extent in a belt southeastwards from Katherine. The subhorizontal strata, up to 70 m thick, range in age from Upper Jurassic to Lower Cretaceous; they are generally duricrusted and give rise to plateaux up to several square kilometres in extent. On

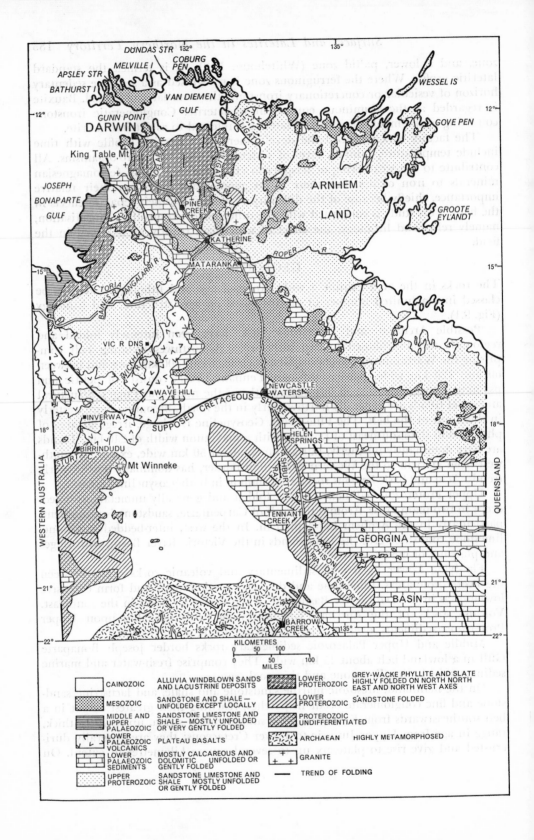

KILOMETRES
0   50   100
0   50   100
MILES

	CAINOZOIC	ALLUVIA WINDBLOWN SANDS AND LACUSTRINE DEPOSITS
	MESOZOIC	SANDSTONE AND SHALE — UNFOLDED EXCEPT LOCALLY
	MIDDLE AND UPPER PALAEOZOIC	SANDSTONE LIMESTONE AND SHALE — MOSTLY UNFOLDED OR VERY GENTLY FOLDED
	LOWER PALAEOZOIC VOLCANICS	PLATEAU BASALTS
	LOWER PALAEOZOIC SEDIMENTS	MOSTLY CALCAREOUS AND DOLOMITIC UNFOLDED OR GENTLY FOLDED
	UPPER PROTEROZOIC	SANDSTONE LIMESTONE AND SHALE MOSTLY UNFOLDED OR GENTLY FOLDED

	LOWER PROTEROZOIC	GREY-WACKE PHYLLITE AND SLATE HIGHLY FOLDED ON NORTH NORTH EAST AND NORTH WEST AXES
	LOWER PROTEROZOIC	SANDSTONE FOLDED
	PROTEROZOIC UNDIFFERENTIATED	
	ARCHAEAN	HIGHLY METAMORPHOSED
	GRANITE	
	TREND OF FOLDING	

Bathurst and Melville Islands, the Lower Cretaceous strata are represented by several hundred metres of marine shale.

Little attention has been paid to post-Cretaceous deposits, and few Tertiary and Quaternary sediments can be dated, although marine deposits of Miocene-Pliocene age are known in the Georgina Basin (Lloyd 1963) and north of Inverway (Lloyd personal communication). Continental sandstones up to 70 m thick on Bathurst, Melville, and other islands have been lateritised and in places bauxitised. They rest with marked unconformity upon Cretaceous rocks and are thought to be Lower Tertiary. Detrital laterite (White 1954) on the coastal plain is overlain by presumed Pleistocene alluvia (Christian and Stewart 1953) and hence is thought to be late Tertiary. In the Pine Creek area, the detrital laterite rests on the 'Minglo Creek beds' (Hays 1960), which are hence thought to be Tertiary. There are also aeolian limestone and sandstone in the Gove area.

Sediments of Tertiary or Quaternary age are distributed sporadically inland, particularly in the south where isolated but in places extensive lacustrine and fluviatile sediments of local derivation are common. Some of these deposits have been calcified during subsequent desiccation, for instance the alluvia of the northwest, which contain a high percentage of carbonate. On the other hand, the siliceous alluvia of the plains around the Ashburton Ranges have not been calcified.

PHYSIOGRAPHIC ZONES

The area reviewed can be divided into three physiographic zones (Fig. 9.2).

(a) *Main Plateau*

This is the most extensive of the zones and covers more than three-fifths of the total area. It is a flat to gently undulating plateau, ranging in elevation from 180 m in the north to about 400 m above sea level in the south. In addition to its general northward descent, there is a gentle rise towards its northwestern and northeastern borders, giving a saucer shape. There is a centripetal endoreic drainage from the rim, except where exoreic streams have cut back through the rim of the plateau and reversed the drainage, as in many headwaters of the Victoria River. All the streams have been recently rejuvenated and have incised their channels into the alluvium which fills their old valleys, but locally even the new channels have become choked as alluviation has proceeded in the flood-out areas. Most of the present streams are underfit. In the central part of the plateau this may be attributed to a climate less humid than that in which the original valleys were formed, but some of the streams near the plateau rim may be underfit because of the loss of headwaters to exoreic streams of the dissected marginal zone.

Scattered ranges and isolated hills with accordant flat tops bevelled across tightly folded rocks rise above the Main Plateau in the south and southwest. Their heights range from less than 15 m to about 150 m in the south, and generally they are separated from the plateau by steep scarps, although there are many exceptions.

(b) *Dissected Margin*

The Main Plateau is bounded on the north by a dissected margin between 150 km

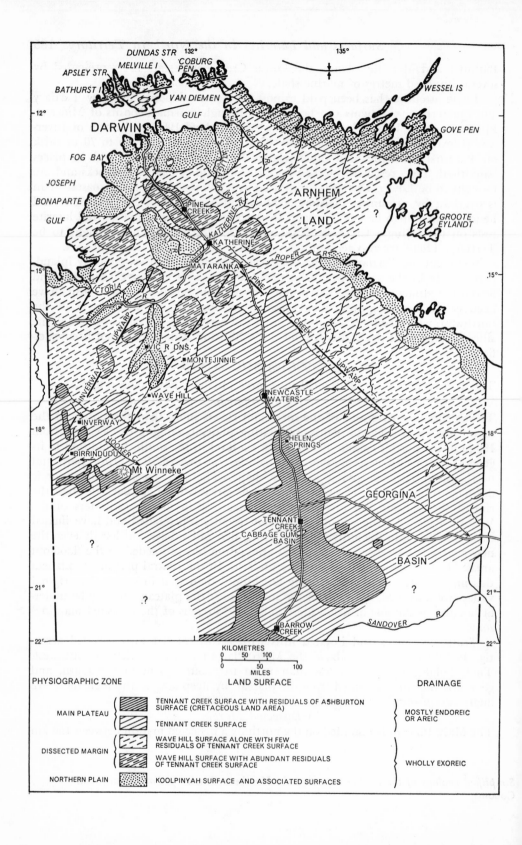

PHYSIOGRAPHIC ZONE | LAND SURFACE | DRAINAGE

MAIN PLATEAU
- Tennant Creek Surface with residuals of Ashburton Surface (Cretaceous Land Area)
- Tennant Creek Surface

DISSECTED MARGIN
- Wave Hill Surface alone with few residuals of Tennant Creek Surface
- Wave Hill Surface with abundant residuals of Tennant Creek Surface

NORTHERN PLAIN
- Koolpinyah Surface and associated surfaces

MOSTLY ENDOREIC OR AREIC

WHOLLY EXOREIC

KILOMETRES
0   50   100

0   50   100
MILES

and 300 km wide, descending in elevation from almost 500 m on the Western Australian border to less than 60 m at Darwin and rising again to about 300 m above sea level in the Arnhem Land and Carpentaria area in the east. Local relief of up to a general maximum of about 180 m has been produced by exoreic streams which have carved narrow, steep-sided valleys showing pronounced structural control.

(c) *Northern Plains*

The Northern Plains include the coastal plain proper and the inland plains of the Daly and Victoria Rivers. The coastal plain is almost 150 km wide southeast of Darwin; in the Gulf of Carpentaria and Joseph Bonaparte Gulf it has a maximum width of about 80 km, but on the north coast of Arnhem Land it rarely exceeds 30 km and is less than 2 km wide in places. It ranges in elevation up to about 75 m inland. Relief is generally extremely small, although scattered low hills occur on some of the interfluves. Streams wind slowly across the coastal plain to the sea, with their meanders locally incised to depths of between 6 and 10 m, but generally lose themselves in swamps near the coast.

CLIMATE

Climate on the Northern Plains is monsoonal, with a wet season from about November to March. Rainfall ranges from about 1600 mm to 1400 mm inland; temperature minima range from 15°C. during June-July to 21°C. during the wet season, and maxima range from 21°C. to 43°C., the extreme high temperatures being restricted to the drier inland parts. Southwards there is a gradual transition from a monsoonal to a fairly arid climate in which annual rainfall decreases to 300 mm. Precipitation is restricted to a few storms and showery periods which are distributed sporadically throughout the year, although commonest in December and January. In the extreme south, winter minima fall as low as 5°C. and summer maxima may exceed 46°C.

LAND SURFACES AND ASSOCIATED WEATHERING PROFILES

Detailed work was concentrated in three areas; the Tennant Creek area, the Katherine-Wave Hill-Birrindudu area, and the Darwin-Pine Creek area. As a result of this work, four mature erosion surfaces were recognised and were traced into adjoining areas where possible (Figs. 9.2, 9.3). The Tennant Creek area is on the Main Plateau where two surfaces, here named the Ashburton and Tennant Creek Surfaces, are easily recognisable. The Katherine-Wave Hill-Birrindudu area lies wholly within the Dissected Margin and the most important erosion surface here has been named the Wave Hill Surface. The Darwin-Pine Creek area extends across the Northern Plains into the Dissected Margin. The dominant surface is that which is here named the Koolpinyah Surface, although the Tennant Creek and Wave Hill Surfaces are also present. Thus, quite fortuitously, the land surfaces were studied in relation to the physiographic zones in areas which could be regarded as critical and complementary.

(a) *Ashburton Surface*

(i) Form and Distribution

This is the oldest and locally the highest surface and it lies wholly within the

Physiographic zones and land surfaces in the north of the Northern Territory. For Coburg *read* Cobourg

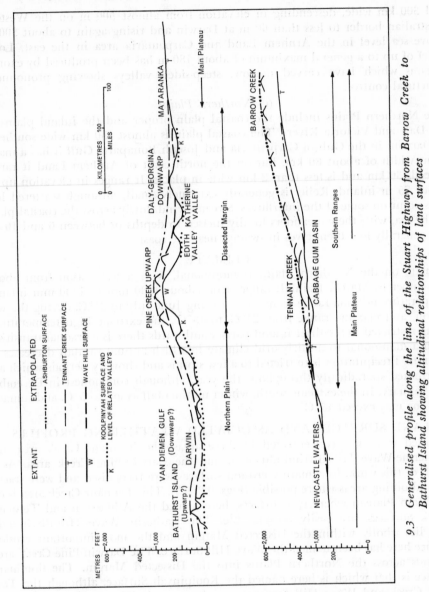

9.3　*Generalised profile along the line of the Stuart Highway from Barrow Creek to Bathurst Island showing altitudinal relationships of land surfaces*

Main Plateau (Fig. 9.2), where it is represented by the accordant hill summits in the south. It ranges in height from about 240 m above sea level in the north to about 550 m inland. Residuals are widely and irregularly distributed, but it can be reconstructed as a surface of wide, shallow valleys and broad, low interfluves with a general relief of less than 60 m, although with slightly greater relief locally on some interfluves. The present fall is between 1 in 1000 and 1 in 1700 to the north and northeast, where the Ashburton Surface merges with the Main Plateau

—which has a northerly and northeasterly gradient of about 1 in 2000—in a zone about 50 km wide. This zone of merging trends easterly to Newcastle Waters and then southeast towards the Georgina Basin, and corresponds to the northeastern shore of the Cretaceous land-mass (Noakes 1960). North of this zone, the Ashburton Surface is lost beneath the Cretaceous cover.

The surface is best developed in the Ashburton and Murchison Ranges and in the ranges between, which surround Tennant Creek and rise between 60 and 90 m above the plains of the Main Plateau to a height of about 400 m above sea level (Plate XIXa). It is a striking topographic feature because of the way in which it bevels steeply dipping Lower Proterozoic rocks with a wide range of lithology and hardness. Although residuals of the surface follow the dominant westerly and northwesterly structural trends, the present drainage tends to be northerly and northeasterly, and no reconstruction of the original drainage pattern is possible.

The Ashburton Surface has not been traced continuously west of Tennant Creek, and appears to be absent from large areas, but it is thought to be represented in the summits of scattered ranges in the southwest, and in the extreme west, where Mt Winnecke carries a weathering profile (Traves 1955). It is also present south of Inverway, where it is seen to descend northwards and merge with the Tennant Creek Surface.

From the apparent coincidence of the northern boundary of the Ashburton Surface and the presumed Cretaceous shoreline, it is assumed that the Ashburton Surface was associated with the land-mass from which the Cretaceous sediments were derived. There are arguments that the dissection to the succeeding Tennant Creek stage could not have been post-Cretaceous. It must have involved removal of between 80,000 km² and 160,000 km² of rock waste and its deposition in or north of the areas now occupied by Cretaceous sediments. Tertiary sediments of such volume are not known in these areas; much of the known Tertiary deposits are younger in that they are clearly derived from post-laterite erosion of the Main Plateau, and much derive from surfaces below. Hence it is difficult to appreciate how material derived from destruction of the Ashburton Surface could have been transported across the Cretaceous rocks without trace. The most satisfactory way of accounting for this sedimentation is to assume that the Ashburton Surface was that from which the Cretaceous sediments were derived. The volume of material involved is of the right order, the rocks eroded would yield sediments of the composition of the Cretaceous rocks, and these rocks are known to have been derived from a land-mass of little relief (David and Browne 1950).

(ii) Weathering Profiles

The residuals are generally flat-topped, have no soil or at most a skeletal soil, and are generally bounded by scarps and pediments. Because a weathering profile somewhat similar to a lateritic profile can be seen in the scarps, earlier workers had considered the residuals to be remnants of a mid-Tertiary peneplain (cf. Woolnough 1927), although Ivanac (1954) suggested that an even older deep weathering profile could be present in the area. Detailed work facilitated by escarpment exposures has in fact confirmed the presence of two old profiles, both resulting from leaching and perhaps from migration of iron (Fig. 9.4).

o

The older profile extends to a depth of about 60 m below tops of residuals on which it has been studied. The lower part consists of slightly leached rock with original structure and texture perfectly preserved; the upper part is thoroughly impregnated with iron oxide except where affected by younger weathering, re-garded as equivalent to the lateritisation of the Main Plateau. Similar profiles have been observed on the Maranboy tinfield in the Pine Creek mining area, and near Darwin. These occurrences are independent of the present watertable, do not appear to belong to the main period of lateritisation, and are thus thought to pertain to deep weathering of the Ashburton Surface before the formation of the Tennant Creek Surface. The occurrences further north are too few and too widely scattered for one to postulate that they have a common origin and that they are all directly related to the Ashburton Surface, although they all extend between 60 and 100 m below this surface or the exposed sub-Cretaceous surface.

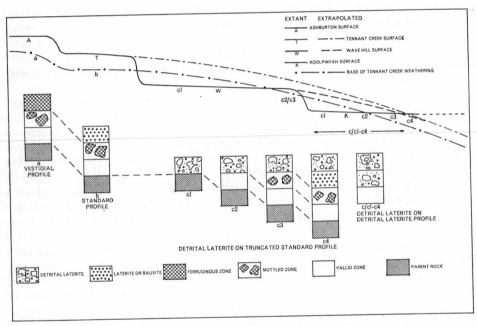

9.4   Relationships between land surfaces and types of lateritic profile

The younger weathered profile is best seen on argillaceous rocks which are abundant in residuals around Tennant Creek. These are composed of greywacke and slate of the Lower Proterozoic Warramunga Group, with iron content ranging from 2·5 per cent for greywacke to 4·5 per cent for slate. The two rock types occur in very intimate association due to folding and inter-bedding, and are here considered as one. No sedentary ironstone has been observed on the residuals, although cracks and hollows may contain a breccia consisting of fragments of country rock in a spongy limonitic matrix. This is thought to have formed in soil-filled hollows and is regarded as the equivalent of laterite.

The country rock in each residual is heavily impregnated with iron to a usual depth of about 6 m, although depths of 20 m have been noted. This impregnation is regarded as equivalent of the ferruginous zone of the main lateritic profile, but differs in that the texture and structure of the parent rock are perfectly preserved and in that there is no separate laterite. The mottled zone of the profile is represented by about 15-25 m of patchily ferruginised and leached rock in which original structure and textures are preserved. The pallid zone is absent from many exposures, mottled zone persisting down to parent rock after a further 15-25 m. Even where a pallid zone appears to be present it may simply be a very large leached patch in a mottled zone. Because of the presence of the limonite breccia and the apparent lateral transition into a standard lateritic profile at Cabbage Gum Basin, discussed below, it is thought that very little stripping of the profile has taken place.

Weathering of quartzite of negligible iron content is demonstrated on other residuals, particularly in the Ashburton and Murchison Ranges, where quartzites predominate. The only evidence here of a ferruginous zone is iron-staining along joints and cracks, and impregnation by iron, locally to a maximum depth of about 10 m. Mottled and pallid zones have not been seen and are thought never to have been formed.

(b) *Tennant Creek Surface*

Previous workers had identified the Ashburton Surface with a mid-Tertiary peneplain on the Main Plateau further north on the assumption that a standard lateritic profile in the northern part of the Main Plateau could be correlated with a somewhat similar lateritic profile on the southern ranges. The discovery of a standard lateritic profile by the author on the plains of the Main Plateau within the southern ranges entailed the recognition of a separate surface below the Ashburton. Named the Tennant Creek Surface, it is the one most extensively developed on the Main Plateau (Fig. 9.2).

The town of Tennant Creek stands about 330 m above sea level in the southern part of the Main Plateau and is surrounded by flat-topped hills about 60 m high (Plate XIXa). The lateritic profiles of the Tennant Creek Surface were revealed in groundwater investigations in the Cabbage Gum Basin on the plains between 8 km and 16 km south of the town. The aquifers were fluviatile and lacustrine deposits in an old drainage line, and the weathered rock beneath showed a complete standard lateritic profile.

The fluviatile and lacustrine deposits consist of reworked lateritic ironstone, and fragments of fresh and lateritised granite and metasediments derived from the eastern and northern margins of the basin, and include a basal conglomerate of laterite fragments. The lower beds contain a high proportion of laterite and lateritised rock in the middle of the basin, but less weathered and unweathered rock fragments become more abundant higher in the succession and towards the northern and eastern margin. The sediments are overlain by windblown sand, and both superficial deposits transgress from above a complete lateritic profile in the centre of the basin on to unweathered rock on the margin (Fig. 9.5).

Extrapolation of the base of the weathered profile below the sediments indicates that the basin was bounded on the north and east by low granite ridges.

These ridges were separated by a fault-guided drainage channel, and the sediments were deposited in the lower reaches of this channel. The ridge crests appear to have been accordant with hill summits around Tennant Creek, 5 km further north. The lateritic profile changes character towards each ridge, and appears to be grading into the younger type of profile found on the hills of the Ashburton Surface, in that the ferruginous and pallid zones become less clearly defined. This transition is confirmed by the composition of the basin sediments, the lower beds of which are derived from laterite and the upper beds from ferruginised rock. Thus the standard lateritic profile of the plains appears to have continued beyond the basin into the deep weathering profiles on the hills, and the two are thought to have been coeval.

Another feature of the basin is an older deep weathering profile, also apparently involving upward migration of iron, the greater age of which is confirmed by its displacement in faults which pre-date the main laterite. This may be related to the older profiles on the Ashburton Surface.

(i) *Extent of the Tennant Creek Surface*

Although exposures are abundant in areas of active erosion, such as the southern ranges and the rim of the Main Plateau in the north, laterite is seldom seen on the plateau proper. In the south, most of the plains are covered by desert sand; in the north, the sand gives way to alluvial and soil covers. Continuity from the southern plains to the northern rim and into the Georgina Basin in the east must be assumed from a few outcrops of laterite, a few patches of lateritic soil, and from data from scattered bores. The evidence is that beneath the superficial cover there are many wide, alluvium-filled shallow drainage channels eroded in and even below a laterite mantle.

The original Tennant Creek Surface on the Main Plateau must have had remarkably little relief—perhaps less than 15 m over distances of many kilometres. In the east, the modern Georgina Basin is a post-laterite erosional feature imposed upon a tectonic basin. The Tennant Creek Surface can be projected across it eastwards into Queensland and northwards into the Dissected Margin fronting the Gulf of Carpentaria, on the evidence of laterite occurrences and accordances of level. The inward slope of the basin continues northwards beyond its present margin, and then there follows a steady, steeper fall to the sea. The conformation of the Tennant Creek Surface in these areas and its northwesterly extension into the Daly River Basin and into the Pine Creek area are assumed by Christian and Stewart (1953, 1954) to result from late-Tertiary warping of a Tertiary land surface of low relief.

Identification of the Tennant Creek Surface in the watershed area near Mataranka is difficult, and features assigned to it there may belong to the Wave Hill Surface, which stands less than 30 m lower. The Bradshaw Surface identified by Wright (1963) in the Daly River Basin appears to be the Tennant Creek Surface. The Tennant Creek Surface is widespread but subordinate in the Pine Creek area, where it is 60 m above the Wave Hill Surface, and also in the fringes of Arnhem Land, where its maximum altitude is about 300 m. Further north, it appears to descend to a little above sea level at Gunn Point near Darwin, where its original maximum height can be estimated at about 45 m from evidence of a

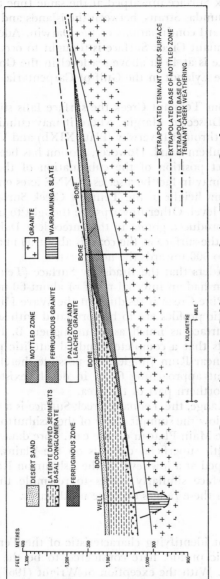

9.5 *Cross-section of the Cabbage Gum basin, Tennant Creek*

truncated lateritic profile. On Bathurst and Melville Islands a standard lateritic profile occurs at an elevation of about 105 m; these islands are assumed to represent the Tennant Creek Surface upwarped at the same time as Van Diemen Gulf subsided. Apsley and Dundas Straits, between the islands and Cobourg Peninsula, probably mark northward continuations of the Darwin, Adelaide, and Alligator river systems. The Tennant Creek Surface is thought to occur on Croker Island; and a lateritised surface is at 45 m above sea level in the Gove Peninsula and at a lower level on Groote Eylandt in the Gulf of Carpentaria. For the rest little is known.

Northwestwards from Tennant Creek the surface falls slightly and then rises again gently into the Dissected Margin, where it may culminate along a north-easterly axis extending through Inverway (Plate XIXb) and Victoria River Downs and eventually into Arnhem Land. However, erosion has been so extensive along this axis that the exact position of the culmination of the surface cannot be determined, and there may in fact be a series of NNE axes en echelon in a north-east belt. The maximum height of the Tennant Creek Surface along the axis is about 500 m above sea level. Other upwarps are thought to occur between it and the coast and to have produced gorges in the antecedent Daly and Victoria river systems. The height of the surface at the coast is about 90 m above sea level, with a continuing fall of 1 to 500 towards the northwest.

Wright (1963) considers that the Bradshaw Surface (Tennant Creek Surface) in the Daly River Basin had an internal relief of about 60 m. Similar relief may have existed north of Pine Creek if residuals at the Wave Hill Surface level with almost complete lateritic profiles are to be correlated with scattered residuals of the Tennant Creek Surface as much as 60 m higher. B. P. Ruxton (personal communication) reports that a complete standard lateritic profile occurs at the lower level on granite near Rum Jungle. It is possible therefore that depressions of unknown extent, but approaching 60 m in depth, existed on the Tennant Creek Surface in the northern part of the area.

In the Murchison Range, the Tennant Creek Surface is a valley phase, heavily lateritised in places, below the summit plane of the Ashburton Surface and tributary to the plains of the Main Plateau on the east. Bore data indicate that lateritised rock occurs beneath superficial deposits on the plains.* Standard lateritic profiles are also developed at a low level in the Ashburton Range, but the profile on the Ashburton Surface similarly comes to resemble the standard lateritic profile as the heights of these ranges decrease northwards.

(ii) Lateritic Profiles

The most important identifying characteristic of the Tennant Creek Surface is the standard lateritic profile, here considered to be the product of a main period of lateritisation. With the exception of Wright (1963), earlier writers discussed the profile only in general terms; hence it was felt necessary to study profiles on as many rock types as possible in order to establish variations with topography and lithology (Fig. 9.4). Profiles have been studied in areas where

---

* Compare the valley phase of the upland surface of the Davenport Range described by Mabbutt (1965).

the Tennant Creek Surface had no original relief, and in areas where there were Ashburton residuals, and these are discussed separately below. An important lithological factor is the iron content of the parent rock, and this has been estimated from Clarke (1924) in the absence of chemical analyses.

(1) *Lateritic profiles in areas of no original relief.* The profiles most studied are those on the Antrim Plateau Volcanics in the west of the area, where the Tennant Creek Surface has been deeply dissected and exposures are abundant. The volcanics are considered to be plateau basalts (Traves 1955) and it is reasonable to estimate an original iron content of between 8 and 10 per cent.

The uppermost horizon of the profiles comprises 12 m of orange to red-brown ferruginous material grading from partly pisolithic at the top through nodular and vermicular to nodular and earthy near the base. This ferruginous zone shows no trace of the texture or structure of the parent rock. It grades downwards over about 1 m into a mottled zone in which the only indication of original structure is the apparent control of mottling by joints which elsewhere determine spheroidal weathering of the rock. The base of the mottled zone has not been observed, but the rock becomes more leached with depth, and a structureless pallid zone has been noted at a lower topographic level in several places. Weathered but identifiable basalt crops out in Mosquito Creek near Birrindudu, 35 m below the top of the ferruginous zone, so that the profile cannot exceed this depth locally unless some of the ferruginous zone has been removed. Similar profiles are to be seen on volcanic rock near Helen Springs.

The profiles next in abundance of exposure are those imposed upon Lower Proterozoic argillaceous rocks and their metamorphic derivatives, and upon Cretaceous shale. The Lower Proterozoic rocks are exposed in the centre and the south of the area and have been studied from wells and bores near Tennant Creek, and the Cretaceous shale is seen in cliffs along the the north coast of the Territory. The average iron content of these rocks ranges from 3 to 4·5 per cent. The ferruginous zones of the lateritic profiles are similar to those on basalt but are much thinner; the thickest observed is about 7·5 m, and even allowing for erosion it is unlikely that the ferruginous zones ever exceeded 10 m. Mottled zones consist of between 12 and 24 m of material mottled red-brown and white with no trace of original texture or structure. The mottled zones grade downwards into 15 m or more of pallid kaolinitic material which in turn passes into fresh rock. Total thicknesses of the profiles mainly range between 35 and 55 m, but in places may be greater.

Profiles on acid igneous rocks have been studied only in the Tennant Creek area, on granite, porphyry, quartz-syenite, and granite-gneiss, although complete profiles have only been studied on the gneiss. Iron content of these rocks appears to range between about 2 and 3 per cent. Ferruginous zones consist of rather less than 6 m of pisolithic, vermicular, and nodular ironstone grading into a mottled zone in which rock texture may be seen through the persistence of original quartz grains. Pallid zones also show this original texture. Combined thicknesses of mottled and pallid zones total about 20 m, although much greater depths of weathering are indicated by truncated profiles near Pine Creek and Rum Jungle, formed in depressions on the Tennant Creek Surface, or constituting relics of an older weathering profile, or representing abnormal profiles in hydrothermally altered rocks. In all profiles examined the gradation from ferruginous zone to mottled zone takes place over a distance of between 1 and 2 m, whereas that from mottled to pallid zone may extend over 12 m.

The only other rock type upon which a complete profile has been observed in an area of no original relief is a Cretaceous sandstone north of Newcastle Waters. The iron content of the parent rock is not known, but since its provenance is to the south and southwest where basic igneous rocks are abundant, there is reason to assume that it would be at least that of greywacke, the average for which is 2·5 per cent. Cretaceous sandstone in the Darwin area is extremely ferruginous. The only difference between the profile in Cretaceous sandstone and that in argillaceous rock is that the texture of the parent sandstone is preserved through the persistence of quartz grains. These persist so abundantly that parts of the ferruginous zone become a highly ferruginous sandstone. The pallid zone consists of kaolinitic sandstone with an abundance of clay, which supports the view that the parent rock was rich in ferromagnesian minerals.

All the profiles described above closely resemble standard lateritic profiles of the literature, and all show an abrupt transition from ferruginous zone to mottled zone, and a gradual transition from mottled to pallid zone and from pallid zone to unweathered rock. Profiles developed on highly siliceous and calcareous rocks, on the other hand, deviate markedly from the standard lateritic profile.

Quartzite is abundant in the Ashburton Range at the level of the Tennant Creek Surface as well as on the Ashburton Surface. Iron content of the rock is negligible and no lateritic profile has been observed, although iron-staining and impregnation occur along joints to a depth of 6 m. It is assumed that no profile was ever developed, although the possibility of stripping cannot be completely discounted. Thus profiles on quartzitic rock on the Tennant Creek Surface do not differ from those on the Ashburton Surface.

Limestones with negligible iron are abundant in the area. Some of them, as near Tennant Creek, are undoubtedly at the level of laterite on the Tennant Creek Surface; others, as on the Barkly Tableland, in the Daly River Basin, and in the upper Roper valley, may be at lower levels. No evidence of a lateritic profile has been seen on any of the limestones, and Christian and Stewart (1954) note the absence of such profiles from some limestone in the Barkly Tableland.

Inter-bedded thin calcareous, argillaceous, and arenaceous strata are abundant near Inverway. Many exposures are at the same topographic level as the laterite, but no lateritic profiles have been observed on them despite the fact that the shales are thought to have had an original iron content of up to 3 per cent. There are two possible explanations. In every section studied, the uppermost horizon was a very quartzitic sandstone of unknown original thickness, and as the maximum depth of lateritisation under favourable conditions appears to have been 35-55 m, the quartz sandstone may have been too thick to permit lateritisation in the underlying shale. An alternative explanation is that the presence of limestone is inimical to lateritisation even where there is iron in adjacent strata.

(2) *Lateritic profiles in areas with Ashburton residuals.* Standard lateritic profiles extend at plain level to within some miles of residuals, but no such

profiles have been observed on fringing pediments, whilst those of the residuals themselves, as already described, are faint shadows of the standard lateritic profile, lacking true laterite and nowhere showing pallid zones of complete decomposition. However, profiles intermediate between these extremes in Cabbage Gum Basin may indicate that laterite formerly extended unbroken from plains to residuals, although the profiles were considerably modified on the latter. Gradients of one per cent were noted on slopes showing these intermediate type profiles, and Condon (1962) has reported local gradients as high as 1 in 4 on lateritised slopes in Western Australia.

(iii) Bauxitic Profiles

The only bauxite known is that on the Tennant Creek Surface on Gove Peninsula. No complete profile has been seen and the parent rock is not yet known, but the nearest outcrops are of granite and assimilated sediments thought to continue beneath the bauxite. The bauxite is pisolithic and nodular above, and vermicular, massive, and earthy below. Blocks of vermicular bauxite have been observed in pisolithic material, and pisoliths occur in cavities in blocks of vermicular bauxite. The alumina content of the pisolithic bauxite and the enclosed nodular bauxite is very much higher, and the iron and silicon contents very much lower, than in the nodular and vermicular variety. Blocks of vermicular material enclosed in the pisolithic layers differ only slightly in composition from the containing pisolithic rock, but very markedly from the non-pisolithic lower layers. These facts may imply that bauxite formed in two stages and that some reworking occurred in the intervening period.

Although a large number of assays is available from Gove, most of them are from that part of the profile in which commercial bauxite occurs. One fact is clear from the assays; the alumina-ferric oxide ratio ranges from 5:2 in the higher grade to 3:2 in the lower grade. Since the ratio for the supposed granitic parent rock may lie between 8:1 and 16:1, the bauxite zone is one of even more marked enrichment of iron than of aluminium, and corresponds to laterite in the lateritic profile.

(iv) Age and Origin of the Tennant Creek Surface

The age of the Tennant Creek Surface and its associated lateritic profiles is not known exactly. In its type area the surface is undoubtedly an erosional one, although there is little evidence of the nature of the formative processes. There has been extensive post-laterite erosion of Ashburton residuals, predominantly by pedimentation and scarp retreat, but gentle slopes occur side by side with scarps, and the granite ridges from which the Cabbage Gum Basin sediments were derived appear to have been bounded by gentle slopes. It would be unwise therefore to assume that the early sculpturing of the Tennant Creek Surface resulted from those same pedimentation processes which the present-day landforms suggest have predominated later.

North of Newcastle Waters the lateritic profiles are imposed upon horizontal Cretaceous sediments, and the Tennant Creek Surface may here lie very close to the original depositional surface of these sediments. Further north, in the Maranboy area, the lateritised surface truncates tilted Cretaceous beds and may locally coincide with the exhumed sub-Cretaceous surface; hence it is predominantly a surface of erosion. Similarly, the Tennant Creek Surface is erosional in most of the Dissected Margin. However, a depositional surface may recur in the extreme north on Bathurst and Melville Islands, where lateritic profiles are imposed upon horizontal terrestrial sediments which can be no older than Lower Tertiary because they rest unconformably upon Cretaceous and older rocks.

If the formation of the Tennant Creek Surface supplied Lower Cretaceous sediments to the north, then the Surface was already in existence in a state inviting lateritisation towards the end of the Lower Cretaceous. The climate was undoubtedly humid, as indicated by the sediments, and the surface was so nearly planate that both surface and underground drainage would have been sluggish, and chemical degradation would have dominated. Consequently, as sedimentation ceased, deep weathering profiles would have developed, culminating in the formation of laterite. Although the climate of the time is not known in detail, it can be reconstructed on the assumption that conditions suitable for lateritisation today were equally suitable in the past. On that assumption a climate comparable to that now prevailing in the Northern Plains would be appropriate. Such a climate is today restricted to a belt less than 300 km wide in the north of the area, but the extent of laterite indicates that it must have prevailed over practically the whole of the Australian land area in Upper Cretaceous time.

It is suggested that such a climate was essentially coastal, and that it would have moved northwards with retreat of the sea, so that lateritisation would be diachronic, beginning with emergence and stopping as soon as the moister climatic belt had passed to the north. Consequently, the time available for lateritisation in any latitude would not have been the whole period from late Cretaceous onwards. Nevertheless it could have been measured in millions or even tens of millions of years. The main effect of northward continental drift (Runcorn 1962) into higher latitudes would be an increase of temperature, which would merely accelerate the processes of lateritisation.

External factors such as temperature and rainfall would have been less important over the long periods envisaged than if lateritisation were condensed into a few hundred thousand years, particularly on a stable, flat surface of maximal chemical weathering. The greater the time available, the less important temperature becomes, provided that no critical threshold temperature is involved.

Since the area formed part of a south foreland for late Cretaceous and Miocene orogenies, it must be assumed that uplift and northward migration of the sea and its related climatic belts would have been far from regular, and that the movement could have been reversed from time to time. Nevertheless, the general picture is one of a land surface ranging in age from late Cretaceous in the south to early or mid-Tertiary in the north, and affected by lateritisation during this time-span.

(c) *Wave Hill Surface*

The existence of an extensive plain below the main lateritised surface was first noted by Jensen (1915) in the Wave Hill area. The Wave Hill Surface is so named because it is best developed at an altitude of 180 m on Wave Hill Station. It is typically one of advanced erosion, and it is characteristically developed in the Dissected Margin, where it stands lower than and encroaches upon the Tennant

Creek Surface and is in turn extensively dissected by the Koolpinyah cycle on its seaward edge. Broad undulations are thought to occur on it, but local relief, apart from that supplied by residuals of the Tennant Creek Surface, is restricted to particularly resistant structures. In the southwest the surface is mostly bevelled across calcareous, arenaceous, and argillaceous sediments of Upper Proterozoic (Victoria River Group) and Middle Cambrian age, and across Lower Cambrian volcanics; in the north, it bevels Lower Proterozoic greywacke and phyllite and Upper Proterozoic rocks similar to those of the Victoria River Group.

In its best preserved state the surface extends from Wave Hill northeastwards at constant height to Montejinnie Station, where the Montejinnie Limestone has produced a localised second level, and southwestwards rising to Inverway, where it ends at about 300 m above sea level in a scarp 90 m high leading up to the Tennant Creek Surface (Plate XIXb).

North of these limits the Wave Hill Surface has been dissected by headwaters of the Victoria and Daly Rivers and survives as dissected plains or in accordant hill summits. It has been traced northwestwards, sloping gently towards Joseph Bonaparte Gulf. North of Wave Hill Station the surface persists as a deeply dissected plain through Victoria River Downs Station and as accordant summits of scattered ranges and groups of hills still further north (Plate XIXc). On the Stokes Range and its continuations northeastwards, the surface descends from 300 m near Victoria River Downs to 180 m above sea level in the Daly River Basin. Hossfeld (1936) had earlier drawn attention to a surface below the main laterite in the Daly River Basin, and Wright (1963) has described *inter alia* a Maranboy Surface here which is to be equated with the Wave Hill Surface. Wright (1963) considers that the level of much of his Maranboy Surface is controlled by a zone of silicification low in the pallid zone of the lateritic profile on the Bradshaw or Tennant Creek Surface. This question is discussed below. In the south of the Daly River Basin, near Mataranka, it is difficult to separate the Tennant Creek and Wave Hill Surfaces because of the similarity of the laterite on both surfaces, the small differences in altitude (both surfaces being about 180 m above sea level), and the presence of the exhumed sub-Cretaceous surface west of Mataranka.

Eastwards, the Wave Hill Surface may be traced into the Roper valley, where its identification is made difficult by the large number of surfaces produced by local structural control in thinly bedded horizontal strata, and into the fringes of Arnhem Land, where it is the dominant surface at altitudes rising almost to 300 m. The surface apparently continues throughout the area to the north and east coast, where the Tennant Creek Surface reappears.

North of the Daly River Basin, the Wave Hill Surface is at about 300 m above sea level throughout the Pine Creek area, where, however, some duplication of surfaces occurs through local control by exhumed land surfaces, by resistant horizontal strata, and by differences in resistance encountered at the base of weathering profiles. The surface falls northwestwards from Pine Creek towards the sea, crossing the coast at about 30 m near Fog Bay. It can also be followed north and northeast to the coast, initially as a deeply dissected plateau, which gradually passes into strings of residuals along the interfluves. The surface has a northward fall of 1 in 500 from Pine Creek to King Table Mountain, the last distinct residual, some 25 km south of Darwin at an altitude of less than 60 m. The plateau upon which Darwin is built is also a remnant of the Wave Hill Surface, at a height of about 30 m. Beyond Darwin the gradient flattens, and at Gunn Point 40 km northeast it is negligible, the surface being about 10 m above sea level, whence it rises to almost 60 m on Bathurst and Melville Islands.

The only evidence of the age of the Wave Hill Surface comes from the White Mountain Formation (Traves 1955) on the Western Australian border west of Inverway. This marine formation of Miocene-Pliocene age (Lloyd personal communication) is here considered to be a depositional facies of the Wave Hill Surface formed in its northern part during a temporary southward transgression of the sea. It is supposed that the formation was uplifted to its present altitude (300 m) before consolidation, that the folding mentioned by Traves is slumping, and that the deposit owes its preservation to its siliceous nature, adjacent non-siliceous deposits having been washed away during uplift. The presence of marine limestone of similar age on Brunette Downs in the north of the Barkly Tableland (Lloyd 1963) indicates that this part of the area was also submerged during the formation of the Wave Hill Surface and that uplift of 300 m must have taken place subsequently.

(d) *Koolpinyah Surface*

This is a multicyclic surface developing at present in the coastal areas and in a few inland basins on rocks of all ages from Lower Proterozoic onwards.

The main development is in the coastal plain east and south of Darwin, (the Subcoastal Plain of Christian and Stewart (1953) and the Northern and Western Plains of Noakes (1949)), extending westwards from the East Alligator River to beyond the Daly River, with a maximum extension inland of about 100 km. The plain ranges in height from sea level to about 60 m at the main inland edge, and to about 75 m in its extensions up the main valleys. It has developed as a large number of panplains eroded into the former northerly and westerly slopes, which have coalesced in the coastal areas but which continue as separate valley floors inland (Plate XIXc). Near Darwin, the panplains of north-flowing and west-flowing streams have coalesced.

The Northern Plains as a physiographic zone are complex, including expanses of exhumed sub-Cretaceous surface, remnants of the Wave Hill and Tennant Creek Surfaces, surfaces of sedimentation, and young erosional surfaces which commonly show geological control. There is much evidence of warping and eustatic changes of sea level in the area. Emerged beaches and strandlines, including wave-cut benches, and extensive alluviation above present baselevel in drowned valleys, point to a former high sea level, possibly an effect of Pleistocene eustatism (Christian and Stewart 1953), followed by a Recent fall of about 6 m, as indicated by the depth of incised meanders in the plains. However, the full history of the plains is not known, and it is probable that more than two changes of sea level are involved. Four depositional episodes can be identified in the Mary River plains north of Pine Creek, where little-consolidated, locally derived alluvium is overlain by detrital laterite, which is overlain by two further generations of alluvium.

Structural differences between the plains south and east of Darwin are reflected in the nature of the limiting scarps (Fig. 9.6). The eastern plains have been formed by closely spaced streams flowing northwards, parallel to the strike of steeply dipping beds, over a land surface of little relief. Following dissection of this surface, the interfluves formed strike ridges, which have since been reduced into strings of residuals decreasing in height and extent to the north. Consequently, the escarpment separating the Koolpinyah and Wave Hill Surfaces is extremely irregular, and the former penetrates as much as 80 km into the Dissected Margin.

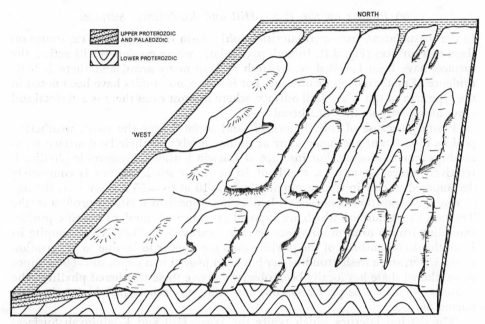

NORTH

UPPER PROTEROZOIC
AND PALAEOZOIC

LOWER PROTEROZOIC

WEST

9.6 Structural control of scarp development in the Dissected Margin Zone

In the southern plains, widely spaced streams flowed down a westerly slope, and were superimposed from flat-lying or westerly-dipping sediments across the older northerly structural grain. In this area the backing escarpments follow the strike; they are well defined and regular, and there is much less encroachment into the Dissected Margin than in the plains east of Darwin.

In the Daly River Basin warping of unknown age has carried flat-lying Palaeozoic and Mesozoic rocks down to a low level and permitted the formation of inland plains simultaneously with the fashioning of the coastal plain. The lowlands connect in a gorge through upwarped Proterozoic rocks.

The inland plains of the Victoria River Basin comprise the Baines, Angalarri, Wickham, and parts of the Victoria River valleys. These are classed with the Koolpinyah Surface because of similarity of age, level, and complexity of origin. The Baines and Angalarri valleys range in height from 15 m above sea level to about 55 m some 80 km inland; they follow a structural trend and occupy what may be a Permian depression or a younger basin of warping. The Wickham valley is about 200 km inland and has a height range of between 40 m and 60 m; it follows the same northeasterly structural trend. The Koolpinyah Surface is currently developing in these areas and has been affected by the same sea-level changes as those described from the coastal areas; there is a high degree of geological control by flat-lying sediments and basalt flows.

Small coastal areas in the north of Arnhem Land, and the extensive plain along the Gulf of Carpentaria, are also mapped as Koolpinyah Surface, but little is known of the areas.

(e) *Profiles on the Wave Hill and Koolpinyah Surfaces*

In the coastal areas, truncated lateritic profiles form the majority of exposures on these two surfaces (Fig. 9.4). Inland, particularly where erosion is still active, the surfaces have been bevelled across fresh rock in many areas, and there is little evidence of modern deep weathering. For instance, no profiles have been noted in the type area of the Wave Hill Surface, where in most cases there is a skeletal soil cover above only slightly weathered rock.

Possibly because of convergence of land surfaces near the coast, weathering profiles of different ages may occur at similar levels and their land-surface relationships remain obscure. For instance at Darwin harbour, Proterozoic phyllite is relatively unweathered to a depth of 10 m below sea level, but is completely decomposed to clay in a zone ranging from -10 m to -55 m; however, the age of this decomposition is not clear. It does not appear to relate to profiles in the Tennant Creek Surface, which are exposed as truncated standard lateritic profiles extending from 5 to 25 m above sea level in nearby cliffs (Plate XXa). Despite its level, the decomposition of the phyllite does not appear to be due to penetration by sea water, since fresh groundwater has been proved to a depth of -60 m. Since unweathered shale has locally been observed above these weathered phyllites, the decomposition may be pre-Cretaceous and relate to deep weathering of the Ashburton Surface.

The detrital laterites which typify the Wave Hill and Koolpinyah Surfaces result from the processes of pedimentation which have predominated in the fashioning and further dissection of those surfaces. These have resulted in the widespread deposition, in front of retreating scarps, of materials derived from higher, weathered levels. The deposits have a wide range of size grade and composition, and contain a high proportion of lateritic fragments in a sandy matrix with an authigenic ferruginous cement (Plate XXb). Locally, they are extremely ill-sorted and contain material of all sizes from clay grade upwards, but they show regional variations which are a function of the character of the parent scarps rather than of distance of transport. Lithology of the deposits is similarly related to the nature of the backing scarp. For instance, deposits having equal proportions of lateritised and fresh rock originate from high scarps exposing complete lateritic profiles and substantial thicknesses of fresh rock. In a few areas with particularly high scarps (120-180 m), slabs and boulders of fresh rock were found to constitute 75 per cent of the detrital laterite. With decreasing height of scarp, and consequent increase in the proportion of the section formed by the laterite, the size of fragments yielded will decrease and the proportion of laterite will increase; hence, detrital laterites in front of low escarpments may consist only of laterite fragments of less than 1·5 cm diameter. Such deposits are easily mistaken for sedentary laterite. Where the parent scarp is itself capped by detrital laterite, a secondary detrital laterite will be formed, containing fragments of the cap from the scarp.

Where a detrital laterite rests upon a truncated lateritic profile, and where the proportion of unlateritised rock is low, a perfect standard lateritic profile may be simulated, particularly where later weathering has redistributed iron oxides in the detrital laterite. Many such simulated profiles have been observed on the Koolpinyah and Wave Hill Surfaces. Wright (1963) describes them on the Maranboy (Wave Hill) Surface in the Daly River Basin, and similar profiles are found on the Wave Hill Surface north of the type area, where it truncates the deep weathering profile of the Tennant Creek Surface and so simulates a complete Tennant Creek profile. The cliffs near Darwin, long thought to exhibit standard lateritic profiles (David and Browne 1950), consist of detrital laterites with only a few fragments of fresh and weathered rock, resting upon a truncated lateritic profile (Plate XXa). Only the original pallid zone remains, and what appears to be a mottled zone is part of this pallid zone stained by iron solutions percolating down from the cover of detrital laterite. Some of these composite profiles show signs of subsequent lateritisation to the extent that they are enriched in iron in the upper 1·5-3 m and impoverished in iron at depth. This is particularly the case in the more humid coastal plain. During the hot wet season the laterite is saturated over wide areas and may even be flooded—conditions ideal for chemical decomposition. During the early part of the dry season the watertable in the detrital laterite falls a few metres, partly through slow drainage into the underlying rock and partly due to evapotranspiration. This fall is accompanied by precipitation of iron oxides dissolved during the wet season. Magnesite nodules were observed to form at the rate of about 12 to 60 cc per square metre of exposed rock in the Adelaide River gorge during the early part of the dry season.

The restriction of such lateritisation to detrital laterite deposits may be illusory. These deposits contain an unusually high proportion of iron, and may locally be classed as iron ore; their occurrence on plain surfaces, their high porosity and high permeability, and the fact that they are underlain by less pervious rocks ensure that saturation and flooding occur very quickly and that their subsequent drying out is slow. Consequently, high, perched watertables form during the wet season and persist during the early, hotter part of the dry season. Conditions within the detrital laterite are thus more suitable for the extensive solution and subsequent precipitation of iron than elsewhere. However, it is possible that similar changes are taking place in adjoining rocks at a rate too slow to detect.

The sole difference between detrital lateritic profiles on the Wave Hill and Koolpinyah Surfaces is that lateritisation is still active on the Koolpinyah Surface whereas there is no evidence that profiles are still being formed on the Wave Hill Surface. This is not surprising since all detrital laterite examined on the Wave Hill Surface was in well drained sites susceptible neither to saturation nor to seasonal flooding.

SILICIFICATION AND LATERITISATION

Wright (1963) has attributed the formation of quartzite and porcellanite in the

Daly River Basin to silicification in the lower part of the lateritic profile on the Bradshaw (Tennant Creek) Surface. However, not all silicification in the area is of this age, nor is it necessarily associated with the formation of a lateritic profile. For instance, siliceous sinter occurs as small nodules in post-laterite sediments near Tennant Creek, and quartz crystals are being formed today from siliceous solutions oozing from sandstones in the Daly River Basin. Silicification preceding lateritisation was noted at one exposure on Birrindudu Station, where silicified material, totally enclosed within the mottled zone and apparently limited by jointing, was invaded and replaced by ferruginous material and was not seen to replace laterite. Quartz sandstones of many ages, but having siliceous cement, are widespread in the northern part of the Nothern Territory. In fact low temperature and low pressure silicification occurs in many areas and at many different horizons, in several rock types, in some places associated with faulting and in other places with no such obvious association.

Many pallid zones are silicified, but others contain no porcellanite. Pallid argillaceous rock, quarried in a soft, wet state in Darwin, sets so hard within two days that tungsten carbide saws are needed to trim it; on the other hand, apparently similar pallid material from the Tennant Creek area showed no sign of setting even after being exposed for three years. It is almost certain that siliceous solutions were produced during lateritisation, but there need be no silicification of the profile where lateral migration of solutions is facilitated by regional uplift or local warping; conversely, downwarping of the Daly River Basin may have resulted in an influx of siliceous solutions into an area rich in carbonate rocks highly susceptible to silicification.

Silicified rocks have clearly exercised an important control over the development of landforms in this area, but it is impossible to generalise concerning the relations of such silicification to the periods of laterisation.

WARPING

There is much geological and geomorphological evidence that minor folding, faulting, and warping have taken place in the area since Cretaceous sedimentation, both before and after the development of the standard lateritic profile. However, warp axes have not yet been confirmed in detail, nor can it be stated beyond doubt that warping has or has not taken place in any particular area at any particular time. Christian and Stewart (1953, 1954) assumed upwarping to have taken place along a northwest axis through Pine Creek, implying relative downward movement along an axis from the Daly River Basin into the Georgina Basin. Wright (1963) directs attention to minor folding in Cretaceous sediments and to the possibility that uplift, greater in the north than in the south, was the cause of dissection of his Bradshaw Surface in the Daly River Basin.

The divides between exoreic and endoreic drainage trend northeast in the northwest and northwest in the northeast, parallel to tectonic lineaments which have been active throughout Australian geological history from at least Lower Proterozoic time (Hills 1946), and which have apparently controlled the plan of the north Australian coastline. It seems logical therefore to suppose that the divides were formed tectonically, and the northeast-trending divide is here called the Inverway upwarp, and the northwest-trending divide the Pine Creek upwarp.

XIXa   Residuals of the Ashburton Surface above the Tennant Creek Surface east of Tennant Creek. Photograph by B.M.R.

XIXb   Laterite-capped residuals of the Tennant Creek Surface rising above the Wave Hill Surface north of Inverway homestead. Photograph by B.M.R.

XIXc   Dissected Wave Hill Surface above valley plains of the Koolpinyah Surface at the Victoria River crossing on the road from Katherine to Wyndham. Photograph by B.M.R.

XXa A truncated standard lateritic profile in the cliffs at Charles Point near Darwin, with detrital laterite above an older pallid zone. Photograph by C. S. Christian.

XXb Boulder of leached detrital laterite at foot of cliff at Gunn Point near Darwin. Photograph by B.M.R.

Some endoreic drainage channels have been beheaded by retreat of the scarp separating the Tennant Creek and Wave Hill Surfaces, and some of their head-waters have been reversed to exoreic streams cutting back into the scarp. Hence the warping which produced the endoreic drainage clearly began before the Wave Hill Surface reached its present limits, and may even have initiated the formation of that surface. The gradual separation of the Wave Hill and Tennant Creek Surfaces westwards from Mataranka indicates upwarping in the west before the formation of the Wave Hill Surface, consistent with the uplift of about 300 m since the Miocene-Pliocene indicated by the marine Tertiary on White Mountain (Traves 1955).

Minor rises and depressions between the Inverway upwarp and Joseph Bona-parte Gulf, and the depression occupied by Sturt Creek on the southeast side of the Inverway upwarp, are also thought to be tectonic because they coincide with the axes of gentle folds. The axes of upwarping intersect the rivers at gorges, and the drainage is thus thought to be antecedent. Noakes (1949) and Wright (1963) attribute the form of the Daly River Basin to the presence of resistant quartzites near the gorge and to softer rocks, subject to more rapid erosion, upstream. This may be true in part, but it is noteworthy that the rocks at the gorge are topo-graphically higher but stratigraphically lower (Proterozoic) than the softer rocks upvalley (Cambrian and Cretaceous), and that the softer rocks have low radial dips into the basin. The Daly River Basin is in origin a Palaeozoic structure, but since the Cretaceous rocks also dip inwards it is considered to be a post-Cretaceous feature as well, parallel to the Pine Creek upwarp and ending downstream at a post-Cretaceous upwarp in the gorge sector. The occurrence locally of folds in the Cretaceous sediments supports the idea of post-Cretaceous warping.

The Wave Hill Surface slopes northwards and westwards towards Joseph Bonaparte Gulf, possibly as a result of downwarping. However, the slopes may be original ones developed on an older structural basin, for late Palaeozoic and early Mesozoic rocks dip radially inwards towards the gulf.

Another basin, elongated easterly, seems to be present off the northern shore of Arnhem Land, its edges marked by the Cobourg Peninsula on the west and by the arc of the Wessel Islands on the west. The Tennant Creek and the Koolpinyah Surfaces appear to converge as they slope into the basin, and dips in surrounding rocks are radial inwards.

From air reconnaissance, Van Diemen Gulf also appears to be the result of downwarping on an ENE axis. The Wave Hill Surface appears to sweep down to the sea in basin form on the south, whilst Bathurst and Melville Islands and the Cobourg Peninsula mark a limiting upwarp on the north side, traversed in Apsley and Dundas Straits by former extensions of an antecedent drainage directed northwards.

Arnhem Land is thought to be a broad upwarp forming a northeasterly extension of the Inverway upwarp. The fact that the Tennant Creek Surface is absent from it, but present in surrounding areas, implies that the present elevated position is due to post-Tennant Creek uplift.

The area formed part of the south foreland of the Laramide and Alpine orogenic belts of Indonesia and New Guinea, and it is to be expected that both orogenies would have some effect, but that those effects would have diminished

P

southwards. This appears to be the case, for warping in the south has not been pronounced and has been controlled by well established pre-Cretaceous trends, whereas the warping in the extreme north has been more severe and its east-west trends are in more direct response to orogenic forces.

CONDITIONS CONTROLLING LATERITISATION

Prescott and Pendleton (1952) have emphasised the importance of saturation and reducing conditions in the formation of the clay minerals of the pallid zone. This seems to be confirmed by the conditions under which lateritisation is operating in the area today, and also by the topographic relations of the lateritic profiles (Fig. 9.4). Precipitation of iron oxide is taking place in a zone of intermittent saturation, particularly in areas of high watertable where there is unrestricted access of oxygen to the groundwater surface. Pallid zones occur at lower levels of permanent saturation and reducing conditions. Well defined laterites and pallid zones occur in areas of low relief where stagnant conditions readily occur below the watertable. The thickness of laterite and pallid zone appear to depend on the porosity and permeability of the parent rock. The deepest profiles are found on argillaceous rock of high porosity and low permeability; the next deepest profiles occur on basalt of low porosity but of moderately high permeability caused by jointing; shallow profiles are found on massive acid igneous rocks of low porosity and permeability, but deep profiles may be formed on them where abnormal conditions obtain, such as excessive jointing or past hydrothermal activity. Presumably the thickness of the laterite depends as much on the mobility of the iron as on the actual iron content of the parent rock.

It was noted that in the standard profiles in which zonal differentiation was best developed, the transition from laterite to mottled zone took place within about 1 m, the mottled zone itself was fairly thin, and the transition from mottled zone to pallid zone was achieved over about 6 m. This may indicate that the final stage of lateritisation would be represented by a profile in which laterite extended down to the permanent watertable and rested upon a perfect pallid zone. Should such conditions be followed by a lowering of the watertable, the upper part of the pallid zone would become partly ferruginised by residual iron from the groundwater and as a result of leaching from the laterite.

Whitehouse (1940) regarded the ferruginous and mottled zones as having formed from the leaching of iron downwards from soil and decomposing rock as well as from the migration of iron upwards under the influence of a steadily rising watertable. The base of the laterite was considered by him to mark the upper limit reached by a rising watertable. However, evidence from the area indicates that either the iron was leached downwards within the profile or it moved into the profile from outside. The great extent of the laterite does not support an outside source, because no source capable of yielding so much iron is known; it is assumed therefore that the majority of the iron in the laterite was introduced by downward leaching, although upward movement of iron can occur under special circumstances.

Evidence of upward movement of iron is seen in the lacustrine and fluviatile sediments of the Cabbage Gum Basin, where there has been removal of iron from a basal conglomerate of pure laterite fragments, accompanied by iron precipitation in the layers above, with results almost identical with the standard lateritic profile in some parts of the basin. A truncated lateritic profile beneath the sediments shows no evidence of subsequent downward movement of iron. No movement of iron was observed over a five year period, and lateritisation is thought to have taken place shortly after the sediments were laid down, perhaps whilst the moist conditions of lake-filling persisted. Somewhat analogous conditions obtain where thin alluvial soils overlie detrital laterites on the coastal plain. Iron is being precipitated in the upper layers of the detrital laterite, perhaps in the zone of capillarity above a seasonally declining watertable; the only obvious source of iron is the lower part of the detrital laterite, perhaps by upward leaching in the season of watertable rise. Both of these examples of upward migration of iron are abnormal in that the sediments concerned are very rich in iron ore and in that climatic and watertable conditions are or were ideal for lateritisation.

The texture of the laterite may indicate the manner in which it was formed and the nature of the parent rock. Pisolithic laterite is restricted to the upper layers and indicates precipitation around nuclei in the soil. Massive, vermicular, and nodular laterites form the lower layers and in many places visibly contain free silica. Where the parent rock is acid igneous, silica grains tend to be angular and irregular, but arenaceous parent rocks yield rounded to sub-angular grains.

Presumably the lower part of the laterite has formed by replacement of parent rock *in situ* beneath a soil; however, there is no indication over most of the area as to what that soil was, and very little evidence of its fate, although much of it must have gone to form the extensive post-laterite alluvia. Even where soil cover is still present, its relationship to the laterite is uncertain. Wright (1963) described lateritic red earths above pisolithic ironstone on the Bradshaw Surface, but it is not certain that these represent the original soil cover. An old lateritic soil occurs beneath 3 m of aeolian sand on the west side of the Cabbage Gum Basin; however, its contact with the underlying laterite could not be examined in detail, and further west where the laterite appears at the surface, the soil cover has been eroded away.

CONCLUSIONS

King (1950) has grouped Australian landscapes into four main cyclic surfaces, namely a Gondwana Surface formed in a pre-Cretaceous cycle of erosion, an Australian Surface formed in erosion lasting from Cretaceous to Miocene, a multi-phase Lake Eyre Surface dating from late Tertiary time, and younger, more local surfaces initiated by Kosciuskan movements.

The Ashburton Surface, as the original surface of the land-mass from which Cretaceous sediments were derived, corresponds to the Gondwana Surface (Fig. 9.7). The Tennant Creek Surface, by virtue of its associated laterite, is considered to correspond to the Australian pediplain. The cycle of erosion which produced it was complex, however, and may be divided into two parts. The first part produced Cretaceous sediments and resulted in the formation of the Tennant Creek Surface in its type area from dissection of the Ashburton land-mass; in the second part of the cycle, the Cretaceous sediments were exposed and eroded to produce the northern extension of the Tennant Creek Surface, thus contributing to late Cretaceous and early Tertiary sedimentation in the Timor Sea and the Gulf of

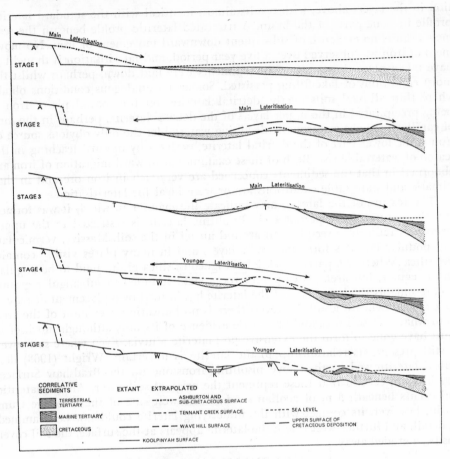

9.7 *Stages in the development of land surfaces in the north of the Northern Territory*

> *Stage 1* Formation of Tennant Creek Surface in the south with advanced planation of Cretaceous land-mass; climate suitable for lateritisation.

> *Stage 2* Extension of Tennant Creek Surface to the north across uplifted and warped Cretaceous sediments. Possibly some Tertiary terrestrial sediments formed in the north. Coastal zone of lateritisation shifts north with retreat of the sea.

> *Stage 3* Continuing uplift exposes terrestrial Tertiary deposits to lateritisation in northward-retreating coastal belt.

> *Stage 4* Uplift in north initiates new cycle and thus ends main period of lateritisation. Wave Hill Surface extends southwards and conditions suitable for younger lateritisation develop in the north. Miocene-Pliocene marine deposits formed during a temporary period of submergence.

> *Stage 5* Warping in the north was followed by development of the Koolpinyah Surface and as this extended relief again became suitable for lateritisation.

Carpentaria. Clearly, the Tennant Creek Surface cannot be regarded as a pediplain outside the type area, for generally speaking its age decreases from the centre outwards, a reversal of normal pediplain sequence. The Wave Hill Surface, dated as probable Miocene-Pliocene, is reasonably correlated with the late Tertiary Lake Eyre group of surfaces. The Koolpinyah Surface was initiated after the Wave Hill Surface, and a large part of it is considered to have been in existence by the Pleistocene; it thus corresponds to the youngest surface of King (1950).

On slight evidence, warping of land surfaces is thought to have occurred under the influence of the Laramide and Alpine orogenies. In the south of the area, the warping followed ancient tectonic trends, but in the north it followed the lines of the modern orogenies.

The conclusions of Prescott and Pendleton (1952) concerning the conditions of laterite formation appear to be confirmed here. Planation, accompanied by virtual cessation of mechanical erosion and the predominance of chemical decomposition, appears to be essential for the lateritic profile to develop completely (Woolnough 1927). By analogy with the coastal plain today, it is supposed that climate during lateritisation was tropical with heavy seasonal rainfall. Such conditions allow upward migration of iron, but it is thought that most of the iron in the laterites has been derived from above, during the formation of an original soil cover.

The age of the laterite on the Tennant Creek Surface is not known exactly, but there is no doubt that it is older than mid-Miocene, since deposits of that age are found on the Wave Hill Surface. It is possible that lateritisation set in as soon as Lower Cretaceous sedimentation ceased, and that the process continued into the Tertiary, being interrupted only by movements of the climatic belt suitable for lateritisation. These movements are considered to have been due almost entirely to geological causes. There is evidence of uplift of the order of 300 m since the Miocene, and it is probable that other similar movements occurred between mid-Cretaceous and Miocene times. Concomitant marked regression would have produced change in climate over wide areas.

REFERENCES

Christian, C. S. and Stewart, G. A. (1953). *General Report on Survey of Katherine-Darwin Region, 1946.* CSIRO Aust. Land Res. Ser. No. 1.
——, —— (1954). *Survey of the Barkly Region, Northern Territory and Queensland, 1947-48.* CSIRO Aust. Land Res. Ser. No. 3.
Clarke, F. W. (1924). *The Data of Geochemistry.* U.S. Geol. Surv. Bull. No. 770.
Condon, M. A. (1962). *Glenburgh, W.A.,* 1:250,000 Geological Series; Explanatory notes. Aust. Bur. Min. Res. Note Ser. G50/6.
David, T. W. E. ed. Browne, W. R. (1950). *The Geology of the Commonwealth of Australia.* Vol. I, London.
Gardner, D. E. (1957). Laterite in Australia. Aust. Bur. Min. Res. Unpub. Rec. 1957/67.
Hays, J. (1960). The Geology of the Mount Harris Tinfield, N.T. Aust. Bur. Min. Res. Unpub. Rec. 1960/2.
—— (in press). The relations between laterite and land surfaces in the northern part of the Northern Territory of Australia. *22nd Int. geol. Cong.*
Hills, E. S. (1946). Some aspects of the tectonics of Australia. *J. Proc. R. Soc. N.S.W.* **79:** 67-91.

Hossfeld, P. S. (1936). *The Tin Deposits of the Buldiva-Collia Area.* A.G.G.S.N.A. Rept N.T. No. 18.

Ivanac, J. F. (1954). *The Geology and Mineral Resources of the Tennant Creek Gold Field, Northern Territory.* Aust. Bur. Min. Res. Bull. No. 22.

Jensen, H. I., *et al.* (1915). *Geological Report on the Country Between Pine Creek and Tanami.* N.T. Aust. Bull. No. 14.

King, L. C. (1950). The cyclic land-surfaces of Australia. *Proc. R. Soc. Vict.* **62**: 79-95.

Lloyd, A. R. (1963). Possible Tertiary marine fossils from the Brunette Downs Limestone, Barkly Tableland. Aust. Bur. Min. Res. N.T. Unpub. Rec. 1963/90.

Mabbutt, J. A. (1965). The weathered land surface in central Australia. *Z. Geomorph.* **9**: 82-114.

Noakes, L. C. (1949). *A Geological Reconnaissance of the Katherine-Darwin Region, N.T.* Aust. Bur. Min. Res. Bull. No. 16.

—— (1960). An outline of the geology of Australia. Aust. Bur. Min. Res. Unpub. Rec. 1960/35.

Owen, H. B. (1954). *Bauxite in Australia.* Aust. Bur. Min. Res. Bull. No. 24.

Prescott, J. A. and Pendleton, R. L. (1952). *Laterite and lateritic soils.* Commonwealth Bur. Soil Sci. Tech. Comm. No. 47.

Runcorn, S. K. (ed.) (1962). *Continental Drift.* New York.

Traves, D. M. (1955). *The Geology of the Ord-Victoria Region, Northern Australia.* Aust. Bur. Min. Res. Bull. No. 27.

White, D. A. (1954). Observations on laterites in the Northern Territory. *Aust. J. Sci.* **17**: 14-18.

Whitehouse, F. W. (1940). The lateritic soils of Western Queensland. *Univ. Qld Pap. Geol.* **2** (N.S.) (1): 2-22.

Woolnough, W. G. (1927). The duricrust of Australia. *J. Proc. R. Soc. N.S.W.* **61**: 1-53.

Wright, R. L. (1963). Deep weathering and erosion surfaces in the Daly River basin, Northern Territory. *J. geol. Soc. Aust.* **10**: 151-64.

10

Landscapes, Laterites and Soils in Southwestern Australia

M. J. MULCAHY

INTRODUCTION

The map of southwestern Australia shows a number of physiographic features that individually are peculiar and of considerable interest, and taken together form a landscape which is perhaps unique. The rivers of the marginal zones are generally short and flow mainly in winter, becoming dry or merely a string of pools within a short distance of the coast at other times of the year. The extensive lake systems of the interior, so prominent on any map, are commonly chains of dry white saltpans, although those in the area considered may fill and have connected flow in exceptionally wet winters. This is only in part a consequence of the climatic pattern, semi-arid in the interior, but with relatively high rainfall in the coastal areas. The principal factor responsible for these features of the drainage is undoubtedly the extremely gentle fall seawards from the highest general elevations, which approach 600 m at a distance of 400 km from the coast. Hills (1955, 1961) describes southwestern Australia as a typical shield landscape, broadly upwarped, an 'ageless and undateable oldland', eroded continuously since the lower Palaeozoic. Late Tertiary epeirogenic uplift of the peneplain formed the 'old plateau' of southwestern Australia (Jutson 1934), only marginally dissected by a resulting rejuvenation of the drainage.

The area treated in this essay, the southwestern corner of the continent, roughly southwest of a line from Geraldton to Esperance (Fig. 10.1), comprises but a small part of the vast Precambrian shield of west and central Australia. Here it slopes down gently west and southwest, rises again marginally to over 330 m in the Darling Range, and ends at 220 m above sea level along the north-south line of the Darling Scarp. To the west of the scarp the shield is flanked by the great thickness of sedimentary rocks of the Perth basin, ranging in age from Palaeozoic to Recent, which form a narrow coastal plain. To the south the shield rocks run into the Southern Ocean; here they carry locally a thin sequence of Tertiary and Recent sediments, the former becoming more extensive north and east of Albany (McWhae et al. 1956). The climatic range is considerable, from an annual rainfall of 100-150 cm in the west and southwest, with a marked winter incidence, to below 25 cm per annum in the semi-arid interior, where seasonal distribution is more uncertain. Winters are cool and mild, and summers hot.

Prevailing conditions of low relief in the interior might well be expected to be associated with and to favour the preservation of landscape elements of considerable age, marked by zones of deep weathering and extremes of soil development. That this is indeed the case was recognised long ago by Woolnough (1927) in his paper on the chemical criteria of peneplanation. He argued that with high temperatures, alternation of wet and dry conditions leading to the solution and

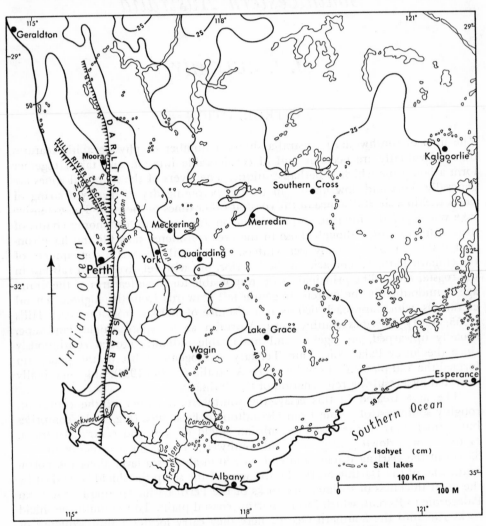

10.1   *Study area of southwest Australia in relation to the 25 cm isohyet*

irreversible precipitation of iron and aluminium oxides favours the formation of lateritic duricrust or 'ironstone' on stable peneplains, while the underlying permanently saturated levels, with loss of iron, aluminium, combined silica and bases, become the white, kaolinitic horizon here termed the pallid zone. It is clear from the literature reviewed by Prescott and Pendleton (1952) that such abundance of lateritic materials as is found in southwestern Australia is exceptional.

The extent of the rejuvenation of the drainage due to uplift has been delineated by Jutson (1934), and defines the inner limit of his physiographic division of Swanland. Beyond it, where there has been no such rejuvenation, he considered erosional modification of the landscape to be due to 'levelling without base-levelling' (after Davis 1905). Today, with better topographic maps, extensive aerial photography, and a number of studies relating soil distribution to landscape history, Jutson's conclusions are largely confirmed, though there are some differences in interpretation and some modifications are required. His 'levelling without base-levelling', that is, alluviation and colluviation working to local baselevels, with some lowering of valley floors by deflation, has operated extensively and has affected the whole area to some degree. These processes are major factors influencing the landforms and soils of the shield today. Their operation under the control of climate, which becomes more arid inland, and of relief, which is related to the stage of rejuvenation of the drainage, is the main theme of this essay.

DRAINAGE AND LANDSCAPE ZONATION

The drainage pattern, already briefly mentioned, must be considered in a little more detail to provide a basis for discussion of landscapes and soils. It is illustrated in Figure 10.2, from which it is evident that there is a clear division on the basis of intensity of drainage, along a line running southeastwards from beyond Moora in the north through Meckering and Wagin. This is the line marking the inland limit of Jutson's Swanland (Jutson 1934), and it forms, as will become even more apparent later, a physiographic boundary of considerable significance. Since it will be referred to frequently in the following pages it is called here the Meckering Line. Woolnough (1918) used the term 'Meckering Level' to indicate the level of the broad flat-floored valleys with salt lakes, such as that which ends immediately to the east of Meckering township. In effect the Meckering Line marks the downstream limit beyond which such valleys are not found as a connected system, as is shown in Figure 10.2.

Inland of the Meckering Line there is thus a sparse, open drainage network, with extensive chains of salt lakes in the trunk valleys regarded as the remnants of ancient rivers (Gregory 1914; Browne 1934). Those valleys running westwards form the main drainage of the area, and have been shown in Figure 10.2 as a connected system, since there is still flow along these courses, though only in exceptionally wet years. Beyond the regional divide marked by the 450 m contour (Fig. 10.2), the pattern of salt lakes suggests a southeasterly drainage to the Tertiary sea, now represented by the marine sediments of the Nullarbor Plain.

The valleys of these old river systems are shallow, wide, and ill-defined, and have little fall, so that drainage is sluggish. The trunk valleys may be as much as 15 km across, while even the larger tributaries may be up to 8 km wide; they lie only about 60 m below the smooth, gently rounded divides. Despite the width of the valleys, they are narrow in comparison with the extent of the uplands between them, which carry broad areas of sandy deposits (Mulcahy 1960) and which are commonly known as sandplains (Plate XXIa). Thus to the eye the

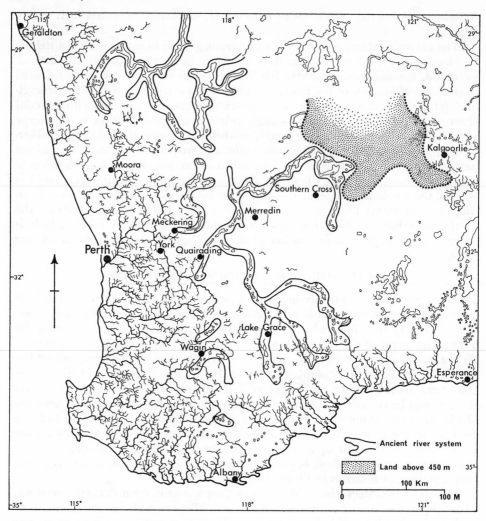

10.2   Drainage systems of southwest Australia. Position of the 450 m contour estimated from 1:1,000,000 maps of the Australian Geographical Series

landscape is gently undulating and on the whole featureless, except for a number of large granite bosses found occasionally on the highest parts of the divides or more commonly on the valley slopes. This broad area of low relief and sluggish drainage corresponds very roughly with the southern half of Jutson's Salinaland (Jutson 1934).

The broad valleys with salt lakes break off suddenly at the Meckering Line, but the drainage continues in valleys which are narrower, though still flat-floored, and fed by a closer network of more sharply incised tributaries. The streams, here with greater fall, flow each winter in defined channels well adjusted to geological structure. In Figure 10.3 the situation is illustrated in more detail for the Salt

River flats-Mortlock River-Avon-Swan River system, which flows through Meckering and Northam. It can be seen that there are a number of zones differing in intensity of drainage, and at the Meckering Line and at succeeding zone boundaries downstream there are sharp increases in the gradients of the valley floors. There are also associated changes in characteristic landforms and soils, in general the change being towards greater relief and younger soil parent materials with distance downstream (Mulcahy 1961).

The zones to be described thus provide a basis for the classification and mapping of the drainage and its associated relief and soil patterns. Their names, indicating their characteristic weathered mantles and superficial deposits, are in downstream succession: the zone of salt lakes and sandplains, the zone of younger laterites, the laterite-free zone, and the zone of detrital laterites.

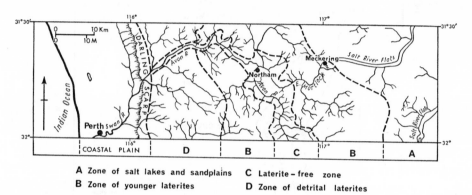

A Zone of salt lakes and sandplains   C Laterite – free zone
B Zone of younger laterites   D Zone of detrital laterites

10.3   Drainage patterns in the Swan-Avon-Mortlock-Salt River flats system in relation to landscape zones (after Mulcahy 1961)

Further field mapping is required before any adequate representation of the extent of the four zones outside the area of Figure 10.3 can be given, though this is only a matter of time, since each is readily recognisable in the field. However, the position of the Meckering Line is easily determined, and the inland margin of the zone of detrital laterites is roughly equivalent to that of the Jarrah forest formation (Gardner 1942), so that for the purpose of this discussion the distribution shown in Figure 10.4 may be taken as an approximation. The laterite-free zone is not shown, since it is restricted to narrow areas in the lower courses of the principal river valleys. Thus the zone of salt lakes and sandplains consists essentially of the country inland of the Meckering Line, of lowest relief and greatest extent, representing the landscape of the shield least affected by regional changes of baselevel, though much modified by erosional processes working to local baselevels. It has been argued (Mulcahy 1961) that the valleys of the zone of younger laterites (Plate XXIb) represent a first stage in rejuvenation, though sufficient time has elapsed since the rejuvenation began for the formation of lateritic profiles in them. The laterite-free zone represents a second stage entrenched in the first. The zone of detrital laterites consists essentially of the Darling Range, a belt of relatively high country which lies across the path of the westward-trending drainage.

It rises in places to over 330 m, possibly reflecting warping up of the shield during the Kosciusko Uplift (Clarke *et al.* 1948; King 1962). Drainage from the salt lake systems passes through this zone by only a few rivers; in fact all the country to the east of the Meckering Line drains to the coast through the Moore, Swan-Avon, Blackwood and perhaps the Frankland-Gordon Rivers. More numerous though shorter rivers such as the Murray and the Collie reach back to the zone of younger laterites, but all, where they pass through the Darling Range, are deeply incised. For example, the Avon flows 150 m or more below the plateau level for much of its course, though its valley is often only about 1 km wide (Plate XXIc). The

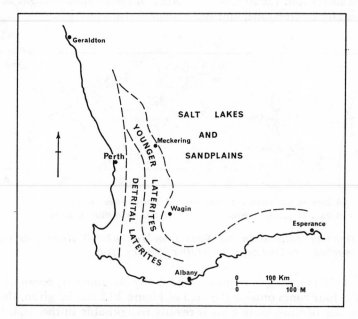

10.4 *Approximate extent of landscape zones of characteristic landforms, superficial deposits, and soils. The small laterite-free zone has been omitted because of scale*

streams with catchments entirely within the Darling Range, on the other hand, though sharply and deeply incised in their lower courses as they approach the Darling Scarp, commonly head in broad, shallow valleys, often with sandy floors. Locally the zone of detrital laterites has broad divides carrying what can be recognised as remnants or outliers of the zone of salt lakes and sandplains, a notable example being that on which lies Lake Muir and other smaller lakes. But overall there is a close pattern of streams, and residuals of the old plateau are limited in extent. Steep V-shaped valleys are common, and in such situations the ubiquitous lateritic materials, in the form of ironstone gravels and boulders, are often recognisably detrital, recemented with iron oxides where there has been seasonal seepage or waterlogging.

LANDSCAPE ZONES AND SOILS

(a) *Zone of Salt Lakes and Sandplains*

Geomorphological literature abounds with descriptions of ancient landscapes, though these are often only partly preserved, such that their characteristics must be inferred from those of the remaining fragments. Further, the criteria used in the recognition of these remnants, such as the distinction of 'slopes' and 'flats', concordance of summits and so on, are difficult to apply objectively (Butler 1959), and some forms of cartographic analysis used for the same purpose may be subject to an inherent source of error (Ollier 1963). Here, east of the Meckering Line, is a landscape which is undoubtedly ancient and extensively preserved, in the sense that it has been tectonically stable for a very long period, its river systems have not been rejuvenated, and it has not been affected by the Pleistocene glaciations. Thus its characteristics, in terms both of landscapes and of soils, should provide a standard of comparison in attempts to recognise fragments of old land surfaces elsewhere, whilst in the landscape zones affected by rejuvenation of the drainage this same surface may be seen in different stages of destruction. For these reasons alone the geomorphology of the area must be of considerable general interest and importance. Yet since the observations of Woolnough and Jutson, this southern part of the Salinaland has received but incidental attention, and that mainly in studies of soil distribution. Prescott (1931) and later Teakle (1938) were aware of the importance of geomorphological factors in determining the genesis and distribution of lateritic materials, and Stephens (1946) first outlined the nature of the soil parent materials, on both erosional and depositional surfaces, associated with the dissection of lateritic landscapes by streams. Following this, recent pedological work with a pronounced geomorphological bias has led to a better understanding of the nature and distribution of weathered mantles and superficial deposits, the latter often themselves derived from pre-weathered materials, on which the soils of the present day are formed. This understanding is valuable in the interpretation of at least the later episodes in the development of the landscape.

The zone is typified by the Merredin area, described by Bettenay and Hingston (1961, 1965), who give details of the soils and the principles governing their distribution and characteristics. The main factors are the erosional and depositional modifications of the Tertiary landscape, illustrated in Figure 10.5. This is a diagrammatic section across part of a valley typical of this zone, from the salt lake in the floor to the divides with extensive sandplains. The important point emerges that with the exception of limited areas of pediments and laterite-capped scarps or 'breakaways', the effect of these processes had been to reduce still further an already subdued relief. Mabbutt (1961) has described a similar situation in the northern part of Salinaland.

The sandplains themselves (Plate XXIa) have deep, generally yellowish sandy materials, originally thought to be fossil soils *in situ* (Prescott 1931) which had suffered the minimum of denudation, but now considered to be deposits originating from the weathering of laterite and subsequent colluvial transport downslope (Mulcahy 1960). Such deposits tend to reduce the relief of the divides by filling the depressions, and may also spill down the valley sides, sometimes to the level of the salt-lake margins. They may overlie unweathered rock or other relatively fresh materials, though they are most usually underlain by pallid rock. Deep bores show that the deposits contain, at various depths, ironstone gravel or reddish mottles in bands which are slightly more clayey and which harden on exposure. The bands may mark changes in texture of the sands and in their degree of sorting, suggesting that these are multiple deposits, and that the conditions under which they were formed may have varied. It is also possible that the bands of gravel represent soil horizons, and therefore periods when deposition ceased. The bands of ironstone may be exposed by further stripping, and with weathering and transport give rise in their turn to yet more yellow sandy deposits. These processes, often repeated, provide a mechanism for the retention of resistant quartz sands within the landscape, while less resistant primary and secondary minerals are progressively destroyed (Mulcahy 1960).

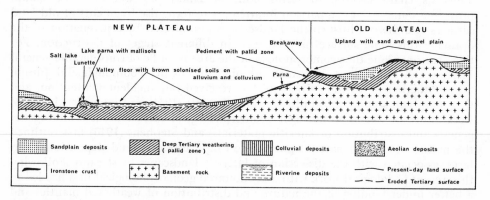

10.5   Modification of the lateritised surface in the zone of salt lakes and sandplains (after Bettenay and Hingston)

It is probable that many of the ironstone crusts now found at the surface formed in this way and so are relatively young, rather than remnants of a Tertiary residual profile. The latter is a possibility only when the ferruginous zone and underlying pallid zone preserve to some degree the fabric of the parent rock, and this is very rarely encountered. It seems, therefore, that in the zone of salt lakes and sandplains the Tertiary laterite on the divides, and with it the Tertiary land surface, has been largely destroyed, and that there has been a general lowering with its removal. It is thus not unusual to find the crests of divides occupied by fresh rock outcrop, though flanked on all sides by sandplain deposits overlying deep pallid zones.

While the upland has been lowered, the valley floors, on the contrary, have been raised, though in general by only a few metres after a slight initial lowering. Active erosion on the steeper slopes of the valley sides, with, in places, scarp retreat and pediment formation, has produced a sequence of deposits only a few metres thick, both alluvial and colluvial, and derived largely from fresh rock. Soils formed on such unweathered parent materials in this environment are fine-textured, calcareous, and alkaline, and have illitic as well as kaolinitic clays, in contrast with the leached, sandy, slightly acid, largely kaolinitic soils of the sandplains. They are in contrast too with the extremely acid clays—pallid weathered granite—up to 20 m and more thick which lie buried beneath them. Bettenay and Hingston (1965), in describing this situation at Merredin, point out that such burial of pallid weathered rock is common in the broad valleys of this zone. That is to say, the deep pallid zones commonly associated with remnant Tertiary duricrust on the divides are equally if not better preserved under the valley floors.

Deposition of this nature in the valley floors, together with a progressive increase in aridity at least since the Pleistocene (Crocker 1959), and perhaps a decrease in valley gradients resulting from the Kosciusko Uplift of the Darling Range, must be the main factors leading to the partial blocking and fragmentation of the ancient drainage system to give the salt lakes or playas of the present day. Their floors are now wind-planed flats, with banks of sandy or gypseous windblown deposits and lunettes (Hills 1940, Stephens and Crocker 1946) on their eastern and southeastern shores. Jutson (1934) described the lowering by deflation of the salt-lake floors below the original valley levels, with migration of the lakes as they are forced upwind by the accumulation of aeolian materials on the lee shores, so that the old drainage lines are not only partially blocked, but distorted and displaced westwards.

All the material derived from aeolian action on the dry lake floors has not been trapped in the lunettes, but a considerable proportion has been carried further and deposited as 'lake parna', discontinuous layers up to a few metres thick which may extend several kilometres downwind from the lake (Bettenay 1962). The parna is a clayey and silty material, illitic, calcareous and high in soluble salts. Sheets of two ages may be found superposed, the older leached of soluble salts and carbonates in the surface and with concretionary lime in the subsoil, while in the younger, salts and finely divided carbonates are distributed homogeneously throughout the profile. Both parna sheets may overlie the alluvial and colluvial deposits of the valley floor, suggesting that the latter predate a past extreme of aridity during which the parna was laid down.

Hydrologically, the zone is normally one of internal drainage in the sense that in most years the salt lakes act as sumps in which drainage water from the rest of the landscape evaporates and salt accumulates. Since, however, the system flows occasionally, the lakes are periodically flushed. If the flow persists for some weeks, as it did in 1955 and 1963, the flowing water decreases in salinity to values as low as about 60 milli-equivalents of chloride per litre (F. J. Hingston personal communication). Thus the gleaming white salt in the dry lakes represents the accumulation merely of a few years, perhaps a decade, and not of thousands or tens of thousands of years. Nevertheless, the landscape does contain a considerable store of soluble salts, the obvious accumulations in the lakes forming only a small proportion of it. Bettenay, Blackmore, and Hingston (1965), from a study of the hydrology of a typical valley draining into the salt-lake system west of Merredin, showed that almost the whole valley is underlain by saline groundwater confined in an aquifer consisting largely of the lateritic pallid zone which extends from divide to valley floor and from the head of the valley to the salt lakes (Fig. 10.5). The main source of the groundwater is the runoff from the relatively restricted areas of fresh rock outcrop which filtrates into pallid rock downslope, continuous with that in the valley floor, where it is contained by a dense clay aquiclude under sub-artesian pressure. Although the groundwater is relatively fresh higher in the system, by the time it reaches the valley aquifers it is extremely salt, with salinities ranging from 400 to 600 milli-equivalents of chloride per litre, and it is also extremely acid with pH values which may be less than 4. Bettenay, Blackmore, and Hingston (1965) calculate that although the valley floor forms only 20 per cent of the whole catchment, the groundwaters beneath it carry 60 per cent of the total NaCl in the whole area, and they consider that the bulk of the salts can be accounted for by accessions of ions in rainwater. The changes in salt concentration are believed to be due to slow upward loss of moisture in the vapour phase through the confining layers, and the changes in concentrations of hydrogen and other ions to exchange processes as the groundwaters move slowly through the highly weathered clayey materials of the aquifer.

Turning to soils, the leached sandy deposits on the broad divides carry sandy yellow earths and lateritic podzolics, while in the valleys the fresher alluvial and colluvial deposits carry fine-textured and calcareous brown solonised soils, the well known 'salmon gum-gimlet' or 'heavy soils' of the wheatbelt. The more saline and calcareous parna sheets give rise to mallisols of extremely loose consistence (Bettenay and Hingston 1961), commonly called 'snuffy morrel' soils. But in addition to the understanding of the distribution of the soils gained, the studies cited (Bettenay and Hingston 1961, 1965; Bettenay, Blackmore, and Hingston 1965) also provide a neat example of the way in which geomorphological analysis of a landscape and an associated knowledge of its superficial geology can point the way to the solution of other pedological problems. The acid subsoils underlying the calcareous and alkaline 'heavy soils' of the wheatbelt have been known for many years, and there have been numerous speculations as to their origin (e.g. Teakle 1938). Most of these assume that all the materials, both acid and alkaline, are part of the same genetic profile, and that the explanation lies in the vertical movement of ions in solution, whether upwards or downwards. The knowledge that the acid clays are older, highly weathered rock materials buried by the younger, fresher deposits at the surface and that the chemical characteristics of the former are due in large part to the lateral movement of groundwater, gives a much sounder basis. Further, the hydrological work, which provides a considerable degree of understanding of the occurrence of soil salinity in an extensive region, would have been meaningless without prior knowledge of the superficial deposits and weathered mantles in which the waters move.

(b) *The Zone of Younger Laterites*

This landscape zone represents the first stage of rejuvenation of the drainage system; in general, too, it experiences a moister climate than the zone of salt lakes and sandplains, and lies west of the 40 cm isohyet, which shows a marked parallelism with the Meckering Line. Soil and landscape relationships have been described by Mulcahy and Hingston (1961) in an area which extends from the zone of salt lakes and sandplains near Quairading in the east to the laterite-free zone represented by the Avon valley in the west (Fig. 10.6). It will be seen that the Meckering Line here runs along the divide between the western drainage through the zone of younger laterites, and the drainage eastwards to a salt-lake

XXIa   Cleared and cultivated sandplain south of Quairading, W.A., in the zone of salt lakes and sandplains. Trees mark fresh granite outcrop near summit.

XXIb   Escarpment-bounded laterite residual, with exposures of pallid zone, flanked by a pediment, near Greenhills, W.A., in the zone of younger laterites

XXIc   The Avon valley near York, W.A., a laterite-free lowland within the zone of younger laterites

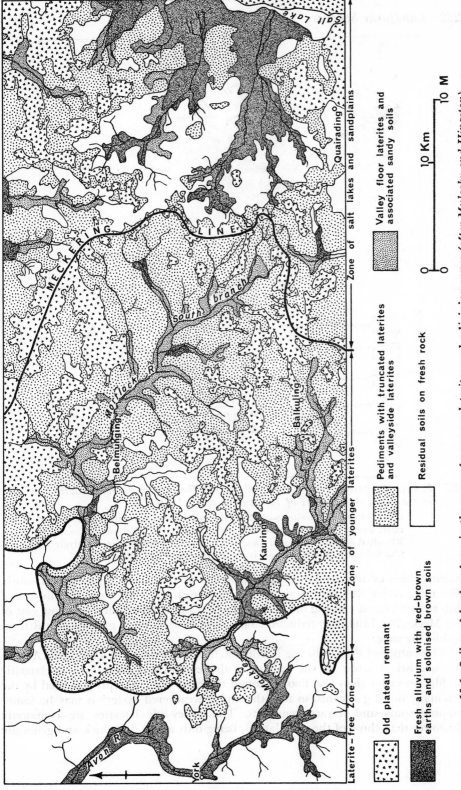

10.6 Soils and land surfaces in the zone of younger laterites and adjoining zones (after Mulcahy and Hingston)

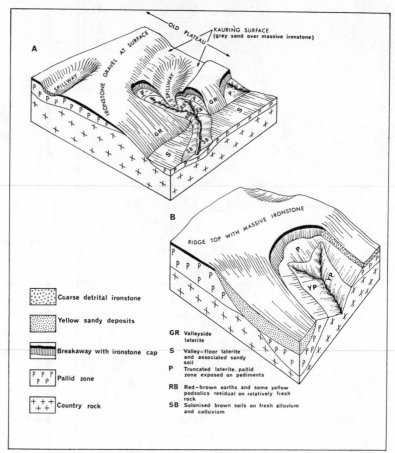

10.7   Landforms, parent mantles, and soils, (A) in the zone of younger laterites, and (B) in the drier, eastern part of the zone of detrital laterites

GR—Valley-side laterite; S—Valley floor laterite and associated sandy soil; P—Truncated laterite, pallid zone exposed on pediments; YP—Yellow and brown podzolics; RB—Red-brown earths and some yellow podzolics residual on relatively fresh rock; SB—Solonised brown soils on fresh alluvium and colluvium.

system which eventually joins the headwaters of the Avon River further south. The more active westward drainage system has carved a network of valleys, and thus reduced the size of the old plateau residuals in comparison with those east of the Meckering Line, the reduction becoming progressively greater downstream within the zone.

The nature of the landscape is illustrated in more detail in Figure 10.7A. The characteristic feature of the valleys is the extensive preservation of lateritic profiles on valley sides and floors, though these are often sharply dissected by the seasonally flowing streams, so that the highly weathered materials may be found capping spurs and terrace remnants. The valley-side laterites are commonly shallower than those of the old plateau, being only about 3 m thick and generally having no pallid zone. Most appear to be profiles developed in bedrock, since there are marked changes in morphology and especially in colour corresponding to changes in the underlying rock. Exceptionally, however, particularly near the foot of the valley-side slopes, the profile is developed in colluvium and may have a pallid zone. The valley floor laterites are underlain by shallow pallid zones which are recognisable as highly weathered deposits, usually water-laid. This is in contrast with the weathered profiles in valley floors east of the Meckering Line, which are much deeper and which have no obvious sedimentary characteristics. In this zone, therefore, the younger, thinner lateritic profiles are thought to represent the sides and floors of valleys cut in the Tertiary landscape at an early stage in the rejuvenation of the drainage system. Soils on these weathered surfaces, except where they have been reduced to small residuals, are waterlogged in winter and dry out to a depth of several metres in summer. In the surface horizons, where these extremes are most pronounced, the ironstone gravels are well rounded, with concentric structure. Particularly in the case of the valley-floor laterites, therefore, where the pallid zones are saturated with water for a great part of the year, it can be argued that the profiles, though old, are still forming. On the old plateau, on the other hand, the laterites are reweathering to give well drained yellow sandy soils.

The old plateau remnants in this zone, though small by comparison with those of the zone of salt lakes and sandplains, have many of the characteristics already described, with some differences which become progressively more important towards the west. Depressions in the undulating surface are likewise filled with yellow sandy deposits in which are bands of ironstone at various depths. But new features are what appear to be fragments of a system of broad, flat-bottomed, perched valleys running locally at about 6 m below the general level of the old plateau (Fig. 10.7A). Whereas on the higher ground ironstone gravel or yellow sandy soils derived from it are the rule, these flats, named the Kauring Surface (Mulcahy 1960), have grey leached quartz sands, devoid of all other minerals, above a massive ironstone which is paler in colour than usual and which has inclusions of pallid-zone rock. A normal pallid zone lies beneath. The profile corresponds very closely with that of a fossil laterite described by Northcote (1946), and judged by any standard it is highly weathered, since even the coatings of iron oxide have been removed from the sand grains of the surface horizon, which is commonly a metre or more thick. Nevertheless, its topographic situation and the pallid-zone inclusions in it suggest that the laterite has formed after some sort of erosional modification of an already lateritised landscape. Its preservation here, and more extensively further west, together with more frequently occurring older upland profiles with evidence of original development from fresh bedrock in the form of inclusions of fresh rock and the preservation of recognisable rock fabric in the laterite, are indications that the old plateau remnants, though smaller, are more completely preserved than those further east. Divides are more commonly marked by the presence of the Kauring laterite than by rock outcrop, so that it seems that the lowering described for the zone of salt lakes and sandplains has not been so effective here. This, together with the more sharply cut valleys and closer drainage network, is responsible for the greater relief and steeper slopes in the zone of younger laterites.

The old plateau remnants in this zone are thus more sharply defined, the limits being commonly marked by the scarps or breakaways which are a feature of the Western Australian landscape (Plate XXIb). Where the line of a breakaway is cut by one of the sand-filled upland depressions, sandy deposits have spilled out and down through the gap, burying the younger surfaces below. These landscape features have been called 'spillways' (Mulcahy 1960), and are shown in Figure 10.7. They function as catchments for relatively good quality water and often end downslope in fresh soaks or small swamps.

The complex formed by the old plateau and the younger lateritised surfaces of the valley sides is being destroyed by the retreat of scarps, the pediments below them giving exposures of pallid rock. In the drier, eastern parts of the landscape zone, the scarps are obviously still active and are scored with gullies which readily extend on to the pediments below where these are cleared for agriculture. Further west, the scarps and pediments have become stable and are commonly mantled with a scree of ironstone gravel and small boulders derived from the ironstone which caps the breakaway, while the pallid rock downslope may be buried by a metre or more of sandy pedisediment.

The upper parts of the pediments are obviously relatively young surfaces, and yet must pre-date those sandplain deposits of the spillways which bury them (Fig. 10.7A). Even so, the spillway deposits may have well developed segregations of iron oxides as soft reddish mottles which harden on exposure. Such formations of ironstone, then, do not take very long to develop and have no value in themselves alone as indicators of long-term stability of landscapes.

Downslope, the pediments end at the V-shaped valleys of seasonal streams. The features shown in Figure 10.7A represent the drier eastern part of the zone of younger laterites, and here dissection of the pediment generally exposes fresh rock. Red-brown earths with subsoils which are occasionally calcareous, and, less commonly, yellow podzolics, are the soils formed. Downslope from such dissected areas, younger colluvial and alluvial deposits bury the valley laterites or their truncated remnants. These younger, fresher deposits carry fine-textured and calcareous solonised brown soils, which contrast with the leached, acid, lateritic materials beneath them. Both the red-brown earths and the solonised brown soils have reserves of fresh, easily weatherable minerals.

Further west in the same zone, with higher rainfall—perhaps west of the 50 cm isohyet—conditions are slightly different. While, as already mentioned, the breakaways tend to be stabilized, fresh rock is not so readily exposed by a comparable depth of dissection by streams, since the pallid zones are deeper. Thus there are extensive areas of meadow podzolic soils characterised by grey sandy surface horizons, probably formed in pedisediment, over slowly permeable clays, low in nutrient reserves, formed from pallid rock. Restricted exposures of fresh rock are associated with yellow and brown podzolic soils rather than the less leached red-brown earths.

To summarise then, the zone of younger laterites is characterised by divides with prominent residuals of the old plateau, bounded by breakaways and carrying a range of sands and ironstone gravels similar to those of the zone of salt lakes and sandplains, with the significant addition of the intact laterites of the Kauring Surface. The residuals decrease in size downstream, more and more of the landscape being occupied by valleys with younger laterites on their sides and floors (Fig. 10.6). Later erosional modifications, forming spillways, pediments, and the V-shaped valleys of tributary streams, are all working to local baselevels, and in sum are tending to reduce the relief created by the early cycle of rejuvenation of the drainage. The broader main valleys carry throughflow every winter, large sump areas or lakes are absent, as also are the aeolian features and deposits associated with them.

(c) The Laterite-free Zone

This is the least extensive of the four landscape zones, existing only where the valleys of a few rivers are sufficiently entrenched on the arch of the Darling Range, or in the country immediately to the east (Figs. 10.3, 10.6). The Avon River with its north-running course through York and Northam is a good example (Plate XXIc). The valley floor has been cut about 30 m lower than that of its tributary, the Mortlock, at comparable distances above the confluence, the valley sides are steeper, and the tributary streams are more sharply incised. The main river and its tributaries have dissected the valley floor to form a main terrace level about 10 m above the Avon.

Lateritic materials are absent from the valley sides, where fresh rock is always close to the surface, giving rise to the red-brown earths characteristic of this district. Colluvial and alluvial deposits with solonised brown soils cover the lower valley sides and most of the flat floor and locally bury highly weathered deposits mottled pink and white, thought to correspond with the pallid zone materials of the younger laterites in the Mortlock valley to the east (Mulcahy 1960). Whether this correspondence is compatible with the rejuvenation which has affected the Avon must, however, remain doubtful, and all that can be said with certainty is that they pre-date the fresher deposits burying them.

Other river valleys which have reached the stage described for the Avon are parts of the north-south course of the Moore River, the Brockman and the Blackwood Rivers, and the Frankland-Gordon system. The part of the Moore River valley falling into the laterite-free zone is similar in many ways to the corresponding sector of the Avon in its climate and soils, but the other three rivers have cut their laterite-free zones in the higher rainfall country of the Darling Range, that is, within the zone of detrital laterites. The sharply cut valleys of the Blackwood and Brockman in particular seem to follow areas of softer and more ferruginous rocks of the shield, which form the parent materials of the commonly occurring kraznozems, that is, deep, red, well-structured, acid soils. Smith (1951) has described a similar stage of downcutting in the Frankland River valley, which drains to the south coast, but here, where the more usual granite and gneiss of the shield are exposed, the common soils are brown podzolics.

(d) The Zone of Detrital Laterites

This westernmost zone corresponds closely with the Jarrah forest, for there has been little agricultural development. The close and largely unbroken forest cover is perhaps the reason for our meagre knowledge of its landscape compared with the other zones, and no detailed investigations of soil-landform relationships have yet been completed.

The fairly close drainage pattern (Fig. 10.2) at once suggests that the Darling Range can by no means represent a well preserved part of the Tertiary old plateau. There is abundant lateritic ironstone, but this is largely detrital and not *in situ*. Remnants of the old surface are generally small, though, as already mentioned, fragments of the ancient drainage system of the zone of salt lakes and sandplains may be preserved on the larger divides. More commonly, however, the major divides in this zone carry broad, shallow, flat-floored, perched valleys with grey sandy soils over light-coloured, massive ironstone. It will be remembered that similar soils and substrates, though not so extensively preserved, were described from old plateau residuals in the zone of younger laterites and were regarded as part of intact lateritic profiles. The perched valleys form the heads of many of the river systems originating in the Darling Range.

With distance downstream the old plateau remnants are reduced to ridges capped with massive ironstone, their flanking slopes mantled with detrital materials derived from it. These mantles range from sands and sandy loams to boulders, and two of the commonest forms are shown in Figure 10.7B, which illustrates conditions near the eastern, drier limit of the zone. On steeper slopes the detritus is in the form of a coarse scree of ironstone gravels, sometimes broken and irregularly shaped, which may be recemented into a massive pavement. Other mantles on gentler slopes form features rather like the spillways further east and, like them, are yellow sandy deposits. Here, however, the sands form a matrix in which are small iron oxide pisoliths. These are evenly spaced through the material and may be so soft as to be rubbed out in the fingers, suggesting that they have formed since deposition of the sands. The detrital slopes have since been attacked by an erosional cycle represented by scarps and pediments which often expose the pallid zone, although many of the breakaways are now no longer active (Fig. 10.7B). The ironstone capping the scarp may be that of the old plateau residuals (in which case it tends to be massive), or of one of the depositional mantles of the dissected valley sides. Among the latter, the yellow sandy deposits with the small iron pisoliths give rise to the pisolithic ironstones which caught the attention of earlier observers.

Where the pediments completely truncate the pallid zone or where there has been deeper dissection by streams, coarse, gritty yellow podzolic soils have developed on the exposed granite and gneiss. This is so in most valleys approaching the Darling Scarp, where they tend to be V-shaped and sharply cut. Breakaways are absent in the higher rainfall country near the Darling Scarp, slopes here being gently concavo-convex. Over the whole zone the ironstone materials are abundant at the surface, so that the dominant soils are lateritic podzolics. Because there has been no pedimentation in the wetter, western portion, pallid zones, though here very thick (up to 30 m under almost the whole landscape), are seldom found at the surface. The exposure of these preweathered clays as a soil parent material is confined essentially to country with an annual rainfall of less than approximately 75 cm.

DISCUSSION

The interpretation of the drainage history of southwestern Australia offered in the early part of this essay differs somewhat from that of earlier writers, who regarded the broad valleys of the zone of salt lakes and sandplains as having been cut in the surface of the Tertiary peneplain. Woolnough (1918) thought they may have been initiated in an early stage of uplift, and Jutson (1934) writes of them as forming his new plateau, cut below old plateau level by arid erosion. Here the view taken has been that advanced by Bettenay and Hingston (1965) who point out that inland of the Meckering Line deep zones of weathering are as common beneath the floors of the broad valleys as under the sandplains of the divides. Rather than rejuvenation of the drainage and downcutting by streams, the more recent landscape development has tended towards lowering of the divides and accumulation of deposits in the valleys following some initial stripping. That is, relief is still decreasing, and peneplanation is still proceeding. Despite its age, the landscape is far from being a level plain, but may vary in elevation from valley floor to divide by as much as 90 m over a few miles. It is characterised not only by low relief and sluggish drainage, but also by surviving deep-weathered profiles and superficial deposits, particularly those of the sandplains. Since most shield areas of comparable tectonic stability consist of acid gneiss and granitic rocks as a source of quartz sand, it may be that the accumulation of such widespread superficial sands as in the sandplains could be a useful criterion of the persistence of landscapes of low relief for very long periods of time. The presence of laterite alone is insufficient evidence, since it and other forms of duricrust may form relatively quickly.

It is possible that the Kosciusko Uplift, though resulting in the rejuvenation of marginal drainage, has contributed to the general lowering of relief through a decrease in gradients in the zone of salt lakes and sandplains. This, aided by climatic change towards aridity, has led to the partial blocking and displacement of the drainage, so that the valleys now function as sumps in which fine sediments and salts accumulate, to be partly redistributed by the wind as lake parna. It would be misleading to classify this part of the salt-lake systems of Western Australia as endoreic, since it is occasionally flushed by continuous flow along it, and thus the greatest store of soluble salts lies, not in the evaporating pans of the salt lakes, but in the sluggishly moving saline groundwaters tributary to them. Their salinity is clearly a secondary development, since the aquifer clays are highly weathered; hence drainage in the past must have been effective in removing the products of weathering in solution.

The landscape modifications described must mean that surfaces and soils of any great absolute age (King 1953; Mulcahy 1961) have not been extensively preserved, and indeed many sandplain profiles consist of yellow sand to loamy sand with little differentiation beyond some darkening of the surface with organic matter. Paradoxically, it is downstream from the Meckering Line, where the old plateau is now reduced to relatively small residuals (Fig. 10.6), that old, highly differentiated soils appear in laterite profiles with their grey sandy A horizons intact. Also puzzling at first is the fact that the zone of detrital laterites, warped up to 330 m and lying closest to the coast, nevertheless has a less dense drainage than the lower-lying zone of younger laterites inland of it. It is in the former zone too, that lateritic materials, though often detrital, are most extensively retained within the landscape. The explanation of these apparently contradictory trends may lie in the interaction of the climatic factor with that of uplift in their effect on the relief and stability of the landscape zones. Thus in the high rainfall area of the Darling Range the secondary cementation of lateritic detritus to give massive boulders and pavements must provide a formidable barrier to further erosion, tend to prevent the full development of potential relief, and help to retain the lateritic materials in place, even on fairly steep slopes. The more effective development of relief is thus in the drier zones—the zone of younger laterites and the laterite-free zone, so that here removal of the older lateritic materials has been most extensive. Inland of the Meckering Line, erosional modifications have been considerable despite the lack of relief, reflecting widespread and frequent landscape instability under the semi-arid conditions, but in the absence of an effective drainage system the resulting superficial deposits have been retained within the landscape.

One of the most interesting landforms of southwestern Australia is the breakaway, the ironstone-capped scarp, exposing the pallid zone in the face and on the pediment which slopes gently away from the foot. They are not unusual features in the zone of salt lakes and sandplains, where they particularly occur on valley sides, but they reach their best development in the zone of younger laterites, where the scarp may be 10 m or more high. Breakaways persist into the eastern part of the zone of detrital laterites (Fig. 10.7), where the scarp and pediment truncate an undulating landscape mantled with ironstone detritus, sometimes recemented. Further west, with annual rainfall greater than 90 cm, they are absent, and slopes are smoothly convex above and concave below. From the onset of pedimentation in such a landscape, a western extension of aridity can be inferred, whilst its subsequent partial withdrawal is suggested by the fact that the scarps in the wetter areas now tend to be stabilized. Even here, where lack of erosion should permit soil development, there has been little pedological change in the materials exposed on the upper slopes of the pediments. Further east, these pediment surfaces carry occasional deposits of lake parna (Fig. 10.5), also to be associated with aridity, and again there has been minimal soil development in the younger sheets. Thus the field evidence indicates a very recent arid period, now past its peak, the arid conditions having withdrawn once more inland. Lange (1960) reaches similar conclusions from an ecological study. However, the pediments must have been initiated much earlier, since their lower ends are truncated by steeper slopes with well developed red-brown earth and podzolic profiles. Thus present day and recent instability of breakaways and pediments may represent only the later phases in history of alternating stability and instability due to climatic fluctuations over a long period.

The chronology of landscape events and the assignment of relative ages to the landforms and superficial deposits presents many problems. At least it can be said that most of the minor erosional modifications described must post-date all stages in rejuvenation of the drainage, since the landscapes of all the zones have been affected by them. Acting under the control of local baselevels, these modifications are not related to changes in relative levels of land and sea due to uplift, but reflect changes in other factors influencing landscape development, either tectonic or climatic, though of these the former seems highly unlikely. The dating of the younger laterites is therefore critical as a datum for later events, but it will not be easily achieved. They may eventually be correlated with the laterites of the Swan coastal plain (McArthur and Bettenay 1960), which would place them in the early Pleistocene. Then, with further uplift, the dissection of the laterite-free zone follows, corresponding in time with the formation of the erosional and depositional surfaces carrying red-brown earths and solonised brown soils. Lastly, during a late Recent aridity, comes the extension of pedimentation into the Darling Range, and parna deposition downwind from the salt lakes. The sand-plain deposits probably span the whole range, since they may be found burying the upper pediments at one extreme, and at the other capping residuals which are bounded by breakaways formed by the exposure and hardening of their buried ironstone bands (Mulcahy 1964).

The exact significance of the Meckering Line in terms of landscape history is hard to estimate. It clearly marks the limit of preservation of the Tertiary drainage system, but what factors have combined to place it in its present position? There is no obvious relationship with Precambrian structure (Wilson 1958), but its marked parallelism with the isohyets suggests a climatic control. The interpretation of the drainage pattern given here stresses the time factor, for the limits of each zone of rejuvenation are largely set by the time available since its initiation, although they must also have been influenced by a combination of climatic factors and available relief. The resolution of such questions poses many interesting geomorphic problems, to be solved perhaps by comparison of landscape processes currently at work, particularly at the upstream limits of each zone. Associated further field studies of soils and of the superficial deposits which form their parent materials must also make a considerable contribution.

References

Bettenay, E. (1962). The salt lake systems and their associated aeolian features in the semi-arid regions of Western Australia. *J. Soil Sci.* **13**: 10-17.

——, Blackmore, A. V., and Hingston, F. J. (1964). Aspects of the hydrologic cycle and related salinity in the Belka valley, Western Australia. *Aust. J. Soil Res.* **2**: 187-210.

—— and Hingston, F. J. (1961). *Soils and Land Use of the Merredin Area, Western Australia.* CSIRO Aust. Soils and Land Use Ser. No. 41.

——, —— (1964). Development and distribution of soils in the Merredin area, Western Australia. *Aust. J. Soil Res.* **2**: 173-186.

Browne, W. R. (1934). Some peculiarities in the drainage-systems of the Australian continent. *Aust. Geogr.* **4**: 13-19.

Butler, B. E. (1959). *Periodic Phenomena in Landscapes as a Basis for Soil Studies.* CSIRO Aust. Soil Publ. No. 14.

Clarke, E. de C., Prider, R. T., and Teichert, C. (1948). *Elements of Geology for Western Australian Students.* 2nd ed., Crawley.

Crocker, R. L. (1959). Past climatic fluctuations and their influence upon Australian vegetation. Ch. XVII in *Biogeography and Ecology in Australia* (ed. A. Keast, R. L. Crocker, and C. S. Christian). Den Haag.

Davis, W. M. (1905). The geographical cycle in an arid climate. *J. Geol.* **13**: 381-407.

Gardner, C. A. (1942). The vegetation of Western Australia, with special reference to climate and soils. *J. Proc. R. Soc. West. Aust.* **28**: i-lxxxvii.

Gregory, J. W. (1914). The lake system of Westralia. *Geogrl J.* **43**: 656-64.

Hills, E. S. (1940). The lunette, a new land form of aeolian origin. *Aust. Geogr.* **3** (7): 15-21.

—— (1955). Die Landoberfläche Australiens. *Erde, Berl.* 1955: 195-205.

—— (1961). Morphotectonics and the geomorphological sciences with special reference to Australia. *Q. J. geol. Soc. Lond.* 117: 77-89.

Jutson, J. T. (1934). *The Physiography of Western Australia.* Bull. Geol. Surv. W. Aust. No. 95.

King L. C. (1953). Canons of landscape evolution. *Bull. geol. Soc. Am.* 64: 721-52.

—— (1962). *The Morphology of the Earth.* Edinburgh and London.

Lange, R. T. (1960). Rainfall and soil control of tree species distribution around Narrogin, Western Australia. *J. Proc. R. Soc. West. Aust.* 43: 104-10.

Mabbutt, J. A. (1961). A stripped land surface in Western Australia. *Trans. Inst. Br. Geogr.* 29: 101-14.

McArthur, W. M. and Bettenay, E. (1960). *The Development and Distribution of the Soils of the Swan Coastal Plain, Western Australia.* CSIRO Aust. Soil Publ. No. 16.

McWhae, J. R. H., *et al.* (1956). The stratigraphy of Western Australia. *J. geol. Soc. Aust.* 4: 1-161.

Mulcahy, M. J. (1960). Laterites and lateritic soils in south-western Australia. *J. Soil Sci.* 11: 206-26.

—— (1961). Soil distribution in relation to landscape development. *Z. Geomorph.* 5: 211-25.

—— (1964). Laterite residuals and sandplains. *Aust. J. Sci.* 27: 54-5.

—— and Hingston, F. J. (1961). *The Development and Distribution of the Soils of the York-Quairading Area, Western Australia, in Relation to Landscape Evolution.* CSIRO Aust. Soil Publ. No. 17.

Northcote, K. H. (1946). A fossil soil from Kangaroo Island, South Australia. *Trans. R. Soc. S. Aust.* 70: 294-6.

Ollier, C. D. (1963). Morphometric analysis and the world wide occurrence of stepped erosion surfaces: a discussion. *J. Geol.* 71: 121-3.

Prescott, J. A. (1931). *The Soils of Australia in Relation to Vegetation and Climate.* CSIR Aust. Bull. No. 52.

—— and Pendleton, R. L. (1952). *Laterite and lateritic soils.* Commonwealth Bur. Soil Sci. Tech. Comm. No. 47.

Smith, R. (1951). *Pedogenesis in the Frankland River Valley, Western Australia.* CSIRO Aust. Bull. No. 265.

Stephens, C. G. (1946). *Pedogenesis Following the Dissection of Lateritic Regions in Southern Australia.* CSIR Aust. Bull. No. 206.

—— and Crocker, R. L. (1946). Composition and genesis of lunettes. *Trans. R. Soc. S. Aust.* 70: 302-12.

Teakle, L. J. H. (1938). A regional classification of the soils of Western Australia. *J. Proc. R. Soc. West. Aust.* 24: 123-95.

Wilson, A. F. (1958). Advances in the knowledge of the structure and petrology of the Precambrian rocks of south-western Australia. *J. Proc. R. Soc. West. Aust.* 41: 57-83.

Woolnough, W. G. (1918). The Darling peneplain of Western Australia. *J. Proc. R. Soc. N.S.W.* 52: 385-96.

—— (1927). The chemical criteria of peneplanation; also The duricrust of Australia. *J. Proc. R. Soc. N.S.W.* 61: 17-53.

11

Soil Periodicity in relation to Landform Development in Southeastern Australia

B. E. BUTLER

INTRODUCTION

Stratigraphic relationships provide physical bases for history in the earth sciences, and it is proposed in this essay to give some illustration of the extension of these principles into soil science, and to examine the consequences of this for our understanding of landform development.

Soils themselves are often used as a basis for conclusions on history, inferred from the internal evidence of the soils. On the assumption that a certain property, such as the presence of ironstone concretions, kaolinitic clay, or the presence of columnar structure or of exchangeable sodium, could not have developed in the soil under the present environment, certain other specified environmental conditions are postulated to have existed previously at the site. Thus a history may be built up but it may be doubted whether the correlations between soil properties and environments are firmly enough established to permit this, especially if the history of soils on which the correlations are based is not known beforehand. It is obvious that the argument is likely to go in a circle unless some independent criterion of history relevant to soils is brought in. Such a criterion is the stratigraphic principle.

(a) Stratigraphic Principles Applied to Soils

For such an enquiry, the individual character of a soil is not definitive; it matters only that there is a soil with definable upper and lower boundaries, and that it has certain spatial relationships to other soils. In this context the soil is significantly studied as a mantle, that is an organised body or layer which is more or less extensive in the horizontal plane. Hitherto the usual basis of soil study has been the profile, a vertical column of small though usually undefined cross-sectional area. Many profiles, and diverse profiles, may comprise a soil mantle, each one merging laterally into and being continuous with another. The stratigraphic relationships apply to soil mantles, not to soil profiles. Soil mantles, though extensive, are discontinuous, and it is the nature of their discontinuities and contacts which is significant. Conformable and unconformable superposition, cut-out emplacement, and special contacts in soil mantles have the same fundamental significance as is awarded them in the general field of geology.

The author gratefully acknowledges the part played by his colleagues, the authors of the transect study areas, in the development of ideas presented here. Particular thanks are due to Dr J. A. Beattie for permission to refer to his unpublished study at Wagga, and to Dr D. C. van Dijk for suggestions on the manuscript.

There are, in addition to the general geologic significance, several special considerations arising from the fact that soils are involved. Soil development takes time; soil represents a stable surface for a time, so that a contact marked by a soil is always at least a disconformity, if not something more significant historically; it represents a still-stand as a surface, even when the sediments above it and below are indistinguishable and entirely conformable. This association of soils with periods of uneventfulness provides a unique form of evidence in the earth sciences. Geomorphology is concerned with the earth's form and the processes of erosion and deposition by which it develops, with the various cycles of development of landscape form, through youth, maturity and old age, in various environments. It would be of interest to know the details of these formative processes, and in particular whether they proceeded continuously and uniformly or by an alternation of active and inactive phases. From a misuse of the doctrine of uniformity, it is often assumed, without any enquiry, that the former is the case. However, soil data can be definitive on this question, because if soils occur within the erosion/deposition record then there have been still-stands in the processes. To neglect the still-stands or to average out the data for the overall period would be a falsification of history as well as a misreading of the nature of the processes by which the changes were effected.

In an earlier publication (Butler 1959) I have formalised this aspect of soil work, and proposed the concept of groundsurface to cover the notion of soil mantle as described above. The chronologic order of groundsurfaces is set by their stratigraphic order and this is designated K_1, K_2, K_3, K_4 etc. from the uppermost (most recent) to the consecutively lower and older ones in each locality. As an expression of these data in terms of events the concept of 'K cycle' has been introduced, with its unstable phase of erosion/deposition,* and its stable phase of soil development. Thus we can establish a chronological framework for the locality, consisting of alternating stable and unstable phases of the K_1, K_2, K_3, ... K_n cycles, and use this framework for the chronological placing of associated local events.

In each of the local studies which are discussed below their authors have allotted distinctive names to their groundsurfaces, helping to emphasise their local significance and also the essentially local significance of their K cycle designation. However, in this study the local names will not be used as this would involve prolixity. The K cycle designation in each locality is used instead, but it must be emphasised that at this stage no correlation from one study area to the other is intended.

(b) *Transect for Study*

Studies using these concepts have been made in recent years along a transect in southeastern Australia extending from Nowra to Swan Hill. The study areas are discontinuous (Fig. 11.1), but there is enough similarity in the data from one to another to make them worth examining together. Each of these study areas shows evidence of a history of climatic variation, hence the relevance of the present

---

* The notation 'erosion/deposition', which is used throughout this essay, refers to landscape instability without discriminating between its erosive and depositional aspects.

climate to any overall study may be queried. Nevertheless it is likely that similar climatic gradients have existed across the region for the last million years. Data on the present climate at each locality are given in Table 1.

The transect is one of hilly, moderate rainfall areas in the east passing to drier alluvial plains in the west, and eventually to the semi-arid dune landscape at Swan Hill. This study accords only little attention to the littoral zone (though mention will be made of such features at Nowra), to the steep coastal escarpment,

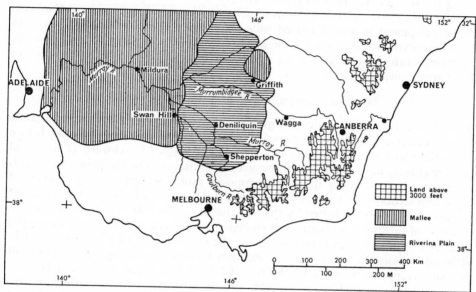

11.1 *Sketch map of southeastern Australia showing places mentioned in the text*

TABLE 1

Mean annual climatic data for towns in southeastern Australia

	Swan Hill	Deniliquin	Griffith	Wagga	Canberra	Nowra
Rainfall mm	330	394	386	544	584	1016
Temperature °C.	16·6	16·6	16·6	16·6	13·4	17
Elevation m	69	93	126	154	551	15

From Commonwealth Bureau of Meteorology (1956)

the groundsurfaces of which are described by Walker (1963), and to the higher ranges of the plateau with their solifluction and glacial features, for these comprise only a minor proportion of the region. However, a range of landscapes from hilly terrain to aggradational plains is considered in a climatic setting ranging from moderate to low rainfall.

STEPPED VALLEY PLAINS NEAR CANBERRA

The study begins with a description of the data at Canberra, and this is presented on the basis of van Dijk's (1959) survey. The terrain consists of a series of table-lands, recognised by earlier writers (Craft 1933) as planation surfaces, extending back to Tertiary and Cretaceous times. These landsurfaces are separated by nick points, and the region as a whole is above other nick points on the rivers. In this landscape there is a marked development on each level of valley plains and straths along the smaller stream lines (Plate XXIIa).

Van Dijk made use of data from trenches for deep drainage works of Canberra city development in which buried soils are exposed (Plate XXIIb). These data have been extended throughout the locality by the examination of any naturally occurring cuttings such as erosion ravines or road cuttings, and by traverses of hand auger bores up to 5 m deep.

(a) Groundsurfaces and Mantles on Hillsides

Studies in hilly country frequently give evidence of unconformably superimposed groundsurfaces. The basis of proof of this situation will be discussed before proceeding with the description of the Canberra data. Churchward (1961b) and Walker (1962a) have previously discussed this principle. For the general case it is necessary to prove firstly that each proposed groundsurface is an independent layer, and secondly that it has soil profile development in it. The separateness of the upper layer is established by the fact that it can be found extending across a diversity of substrates without itself changing with them. The status of the upper layer as a groundsurface is established by the development of a soil profile in it, although in some places it may be too thin to contain a recognisable ABC soil horizon arrangement and must be traced laterally to a point where it is thick enough to contain such a recognisable profile. Similarly with the substrate, this may not be identifiable as another groundsurface because no recognisable soil profile is seen, but only various horizon remnants of truncated soil profiles. How-ever, it too may be traced laterally—it may be necessary to traverse 5 or 500 m—until a complete, recognisable profile is discovered. By these means even a simple looking profile might be proved to be a composite of two or more, but obviously not all profiles are composite, so the test of independence should be continually applied. The type of situation is illustrated in Plate XXIIc, and in Figures 11.2a and 11.2b.

The still-stand, which is of prime significance in these studies, is indicated by the soil development, profile differentiation and mineral weathering which had occurred on the lower layer before it was eroded and then buried by the upper layer. Detailed traverses have shown that each groundsurface has a restricted range of soils on it. This relationship must be soundly established, but once it is, the task of delineating groundsurfaces is greatly facilitated, becoming only a matter of delineating certain changes in soil type. The difference between soils on the different groundsurfaces of a locality may not be of a high order in terms of the general soil classification. It is often most consistently expressed in some detail of horizon contrast or of soil fabric, and this feature should then be awarded a high order of significance because of the historical differences relating to it.

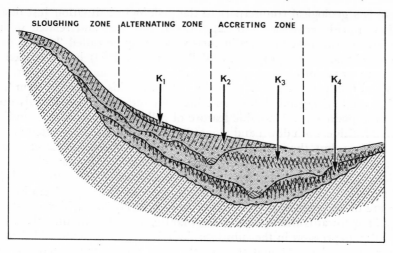

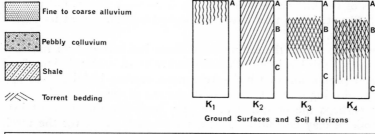

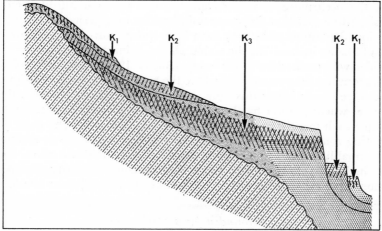

11.2a *Diagrammatic cross-section showing the common groundsurface situation at Canberra*

11.2b *Diagrammatic cross-section showing the common groundsurface situation at Nowra. For* torrent *read* current.

There is a geological counterpart to the pedological situation just described, and this comprises erosional and depositional processes and related sediments. Studies have shown that these sediments—which may be called 'hillside mantles' here—have characteristic properties. Walker (1962a, 1964) has described them, calling them by various names—pediment mantles, mass movement layer, hillside deposits and the 'pedi-sediment' of Ruhe (1956). In this paper the term 'hillside mantle' is used in a general way and includes the surficial materials on both hillsides and pediments. A notable feature of hillside mantles is their uniformity on a given hillside, both down and along the contour lines. They often mantle an uneven surface, but themselves present a surprisingly even surface; sometimes there is evidence that only a metre or so of translocation is involved in their formation. They consist of poorly sorted, unbedded, unoriented, and loosely packed material. There is an unoriented arrangement of pebbles 1 cm in size, but the texture of the matrix is sandy loam to sandy clay loam. Texture gradually becomes finer towards the surface of the mantle, and not infrequently where the mantle fills a depression in the substrate there is coarse, current-bedded material. From the toe of the pediment the mantle often merges without break into an alluvial sheet across the adjacent basin or valley bottom. The alluvial sheet lacks the pebbles of the hillside mantle and is a little more clayey, but it is otherwise very much like it; it too may have current-bedded material at its base where it fills prior ravines.

The evidence is that the sedimentary phase has included an initial phase of erosion, but that this has been followed quickly by an accumulation of sediments, only a small proportion of which—from their current bedding—was apparently deposited by flowing water. The origin of the rest of the material is not so readily apparent; perhaps the entrainment of very high density sediment loads from erosion upslope may be indicated as a mechanism. Whatever the mechanisms, however, the occurrence of well developed soils on each hillside mantle and alluvial sheet indicates that they were stabilized for long periods. The duration of each erosion/deposition phase may have been quite short—in a geologic perspective it could be an instant, but the stable phases of inactivity were certainly long.

Hillsides will often show three zones (Butler 1959) of mantle activity: the 'sloughing zone' on the steeper part, where the mantle is completely stripped away at each erosive phase; below this zone and on slightly flatter grades is the 'alternating zone' where erosion has been less effective, and variably truncated soils occur below each mantle; and finally, on the adjacent pediment slope or basin, the 'accreting zone', where erosion between sedimentary phases is effectively nil, and conformably superimposed groundsurfaces occur. These three zones are apparent in Figures 11.2a and b; there is often complementary expansion and contraction of adjacent zones at the one locality in passing from one K cycle to the next.

(b) *Groundsurfaces at Canberra*

Van Dijk's study at Canberra reveals five groundsurfaces (Fig. 11.2a). The same range of groundsurfaces occurs on each of the planation levels, thus proving that their origin is independent of and subsequent to the related baselevel changes. On the sloughing zones of the hillsides K_2 groundsurface occurs alone. Lower

XXIIa   Typical landscape in the Canberra region

XXIIb   Buried soil exposed in drain-age trench at Canberra

XXIIc   Section showing unconformity between soil mantles

XXIIIa Landscape near Nowra

XXIIIc Railway cutting at Marinna (Wagga district) showing soil mantles overlying pebbl hillside K₄ mantle and reticulately mottled K

XXIIIb Typical landscape in the Wagga district

down the slope, in the alternating zone, variably truncated remnants of K_3 and K_4 groundsurfaces occur as substrates to this groundsurface. Immediately beyond the toe of the hill the record of superimposed groundsurfaces is more complete, whilst the older groundsurfaces successively emerge further out.

The Canberra K_1 groundsurface, the most recent one, comprises a very small proportion of the area; the soil in it is consistently a dark minimal prairie soil,* weakly acid, soft, and friable. The Canberra K_2 groundsurface occurs at the surface over one-third of the area; the soils in it vary from red earth in well drained sites to yellow earth and grey earth with buckshot in poorly drained sites. All of these soils described as 'earths' have a profile which is porous and weakly acid throughout, with gradual horizon changes. The soil is characteristically apedal (Butler 1955), that is not naturally in the form of aggregates, nor does it break up into aggregates upon drying (pedal material is in the form of aggregates). The red earth on the sloughing zones of the hills is often stony.

The Canberra K_3 groundsurface probably occurs over more than one-third of the area at the surface and is even more extensive as a variably truncated and buried layer. The catena of soils in this groundsurface has a red podzolic soil in well drained sites, and yellow podzolic or solodic soils in less well drained sites. These soils have a strongly contrasting, pedal clay B horizon, and those referred to as solodic among the yellow members are alkaline in the subsoil and may contain lime or soluble salts. The podzolic soils are moderately acid throughout. In the most poorly drained sites there is a solodic soil with a dark grey B horizon.

The Canberra K_4 may occur as a surface exposure but it is more common as a variably truncated buried layer. The catena is similar to that on K_3 but the B horizons are thicker, with denser clay, and in poorly drained sites it may include a calcareous gilgai soil. Below the K_4 at Canberra may be found red and white reticulately mottled, highly weathered soil material, sometimes with sesquioxide concretions. This material is lime-free and may be either residual or transported. It may be the fifth groundsurface.

(c) Distribution of Canberra Groundsurfaces

The pattern of the groundsurfaces in the Canberra area has been shown by van Dijk and Woodyer (1961) to be extremely complex, though it is systematically related to the hillslopes and to the streams. The K_1 occurs sporadically as silty terraces along streams and trunk rivers, as small alluvial sheets below steep slopes, and as segments in alluvial cones. The K_2 occurs extensively as hillside mantles on the lower two-thirds of the slope and as stony shallow soils higher up. It may extend as an alluvial sheet across the adjacent basin where the hills are close together; otherwise it tails out leaving the K_3 groundsurface exposed on the alluvial flat. K_2 also occurs as small terraces flanking minor streams and as sand sheets blanketing the country adjoining the Molonglo River.

The K_3 at Canberra is generally on the more extensive, level parts of the landscape, though it occurs also on a large proportion of hillsides as a truncated buried layer. It forms hillside mantles and extensive alluvial sheets and constitutes terraces along streams, though only to a very minor extent along the main rivers.

* Soil names largely follow Stephens (1962).

R

From these main rivers, however, K_3 sand sheets extend up to 700 m in places. A large proportion of alluvial cones in the area belong to the K_3 groundsurface. The K_4 at Canberra is known mainly as a buried layer or remnant below K_3 but may occur as a surface exposure.

The still older, highly weathered red and white material occurs as sparse gravel terrace residuals adjacent to the main streams, and there are occasional relics of it on the lower hillsides, where it may be *in situ*.

Such a large volume of detrital material on hillsides and valley slopes is noteworthy. Much of this material is in the higher parts of the landscape, beyond the level of any stream activity. The main river valleys have less alluvial accumulation than the tributaries, whilst perched basins and higher-level valley plains with grossly underfit streams may have as much as 12 m of sediment. The studies show that movement of these materials has been highly spasmodic; the same material may have been reworked and moved on its way out in several stages, but has been stationary for periods long enough to be significant pedologically. The ground-surface, comprising the hillside mantle and its soils, is the operative unit for the study of these surficial phenomena.

It is significant that the groundsurfaces are continuous from hillside mantles on to stream and river terraces, and this is taken to indicate that terrace aggradation and erosion/deposition on hillsides were concurrent. Sand sheets grew from river terraces concurrently with colluvial accumulation on hillsides. The indications are that erosion and deposition were widespread over the whole landscape on several occasions, and that their initiation was on the hillsides. Van Dijk proposes that these periods of landscape instability were associated with more arid or stormy climatic phases; that there were several such phases, and that the intervening phases when soil development proceeded strongly were more humid and equable.

MATURELY DISSECTED LANDSCAPE AT NOWRA

The landscape at Nowra is maturely dissected, with local streams heading in an adjacent scarp. The main river, the Shoalhaven, rises in a stepped valley-plain landscape as described for Canberra, traverses a long gorge section, and enters the sea at Nowra by a delta which fills a drowned valley. Walker (1962a, b) has described the soils and groundsurfaces of the hilly country adjacent to Nowra, and of the delta area (see Plate XXIIIa; Fig. 11.2b). He found evidence of three groundsurfaces. The youngest, K_1, has soils of a minimal prairie type, being dark grey to black, with weak or no horizon differentiation, and of a crumbly organic nature. The Nowra K_2 groundsurface has a range of soils, all of which are earths as defined above. Very occasionally a red earth profile is the well drained member of this groundsurface, but more frequently the soil is a 'grey-brown soil' (after Walker), answering the general description of an earth profile, but brown-grey throughout. The profile in poorly drained sites is rather a neutral grey, with rust-coloured flecks and a trace of fine soft concretions throughout. In all cases the texture is uniformly sandy-loam or sandy-clay-loam.

The Nowra K_3 groundsurface has podzolic soils, and in these the A horizon is dense, generally of sandy-loam to sandy-clay-loam texture, and the B horizon is a plastic clay, moderately pedal and with angular blocky structure. In the well drained site in this groundsurface the profile is red podzolic with a strong red-brown B horizon; downslope, however, the profile is yellow podzolic, and in the poorly drained site the soils are 'meadow podzolic' with a dark grey or black B horizon. Alkaline subsoils such as occur at Canberra are not found in this ground-surface at Nowra: neither lime nor soluble salts have been encountered.

The distribution of groundsurfaces in the landscape at Nowra has many points in common with that in Canberra. The commonest form of the ground-surfaces is as hillside mantles, with the unsorted and unbedded sedimentary characteristics already described. In the study area, Walker found the K_1 ground-surface extending over the steeper parts of the hillslope (above 20°), with either bedrock or residuals of K_2 as substrates. Further downslope, K_2 hillside mantles were general, with substrates of bedrock or residuals of K_3. On slopes less than 10° the K_3 predominated at the surface, though terraces or overlays of K_2 and K_1 occurred along streamlets across this K_3 terrain. Walker records massive accumu-lations of hillside mantle material in the upper catchments and hillslopes, with bulky terrace accumulations in the heads of tributary valleys. These accumu-lations are probably more massive than at Canberra, though following the same trend. River terraces become less massive downstream on the trunk rivers, though the K_3, K_2, and K_1 terraces are still considerable there.

A nick point on the local stream studied by Walker isolates its headward sector from the influence of sea-level changes. Nevertheless the same ground-surfaces can be found in the delta zone of the main river and in the headward sector of the local stream. In the delta zone the K_3 is overlain by the K_2, and the K_2 by K_1, but borings show the K_3 as continuing to slope downwards as sea level is approached. This slope is less marked for K_2 and K_1, which tend to level out; however, the relevance of their levels for dating on the basis of sea-level corre-lations is doubtful, since the coastline has numerous indications of subsidence. Although the flattening of terrace gradients on approaching the sea indicates that terrace aggradation occurred at times of high rather than low sea level, the simi-larity of groundsurfaces above and below the local nick point shows that sea-level change was not the cause of it. Walker has dated his groundsurfaces by carbon-aceous material found in them, the dates being K_1—400 years, K_2—3750 years, and K_3—29,000 years.

Walker concluded that climatic change was the cause of the three alternations between erosion/deposition, and soil formation in his study area. This conclusion is based on the isolation of the area from sea-level changes, and on the nature of the erosion itself. The erosion was hillside erosion and hillside mantle movement, and this would be favoured by decreased rainfall. Soil development phases, by contrast, Walker thought would be associated with more humid, equable climates. It seems *a priori* out of the question at Nowra, though less clearly so at Canberra, to invoke any form of periglacial action to account for the hillside erosion and mantling, and since the phenomena are so similar at both places it is concluded that solifluction need not be seriously considered at Canberra either.

A LANDSCAPE OF BROAD LOW RELIEF AT WAGGA

The landscape in the Wagga region has a widely spaced drainage and is characterised by long, even slopes, and rounded hilltops (Plate XXIIIb). Along the main drainage lines of the area there has been considerable aggradation, though the streams, such as Houlaghan Creek, are presently inactive. In the Wagga district the main through-going stream, the Murrumbidgee River, has developed a broad floodplain.

(a) *Groundsurfaces and Soils*

In a study of the soils of the Wagga region, Beattie (in press) recognised five groundsurfaces, as shown in Figure 11.3a. The Wagga K_1 groundsurface is confined to riverine sediments, occurring continuously along the Murrumbidgee River but only locally on the smaller tributary streams, the soil in this groundsurface being a minimal prairie soil.

The Wagga K_2 groundsurface is almost ubiquitous as a surface exposure, extending over valleys and hillsides, saddles and broad hilltops, as well as forming sand sheets adjacent to the floodplain of the Murrumbidgee. It occurs rarely as small terraces on tributary streams, but fairly generally as a buried riverine layer along the Murrumbidgee River. The soils on the K_2 groundsurface vary according to drainage and relief. On well drained sites, the profile is commonly a red earth with a gradual increase of clay to an apedal, porous B horizon, weakly acid and becoming neutral at depth, but in about half of the occurrences the well drained member is a red podzolic profile. In lower sections of the landscape and on broader plains the soil on the K_2 groundsurface is a red-brown earth, and further out, on flatter terrain, the profile approaches that of grey and brown soils of heavy texture, with a certain amount of gilgai development and with calcareous self-mulching surfaces.

The Wagga K_3 groundsurface is the substrate to the K_2 groundsurface over most of the area. As a buried soil it most commonly has the general form of a red earth, but this name is not very suitable and the expression 'red subplastic soil' will be used here. This soil has gradual profile changes and its clay content is high, but in its handling properties it is quite unlike a clay, being more like a sandy loam. This property is called 'subplasticity' (Butler 1955). The profile, particularly in the lower part, is highly pedal, breaking down to sub-peds of 1 mm size and having coatings or 'cutans' (Brewer 1960) on the peds of clay, manganese, and iron oxides. The profile is weakly to moderately alkaline, and lime concretions occur at about 1 m depth. Less commonly the soil shows strong textural contrasts between the A and B horizons, although with many of the characteristics described above. In the poorly drained end of the catena the soil in the Wagga K_3 groundsurface is a grey-yellow version of the red subplastic soil, and it passes via a grey form of the same soil into a fully plastic grey soil which would fit reasonably into the grey soil of heavy texture group (Stephens 1962). In two areas the K_3 groundsurface has been mapped as a surface exposure, as a red earth in one area, and a solodised solonetz with strong texture contrast in the other.

The Wagga K_4 groundsurface is probably little less widespread than the K_3; however, as it occurs as a fairly deep buried layer (usually 3 m and more), acquaintance with it is more restricted. The K_4 profile is generally a red or a grey-yellow subplastic soil, highly subplastic and highly pedal, with large lime concretions

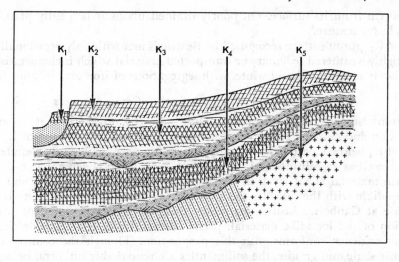

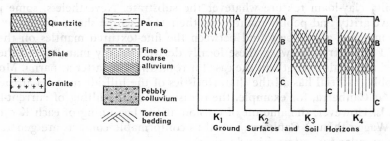

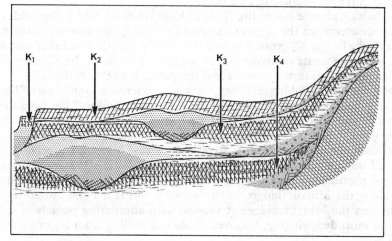

11.3a *Diagrammatic cross-section showing the common groundsurface situation at Wagga*

11.3b *Diagrammatic cross-section showing the common groundsurface situation at Griffith. For* torrent *read* current

120-150 cm from its surface. On poorly drained plains it is a fully plastic grey soil of heavy texture.

The K_5 groundsurface recognised by Beattie is met with only occasionally, and is in highly weathered sedentary or transported material which is characteristically reticulately mottled red and white, with segregations of iron and without lime.

(b) *Distribution and Layering of Groundsurfaces*

The groundsurfaces at Wagga contrast with those at Canberra in that the mantles are thicker and more extensive (Plate XXIIIc). Conformable contacts of K_3 below K_2, and K_4 below K_3 are most common, extending over the broadly rounded hillcrests as well as on hillsides and valley floors. Evidence of a general accession of a uniform material at all levels of the landscape is thereby indicated, and this is incompatible with the hillsides themselves being the source of the material, as is the case at Canberra. Beattie maintains that the facts are consistent with the accession of the loess-like material, parna (Butler 1956), from outside the area. Further evidence conforms with this proposition. Though the country rock is variously shale and granite, the soil mantles are remarkably uniform, being of an even, silty clay-loam texture whatever the substrate. Nevertheless, some peaked hills have gritty and pebbly mantles on their tops, whilst sheets of similar gritty, pebbly material are to be found between the fine-textured mantles on the slope below. The contrast between these locally derived pebbly mantles and the finer-textured materials strengthens the case for regarding the latter as parna. Moreover the pebbly material has all the characteristics of the hillside mantles already well known at Canberra, for example, the occasional ravine filling of current-bedded materials. However, the amount of erosion at the beginning of each K cycle was less at Wagga than at Canberra, and thus conformable contacts are general here, though angular unconformities do occur.

The pebbly mantle below the K_4 is 120-300 cm thick and lenses with current bedding are common; the parna component of this groundsurface is often about 300 cm thick. In the K_3 groundsurface the pebbly mantle is thinner and may be absent, while the parna component is about 180 cm thick. In the K_2 groundsurface the pebbly mantle is usually absent and the parna is 45-90 cm thick.

Along the Murrumbidgee River there are extensive sand sheets. These are commonly 75-120 cm thick and extend for a distance of up to 2 km from the floodplain on to the adjacent slopes. They can be related to the K_2 and K_3 groundsurfaces since they merge into the corresponding parnas on the hillsides. In the floodplain of the Murrumbidgee, K_1 alluvium can be found overlying the soil developed on the alluvial K_2 groundsurface, and there is evidence of entrenchment and meander-swinging between K_1 and K_2. No K_3 river terrace has been found along the Murrumbidgee in this locality, but it may be buried by the K_2. It seems that the Murrumbidgee at Wagga, with alternating periods of entrenchment and meander-swinging, has overall been aggrading from K_3 to K_2 and from K_2 to K_1.

The evidence at Wagga has been interpreted by Beattie as indicating periodic stability and instability in the landscape; unstable phases of erosion and local deposition on the hillsides alternate with periods of groundsurface stability when the soils developed to a marked degree. The periods of instability, he considered, would be drier or more seasonally contrasting or stormy. The accession of parna is related less to conditions in the accession area than to conditions in the source area. The source area was to the west and will be discussed more fully later; it was undoubtedly arid and it is arguable that phases of great aridity in the west would also be relatively drier phases in the east. The deposition of parna immediately following the onset of hillside erosion at Wagga, with no intervening soil development, could thus be reasonably associated with the one climatic trend. At Wagga, as at Canberra, hillside erosion is associated with riverine deposition and with the blowing of sand sheets from river flats. With the exception of the parna accessions at K_2, K_3, and K_4, Beattie's proposal for Wagga is similar to van Dijk's for Canberra—four alternations of widespread erosion/deposition with phases of prolonged stability and soil development.

Beattie points to a number of characteristics of the groundsurfaces at Wagga which he associates with the desert origin of the parna. These include the presence of palygorskite, the marked development of segregations of lime, dolomite, and barytes, and a high degree of subplasticity in the clay. Palygorskite is associated with salinas, and both it and the other materials are apparently foreign to the weathered substrate of the country rock as in the K_5, for this is low in bases. The phases of sedimentation along the Murrumbidgee River at Wagga have points in common with those at Canberra, but differ in that the overall record of the river at Wagga has been one of superimposed aggradation. In this respect, the river valley at this point may be regarded as an extension of the Riverine Plain to be discussed later.

THE RIVERINE PLAIN

It is convenient to consider soil and depositional data on the Riverine Plain at several points, but a preliminary description of it as a whole is needed. The Riverine Plain (Butler 1950, 1958; Langford-Smith 1960) of some 82,000 km², has been shaped by the deposition of vast alluvial fans by the precursors of the present rivers—Murrumbidgee, Murray, and Goulburn—which flow across it from the east and from the south. Rainfall diminishes towards the northwest of the plain, where the climate is arid. A characteristic aeolian landscape called 'mallee' flanks the plain on the west and occurs as pockets in the north. It is flanked on the north, south, and east by the low foothills of the main mountain zones in which its rivers arise.

Three areas are described below. Griffith is on the fringe of the foothills at the northeastern edge of the plain, Deniliquin is centrally placed, and Swan Hill is on the mallee boundary on the west.

(a) *Griffith*

At Griffith the low foothills merge gradually into the main Riverine Plain, which in this section has been built by precursors of the Murrumbidgee River. However, the study area is some 30 km from that river, and the sources of its riverine sediments are tributary streams and local hillside drainage.

Van Dijk (1958) has described the surface deposits and soils in the Griffith district. He has given local names, but not K cycle designations, to each depositional system; however, the K cycle designation as given by Butler (1959) will be used here instead of these names. There are three groundsurfaces at Griffith—K_2, K_3, and K_4 (Fig. 11.3b). The K_2 occurs as the general surface except where it is entrenched by the Murrumbidgee River and overlain by another groundsurface, the K_1.

The Griffith K_2 groundsurface has a range of soil profiles varying with drainage. In well drained sites the soil is a red-brown earth with a calcareous B horizon at about 35 cm. On flatter areas and in other less well drained sites, the soil is a grey-brown soil transitional between the red-brown earth and the grey soil of heavy texture. In the poorly drained and flattest sites the soil is a grey soil of heavy texture in gilgai micro-relief and with calcareous puffs.

The K_3 groundsurface occurs only as a buried layer, appearing at 80 to 240 cm from the surface and varying in thickness from 120 to 300 cm, its profile varying with its drainage state. The profile is a red subplastic soil in the well drained sites and merges by stages to a plastic grey soil of heavy texture in the poorly drained sites. These soils are very similar to those on the Wagga K_3 groundsurface. The red subplastic soil is leached of lime to 150 cm, whereas the grey soil of heavy texture is leached of lime to only 30 to 45 cm. The K_4 groundsurface occurs only as a buried layer below K_3 and is very similar to it, being highly subplastic in well drained sites and a grey plastic clay in poorly drained sites.

Distribution of groundsurfaces

The K_2 at Griffith occurs as a mantle on hills, on footslopes, and on the Riverine Plain. In different sites it overlies Devonian quartzite, the K_3 soil as described above, and various unweathered deposits, both fine sandy clays on the Riverine Plain and gritty lenses and sheets on the hillsides. Because of its uniform fine sandy and clayey nature, and because of its uniformity over varying topography despite a diversity of substrates, van Dijk considers that the bulk of the K_2 material consists of parna. The K_3 groundsurface has a similar distribution to the K_2, below which it occurs, and is also considered to consist of parna. However, it is obviously a much older parna, since deeply leached soils developed on it before its burial. The sandy riverine sediments and gritty-gravelly hillside materials which occur below the K_3 are more extensive and thicker than those below the K_2, but are of a similar nature. In neither groundsurface is there soil development on these alluvial and colluvial materials, but only on the overlying parna. The K_4 groundsurface is not so well known, largely because it occurs at depth; it has a well developed soil in it, however, and it seems to consist of both parna and gritty hillside deposits at different sites.

The similarity between the character and distribution of soils and surficial mantles at Griffith and Wagga is apparent; the main difference is the frequent occurrence of unweathered riverine sediments below the parna at Griffith. This is characteristic of the main extent of the Riverine Plain, where, of course, hillside mantles do not occur. Subplasticity and the presence of palygorskite are common to the old parnas at Wagga and Griffith. Apparently similar materials also occur at Katandra near Shepparton in Victoria, on the southeastern fringe of the Riverine Plain (Cockroft in press).

Van Dijk proposes climatic oscillations to account for the data which he presents. He attributes the deposition of riverine and hillside sediments followed by accession of parna to more arid phases, and he postulates more humid intervening phases during which extensive soil development occurred. He considers that the source of the parna was towards the west, but that a more calcareous component was added from local sources.

(b) *Deniliquin*

Through most of the Riverine Plain the physiographic situation and the alluvial deposits seem to be the same, whether attributable to the Murrumbidgee, Murray, or Goulburn Rivers. This is a plain of fluvial aggradation, with its riverine deposition patterns still clearly marked (Plate XXIVa). Soils and depositional systems on the Riverine Plain have been described by Butler (1958). The K cycle designation was not in use in the original paper but was applied to it later (Butler 1959). Three groundsurfaces are identified (Fig. 11.4a).

The Deniliquin K_1 groundsurface occurs as a small, low aggradation terrace adjoining the present river channels. It also occurs, though very rarely, as a surficial alluvial sheet in the west of the region, as for instance to the southeast of Swan Hill (Churchward 1961a), where there are a few square kilometres of it, about 30 cm thick. The soil on this groundsurface is a minimal prairie soil, of soft, silty, clay-loam texture, with no eluviation of clay.

The Deniliquin K_2 groundsurface is the ubiquitous surface exposure on the plain, and comprises a range of soils from red-brown earths in well drained sites through intergrades to grey soils of heavy texture in poorly drained sites and flatter areas. Many of the soils are saline in the subsoil, increasingly so towards the west.

The Deniliquin K_3 groundsurface is known only as a buried soil; it occurs occasionally as close to the surface as 60 cm but a depth of 180 cm is more typical. The most common soil profile is a grey soil of heavy texture, often leached of lime and acid in its upper part. On local more elevated sites the soil is a red-brown earth, sometimes subplastic. Soil borings have rarely encountered materials older than K_3, but occasionally material with comparable soil development is encountered below K_3, and this would be K_4.

The K_2 groundsurface comprises riverine depositional sheets and a parna sheet; and these have been compared by Butler and Hutton (1956) and Butler (1958) in terms of particle size grading and geographic patterns of particle size variation. The parna is more uniform than the riverine sheets, both in particle size grading and in calcareousness; it is uniformly a calcareous clay. The riverine sheets, by contrast, vary in particle size grading from coarse sands and even gravels at the streambed, through sandy loams in the levee to heavy clays in the far floodplain. They are calcareous only in the levees. The soils on parna and alluvium are similar save that the red-brown earth on parna is subplastic.

Two riverine sheets and an intervening parna sheet are the three 'components' (Butler 1959) of the Deniliquin K_2 groundsurface. Only one soil mantle is associated with the three components, no matter which one occurs at the surface, and neither layer when buried shows either weathering or soil development. Butler (1958) has interpreted this as indicating that the three layers followed one another closely, and that there has followed a long phase of non-deposition. Since parna

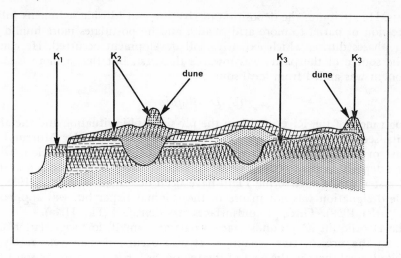

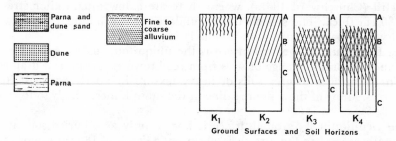

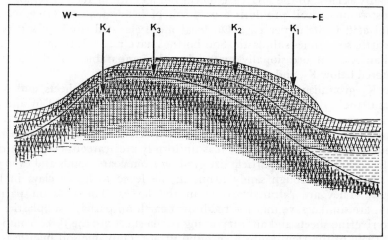

11.4a   *Diagrammatic cross-section showing the common groundsurface situation on the Riverine Plain*

11.4b   *Diagrammatic longitudinal section of dune and swale at Swan Hill*

is to be associated with maximum aridity, the riverine depositions are attributed to like climatic conditions closely preceding and following such a climax. Pronounced soil development has occurred subsequently on the exposed surface, with leaching of lime and movement of clay; this is associated with more humid conditions.

The K_3 groundsurface is similarly composite with riverine and parna sediments and has strongly developed soils. It seems to be a parallel development to K_2, but on a larger scale in all respects.

The riverine deposits have given their form to the plain, and where parna overlies them the shape of the plain is unaltered. This shape comprises the waning longitudinal gradients of the prior streams and the steeper transverse profile of levees to the floodplain. Some of the prior stream forms are K_2 in age, whilst others are K_3, but with a K_2 parna overlay some 60 to 180 cm thick.

Sand dunes are scattered along the river ridges, and in these may be found red-earth profiles for K_2, and strongly contrasting podzolic or solodic profiles for K_3 groundsurfaces. The pattern of soils in the sand dunes is complex, owing to blow-out erosion between K_2 and K_3 (apparently in the arid unstable phase of K_2) and also between K_3 and K_4 times. Occasional lenses of parna are found high up in the sand dunes, but generally parna is absent from the dunes, and such clayey horizons as occur there seem to have been produced by mineral weathering *in situ*. In such cases clay content is low, though the soil material is highly coherent, and lime is absent.

Butler (1958) proposed a repetition of more humid and more arid climatic cycles—three of them—to account for the three groundsurfaces described, with indications that K_4 would be another similar cycle.

Cockroft (in press) has described similar and comparable riverine and parna layers in the Goulburn valley area of Victoria.

(c) *Seif Dune Plains at Swan Hill*

The name 'mallee', which is applied to the country to the west of Swan Hill, refers specifically to a type of eucalypt vegetation. As a whole this country is a broadly undulating plain with a close pattern of seif dunes and swales superimposed (Plate XXIVb). There is no local stream system but the Murray River traverses the region.

Churchward (1961b, 1963a, b, c) made a detailed study of the structure of the seif dunes and swales and found evidence that the dunes had been periodically eroded on their western ends, with associated accumulation along their crests and at their eastern ends. The application of the same principle of unconformity described above for the alternating zone of hillsides enabled Churchward to distinguish four groundsurfaces in the seif dunes and swales (Fig. 11.4b).

The soil on the Swan Hill K_1 groundsurface is weakly developed, soft, with a uniform organic colouring and structure. Lime is leached to about 15 cm, but there is no differentiation of clay. The soils on the Swan Hill K_2 groundsurface form a catena having a red-brown earth with lime leached to about 35 cm at well drained sites, and passing through intergrades to a calcareous grey desert soil in poorly drained sites. The K_3 groundsurface occurs only as a buried layer, frequently truncated, but its full profile would probably be a red-brown earth with some red earth features and with lime leached to 1 m. With intergrades this catena merges to calcareous grey soil of heavy texture in poorly drained sites. The K_4 groundsurface also occurs only as a buried layer: its range of profiles resembles that on the K_3, but lime in well drained soils is leached to 180 cm or more, and the clay is more highly segregated within the soil fabric.

The distribution of the groundsurfaces at Swan Hill is related to the topography: on the dunes they are arranged unconformably, with successive erosion scars at the western end merging toward superimposed groundsurfaces at the eastern end; in the swales or interdune corridors they are conformable. The K_1 occurs only discontinuously and with small extent as downwind caps on the dunes. It has the form of a wind-blown sand sheet or lens on the crest, merging into a sandfall at the end of the dune. K_1 also occurs as a riverine sheet in a very small proportion of the adjacent lower country.

Churchward has studied the relationship between the wind-eroded zone on the western end of the dune and the deposited sand sheet which extends downwind from it. He finds, following Chepil (1958), progressive erosion, abrasion of aggregates, and ablation of finer components along this traverse. The sand sheet becomes progressively more highly sorted, less clayey and less calcareous with distance from its source at the erosion scar. The component finer than 100 μ, including the lime, is removed as dust; and this process of wind erosion and ablation acting on the soils is proposed to explain the origin of parna. The parna is the dust component which moves in suspension in the air and may settle out over vast distances downwind. Indications of the sorting effected by this process are given by Butler and Hutton (1956).

Churchward finds that these erosion and ablation relationships apply to contemporary blow-outs and to the K_1 aeolian groundsurfaces, but there are complications with the K_2 and K_3 aeolian groundsurfaces. These have undoubtedly been formed by erosion and sand-sheeting, because of their position on the dunes and their unconformable contacts with the K_3 and K_4 respectively, but the component finer than 100 μ and the lime are still much in evidence. They are very minor in the sand sheet on the crest of the dune, increasing progressively downslope from there. It is significant that there are conformably buried K_3 and K_4 surfaces extending across the swales and that the constituent material is parna. Thus it appears that whilst the sand dunes were a source of parna in K_2 and K_3 times, there was also general accession of parna to the whole area from further west. Clearly, it is not impossible for an area to be both a source and a receiver of dust. Swan Hill is on the eastern margin of some 100,000 km² of similar mallee country, so there is an ample dust source.

The accession of parna on the dunes in K_2 and K_3 times is indicated by the bi-modality of the sands there; the characteristic mode of parna on the dunes is about 80 μ, whilst the saltation sand averages 300 μ (Churchward 1963a). The proportion of parna increases downslope away from the crest of the dune, thus reversing the size-grading trend which Bagnold (1941) found to characterise the sands of the Libyan dunes.

Churchward's borings indicate that the form of the K_4 groundsurface within the dune is itself dune-shaped. Thus aeolian action shaped the landforms in K_4 times as well as in K_3, K_2, and K_1. However, there is evidence for long periods of stability on the dunes between these unstable phases in the form of soil development of a high order, involving leaching of lime and movement of clay.

Churchward's work extended to parts of the plain and inter-dune corridors where riverine deposits occur, and he was able to correlate the dune and parna phases with the riverine phases. There is no soil development or mineral weathering on alluvium where it is overlain by parna of K_2 or K_3 age, thus indicating close association in time of fluvial and aeolian deposition. Parna soils overlying micaceous riverine sediments are also recorded on terrace levels along the Murray River further northwest in the mallee region. The Karadoc and Koorlong soil types of the Mildura soil survey (Penman *et al.* 1940) have shown this relationship.

The suggestion by Churchward that arid climatic conditions were associated with the unstable phases on the dunes at each K cycle seems entirely convincing, whilst the association of dune instability with parna entrainment and deposition, and of parna deposition with riverine deposition is established. In contrast, humid climate phases are associated with the intervening periods of soil development in each K cycle.

DISCUSSION

The foregoing data reveal that erosion/deposition has been markedly intermittent rather than having proceeded at a steady rate. In discussing this, attention will be given to the initiation of phases of more active erosion, the conditions to be associated with these, and the possibility of correlations in time. Consideration will also be given to the implications of the data for the general question of the development of landscape form.

(a) *The General Incidence of Erosion*

Erosion is familiar as the 'accelerated' erosion (Bennett 1955) induced by malpractices in land use, and both the contemporary hillside erosion and gullying at Canberra and the wind erosion on wheat farms at Swan Hill are instances of it. These instances have all the features found in the older phases of erosion/deposition except in their scale of magnitude. The older record shows erosive phases of far greater severity and comprehensiveness than any man-made, accelerated erosion. Accelerated erosion is generally contrasted with 'geologic' erosion (Bennett 1955), which is supposed to proceed very slowly and continuously. Since it is hard to imagine that the processes of accelerated erosion could be reduced in rate very considerably without their nature and manifestations being changed, we should look for evidence of some other kind of erosion/deposition in the record to represent periods of geologic erosion. However, the only evidence in the record other than that of accelerated erosion is that of soil development. This points to alternation of erosive and non-erosive phases, and the supposed contrast between accelerated and geologic erosion must be judged irrelevant.

Bennett (1955) shows that with various kinds of vegetative cover and soil exposure, other conditions being the same, erosion may vary by a factor of up to 10,000. A full grassland cover gives a high degree of protection from erosion, and it may well be expected that a forest cover with several inches of leaf mulch would also present a very stable surface. Experience of erosion indicates that the greatest protection is in the layers of organic matter above and at the surface of the mineral soil, and that most soils become increasingly liable to erosion the more this layer is penetrated. With increasing penetration, not only the mechanical protection of the surface litter is removed, but also the more durably structured soil. With increasing depth in the soil there are fewer plant nutrients and a less resistant physical structure; thus the more a soil is eroded the more it is liable to erosion. It would seem that a severe phase of erosion could be initiated by a relatively small change, if it involved penetration of the protective mantle of the soil. The very nature of the relationship between plants, soils, and erosion itself thus conspires to give a spasmodic erosion rate rather than a steady one: the most likely steady state is that of no erosion.

This picture of the erosion process conforms with the historic record, and points to the crucial part played by vegetation. Thus, in considering the incidence of erosion, attention is directed to changes which could be of biological significance, to humidity and temperature, and their seasonal variation. It is likely too that purely biological considerations have an important role; such would be inertia in plant communities, that is the tendency for them to hold the site for some years after the conditions required for their regeneration have passed. Their capacity for speedy migration is relevant, especially where climatic gradients are low and a replacement plant community must travel perhaps hundreds of kilometres. Also of significance is the combination of short-term climatic oscillations with long-term trends, which can bring a run of seasons providing a catastrophic onset, and yet forming part of a progressive deterioration.

These thoughts throw some light on the nature of the changes that could cause the onset of general erosion over such a wide climatic range as discussed above. It appears that climatic change itself, rather than the climatic levels so reached, is the significant control. A change towards aridity at Nowra (present rainfall 1016 mm) would hardly bring its rainfall as low as that of Swan Hill (330 mm). Even so, Swan Hill has a full vegetative cover, and apart from man's interference there is little or no erosion there now. Nevertheless the periodic occurrence of general erosion at each locality across the transect from Nowra to Swan Hill is indubitable. The significant climatic changes are those which cause biological degeneration, such as changes towards aridity or towards cold or towards stronger seasonal contrasts. The authors of the studies under discussion have favoured increased aridity or increased seasonal contrasts and storminess.

It will be realised that local 'incidents' quite independent of climatic change could similarly cause an erosive phase. Such events as bushfires, the pandemic incidence of a killing disease, or parasitic attacks could also be effective in causing erosion, and one must have confirmation on a regional scale of evidence from a variety of sources before erosion can be attributed to climatic change.

(b) *Local Differential Incidence of Erosion*

Whilst the foregoing considerations apply to the incidence of erosion over a region as a whole, other controls are superimposed, and these determine its incidence at a given site. The incidence of erosion is controlled by length and angle of slope (Bennett 1955) so that under given climatic and biological conditions certain slopes will be actively eroding and depositing, whilst others will be stable. The incidence of wind erosion, too, is differentially determined by the nature of the ground; sandy soils are particularly susceptible to attack (Chepil 1958), as are the salty cracking clays of lake beds.

It is significant that in all the study areas cited the evidence is repeated throughout the district—on each hillside, in each valley bottom or on each dune. The indications are that erosion/deposition began at many points throughout the region, that in many instances there was no physical connection between such points of outbreak, and that these could be on different landsurfaces, on different hills or dunes as the case may be. Yet the outbreaks were contemporaneous within the K cycle since they are associated with a common groundsurface.

When considering the initiation of a phase of erosion in a locality one can distinguish two cases. One is when the erosion begins at many separate places at once throughout the landscape; the other is when it is initiated at a front which advances across the district. All the phases of erosion discussed above are of the first kind, and it appears that no factors other than those familiar to the soil conservationist need to be invoked. These factors are the nature of the vegetative cover, soil character (particularly texture), and length and angle of slope. Given a landscape in which the last two vary at different sites, any degeneration of vegetation will initiate erosion at scattered points. The initiation of this kind of erosive phase is thus biologically determined.

The second kind of erosive phase—one that is initiated on a front—is probably more familiar in the literature, and is perhaps the concept which automatically comes to mind when the phrase 'an erosive phase was initiated' is used. Such a phase of erosion is initiated by a change of baselevel, and advances from the line of initiation—the fault line or warp axis, or the coastline in cases of sea-level change—firstly up the streams and then up the valley sides. Though biological changes may influence the rate of advance of such an erosive phase, they are not the cause of it, nor will they modify its distinctive pattern. Judged on the basis of pattern of incidence in the landscape, none of the phases of erosion/deposition described above are to be associated with baselevel change as a cause; rather have they been biologically initiated, presumably through climatic change. Nevertheless in many instances baselevel change has resulted from them, for instance the general aggradation of streambeds.

A further reason for making this distinction between two types of initiation of erosive phases lies in their different significance in terms of time. Phases of erosion initiated by biological changes may, and in the case above do, have a single time significance, whereas the erosion initiated by a baselevel change can have no single time significance. Its commencement may be dated, but its advance across the region takes time, and hence the surfaces and soils created by its activity range in age from its commencement to as long as the advance continues. In studies of the soils in terrain where the phases of erosion have been geologically induced this lack of temporal significance of the landsurfaces must be recognised (e.g. Mulcahy and Hingston 1961).

(c) *Correlation of Groundsurfaces*

The opportunities for correlation of data from centre to centre are numerous. There are apparent similarities between the soils and also between the sedimentary characteristics of the corresponding groundsurfaces at different centres.

Matching sedimentary sequences have often been used as a basis for correlation (e.g. Frye and Leonard 1952), as have matching sequences of buried soils (Richmond 1950). In the regional studies discussed in this essay soil and sedimentary data are integrated as the groundsurface, and both may be used together.

All centres show similar sequences, and these have the general form of a very minor phase preceded by three much larger phases, each larger than that following, whilst these in turn are preceded by a major phase of a different kind. This sequence can be seen in soil development, in erosion/deposition sequences and in relative degrees of weathering.

General hillside erosion/deposition has been the common event, except of course on the plains, where riverine deposition and accretions of parna have been the main events. However, at different centres, hillside erosion can be correlated with riverine deposition, parna accession with both hillside erosion and riverine deposition, and dune erosion with parna entrainment. All of these groupings of events are separated by soil-forming intervals.

Parna accession is probably the best basis for correlation between centres. Its entrainment resulted from dune erosion in the mallee region, and its deposition at Deniliquin, Griffith, and Wagga provides a basis for correlating groundsurfaces at all these centres. At each centre the K_1 groundsurface has no parna, but K_2, K_3, and K_4 have, and the nature of dust accession is such that it must have been simultaneous and general.

Correlation between Wagga, Canberra, and Nowra, however, must be on other grounds. Parna has not been identified at Canberra, though it is most likely present, since dust accession does not cut out suddenly but gradually decreases with distance from its origin. Perhaps some of the calcareousness of Canberra subsoils (of K_3 and K_4 groundsurfaces) is due to such a source, but at present this is only conjecture. The Murrumbidgee River system flows through Canberra and Wagga, and the groundsurface record indicates phases of terrace building and windblowing of sand from these terraces in K_2 and K_3 times at both centres. If we assume that a river which has several nick points between the centres in question would have a common depositional régime at any one time, and this seems most likely, then a correlation can be established between Canberra and Wagga groundsurfaces on the basis of these sand-sheetings. But there is no such opportunity for correlation between Canberra and Nowra; the parallelism of the data mentioned above, and the probability that climatic changes in contiguous regions will coincide, must suffice. However there is still no evidence as to which K cycles at Canberra and Nowra correspond. This is unfortunate because Nowra is the only locality where absolute dates of the groundsurfaces have been obtained so far.

Consistent trends in soil development in the similarly numbered groundsurfaces at each centre lend support to their correlation. The K_1 groundsurfaces at all centres have a minimal prairie soil. The soils in well drained sites in the K_2 groundsurface show a consistent trend from centre to centre, a brown-grey earth at Nowra, a red earth at Canberra, a red earth at Wagga with a red-brown earth next down the catena, a red-brown earth at Griffith, Deniliquin, and Swan Hill. The K_3 groundsurfaces at Nowra and Canberra have red podzolic soils, whilst at Wagga and Griffith they have 'red subplastic' soils.

Although an outline of soil and landscape events can be got from these

XXIVa   Vertical air photo near Deniliquin showing riverine deposition pattern. Photograph by R.A.A.F.

XXIVb   Vertical air photo near Swan Hill showing seif dune formations. Both roads and water reticulation canals appear in the photo. Photograph by R.A.A.F.

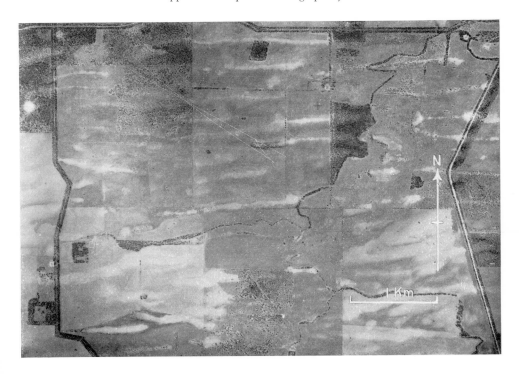

similarities, a great deal of elaboration is needed. This could be through C_{14} datings, palaeo-ecological investigations, and palynology, as well as through soil and sedimentological studies.

(d) *Implications for the Development of Landforms*

All of the data discussed above indicate that the processes of erosion and deposition have occurred in separate phases. The development of the main physiographic setting has not been the subject of investigation here, and indeed the major forms have not been greatly altered by any of the phases described. Nevertheless, data of this sort offer a unique opportunity of studying the nature of landform development. Small successive phases may be examined separately and these are likely to be more meaningful than mere examination of the overall change, in which the effects of conflicting processes can be lost.

On the question of the nature of slope development, the data are quite specific: each later step has led to a reduction of slope. There has been some loss in the sloughing zone and some accretion lower down the slope, and this process has been repeated, at different scales, in each of the last four or five steps or K cycles. Steps of this kind presumably extend far back in time at Griffith and Wagga, and deeper borings in accretion zones there would reveal a longer succession of groundsurfaces. But in the accreting zones at Canberra and Nowra there is no such long record of slope reduction. The evidence there is that in times earlier than K_4 and K_3 respectively the process of slope development was one of valley lowering which, of course, means slope increase. This process could not have been due to baselevel lowering, since the same evidence occurs on successive landsurfaces of the benched landscape. The inference is that this valley lowering is to be associated with some climatic state; one which would give high protection to hilltops and hillsides, but allow vigorous streambed erosion. The protection would be through the agency of vegetation, and a very humid equable climate is suggested.

The evidence thus shows that processes of both slope reduction and slope increase have gone on at different times. The cause of either seems to have been in climatic conditions, which are only to be inferred from their effect on the stability of soil surfaces and on the entrainment and transport of surficial sediment.

Alternation of slope reduction and slope increase has resulted in 'skinning' of the old landsurfaces in the Canberra region, as it might be inferred that it would. Continued phases of slope reduction such as have occurred since K_4 time would probably have left a higher proportion of old groundsurfaces at Canberra than now occurs, owing to the reduction of erosion rates as gradients declined. As it is, phases earlier than K_4 were ones of active streambed lowering with removal of older alluvia from the valley floors, and this maintained steep gradients and the opportunity for active erosion in appropriate phases on the hillsides. The result is that the groundsurface materials, soils, and patterns are very similar on the 'old' landsurfaces at Canberra and on the younger landscape at Nowra.

S

References

Bagnold, R. A. (1941). *The Physics of Blown Sand and Desert Dunes.* London.

Beattie, J. A. (in press). *Groundsurfaces of the Wagga Wagga Region N.S.W.* CSIRO Melb. Soil Publ.

Bennett, H. H. (1955). *Elements of Soil Conservation.* New York.

Brewer, R. (1960). Cutans: their definition, recognition and interpretation. *J. Soil Sci.* 11: 280-92.

Butler, B. E. (1950). A theory of prior streams as a causal factor of soil occurrence in the Riverine Plain of South-Eastern Australia. *Aust. J. agric. Res.* 1: 231-52.

————— (1955). A system for the description of soil structure and consistence in the field. *J. Aust. Inst. agric. Sci.* 21: 239-49.

————— (1956). Parna, an aeolian clay. *Aust. J. Sci.* 18: 145-51.

————— (1958). *Depositional Systems of the Riverine Plain of South Eastern Australia in Relation to Soils.* CSIRO Aust. Soil Publ. No. 10.

————— (1959). *Periodic Phenomena in Landscapes as a Basis for Soil Studies.* CSIRO Aust. Soil Publ. No. 14.

————— and Hutton, J. T. (1956). Parna in the Riverine Plain of South-Eastern Australia and the soils thereon. *Aust. J. agric. Res.* 7: 536-53.

Chepil, W. A. (1958). *Soil Conditions that Influence Wind Erosion.* U.S. Dept Agric. Tech. Bull. No. 1185.

Churchward, H. M. (1961a). *Soils of the Lower Murrakool District, N.S.W.* CSIRO Aust. Soils and Land Use Ser. No. 39.

————— (1961b). Soil studies at Swan Hill, Victoria. I. Soil layering. *J. Soil Sci.* 12: 73-86.

————— (1963a). Soil studies at Swan Hill, Victoria. II. Dune moulding and parna formation. *Aust. J. Soil Res.* 1: 103-16.

————— (1963b). Soil studies at Swan Hill, Victoria. III. Some aspects of soil development on aeolian materials. *Aust. J. Soil Res.* 1: 117-28.

————— (1963c). Soil studies at Swan Hill, Victoria. IV. Groundsurface history and its expression in the array of soils. *Aust. J. Soil Res.* 1: 242-55.

Cockroft, B. (in press). *Pedology of the Goulburn Valley Area.* Vict. Dept Agric. Tech. Publ. Ser. No. 19.

Commonwealth Bureau of Meteorology (1956). *Climatic Averages Australia.* Melbourne.

Craft, F. A. (1933). The surface history of Monaro N.S.W. *Proc. Linn. Soc. N.S.W.* 58: 229-44.

Dijk, D. C. van (1958). *Principles of Soil Distribution in the Griffith-Yenda District, N.S.W.* CSIRO Aust. Soil Publ. No. 11.

————— (1959). *Soil Features in Relation to Erosional History in the Vicinity of Canberra.* CSIRO Aust. Soil Publ. No. 13.

————— and Woodyer, K. D. (1961). *Soils of the Yass River Valley.* CSIRO Aust. Rept No. 6 of Reg. Res. & Ext. Study Southern Tablelands N.S.W.

Frye, J. C. and Leonard, A. B. (1952). *Pleistocene Geology of Kansas.* Kansas Univ. Geol. Surv. Bull. No. 99.

Langford-Smith, T. (1960). The dead river systems of the Murrumbidgee. *Geogrl Rev.* 50: 368-89.

Mulcahy, M. J. and Hingston, F. J. (1961). *The Development and Distribution of the Soils of the York-Quairading Area, Western Australia, in Relation to Landscape Evolution.* CSIRO Aust. Soil Publ. No. 17.

Penman, F., *et al.* (1940). *Soil Survey of the Mildura Irrigation Settlement, Victoria.* CSIR Aust. Bull. No. 133.

Richmond, G. M. (1950). Interstadial soils as possible stratigraphic horizons in Wisconsin chronology. *Bull. geol. Soc. Am.* 61: 1497.

Ruhe, R. V. (1956). Geomorphic surfaces and the nature of soils. *Soil Sci.* **82**: 441-55.

Stephens, C. G. (1962). *Manual of Australian Soils.* 3rd ed. Melbourne.

Walker, P. H. (1962a). Soil layers on hillslopes: a study at Nowra, N.S.W. *J. Soil Sci.* **13**: 167-77.

—————— (1962b). Terrace chronology and soil formation on the South Coast N.S.W. *J. Soil Sci.* **13**: 178-86.

—————— (1963). Soil history and debris-avalanche deposits along the Illawarra scarpland. *Aust. J. Soil Res.* **1**: 223-30.

—————— (1964). Sedimentary properties and processes on a sandstone hillside. *J. sedim. Petrol.* **34**: 328-34.

12

Some Karst Areas of Australia

J. N. JENNINGS

INTRODUCTION

Lithology, tectonic structure, and climatically determined exogenic processes combine to control landscape development, but all these factors, even lithology, may have varied during the lifetime of present landforms. In consequence modern interest in climatic morphology has stimulated use of the simplifying device of comparing the terrains associated with a particular rock type in different climates (Tricart and Cailleux 1955; Wilhelmy 1958). Karst has long constituted an almost autonomous field within the scientific study of scenery, and comparison of limestone terrains has been commonplace. Nevertheless this field also has partaken of the modern stress on the climatic control of landforms through process (Lehmann 1954, 1960; Birot 1954).

Classical studies chiefly relate to the karst of Yugoslavia (Cvijic 1960; Blanc 1958) where the dominant forms are those of reduction, the closed depressions. These range from the simplest and most widespread, the dolines, to the more complex uvalas, and to the largest, the poljes, which have been increasingly recognised to be distinct from the others in origin. Substantial residual forms are few and scattered—the hums projecting from the flat polje floors. Bare rock, much ornamented by *Karren* (minor surface solution features), is typical of much of the Yugoslavian karst, but this characteristic was realised as not obtaining always, even when attention was restricted to pure limestones.

In this earlier period it was thought possible to set limestone landforms from widely differing environments such as Jamaica and Java in sequence with the Yugoslavian ones in order to construct a theoretical karst cycle (Cvijic 1960; Grund 1914), in which the tropical terrains were regarded as elaborations of the temperate karst, to parallel the Davisian model. At this time departures were thought to be entirely lithological and structural in origin as, for instance, in the distinction between the holokarst and the merokarst of Yugoslavia, the former being developed in a great thickness of pure limestone reaching below ultimate baselevel, the latter in impure limestone formations, often surrounded and overlooked by impervious rock terrain and not extending below sea level.

But later there came reaction to this lumping together in one system of the karst landforms of temperate and tropical latitudes. H. Lehmann (1936) was one

Dr M. M. Sweeting kindly allowed me to make use here of both published and unpublished results of our collaborative work in Tasmania and West Kimberley. I am grateful to the Tasmanian Caverneering Club for access to their records and surveys and to R. T. Sexton of the Cave Exploration Group of South Australia for much co-operation over cave surveys. Mr C. D. Ollier made valuable comments on the manuscript. Finally, it is my pleasure to acknowledge my debt to all those Australian cavers, too numerous to name, with whom I have spent so much time underground, not least my fellow members of the Canberra Speleological Society.

of the first to maintain that tropical humid karst had its own rationale and that
the classical karst could not be conceived of as ever developing into the cockpit
karst of Jamaica or the towerkarst of southern China and Indochina. Thus the
notion of separate morphogenetic systems associated with major climatic types
entered into karst investigation and has been applied elsewhere; the effects of
altitudinal climatic change have also been considered in some degree (Rathjens
1954; Jennings and Bik 1962; Verstappen 1964).

Though not richly endowed with limestone and karst, Australia has too much
for this essay to be comprehensive or even fully representative (cf. Maksimovich

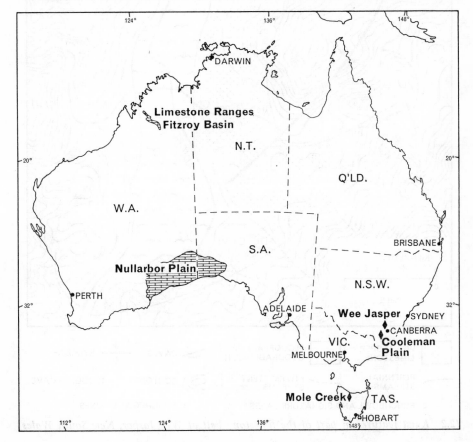

12.1   Selected karst areas of Australia

1962). Perforce it will dwell only on a few examples (Fig. 12.1), with which the
writer is familiar, and which can be used to illustrate some of the themes of karst
morphology and the kinds of problems confronting any attempt to explain
variation of limestone topography in terms of the various controlling factors,
including climate.

SIGNIFICANCE OF LIMITED AREA AT WEE JASPER,
NEW SOUTH WALES

At Wee Jasper about 50 km northwest of Canberra is a karst area structurally typical of many of the tiny limestone masses in the eastern highlands of Australia (Fig. 12.2). A pure, thick-bedded, compacted and in part biostromal limestone of Middle Devonian age here crops out along a belt some 15 km long but less than 1 km wide (Edgell 1949). Elongated along the NNW regional strike, it is exposed along the western side of the wide floor of the deep, steep-walled valley of the

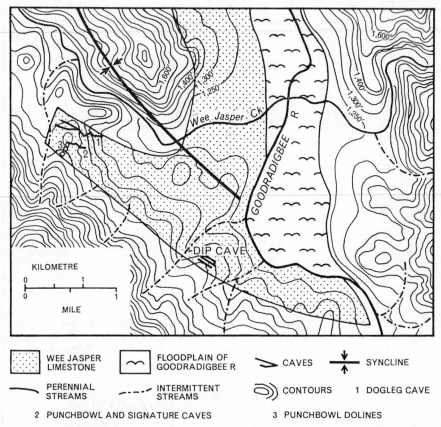

	WEE JASPER LIMESTONE		FLOODPLAIN OF GOODRADIGBEE R	CAVES	SYNCLINE
	PERENNIAL STREAMS		INTERMITTENT STREAMS	CONTOURS	1 DOGLEG CAVE
2 PUNCHBOWL AND SIGNATURE CAVES				3 PUNCHBOWL DOLINES	

12.2   Karst features in part of the limestone belt at Wee Jasper, New South Wales

Goodradigbee River. At its southern end, the outcrop curls round the nose of a pitching syncline and extends with WNW strike a short distance up the tributary valley of Wee Jasper Creek. The limestone dips into the synclinal axis almost vertically.

Partly concealed beneath alluvium, the limestone chiefly forms valley-side benches sloping eastwards to the river and dissected by shallow tributary valleys which extend from steep gullies in the mountain wall of conglomerate and porphyry above. The benches, 30-75 m above the present floodplain at 335-365 m, are remnants of a former valley floor and carry gravels in places (Edgell 1949). This halt in the downcutting of the valley represents a late phase in its excavation below a surface of mature relief at 610-730 m, partly overlain by Tertiary basalts. Formerly it was assumed that such basalts in the Southern Tablelands were Pliocene and that the incision followed Pleistocene uplift, but recent work on the basalts in the Snowy Mountains (Gill and Sharp 1956) attributes them to the Lower Tertiary. The formation of the benches cannot therefore be excluded from the Tertiary though it is more likely to be Pleistocene in age. In a few places the limestone rises a little higher than these benches in small hills and spurs.

(a) *Drainage and Surface Karst*

The shallow valleys crossing the limestone belt athwart the strike vary hydrologically. Wee Jasper Creek, the largest tributary of the Goodradigbee to fall in this category, flows almost perennially over coarse alluvium. Smaller creeks are generally less effectively insulated from the pervious bedrock in this way and flow only intermittently. However, under the subhumid warm temperate climate prevailing, intermittently dry river beds are not restricted to limestone; all small creeks dry up for varying periods, especially in summer, since rainfall and potential evaporation are both of the order of 1000 mm. However, the limestone creeks lose much water by percolation also. There are in addition shallow dry valleys without stream beds; some head within the limestone belt but others are continued upwards in mountain-side gullies, the water sinking inconspicuously near the break of slope at the foot of the valley side. Progressive development of underground drainage in the limestone after incision into the former valley floor seems sufficient to explain these dry valleys, without recourse to climatic change.

Closed depressions are few in this small karst area, and chief interest centres on a group of three dolines (Jennings 1963a) in a col on the southern side of Punchbowl Hill, a residual limestone hill at the western end of the outcrop in the Wee Jasper Creek valley. The name belongs to a shallow, elliptical, bowl-shaped doline with its central part so well mantled with soil that much digging would be needed to reveal to what extent surface solution and to what extent collapse into a cave below has produced it. It is, however, intersected on the north by a deeper, very steep-sided, angular doline, floored with a talus slope which extends into shallow caves beneath an overhanging northern wall. This talus slope is continued in the Far Chamber of Punchbowl Cave so that this doline is of collapse origin and in a young state. On the other side of the smooth Punchbowl but at a distance of some 30 m from it is the third doline, a deep, conical one, with little rock cropping out on its sides; again it is uncertain whether it is a solution doline or a degraded collapse doline.

Much of the surface of the limestone belt is soil-covered but there are significant areas of bare rock, which are very rough in detail through the development of big grikes or solution slots (*Kluftkarren*) along the bedding planes and even more frequently of strike ribs of rock which project from the general surface and correspond to particular beds (*Schichtfugenkarren*). Where well developed, these ribs carry 'beehives' of rock standing several feet high. On the steep eastern end of

Punchbowl Hill, the relief becomes more rugged, with small pinnacles of rock up to 6 m high, often capped with beehives which can, however, slip off along joint planes truncating the pinnacles.

Well developed solution flutings (*Rillenkarren*), associated with solution bevels (*Ausgleichsflächen*), are found on many outcrops but particularly on beehives and best of all on the pinnacles. On the latter, broader flutings of the *Regenrinnenkarren* type of Bögli (1960) occur sparingly over nearly vertical faces. The good development of these gravity-controlled minor surface solution features may be attributed to the subhumid climate and to the dry eucalypt woodland which covered the limestone before settlement and which was open enough to permit rain to fall directly on the outcrops and fashion them. Though some frosts are experienced, the occurrence of the solution features shows that mechanical breakdown by frost action is not significant.

(b) *Caves*

A number of small caves and several larger ones are known in the area. Three representative systems from the southern end of the outcrop will now be discussed; they illustrate that with the help of allogenic drainage quite elaborate and varied cave development can take place even in a small body of limestone (Fig. 12.2).

(i) *Dogleg Cave*

West of Punchbowl Hill a small intermittent tributary of Wee Jasper Creek flows over gravel along the western margin of the limestone outcrop. Where gullying due to clearance and grazing has exposed the bedrock, the creek loses some or all of its discharge underground to reappear in Dogleg Cave, an intermittently active river cave opening on the far side of the hill (Fig. 12.3). The cave length of about 800 m is considerable for Wee Jasper, but in other dimensions it is small; it is a simple cave with only one sizeable branch and is for the most part developed at a single active level. It possesses certain reaches which are rectilinear along the strike owing to solution along bedding planes, but other parts have a much more swinging plan, owing to meanders reducing structural influence. In such parts the cave is low and typically has the flat, elliptical form commonly associated with epiphreatic flow (Glennie 1958). The westernmost or headward parts of the cave have a gentle, fairly uniform downstream gradient, but are followed by a sector with three watertraps, which may act as true siphons at flood stages. In the lowermost course, where meandering is most obvious, there is an extremely gentle convexity in the long profile so that water descending a shaft from the surface after a drought here feeds both ways until the upstream portion fills up and a continuous outward flow is established. The surface outflow is located at the contact of the limestone and impervious rocks and the level of this contact has governed the development of the cave. Nevertheless, the lowest part of the watertrap sector is lower than the outflow and yet can drain dry; this shows that the cave is beginning to develop a lower circulation, which will ultimately enlarge and render part of the present system permanently inactive.

Thus Dogleg Cave is an intermittently functioning cave, mainly occupied by a free surface vadose stream of low gradient but having small reaches which act as

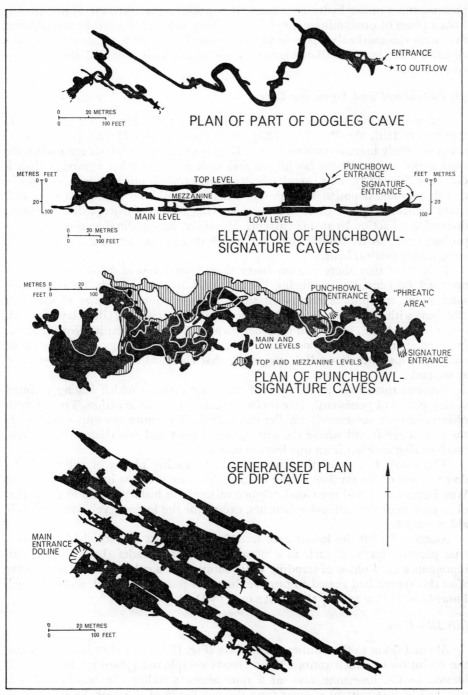

PLAN OF PART OF DOGLEG CAVE

ELEVATION OF PUNCHBOWL-
SIGNATURE CAVES

PLAN OF PUNCHBOWL-
SIGNATURE CAVES

GENERALISED PLAN
OF DIP CAVE

12.3 Dogleg, Punchbowl-Signature, and Dip Caves, Wee Jasper

pressure tubes under hydrostatic head. It is possible that the cave is just passing from a phase of predominantly epiphreatic flow, although it must be remembered that with the markedly variable precipitation characteristic of most Australian climates water levels oscillate vigorously and epiphreatic flow will almost always be episodic.

(ii) Punchbowl and Signature Caves

Lying very close to and parallel with Dogleg Cave but at higher levels in Punchbowl Hill, the Punchbowl-Signature Caves system (Jennings 1964) comprises presently inactive predecessors of Dogleg Cave and was fashioned when the creek supplying the latter lay higher and sank a little farther upstream than it does now (Fig. 12.3). This completely dry system reveals much of its history in its morphology and deposits. Though some chamber walls and some passages exhibit strike control in plan, there are many curving elements disregarding structure due to lateral action by strong currents. Moreover, longitudinal sections show the predominance of horizontal roofs for which there is no structural guidance in these nearly vertical beds.

It is clear that there are no fewer than four levels at which river action operated horizontally, producing flat elliptical passages chiefly by epiphreatic solution of an episodic nature, at times of high runoff. Patches of allogenic alluvium with graded beds which range from fine gravel to silty clay were left behind at all levels, usually in meander niches, so some mechanical corrasion was involved, particularly of floors and lower sidewalls. Ceilings show a delicate etching of fossils in low relief, suggesting that chemical corrosion predominated at the end.

Between these four levels are roof and floor canyons which belong to intervening phases of persistently free surface streams and vadose action. The intervals of incision were successively smaller downwards. The more spacious chambers of the system are found where the underground river did not change its position much during incision from one level to another.

The whole history of the cave reflects alternating phases of still-stand and downcutting of the outflow stream in its surface course across impervious rocks to Wee Jasper Creek and the Goodradigbee valley. This history relates to the period of formation of the valley-side benches, except for the lowest level, which is probably younger.

Associated with the lowest cave level is a small part characterised by typical true phreatic features, such as a network plan and blades (Bretz 1942). This represents a final phase of standing water solution in a cul-de-sac area of the cave after this system had ceased to provide the main passage for creek water through Punchbowl Hill, a role by then taken over by Dogleg Cave.

(iii) Dip Cave

About 1·5 km to the southeast, Dip Cave (Fig. 12.3) is another inactive system, the evolution of which cannot be so clearly deciphered (Jennings 1963b). It is located in the limestone nose of a spur above a valley-side bench, which is trenched by intermittent streams from the two flanks of the spur. Extreme dominance of structural control is evident in the plan of the cave, which consists of five parallel series of passages and chambers along the strike; particular beds, presumably the more readily soluble, have been removed, and transverse sections reveal the dominance of bedding plane walls. Cross-connections are few and exiguous but make the cave a network rather than a branching pattern. Systematic trends in longitudinal profiles are hard to discern, though the roofs give some suggestions of gradients in particular directions, with which weak solution current markings are consistent. But the directions are not all in the same sense. Flow to the WNW occurred in some parts, though the opposite direction is more common.

Cave breakdown, chiefly in the form of wall-slab (Davies 1949), is very prevalent and has greatly modified the solutional forms which might have revealed the cave history more clearly. However, despite the general paucity of small-scale phreatic features, it seems that the present morphology still owes a great deal to an initial true phreatic phase before the valley-side bench below the spur containing the cave was fashioned. At a later stage, probably when the bench was being cut, more pronounced currents of an epiphreatic nature developed in the cave, causing some modification of the cave morphology. Vadose flow seems to have had but little effect.

Thus Dip Cave is older than the Punchbowl-Signature Caves system, which in its turn is older than Dogleg Cave. Cave deposits have not yet yielded evidence which might give precision to these vague and relative ages based on morphological analysis. Apart from living species, a giant kangaroo (*Sthenurus* sp.) is represented in a collapse breccia in Dip Cave and a very large diprotodontid vertebra has come from waterlaid clays in the lowest level of Punchbowl Cave. Though they are not thought to go back into the Tertiary, the range in Quaternary time of these large marsupials is not yet defined.

(c) *Summary*

In this small limestone area dominated by high ranges of impervious rocks, only particular traits of karst morphology and hydrology have developed. Underground percolation increases the stream intermittency inevitably associated with the subhumid warm temperate climate. Of enclosed depressions, only dolines occur and there are few of these; on the other hand, quite elaborate minor surface solution forms have appeared beneath an open woodland. Cave development is quite elaborate and the marked contrast in evolution of two of the larger systems only a short distance apart underlines the difficulty of generalising about speleogenesis, even for so restricted a limestone terrain as this.

IMPACT OF REJUVENATION AT COOLEMAN PLAIN, NEW SOUTH WALES

At an elevation of 1250 m, Cooleman Plain lies near the head of the same deep valley in which Wee Jasper is located (Fig. 12.4). Between the deeply cut valleys there are a number of high plains at about this altitude in the southern part of the Southern Tablelands of New South Wales, and the ridges which separate these plains show summit concordance. Miocene and Pliocene dates have been given to these successive planation levels (David and Browne 1950) but doubt has been cast on these datings by Gill and Sharp (1956), whose suggestion of a Lower Tertiary age for the higher one is more probable. Stevens (1958) has maintained that Cooleman Plain is exhumed from beneath a Devonian lava cover, but there are strong morphological arguments for the view that it is a relict planation surface of probable Upper Tertiary age, along with the neighbouring plains.

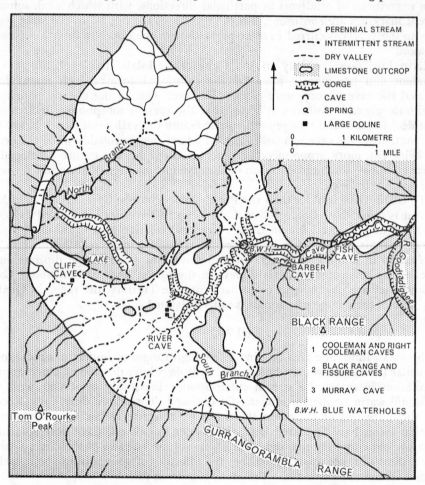

12.4   *Drainage and associated karst features on Cooleman Plain, New South Wales. The unshaded area is the limestone outcrop.*

The karst is developed in a pure, compacted and partly crystalline Upper Silurian limestone. The outcrop of limestone is divided by Devonian lava and by overlying Silurian chert and sandstone into a smaller northern area and a larger southern one; together they add up to no more than 12 km². The plain is drained eastwards through a gap in the surrounding ranges of igneous rocks by Cave Creek, which drops steeply in a gorge, partly in limestone, to the Goodradigbee River

3 km to the east and 150 m lower. Rejuvenation has occasioned not only this gorge but other shallower gorges and incised valleys which reach some way into the plain. Above the major nick points the valleys lie less than 15 m below very flat and broad interfluves, which constitute the original surface of the plain and which bear gravel unrelated to present drainage lines. The Tertiary ferruginous sandstone of Stevens (1958) is similarly disposed and there are pieces of haematite, probably derived from it, scattered over the plain. Together these deposits suggest a general cover of waste prior to rejuvenation.

Other superficial deposits are associated with relief developed since rejuvenation as well. These include solifluctional covers and blockstreams, evidence of a past periglacial climate that might be inferred *a priori* from the occurrence of late Pleistocene glaciers in the nearby Snowy Mountains. Thus the valley sides of the south branch of Cave Creek, where they lie below cappings of Devonian lava, bear sheets of lava blocks in a fine matrix, which have moved down slopes now below the present minimum angle of sliding friction for such material, in fact slopes as gentle as 8°. In places the fines have been washed out to leave small blockstreams. Other solifluctional spreads are found round the margin of the plain.

(a) *Drainage and Surface Karst*

Compared with neighbouring plains and valleys on impervious rocks, there is a sharper contrast between the marked horizontality of the interfluves of Cooleman Plain and the vertical or nearly vertical walls of the gorges near its eastern outlet. Before being affected by rejuvenation, Cooleman Plain was much more perfect than its neighbours, Long Plain to the west and Currango Plain to the south, both on impervious metasediments and igneous rocks. When limestone terrain is baselevelled, the solutional processes involved produce a more nearly horizontal surface than do corresponding processes on other rocks, or else achieve this more quickly, and so such perfection is of more frequent occurrence. Similarly the limestone gorges of the Southern Tablelands are more nearly perfect canyons than those cut in other rocks. The rapid percolation of rainwater underground on limestone inhibits runoff and reduces mass movement to a minimum, so that incision by rivers in limestone country is not accompanied by the many processes which normally cause valleys to flare out.

The irregular centripetal drainage of the plain converges on the Blue Waterholes, whence a single watercourse runs through Clarke and Wilkinson gorges to the Goodradigbee. At these high levels, where a humid cool temperate climate prevails, perennial drainage is characteristic. However, in Cooleman Plain many features of karst hydrology are found. Perennial or long-flowing intermittent streams flow down the slopes of the surrounding ranges, but when they pass on to limestone all or part of their flow goes underground. Many drainage lines have continuous stream beds, but the length of flow along them varies with weather and season. Frequency of flow is reflected in the stability of gravels and plant colonisation of the beds. The most persistent surface streams are found in the northern part of the plain, which has been scarcely affected by rejuvenation. For most of the year, the north branch of Cave Creek flows right across the limestone, then through a gorge in the overlying impervious beds, passing on to limestone for the second time and generally sinking here after a shorter or longer course.

However, the north branch does manage to flow over its whole course a few times most years for short periods after heavy rains or snowmelt, whereas the south branch has a short reach above its junction with the north branch where the state of the bed indicates that it is rarely, if ever, used. Other streams go completely underground and the drainage lines are continued in grassy dry valleys, without stream channels and in some cases without continuous gradients (Plate XXVb). The watersinks vary in nature; small streams often disappear in sloping bogs where water soaks underground without obvious sign, others end in small earth holes, whereas some larger streams enter fissures in the limestone directly and others seep into bedrock through their gravel beds.

Nearly all the water lost underground resurges in the Blue Waterholes, a group of large risings in or near the creek bed and below which the river is perennial. This major resurgence is well within the rejuvenated part of the plain. Smaller resurgences occur higher up the drainage lines, for example below Cliff Cave, but mostly these waters are lost underground again after a short surface traverse.

Not all the fluvial features of the plain seem to be related to the present climate. Thus there are fills of coarse angular to sub-angular gravels along parts of certain dry valleys, sometimes forming small terraces. Very active surface streams, such as are strange to these valleys today, were required to emplace them. Progressive development of underground drainage following on rejuvenation is a possible hypothesis to explain the abandonment of these fills, as it is for the dry valleys themselves, but a periglacial fluvial origin is more likely for the aggradation. In cold conditions reduced vegetation would allow slope waste to move more readily into the streams and frozen subsoil would minimise underground circulation. Certainly some of the filled dry valleys appear to have irregular bedrock long profiles as if the coarse fill concealed semi-blind valleys (Cvijic 1960). This suggests that karst development had occurred prior to the alluviation and argues in favour of periglacial-fluvial origin of the fills. In addition some of the sloping bogs round the periphery of the plain overlie relict alluvial cones, which can also be attributed to a former periglacial phase.

Dolines are fairly numerous, though small and localised. Very many of them are mere dimples a metre or so deep and 4-8 m across, but some reach 7 m in depth and about 35 m in diameter. Most are soil-covered, though there are rocky ones. They occur in three kinds of situation:

(i) Round the margin of the limestone plain. Here many are in colluvial mantles and others mark the points of sinking of peripheral streams.

(ii) Along the dry valleys and in some cases along intermittent stream courses where the stream fills up each doline along the course in turn before it extends farther down the valley, the characteristic of the semi-blind valley.

(iii) On interfluves but over the probable line of a cave, for example three which lie in line with Murray Cave.

In most cases there is uncertainty as to whether the dolines are of collapse or solution origin, though collapse origin is likely in the case of the third group. In the plain there is also one karst corridor, probably of collapse origin, but more elaborate types of enclosed depression are absent.

Soils and the superficial deposits already discussed cover much of the plain, yet bare rock crops out not only along the gorges but also along some of the dry valleys and over substantial areas of flat interfluve. Natural grassland prevails over most of the plain, with some open eucalypt woodland; despite this favourable condition small-scale solution sculpturing is not much in evidence. Solution fluting is rare and poorly developed; the only sculpturing at all frequent is a tiny rippling on steeply sloping to vertical surfaces (Plate XXVa). These ripples have a height of 1-2 cm and run roughly horizontally 5-10 cm. On the eastern margin of the plain this sculptural poverty finds explanation in a very coarsely crystalline texture due to contact metamorphism. This limestone weathers into a fine gravel and gives rise to rounded outcrops suggestive of exfoliation. Nevertheless a lithological explanation does not apply generally through the plain. Frosts are experienced much of the year because of altitude and temperature inversions due to local topography, and so frost shattering leaves its characteristic products in some degree. However, more important than present conditions may be the probable short length of time that has elapsed since there prevailed the more rigorous climate, attested by the periglacial phenomena already described, which would have destroyed any prior solutional sculpturing.

(b) *Caves*

The purity and competence of the rock and the high and effective precipitation are favourable for the formation of caves, nevertheless caves are few on the plain, and these are neither large nor elaborate.

In the northern part of the plain there are only two very short caves in shallow valley sides where surface streams have simply passed into the limestone for about 30 m and then out again. Lying no more than 4-5 m below the surface, they are of flat elliptical cross-section with level, gravel floors. In normal flow the streams have a free surface in the caves, but after heavy runoff the passages fill to the roof.

In the southern part of the plain there are numerous watersinks round the margin, but at only one has a cave been penetrated more than a metre or so up to the present time. This is Devils Hole, an active vadose inflow cave, short (15 m) and steep, descending 13 m rapidly in two waterfalls. Not far away and possibly connected with it, though lava covers the limestone between, is Cliff Cave, a short abandoned outflow cave with an impenetrable active stream passage 7 m lower down, which feeds the spring mentioned above. At flood, water backs up into the penetrable cave above but no outflow occurs at this level. Resurgence here is the result of contact with overlying mudstone.

The larger caves are found where rejuvenation has caused entrenchment below the plain. Opening into the gorge wall of the north branch of Cave Creek is Murray Cave, a nearly horizontal outflow cave about 270 m long with two distributary branches. A tight watertrap at the inner end of the main passage has so far blocked further exploration. This cave is on the threshold of inactivity since only occasionally after heavy runoff does water rise in the trap and outflow occur for short periods. River Cave lies 800 m to the SSW, with its entrance immediately above a rock bar in a dry valley. Formerly, surface flow reached to it when the valley was semi-blind. The former inflow cave here winds down to join an active river cave of large dimensions, which can be followed upstream and downstream to watertraps, so it falls into the category of *Zwischenhöhle*. The south branch of Cave Creek normally sinks at a point about 500 m southwest and it is inferred that River Cave is supplied from there. At the sink, the inflow cave is buried by the debris of a former entrance arch, which may have collapsed through frost action in periglacial conditions, and by coarse alluvial fill beyond the capacity of the present stream. A flood inflow cave a little further down the south branch valley has been explored for about 30 m.

Between 300 and 600 m upstream of the Blue Waterholes, in the left bank wall of the gorge of Cave Creek, is the Cooleman-Right Cooleman system. These interconnecting dead caves are former outflow caves, where the main artery at the Waterholes, about 6-7 m higher than the main resurgence, reached the surface. Collapse material blocks the upstream end of this system and in Right Cooleman there is a good deal of flat elliptical passage suggestive of epiphreatic solution, such as may well be going on behind the Blue Waterholes today.

Downstream of the resurgences in Clarke gorge, Barber Cave is a through cave; a tributary from the Black Range of impervious igneous rocks passes through a limestone spur by means of it. There are two entrances, one active and one inactive, at each end and inside the cave the active passage crosses the inactive one twice. The nearby Black Range Cave, a simple linear cave, nearly punctures the wall of the gorge from a dry valley; though there is still a small stream inside the cave, no surface stream runs into its entrance doline nowadays. Higher up in the same spur, Fissure Cave fulfilled the same function at an earlier stage.

Thus the cave development of Cooleman Plain is modest, but is most advanced near the gorges cut in the plain. This limited development can be related to the fact that rejuvenation has not affected the whole mass of the limestone. Even where it has penetrated, perhaps, insufficient time has elapsed for much cave elaboration, though some caves have already ceased to function as drainage channels, and another (Murray Cave) is almost inactive.

(c) *Discussion*

Though less dominated by impervious ridges than Wee Jasper, Cooleman Plain is yet a 'karst barré' (Blanc 1958) and much influenced by the alien surround. The plain remains traversed by a dendritic pattern of valleys, though the intermittency of flow along many river beds and the occurrence of dry valleys in that pattern are a more positive indication of karst hydrology than at Wee Jasper, since the cooler, rainier conditions here must otherwise result in perennial surface drainage. Small dolines are the only closed depressions; more frequent than at Wee Jasper, they remain localised and do not coalesce into fields.

Limited development of surface karst is partly an expression of limited time. The well planed floor of a hill-girt basin inherited from the Tertiary landscape has been only partially encroached on by a young valley system. This is an indication that rejuvenation is young here, whatever the time of its initiation farther down the Goodradigbee-Murrumbidgee drainage.

Cave development is also moderate and is predominantly associated with the rejuvenated parts of the limestone relief. In relation to the Davis-Bretz theories of cave origin (Davis 1930; Bretz 1942), it is significant that the caves here have not inherited forms from any true phreatic activity of the planation stage, but are the product of strong current action above or close to the water rest level.*

Climatic history is undoubtedly another geomorphogenic factor here. During a period of Pleistocene periglaciation, frozen subsoil must have hindered underground circulation. Joined with the recency of rejuvenation, this could account for the limited karst development. Minimal development of surface solutional sculpture may be related to frost destruction at that time; the subsequent period has been short and not very favourable climatically for refashioning. Relatively impervious periglacial-fluvial deposits have certainly resulted in some re-establishment of surface drainage and may have restored continuous downward gradients to some valleys which had previously lost them.

COMPLICATION BY CLIMATIC CHANGE AT MOLE CREEK, TASMANIA

Extending over an area about 22 km by 8 km, the limestone area near Mole Creek is another comparatively small and interrupted karst within a higher frame of impervious rocks (Fig. 12.5). Structure and climatic change have rendered it complex, however, and only salient features especially relevant to the present theme can be discussed here. This is based on a meagre literature of which the most important items are by Burns and Rundle (1958), and Brown and de Vries (1958), and on unpublished work by the writer and M. M. Sweeting. The present climate is cool temperate and humid, with 1000-1500 mm of well distributed rainfall. Frost is much less frequent than on Cooleman Plain, and in any case its geomorphological effects are minimised by a natural vegetation of wet sclerophyll eucalypt forest, with patches of rainforest on the Tiers.

Ordovician limestone, predominantly pure, compacted and thick-bedded, is here incorporated in a synclinorium pitching ESE, folded and faulted in at least two Palaeozoic orogenies (Hughes 1957). In consequence, the limestone is cleaved and well jointed. Underlying sandstone overlooks it in Gog Range and Mt Roland to the north and also divides the western half in the median anticline of Standard Hill. On the south the karst is dominated by the Great Western Tiers, a dolerite-capped scarp of weak Permian sandstone, siltstone, and mudstone.

The northern and eastern parts of the limestone outcrop consist mainly of flat plains at 180-300 m above sea level, partly alluviated, along the Mersey River, Sassafras Creek, Mole Creek, and Lobster Rivulet. The limestone rises above these plains irregularly to heights between 250 and 600 m with little semblance of summit concordance, although at 380-410 m there is an erosional bench in the vicinity of Kansas and Mill Creeks which may be relict from a higher surface.

(a) *Superficial Deposits*

The limestone is covered by a variety of superficial deposits of sufficient extent and relevance to the karst to warrant some separate discussion.

* This now calls for qualification; two of the recently discovered caves on the plain appear to be phreatic in nature and may belong to the time of planation.

T

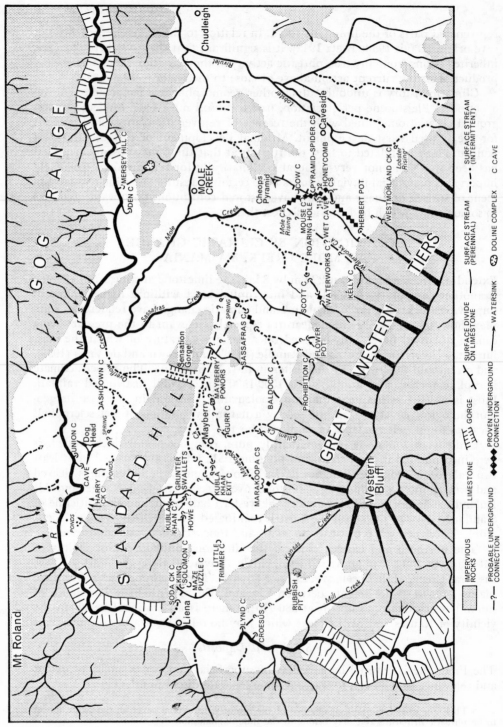

12.5   *Drainage and associated karst features at Mole Creek, Tasmania*

The Mersey River has cut gorges in older, more resistant rocks upstream and downstream of the limestone area, and also through the sandstone of Standard Hill in between, but on the limestone it has broadened its valley greatly by lateral planation and has spread coarse gravels. These are disposed in several terraces of probable Pleistocene age and glacifluvial origin (Rundle 1961). The lowest surface, Den Plain, is still liable to flood and carries a pattern of grassy braided channels, which may, however, be relict.

Valley trains of gravel can be traced up the Mersey tributaries to the foot of the Tiers where they pass into piedmont gravel fans with calibre rapidly coarsening upwards. These are clearly relict, since they were forested before white settlement and have largely lost their channels. This inactivity is not simply a karst effect, though this is a contributory factor in their desuetude, but primarily they are relict from a former cold climatic period and the question arises whether they are glacifluvial or periglacial-fluvial in origin.

Since Pleistocene ice buried most of the plateau behind the Tiers above Mole Creek and overlapped the latter over long stretches (Jennings and Ahmad 1957), the probability of glacifluvial fans at the escarpment foot is great. The relationship with glaciation may be even closer. At two places at the foot of the Tiers—west of Scott Cave and east of Westmorland Creek—there stand out masses of bouldery drift with a silty clay matrix. Their hummockiness and the way they spread out distally with a bulging lower margin are features in favour of an end-moraine rather than a solifluctional origin. Similar material is found between Western Creek and Dale Creek, with less clear-cut morphological evidence to support this interpretation. Referring to this easternmost example, Burns (1957) adopts a somewhat intermediate position, referring to it as a rock-glacier, formed 'of glacial till shovelled over the edge of the Tiers' and moved downhill with the help of 'ice lubrication'.

On the other hand there are indubitable solifluctional deposits in the area. Much of the Quaternary 'talus' of dolerite, basalt, and quartzite of the 1/63360 Middlesex Geological Survey sheet has the characters of solifluctional cover. At many points these angular materials spread down over limestone at gradients well below the present angle of rest for such debris, and with preferred orientation downslope. Closely associated with some of these, for example along the foot of the Gog-Mt Roland Range, there are inactive fans which we may conclude to be periglacial-fluvial fans of similar age. So it cannot be assumed that all the fans at the foot of the Tiers are glacifluvial. Indeed the more westerly ones such as the one in the Loatta depression seem to be of this periglacial nature, since they are commanded only by the small mass of Western Bluff which largely escaped glaciation.

Burns (1957) considers that some 'talus' masses at the foot of the Tiers have yet another origin, namely that they represent the former fill of enclosed depressions in the limestone left behind when the surrounding limestone had been completely removed. A further possibility is that some may be slumped masses of formations overlying the limestone and undermined by solutional removal of the latter (cf. Thomas 1963).

(b) *Drainage and Surface Karst*

On climatic grounds one would expect streams here to be largely perennial; however, the Mersey River, large on entering the limestone and lying low in it, is the only one. All other streams lose sufficient water underground either to abandon reaches of their channels for periods of time or to have permanent underground courses over part of their length. This karst hydrology is illustrated by the following examples.

The Lobster Rivulet is the least affected by the limestone since it flows perennially from a large spring at the foot of the Tiers; however, above the Lobster Rising it has nearly a kilometre of bed which is liable to go dry (Fig. 12.5). It is not known whether the water sinking in the bed of the Lobster follows the strike and resurges at the Lobster Rising itself. An alternative feeder for the Rising is Westmorland Creek nearly a kilometre further west, which on encountering the limestone enters a cave, trending ESE along the strike for 140 m. However, a not completely conclusive fluorescein test (Jennings and Sweeting 1959) suggested that this water did not reach the Lobster.

Indeed it is possible that this cave feeds the largest rising in the area, that of Mole Creek itself, which was observed by the writer to reach an estimated flow of 10 m³ per second after heavy rains in August 1961. Since there is no likely alternative, it is probable that several other creeks westward of Westmorland Creek and sinking at the foot of the Tiers also feed the Mole Creek Rising. However, only one connection has actually been traced: a small stream entering Herbert Pot at 420 m on the Tiers emerges from Wet Cave 1200 m away at 305 m (fluorescein test by M. de Vries, personal communication). After a very short surface flow the Wet Cave stream enters Honeycomb 1 Cave and a test (Jennings and Sweeting 1959) has shown that thence it goes to Mole Creek Rising 1600 m away and 30 m lower, appearing in between for a very short surface course of 30 m in Blackberry Hole. In this fashion the underground drainage crosses the surface divide between the Lobster Rivulet and Mole Creek valleys. Below its rising, Mole Creek normally persists in surface flow, but its behaviour higher up justifies its own apt name and the selection of this name to designate the whole karst area.*

Short, very steep, dry valleys often continue the line of streams sinking near the foot of the Tiers. These run down the dip, but dry valleys also occur along the strike down the flanks of the limestone divides running NNE from the Tiers. To what extent, if any, these dry valleys are a consequence of periglaciation remains to be investigated, though their disposition is so closely related to the present relief that it is hard to think of them as the product of an initial phase of surface drainage on a former high-level surface.

The long profiles of many dry valleys are interrupted by dolines (Plate XXVc). Dolines are in fact numerous—Burns and Rundle map over 400 and this falls far short of the total—and are widespread except in some of the flat plains of the

---

*Within the last year new caves between Herbert Pot and Wet Cave have been explored and fluorescein has proved a connection between Kelly Pot lying farther west along the Tiers and one of these caves. So some at least of the water emerging at the Mole Creek Rising makes a double crossing of the divide between Mole Creek and Lobster Rivulet.

north and east. On the average they are larger than those of Cooleman Plain and more varied. On fairly flat river terrace, fan, and solifluctional covers, they range from conical through basin to dish and saucer shape. Circular ponds of a permanent or semi-permanent nature occupy many shallow ones. The strike of the covered limestone is often reflected in the shapes and arrangement of the doline which may coalesce to form elongated depressions. On steeper slopes, as on the north side of Standard Hill where the solifluction material has spread down as an apron over the limestone, dolines are particularly frequent. On the margins of the bodies of superficial deposit, they become asymmetrical in both plan and section. A straight steep slope develops in the outcropping limestone, faced by a more gently sloping amphitheatre on the debris mantle side; examples occur along the southern side of Dog Head.

These dolines in cover deposits can be regarded as subsidence dolines in that the insoluble superficial deposits have slid down into limestone cavities beneath, but whether these cavities are due to solution at the buried surface of the limestone or to collapse into caves within the limestone is not readily ascertained. Where the dolines are arranged in a line the collapse explanation is likely, but where they tend to form fields more or less covering an area, as south of Standard Hill between Sassafras Creek and Sensation Gorge, the solution hypothesis is more satisfactory.

Where the limestone is exposed or only thinly covered with residual soils, the dolines tend to be elongated along the strike, angular in plan, and to have steep sides, including vertical rock walls. These characteristics suggest a collapse origin. Such are common on the divide between Sassafras Creek and the Mayberry basin and especially on that between Caveside and South Mole Creek. Similar but shallower depressions, often water-filled, occur in the northern limestone plain near the head of Overflow Creek.

There are larger, more complex depressions in the Mole Creek karst which cannot be termed dolines. Thus, north of Mole Creek village the Tertiary basalt capping of the wide, flat-topped divide, Mersey Hill, is punctured by an enclosed lobate depression about 25 m deep and 350 by 250 m across. It formed by the inosculation of three fairly large and eleven smaller dolines of conical or basin shape developed in the underlying limestone, which is exposed in little cliffs and crags on their sides, and it can be placed in the category of uvala in the classical Yugoslavian karst terminology.

The Loatta enclosed depression, about 3 km by 2 km, is bounded by impervious rock ridges to the north and south but has limestone divides on the west and east (Fig. 12.5). It is divided into a number of compartments by low limestone ridges mostly along the strike. The lowest compartment in its northeast corner is elongated NNE through fault or dip joint guidance, and has a flat alluvial floor, which in April 1961 became a temporary lake of over 3 hectares of 5-6 m depth. Normally, streams from Standard Hill to the north sink in caves at the base of the limestone divide on the east, but less frequently used stream beds cross the alluvial floor, which is itself punctured by dolines and slump pits. The western half of the depression is largely floored by a relict fan of mainly angular waste from the Tiers. Northeast of it is a small circular lake, and to the northwest are a series of shallow bedrock corridors leading to small caves in the divide which separates the Loatta depression from the Mersey valley. The whole feature does not fit easily into any of the standard categories of karst depression.

The most interesting landform in this limestone area is the Mayberry basin, which is about 5 km by 3 km, with limestone divides to the west and east (Fig. 12.5). On the south the Tiers shed the most important drainage into the basin, whilst on the north is Standard Hill, breached by the sawcut of Sensation Gorge. This is a gorge of superimposition produced in the sandstone anticline as the Tiers retreated southwards and a stream flowing over the Permian cover eventually cut through into the folded Palaeozoics beneath. Above this gorge, the stream has etched widely in the weaker limestones. Waterfalls over 50 ft high in the gorge constitute a nick point reached by rejuvenation from the Mersey valley. To the east, Sassafras Creek slid sideways down the pitching nose of the same anticline when it encountered the tough sandstones, and in consequence rejuvenation has passed south of this obstacle, bringing the Creek lower than the floor of Mayberry basin. From this relationship stems the present poised hydrological situation of the basin. Only once or twice a year do floodwaters overflow through Sensation Gorge; normally drainage is underground through the limestone at its northeast corner.

Much of the Mayberry basin has an alluviated floor locally interrupted by knolls and bars of limestone. Marakoopa Creek, the chief stream, has a continuous bed from its two resurgences at Marakoopa Cave to the lowest point in the basin, first through a dissected fan and then below Mayberry village through a flatter alluvial fill with terrace remnants. Here sections show coarse gravels overlying silty clays at several points. The river normally ends in a ponor complex of intersecting conical hollows in the northeast corner, the deepest reaching 9 m below the alluvial plain. When the creek is dry, three points of sinking into limestone cracks in the bottom of the hollows can be seen, but there are other points of infiltration. After heavy rain the whole area of hollows fills up; indeed, in August 1961 the lower parts of the plain as well were under water. In these circumstances a shallow channel about 1 m deep leads from the ponors into Sensation Gorge to provide surface connection with the Mersey.

The widely held view that the Mayberry ponors feed water along the strike to the Sassafras has not been proven by rigorous watertracing methods, but the structure seems to allow no other possibility. Local reports state that sawdust was seen in the Sassafras at a time when a sawmill was in action in the Mayberry basin but none higher up the Sassafras. There are several springs appropriately placed on the left bank of the Sassafras, and the largest one at the head of a short 'steephead' valley was seen to pour forth very large volumes of turbid water during the floods of August 1961 when the Mayberry ponors were full and when there was overflow through Sensation Gorge.

These various characteristics place the Mayberry depression right at the point of transition from a basin with surface outflow to a structural polje.

The limestone divides of the area are marked by the development of rounded ridges along the strike. In lower parts these give place to short whaleback residual hills, surrounded by bedrock plains or alluvial covers and resembling the hums of Yugoslavian karst. Some few have acquired a pyramidal shape, for example Cheops Pyramid about 30 m high near South Mole Creek. Dog Head in the

Mersey plain with a height of 250 m above its basement is the only one achieving the full dimensions of a hum; it remains slightly elongated along the strike and has a steeper anti-dip side.

The rounded smoothness of the residual ridges and hills is often paralleled on a finer scale in the smaller rock outcrops. Only in a few steep and exposed situations can one find such gravity-controlled forms of bare karst as solution flutings. These occurrences are on the blunt western end of Dog Head, on the sharp crest of a residual hill near the junction of Mole Creek with Mersey River, and on an isolated crag in the middle of Den Plain. In natural conditions these points were probably exposed to rain under open canopy woodland, as is still the case at Dog Head. The rest of the karst was, and in parts still is, under wet sclerophyll forest, with its outcrops covered in forest litter or largely coated with mosses, lichens, and liverworts. If such coverings are removed, rounded weathering forms are found beneath. Where clearance has bared limestone knolls, as north of Mole Creek near its junction with Sassafras Creek, smooth boilerplates of limestone have something of tropical sugarloaf appearance. Platy desquamation parallel to surfaces is certainly taking place now, but this may be due to man-wrought exposure to frost action and diurnal temperature change. Rounded solution grooves (*Rundkarren*) can also be found fairly frequently where the forest cover has been removed; these form on steep rock slabs beneath forest litter or soil, and their appearance at the surface is an indication of the stripping of such mantles.

(c) *Caves*

This small karst area is rich in caves—over 70 are known—and space precludes more than a summary and selective treatment of the variety of their geomorphological settings. Nearly all of them have predominantly vadose characteristics and contain allogenic gravels, some in active movement and some as fill remnants.

Along the Tiers is a series of very steep and very active inflow caves where acid mountain streams are engulfed after short courses over the limestone. It is significant that the Pennine name 'pot' has been given to several of these. Waterfalls are frequent in them and great masses of boulders and gravel are in rapid transit. Kelly Pot typically descends about 80 m in a not much greater horizontal distance, though its gradient flattens towards the lower limit of exploration since by then it is down at the level of the foot of the Tiers. The main watercourse in the cave goes directly down the dip of the rocks. Drainage from Standard Hill has also created inflow caves, such as Howe Cave in the Loatta depression and Harry Creek Cave on the southern flank of Dog Head.

Kubla Khan Cave is a *Zwischenhöhle* in the divide on the east side of the Loatta depression. Roof collapse here allows descent to an active river passage which can be followed some way up and downstream but not to daylight. This cave is part of the main drainage eastwards from Loatta into the Mayberry basin, and on the other side of the divide opposite is a large spring with a water-filled cave behind. This has been named Kubla Khan Exit Cave, although the inferred connection has not yet been proven by watertracing. On the western side of the Loatta depression is King Solomon Cave, a heavily decorated, dead cave which appears to be a high-lying inflow cave whereby drainage formerly escaped westwards through the divide into the Mersey valley. Maze Puzzle Cave is a small cave with a similar former function close to the present level of the depression floor.

There are two particularly interesting caves in the Sassafras Creek valley. Sassafras Cave, although lying just inside the western valley wall, interrupts the surface course of the creek for some 500 m. Above and below the cave there is a river channel which is occupied intermittently, but alongside the cave there is no channel, merely a gravel veneer on the valley floor. In parts this gravel is disappearing into grikes, exposing a level limestone pavement. The fact that Sassafras Cave is for the most part at the same level as the alluviated valley floor outside suggests a genetic connection. Probably the gravels were brought down from the Tiers in a period of cold climate when glaciers fed heavy loads of morainic material into the streams. Summer flows braiding over the gravel surface would be insulated in some degree from the limestone beneath, and some passing along the margin of the gravel train would be able to enter the limestone on the flank and to develop a parallel flow at the same level within the mass of the rock.

This possibility is underlined by evidence from Baldock Cave, which roughly parallels the valleyside higher up the same valley. A small stream now operates at a low level in this cave, but the inactive passages are largely filled by coarse gravels, indicating a formerly much greater flow, and one can envisage cave enlargement by strong currents of cold water concomitantly with deposition of the gravel.

This postulated association of cave elaboration with cold climate finds strongest evidence in the divide between the Lobster Rivulet and Mole Creek valleys. Wet Cave, which has been penetrated upstream for over 1000 m, runs roughly parallel to the eastern side of the divide, which is impinged against by the gravels of a glacifluvial fan. Right along the contact is a dry valley with shallow dolines, a former peripheral channel of the fan. Evidently much meltwater flowed along the limestone hillside with a strong chance of feeding some discharge into Wet Cave. The outflow from Wet Cave runs precisely along the southern flank of a strike ridge to enter Honeycomb 1 Cave (Sexton 1960), which carries the waters round the nose of the ridge and along its northern flank just inside the limestone hillside (Fig. 12.6). Numerous entries round this margin were points where water and gravel could be fed into the system from the glacifluvial fan. A peripheral depression and dolines mark the contact of the fan with the next strike ridge to the north, through which Honeycomb 1½ and 2 Caves carry some of the water originating from Wet Cave. Even at low stage, there are at least two routes from Honeycomb 1 to Honeycomb 2, and it is quite certain that this division is multiplied at flood stage when several different levels in the caves are in action. This makes it unnecessary to explain the network pattern of Honeycomb 1 as an inheritance from a former phreatic phase. Rather can it be likened to the anastomosing channels of a braiding surface stream, except that in a cave the braiding can occur in a vertical as well as in a horizontal plane.

Lying fairly centrally in the divide between Honeycomb Caves and Mole Creek Rising, the Spider and Pyramid Caves system has a low-level stream passage, the provenance of which is not yet known. However, the high levels were observed in the floods of August 1961 to be occupied by a temporary but big flow from the

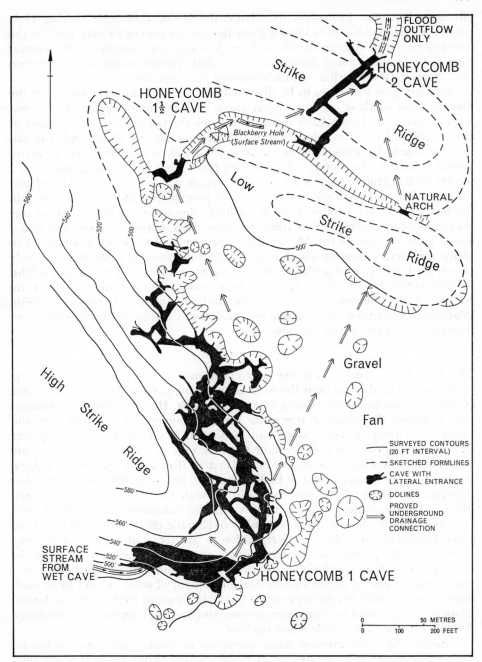

12.6 *Honeycomb Caves, Mole Creek. The cave plan and part of the surface detail are due to an A.S.F. survey party led by R. T. Sexton*

Honeycomb system. Just across the divide, the Mouse Cave and Roaring Hole system, a *Zwischenhöhle,* is known from fluorescein testing to take part in the low-stage drainage through the divide here (Jennings and Sweeting 1959), whereas Cow Cave, another active *Zwischenhöhle,* a little further north on this western side, seems to be on a tributary, underground drainage line.

The last group of caves to be discussed is a series of outflow caves near the Mersey. Most of these are fairly level caves, but not necessarily at the present level of the river. Union Cave opens into it on the north side of Dog Head at river level, and Den Cave flows out at the level of the Den Plain, which is still liable to flood. An unnamed cave at the western end of Dog Head has an active stream passage at river level; a dry bedding plane cave, 16 m above, represents a former level. Lynd Cave near Liena has a stream passage at river level and two dry exits, 6 m and 16 m above, but the river passage quickly rises inside to join the uppermost level. Croesus Cave has a long, almost horizontal stream passage over an impressive series of low rimstone dams. This debouches about 3 m above a 6 m gravel terrace of the Mersey River. Mersey Hill Cave opens about 30 m above the Mersey close to where it leaves the limestone; it is an intermittently active, level outflow cave probably related to river terrace remnants at that height. Rundle (1961) boldly claims that all these caves and their various levels are related to the different Mersey terraces and floodplain (cf. Sweeting 1960). Whether the relations are as simple and uniform as this needs investigation, but it certainly seems to be true in some cases.

(d) *Discussion*

The Mole Creek karst area is the most elaborate example discussed so far; one manifestation of this has been the need to make comparisons with a wider range of surface forms from the classical Yugoslavian karst. However, the developments remain within the range of temperate karst phenomena. More numerous and larger caves than at Wee Jasper and Cooleman Plain show that the greater development applies to underground form as well. Contrasts in lithology are insufficient to explain the more elaborate karst at Mole Creek. A partial explanation may be the greater extent of limestone there, but an additional cause is that rejuvenation has reached more generally through the area than at Cooleman Plain and left a greater available relief within the limestone than at Wee Jasper.

There remains, however, the possibility of climatic effects. Compared with the other two areas, the effective precipitation is greater, and vegetation is more prolific with the prospect of greater amounts of biological carbon dioxide in the natural waters. Because of higher carbon dioxide saturation equilibria in colder waters and because of higher carbon dioxide content of snow air and so of meltwater, Corbel (1957) has perhaps unwisely sought to see in cool temperate humid climates the optimum for limestone solution and karst development. Nevertheless they are certainly favourable if not optimal.

Finally, the significance of large quantities of glacial and snow meltwater during Pleistocene cold periods needs to be assessed in regard to this question. On the Mersey plains this has probably been partly responsible for the development of wide limestone plains with gravel veneers and has probably promoted the isolation of one large as well as smaller residual hills. Higher up the margins of limestone divides and residual hills have been steepened by the braiding streams of gravel fans and valley trains, and cave systems have been enlarged by the entry of meltwater into the limestone from such aggradational surfaces. Indeed the underground breach of the Mole Creek-Lobster Rivulet divide has been suggested as of this origin (Jennings and Sweeting 1959). One may speculate also on a further possible consequence; the incipience of the Mayberry tectonic polje could be only apparent in that glacifluvial and periglacial fluvial gravels may have aggraded its floor back to the level of a previously abandoned surface overflow through Sensation Gorge, the underlying silty clays relating to a former state of complete underground drainage through the present ponors.

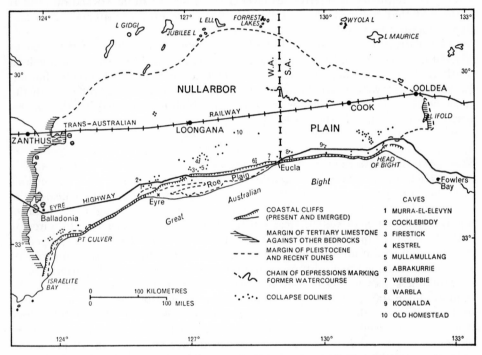

12.7   Selected physiographic features of the Nullarbor Plain

RETARDATION BY DROUGHT IN THE NULLARBOR PLAIN

The Nullarbor Plain is Australia's largest karst region (Fig. 12.7) and one of the world's large ones, a continuous slab of Tertiary limestone of about 165,000 km² (Jennings 1961, 1963c).* A low vegetation of saltbushes, samphires and ephemeral grasses associated with a hot desert climate of 130-200 mm annual rainfall is found in the plain proper, but the same geological structure and relief extend to the coast and so into a belt of slightly higher winter rainfall (200-275 mm), which supports a *Eucalyptus-Acacia* scrub of semi-desert aspect.

* New topographical maps of the Nullarbor require a revision upwards of this figure to 195,000 km².

The geological structure could not be simpler, consisting everywhere of almost horizontal beds. At the surface the Lower Miocene Nullarbor Limestone, partly crystalline, fine-grained, well jointed, and competent, has a thickness of 15-30 m. Below is the friable, white, chalky, Upper Eocene Wilson Bluff Limestone. Porous and with few joints, it is over 200 m thick centrally but wedges out to the margins of the former sedimentary basin.

Much of the coast consists of unbroken vertical cliffs, the product of wave attack on horizontal, pervious and uniform limestones in a dry climate. Almost equally unbroken, the cliffline runs inland for 290 km as an emerged feature behind Roe Plain, a coastal lowland on which Pleistocene coquinas have been found. The sequence of relative sea-level changes has yet to be worked out, but it is thought that there has been a Recent emergence of approximately 3 m and higher Pleistocene stands up to the order of 35 m.

The plain is an impressively flat plateau rising from 45-80 m at the coast to 135-180 m on the inland margin (Plate XXVIc). The surface falls from north to south at about 1 in 2000, and from west to east at about 1 in 10,000. This flatness has amazed everyone from the first explorers onwards, and it is reflected in the construction of the Transcontinental Railway, which it is claimed has the longest perfectly straight line in the world.

(a) Surface Karst

Some parts of this wide area are almost geometrically flat but generally there is a micro-relief. Large parts have gentle undulations, low ridges and depressions 400-1600 m or greater wavelength and of 1·5-3 m amplitude, though nearer the coast the rise and fall can reach 8 m. These undulations are straight and parallel but the trend changes systematically through the plain. There are also circular hollows, 400-1600 m or more across and a metre or two deep, often arranged in lines parallel to the undulations. All these features can be explained in terms of slight differential surface solution of the limestone guided by joint patterns.

Much less frequent are well defined enclosed depressions resembling the cenotes of Yucatan and lacking only the lakes of the latter. Most are circular or oval depressions with vertical to overhanging rock cliffs (Plate XXVIc). They vary from 5 to 30 m deep and from 15 to 100 m in diameter with talus floors, and are obviously collapse dolines due to breakdown of cave roofs. Examples are found at Warbla and the Kestrel Caves (Lowry 1964). Others have suffered slope degradation since collapse but are still recognisably of this origin. A very few, for instance at Cocklebiddy Cave, are so elongated as to resemble short blind valleys, where there may have been collapse at one end followed by spring sapping working headwards from that point.

All these collapse features are restricted to a rainier coastal belt within 40 km of the present or the emerged cliffline (Fig. 12.7). Moreover the total number is only about 150, a very small figure for the area concerned; they are few and far between.

Valleys are exceptional on the plain, the exceptions being so few as to prove the rule. Near the coast there are a very few shallow straight valleys several kilometres long, which clearly follow major structural lineaments. Near the northern and western margins, a few very shallow, meandering valleys run out from the bounding impervious country for a little distance over the limestone plain. Very few function now and in their northward extension they are crossed by vegetated longitudinal dunes of the Great Victoria Desert.

A related feature of some importance runs for 150 km WNW from a point near Cook on the Transcontinental Railway. It is not a continuous valley but a chain of elongated enclosed depressions up to 15 m deep, 1·5 km across, and 12 km long. In certain parts this delineates unmistakably the meanders of a large river, which formerly followed the maximum gradient of this part of the plain.

Although the plain is largely soil-covered, outcrops occur on the low rises. There is little small-scale surface solution sculpture, however, just a few solution pans (*Kamenitsa*) and also rock holes a metre or so deep in unjointed outcrops. In and around the collapse dolines there is slightly more solutional work, but it only consists of tiny pitting and small solution pans. Horizontal pan bottoms on tilted, unstable talus blocks indicate present-day activity, however slight.

Altogether it is clear that surface karst landforms are extremely limited, being most in evidence in the coastal belt where rainfall is highest today and was presumably already so in past climatic phases.

The nature of the surface in the large calls for comment, since it cannot be a planation surface or a structural surface in the sense of a stripped sedimentary surface. Planation must surely have removed the thin Nullarbor Limestone from some portion of this large area, or have left outliers of some younger formation if the surface were erosional; neither condition appears to hold. Instead the plain seems to be an ancient sea floor of Miocene age raised bodily above sea level and scarcely modified since. It has no relief because virtually no tectonic relief was created initially, pure limestones have precluded surface drainage almost everywhere, and low rainfall has prevented surface karst development to any marked degree.

(b) Caves

The grouping of the caves into 'shallow' and 'deep' (Thomson 1950; King 1950) appears to have a generic basis. Lying within about 25 m of the surface, the shallow caves lie in the hard, well joined Nullarbor Limestone. Their entrances range from vertical shafts with evorsional hollowings, through roof windows enlarged by collapse along joint planes, to lateral entries in collapse material at the side of shallow dolines or large lateral entrances at the foot of doline cliffs.

At the most they are 100-200 m in length. Some are simply bottle-shaped potholes, others have a complex arrangement of small passages in underground collapsed rock masses leading from a shaft bottom, whilst large but shallow flat-roofed chambers, with small passages leading off, also occur below short shafts. Roof collapse eventually produces a gaping cavity with no more than rock shelters around.

It has been claimed that these shallow caves are vadose caves; the bedrock shafts and irregular watercourses in silt and gravel below, intermittently followed by descending waters, bear witness to such activity now. However, it is clear that a previous phase of true phreatic preparation of the rock below a massive surface layer of 3-6 m thickness has produced much spongework and anastomosing solution tubes not limited to joint and bedding planes. The intensity of this action of slowly circulating waters beneath a regional watertable accounts for pronounced cave breakdown and the present irregularity of walls and floors. Many shallow cave characteristics are due to this earlier phreatic phase.

Leading off from the bottom of deep collapse dolines at 25-30 m below the plain, the deep caves are developed in the chalky Wilson Bluff Limestone, and are exceptionally large caves to be developed in such mechanically weak limestones (Plate XXVIb). They descend steeply to more or less horizontal levels at about 45 m and 75-90 m below the plain, where they are made up of big halls, 12-18 m high, and 25-35 m wide, with arched walls, flat roofs and apse-like ends. Big domes interrupt them, up to 60 m high and 60 m across, and with rock piles up to 30 m high as in Koonalda Cave. The overall length ranges from about 250 m up to the longest known extent of over 3 km (Anderson 1964).* They are largely floored with angular rockfall and chalk dust but also contain brackish lakes up to 12 m deep as in Weebubbie and Koonalda Caves. Cocklebiddy has intermittent stream courses from the surface over much of its length, and Abrakurrie throughout, with decreasing calibre of load downwards.

The almost stagnant lakes 80-90 m down lie in a regional watertable of which the piezometric surface has been mapped from bores (Ward 1946). The idea of a karst watertable is probably acceptable in this context of horizontal structures and a very permeable limestone, with a primary porosity of 26 per cent (King 1950).

It has been claimed that the caves are phreatic, but in the Davis-Bretz sense this is not likely. The arched and domed sections are the most stable forms which cave breakdown in weak, uniform materials can produce. They are clearly not due to phreatic solution, since the floors are littered with angular blocks showing no sign of solution. Similar talus is found on the bottoms of the lakes, which now are saturated with carbonate. More relevant is Glennie's modification of Swinnerton's 'watertable-stream' theory to explain Yorkshire caves (Glennie 1954). After an initial, small-scale true phreatic development, rising water-filled passages develop at the points of outflow, which by promoting circulation induce an emptying of the upper phreatic tubes. This emptying causes modification by vadose action and cave breakdown in this sector. But the most substantial cave development takes place at the lower ends of the drained upper levels where water banks up after rains and levels oscillate markedly. Here 'master caves' develop, described in Yorkshire as 'big, level railway tunnels', a depiction most appropriate for the Nullarbor deep caves. Despite the fact that present or relict outflows along the coast are not yet known, Glennie's theory appears to be the best working hypothesis to account for the deep caves here.

Only fourteen deep caves are known at present and all fall within the coastal zone of the collapse dolines given above. Though structural explanations have been offered to explain this restriction, control by past and present rainfall gradients is the most convincing hypothesis.

It is evident that little cave development is taking place today other than breakdown, testified by changes noted between successive visits (Thomson 1950).

---

* Further exploration has increased the overall length of Mullamullang Cave to about 6 km and the total length to about 8 km.

Low rainfalls and high evaporation severely limit amounts of water for cave excavation, and restrained plant growth cuts down the supply of biological carbon dioxide, the chief source to render water aggressive towards limestone. So King (1950) has claimed that the caves are chiefly relict from Pleistocene pluvials, for which there is some evidence from within and around the plain. However, the indications of climatic change do not appear to warrant this as a sufficient cause of the rise of watertable of about 90 m implied by the small-scale phreatic preparation of the shallow caves. An alternative cause can be sought in changing sea level, for it is known that sea level relatively at least 30 m higher occurred in the Pleistocene. This must have played an important part in raising watertables to produce those horizontal levels in the deep caves which lie above the lakes and present watertable, and possibly in the shallow caves also. Inter-glacial high sea levels may have been times of phreatic preparation and glacial low sea level times of important vadose and watertable stream action. As yet, however, the correlation of pluvial with glacial periods in Australia is little more than an assumption. Moreover the possibility that the phreatic preparation at the level of the shallow caves goes right back to a period shortly after the emergence of the plain cannot be discounted.

Cave decorations—stalactites, stalagmites and other concretionary forms—are poorly developed in the shallow caves and almost completely absent from the deep caves. The primary porosity and few joints of the Wilson Bluff Limestone are no doubt important in the latter case, allowing the broad diffusion of seepage water instead of canalising it, but the poverty in seepage water is the primary cause of this lack of decoration as a whole.

(c) *Discussion*

There are a number of caves known in the Nullarbor and many more will be found, but this is very much a factor of area, for the caves are actually very thinly scattered. Underground karst development has been as limited as surface karstifi-cation, and in so far as the distribution of collapse dolines and deep caves is a measure, such karst development as has taken place shows a correlation with the rainfall gradient. The conclusion must be that the area has never been much more humid for any very long period since it emerged from the Miocene sea. There has been enough time but not enough water. This karst is essentially of the temperate doline type, but it has remained retarded and immature despite a long history. Thus the Nullarbor karst is pronouncedly a morphoclimatic phenomenon in nature.

DISTINCTIVENESS THROUGH CLIMATE IN THE LIMESTONE RANGES, FITZROY BASIN, WESTERN AUSTRALIA

Though tropical humid karst has, as we have seen, attracted considerable atten-tion in recent decades, few limestone areas in tropical monsoonal or savannah climates have been studied (but see Tricart and Silva 1960). The Limestone Ranges of the Fitzroy basin provide possibly the best Australian instance in terms of extent and available relief to help fill this gap in our knowledge (Jennings and

Sweeting 1963a). Though the country is semi-arid, with rainfall of only 450-640 mm, the precipitation is concentrated seasonally into four summer months, with very intense falls causing much sheet flood action. Temperatures also soar; there are usually more than 100 days of over 38°C., with correspondingly great evaporation. Vegetation varies from open tussocky grassland on soil-covered, undissected limestone to almost nothing but scattered spinifex hummocks on the dissected limestone, though there is open woodland along some alluvial land.

Between the Precambrian heart of the Kimberleys to the northeast and a Mesozoic sedimentary basin to the southwest, the Limestone Ranges derive from a Devonian barrier reef system and have been little disturbed tectonically (Fig. 12.8). Now they form a series of narrow ridges and low plateaux which rise abruptly 30-90 m above surrounding plains, over a distance of 290 km and reaching a maximum width of 30 km. Truncation by a well perfected Mesozoic —mid-Tertiary planation surface was followed by Upper Tertiary rejuvenation and subsequent encroachment from front and rear by a modern planation surface of high perfection also and closely related to present baselevel (Wright 1964). Superimposed gorges of rivers from the oldland of the heart of the Kimberleys reveal the structure of the reef complex most clearly (McWhae *et al.* 1958), and several facies can be recognised:

The Barrier Reef Proper. The *in situ* accumulation of calcareous algae, stromatoporoids and other organisms, forms a winding belt of unbedded limestone only 100-200 m wide, comprising perhaps 10 per cent of the whole complex.

Forereef Facies. Talus deposits on the former seaward side of the narrow reef now constitute well bedded calcarenites chiefly, with primary depositional dips of 15-30°, though they include small biohermal masses of fine-grained, unbedded algal limestone.

Algal Reef Facies. These represent tongues of reef growing down the foreslope of submarine talus and occur as massive bodies.

Backreef Facies. In the lagoons there accumulated usually horizontally well bedded limestones, mainly calcarenites from reef erosion but including biostromes of sessile organisms also.

However, with the exception of the reef proper, these differences of facies give rise to only minor geomorphological differences, apart from one important respect. The backreef facies is more likely to be rendered impure by terrigenous sediment and to be inter-bedded with siltstones and mudstones; this is important because full karst effects seem to require about 90 per cent purity in limestone formations and 60 per cent is a rough limit for any karst effects at all (Corbel 1957). In consequence much of the backreef and even some of the forereef do not give rise to very much in the way of karst peculiarities and these impure facies will be neglected here.

(a) *Drainage and Surface Karst*

In the middle of the wider parts of the Limestone Ranges, the mid-Tertiary planation surface survives almost intact as grassy plains with deep, fine-textured black clay soils. A very open pattern of shallow seasonal drainage lines diversifies the gentle surface of the largest remnant, the Oscar plateau, but most rain sinks underground without even the development of dolines.

XXVa Solution effects on a limestone outcrop, Cooleman Plain, New South Wales. *Above, sub-aerially formed ripples; below, smooth subsoil surface exposed by soil erosion.*

XXVb *Dry valley with shallow dolines, Cooleman Plain, New South Wales, eroded in a planation surface in Silurian limestone surrounded by igneous ranges*

XXVc *Large doline, with active slump pits in earth fill, found in Ordovician limestone in alluviated depression at Mayberry near Mole Creek, Tasmania*

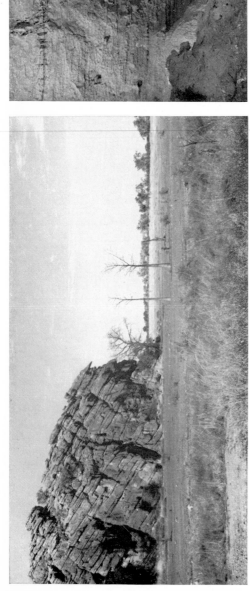

XXVIa Oscar Range, Fitzroy basin, Western Australia. Soil-covered pediment backed by marginal bluff cut in Devonian foreref limestone with depositional dip of 30°.

XXVIb Koonalda Cave, Nullarbor Plain, South Australia. Arch in friable Eocene limestone; floor of collapse blocks and chalky dust. Photograph by E. H. Fairlie-Cuninghame.

XXVIc Murrawijinie No. 1 Cave, Nullarbor Plain, South Australia. A shallow collapse doline in

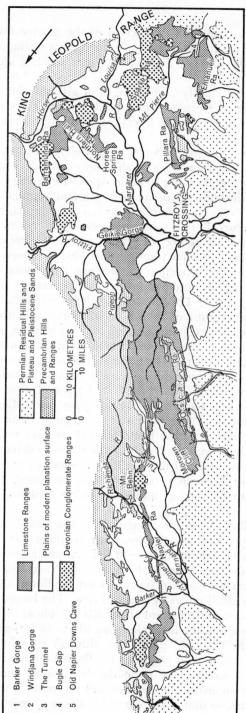

12.8 The Limestone Ranges and their physiographic setting, Fitzroy basin, Western Australia

1   Barker Gorge
2   Windjana Gorge
3   The Tunnel
4   Bugle Gap
5   Old Napier Downs Cave

Limestone Ranges

Plains of modern planation surface

Devonian Conglomerate Ranges

Permian Residual Hills and
Plateau and Pleistocene Sands

Precambrian Hills
and Ranges

0   10 KILOMETRES
0   10 MILES

U

The margins of the plateaux and the full width of the narrow ranges have been and still are being dissected in the process of replacement of the upper surface by the modern one below, so that there can be seen the full sequence of landform development.

Where the upper surface has simply been stripped of soil, solution pans predominate amongst solution micro-features. Their level bottoms carry veneers of clay, silt, and algal remains, which promote lateral solution and so tend to keep the surface flat.

Near the range margins or the gorges, water gets underground much more readily and the surface is etched into fields of sharp-toothed ridges and blocks separated by widened joint planes, familiar in basic type but extreme in development. On steep surfaces solution flutings occur in length and abundance greatly exceeding those of temperate climates; they are broken by rainpits, suggesting that vigorous solution still occurs. Larger solution grooves (*Rinnenkarren*), more characteristic of tropical than of temperate karst, are well developed, and solution pits and wells proliferate at joint intersections. Always, however, vertical corrosion is accompanied by the tendency to produce flat floors on which protective films of impervious fines accumulate and direct solution laterally to steepen the intervening projections. This twofold tendency to vertical incision and lateral sidecutting is characteristic of the whole landform sequence.

On a larger scale, solution-widened joints develop into big features up to 20 m deep, 3-10 m across and hundreds of metres long, which occur in networks due to joint systems. Larger and more numerous than the related solution corridors or bogazi of Yugoslavia, they produce what can be termed 'giant grikeland'. Fissure caves link the corridors underground. This is the initial phase of dissection.

From these networks of corridors and caves, roof collapse and surface solution produce integrated valley systems of box form and rectangular pattern; divides are either nearly flat or like narrow walls. These box-valleys have much planed rock floor, which is frequently so well graded as to allow one to drive right into the heart of the dissected limestone until the way has narrowed so much that the vehicle has to be backed out between vertical walls of limestone. Ephemeral streams flowing over their floors sink at numerous points without producing dolines.

Apart from the giant grikes, there are comparatively few closed depressions; indeed, conical or basin-shaped dolines are rare. More frequent are flat-floored, vertical-walled, rectangular, closed depressions with residual soil, alluvial, or bare-rock floors. Ephemeral streams may traverse the floors from cave to cave. These features do not fall easily into the classical types of karst landform, though they can perhaps be thought of as small poljes of a special type. The largest, near Old Napier Downs homestead, is 1·5 km long and about 300 m wide at the most.

Intermediate between these and the box-valleys are what can be termed marginal amphitheatres, where the marginal plains pass through gaps in the range margins and spread out just inside with gentle or flat floors between steep walls.

As these various elements—box-valleys, polje-like depressions, and marginal amphitheatres—develop, they intersect one another and the relief is thus cut up into isolated blocks and pillars, so that what remains is a type of towerkarst. It is on a small scale vertically, however, since available relief is small and the highest tower is only about 45 m high; withal, the basic character of this stage makes it resemble the towerkarst of tropical humid climates rather than any aspect of temperate karst. But there is one important difference; the planed surfaces which separate the towers are not generally alluviated but are often rock-cut pediments. The significance of this attribute becomes more apparent if the perimeters of the ranges are considered.

The Limestone Ranges rear up suddenly from the plains around and between them, the gentlest margins consisting of rocky scarps of 20-30° in the forereef beds with their depositional dips (Plate XXVIa). Horizontal backreef facies frequently gives rise to steeper walls but the algal reef facies is associated with the most massive features, for example Morown Cliff which is not far from vertical and 60-90 m high.

Some cliffs have alluvium at their feet, especially near the points where the great rivers from the inner part of Kimberley enter and leave their gorges through the ranges. Here they spread out laterally in flood season, lap the foot of the ranges, and corrode them with acid waters. Thus lateral solutional undercutting so important in tropical humid towerkarst (Lehmann *et al.* 1956) does occur.

But much more of the margins consist of pediments inclined gently away from the range fronts. These may be straight, convex or concave in transverse profile and along them vehicles can usually be driven over continuous rock-cut surfaces with comparative ease without road preparation. Occasional small towers diversify them in places.

Pediments occur on other rocks than limestone in this tropical semi-arid region; nevertheless there are special reasons why the upper parts of the pediments are so well formed here and the piedmont angle so abrupt. In the first place the perfection of the pediments can be related to the exceptional responsiveness limestone must have to sheet flood action through lateral corrosion of projecting rock. Secondly the presence of cliff-foot caves must be noted; here water emerges from the limestone and undercuts it. Rock debris falling from the undercut cliff may form low ridges directing the outflow laterally and so extend the cave and its effects sideways. In this respect also limestone is in effect reinforcing through its peculiar properties processes common to the morphogenetic system of the region as a whole because cavernous weathering, particularly at the base of bluffs, contributes on various rock types to the retreat and maintenance of steepness of slopes. Thirdly the pediment may also be perfected through the effect of calcrete ridges, which tend to develop parallel to the marginal walls and bank back drainage along the foot of the range.

(b) *Caves*

Little is yet known of the caves of the Limestone Ranges; few have been explored and fewer still mapped (Jennings 1962). Innumerable small and fragmented caves are to be found in the dissected parts of the ranges but comparatively few extensive systems are known. The causes are various; the available relief is not great, and surface solution seems rapid in comparison with underground action, so that roof removal and collapse easily break up and destroy cave systems. Moreover, the superimposed rivers have tremendous, if short-lived, flows, which are not readily displaced from their superficial courses through gorges into alternative underground passages in the ranges. A lesser stream, Cave Spring Creek, does indeed pass through the range east of Bugle Gap in a chain of short caves separated by reaches in canyons and polje-like small depressions. Old Napier Downs Cave in the Napier Range is a fairly substantial outflow cave incompletely explored, which drains the largest enclosed depression of the whole area already mentioned. Perhaps the most interesting cave of all is The Tunnel, through which Tunnel Creek breaches a narrow part of the Napier Range (Jennings and Sweeting 1963b). The cave underlies a wind-gap in the range, which is relict from a gorge of superimposition related to a stage when the outer and inner marginal plains stood considerably higher but still some 25 m below the level of the Tertiary summit planation surface. The cave thus seems to represent a case of autopiracy though there are some problems attaching to reconstruction of the cave's evolution.

Though richer than the Nullarbor caves in cave decoration, those of the Limestone Ranges lag well behind most of the caves of southeastern Australia in the elaborateness and freshness of secondary precipitation forms. The long dry season is the likely explanation.

(c) *Discussion*

There is thus a distinctive karst here, with some characters due to structure, some to small available relief, but others to climate. In so far as pedimentation is involved, the link with the regional climate is obvious. It departs in many ways from temperate karst yet it is not wholly of tropical humid type. The giant grikeland phase shows extremely strong structural control of surface solution and, of course, structural lineaments are etched out more distinctly in arid morphogenetic systems generally. The larger enclosed depressions and marginal amphitheatres stress the importance of lateral corrosion, a process more widely operative in tropical humid than in temperate karst. The residual towers also link the karst here to tropical humid karst. but with differences due to the pediment factor. Thus it may be that there is here a semi-arid tropical monsoonal karst type.

Thus far the discussion has implied that the relief below the Tertiary surface is entirely to be interpreted in terms of present climate. It may be that past periods of wetter climate have intervened; earlier tropical humid karst may have been modified by later semi-arid pedimentation. This is not impossible, though as yet the only direct evidence of climatic change within the area since the Tertiary planation and the formation of the associated laterites is not of wetter climate but of a drier Pleistocene phase. All the landforms seem to be developing today, if but slowly, and a year's climate virtually consists of the seasonal alternation of tropical humid and tropical arid conditions. It is more economical of theory to regard the karst as adjusted to contemporary morphogenetic conditions.

CONCLUSION

Though the limestones of the karst areas dealt with are by no means identical, they have much in common as regards the lithological characters likely to affect landforms—purity and competence in particular. The chief exception to this is the Wilson Bluff Limestone of the Nullarbor Plain. Though finding some expression in the forms of the deep caves, its friability would have had more substantial effect on the landscape if it were not overlain by the more competent Nullarbor Limestone. But in substantial degree this factor of variability has been excluded from this essay; for instance it may be recalled that, wherever low in impurities, both backreef and forereef facies gave rise to essentially the same kind of relief in the Limestone Ranges of West Kimberley. However, it would not be possible to present a fully representative account of Australian karst without introducing significant lithological variation. Thus a highly characteristic limestone of this continent is aeolian calcarenite and karst in this rock can be at least partly syngenetic. Karst landforms and drainage have not been impressed on a finished product in terms of lithification, but have evolved simultaneously with the diagenesis of the terrestrial calcareous sands which have made up this particular carbonate rock. The special syngenetic nature of karst in aeolian calcarenite has only recently been recognised and still needs investigation.

Though another uniform factor in the regional instances is the virtual, though not complete, absence of neotectonics, there is much variation in the static framework of older tectonic structures from the horizontal bedding of the Nullarbor Plain to the folding and faulting of the Mole Creek karst. Many features show structural guidance of solution; an example is the parallelism of much of the outer walls of the Limestone Ranges with the strike of the dipping forereef beds. Cave forms in particular are liable to structural influence; an example discussed was the case of Dip Cave, Wee Jasper. Nevertheless many major geomorphological features within and differences between the areas do not appear to be structural. Thus at Mole Creek, though the impervious rock framework imposes major controls, the important divides between the Mersey valley, the Loatta and Mayberry depressions, and the Mole Creek and Lobster Rivulet valleys do not appear to be related to any tectonic elements in the limestone but are probably due to superimposition.

Planation, rejuvenation and the influence of changing baselevel loom at least as large as structure in the geomorphology of this sample, which, however, it should be noted does not include karst which has suffered Alpine orogenesis. Australia has perhaps no more than one instance of this in the Cape Range of Western Australia, which is almost unstudied (Cook 1962). The pattern of karst development in Cooleman Plain is very much a reflection of the extent of rejuvenation, and it has also been argued that Pleistocene changes in the relative level of land and sea are important for cave development in the Nullarbor Plain.

Much of the variety in karst presented here seems to derive from climatic differences. This is perhaps most widely evident in the matter of minor surface solution features, though this operates in large part indirectly through soils and vegetation. Tricart and Cailleux (1955) have maintained that the morphogenetic influence of climate is effected indirectly more importantly than directly. In terms of larger karst features, also, it is clear that the Limestone Ranges, the Nullarbor Plain, and the southeastern examples fall into three distinct morphoclimatic groups. But, apart from the aspect of minor surface sculpture, it is not certain whether there are important differences attributable to climate within the southeastern Australian karst group discussed here; Wee Jasper and Cooleman Plain are too small for adequate comparison in this regard. Moreover differences in Davisian evolutionary stage, that is in the factor of baselevel change and adjustment to it, confuse the picture.

Effects of past contrasting climates complicate interpretation. In three of the karst areas—Cooleman Plain, Mole Creek, and Nullarbor Plain—it is certain that inheritance from different morphoclimatic systems is involved, though knowledge remains inadequate to assess this factor fully. In regard to a fourth, the Limestone Ranges, the criteria available remain insufficiently sharp for certainty as to whether the karst peculiarities found there represent solely the consequences of present climate or whether there is some form of inheritance from wetter climatic conditions of which as yet there is no direct evidence. This inheritance may have the character not of relict, but of bastard landforms in the sense of forms which owe their present nature to more than one morphoclimatic system (Baulig 1952). On the other hand it is thought possible to suggest with regard to the Nullarbor Plain that the present landforms do not allow of very substantial or very prolonged variation from present climate, though there is no doubt that somewhat wetter phases did contribute to the surface and the underground morphology.

The examples are too few to expect to resolve many of the outstanding questions by more detailed work in the areas concerned. Nor does it seem likely that even the full tally of Australia's karst areas, most of which suffer from the limitations of small size and too great interaction with surrounding impervious rock terrain, will suffice to attribute effects accurately to the different factors which may have been involved. Indeed the variables in geomorphology are so manifold and often so little susceptible of measurement and calculation that the question arises whether the whole earth will provide a large enough sample for unravelling all the possible interactions of rock nature and arrangement, land and sea-level movements, climatic and vegetational history in the present landscape, blurred and blotted as it is today in both form and process by the ever more powerful hand of man.

REFERENCES

Anderson, E. G. (1964). Nullarbor Expedition 1963-4. *Helictite.* **2**: 121-34.

Baulig, H. (1952). Surfaces d'aplanissement II. *Annls Géogr.* **61**: 245-62.

Birot, P. (1954). Problèmes de morphologie karstique. *Annls Géogr.* **63**: 161-92.

Blanc, A. (1958). Répertoire bibliographique critique des études de relief karstique en Yougoslavie depuis Jovan Cvijic. *Mém. Docums. Cent. Docum. cartogr. géogr.* **7**: 135-227.

Bögli, A. (1960). Kalklösung und Karrenbildung. *Z. Geomorph.* Suppbd **2**: 4-21.

Bretz, J. H. (1942). Vadose and phreatic features of limestone caverns. *J. Geol.* **50**: 675-811.

Brown, F. R. and Vries, M. H. de (1958). The subterranean hydrology of the Mole Creek Area. *Bull. Tasm. Cavern. Club.* **1** (3): 9-15.

Burns, K. (1957). The Geology of the Dairy Plains District. Dept Mines, unpub. interim rept, Tasm., Hobart.

—— and Rundle, A. (1958). The Geology of the Mole Creek Caverns. *Bull. Tasm. Cavern. Club* **1** (3): 3-8.

Cook, D. (1962). Caves of the Cape Range, North-west Cape, Western Australia. *J. West. Aust. speleol. Grp* 1962: 4-11.

Corbel, J. (1957). Les karsts de nord-ouest de l'Europe. *Mém. Inst. Etud. Rhodaniennes.* No. 12. Lyon.

Cvijic, J. (1960). La géographie des terrains calcaires. *Monogr. Acad. Serbe Sci. Arts.* **391**. Belgrade.

David, T. W. E., ed. Browne, W. R. (1950). *The Geology of the Commonwealth of Australia.* London.

Davies, W. E. (1949). Features of cave breakdown. *Bull. natn. speleol. Soc.* **11**: 34-5.

Davis, W. M. (1930). Origin of limestone caverns. *Bull. geol. Soc. Am.* **41**: 475-628.

Edgell, H. S. (1949). The geology of the Burrinjuck-Wee Jasper district. Unpub. B.Sc. thesis, University of Sydney.

Gill, E. D. and Sharp, K. R. (1956). The Tertiary rocks of the Snowy Mountains, Eastern Australia. *J. geol. Soc. Aust.* **4**: 21-40.

Glennie, E. (1954). The origin and development of cave systems in limestone. *Trans. Cave Res. Grp Gt Br.* **3**: 75-83.

—————— (1958). Nameless streams: proposed new terms. *Cave Res. Grp Gt Br. Newsletters* **72-7**: 22-3.

Grund, A. (1914). Der geographische Zyklus im Karst. *Z. Ges. Erdk. Berl.* 1914: 621-40.

Hughes, T. D. (1957). *Limestones in Tasmania.* Dept Mines Tasm. Geol. Surv. Min. Res. No. 10.

Jennings, J. N. (1961). A preliminary report on the karst morphology of the Nullarbor Plains. *Cave Expl. Grp (S. Aust.) Occas. Pap.* 2.

—————— (1962). The caves of the Limestone Ranges of West Kimberley. *J. West. Aust. speleol. Grp* 1962: 29-34.

—————— (1963a). Collapse doline, Australian Landform examples No. 1. *Aust. Geogr.* **9**: 120-1.

—————— (1963b). Geomorphology of the Dip Cave, Wee Jasper, New South Wales. *Helictite* **1**: 43-58.

—————— (1963c). Some geomorphological problems of the Nullarbor Plain. *Trans. R. Soc. S. Aust.* **87**: 41-62.

—————— (1964). Geomorphology of Punchbowl and Signature Caves, Wee Jasper, New South Wales. *Helictite* **2**: 57-80.

—————— and Ahmad, N. (1957). The legacy of an ice cap. *Aust. Geogr.* **7**: 62-75.

—————— and Bik, M. J. (1962). Karst morphology in Australian New Guinea. *Nature, Lond.* **194**: 1036-8.

—————— and Sweeting, M. M. (1959). Underground breach of a divide at Mole Creek, Tasmania. *Aust. J. Sci.* **21**: 261-2.

——————, —————— (1963a). The Limestone Ranges of the Fitzroy Basin, Western Australia. *Bonn. geogr. Abh.* Heft 32.

——————, —————— (1963b). The Tunnel, a cave in the Napier Range, Fitzroy Basin, W. Australia. *Trans. Cave Res. Grp Gt Br.* **6**: 53-68.

King, D. (1950). Geological notes on the Nullarbor cavernous limestone. *Trans. R. Soc. S. Aust.* **73**: 52-8.

Lehmann, H. (1936). Morphologische Studien in Java. *Geogr. Abh.* 3rd Ser. No. 9.

——————, ed. (1954). Der Karstphänomen in verschiedenen Klimazonen, *Erdkunde* **8**: 112-22.

——————, ed. (1960). Internationale Beiträge zur Karst morphologie. *Z. Geomorph.* Suppbd 2.

——————, Krömmelbein, K., and Lötschert, W. (1956). Karstmorphologische, geologische und botanische Studien in der Sierra de los Organos auf Cuba. *Erdkunde* **10**: 185-204.

Lowry, D. C. (1964). Kestrel Caverns Nos. 1 and 2, Madura. *The Western Caver* **4** (3): 9-14.

McWhae, J. R. H., *et al.* (1958). The stratigraphy of Western Australia. *J. geol. Soc. Aust.* **4**: 1-161.

Maksimovich, G. A. (1962). Karst Australii. *Gidrogeologiya i Karstoredeniye* **1**: 153-71.

Rathjens, C. (1954). Karsterscheinungen in der klimatisch-morphologischen Vertikalglied-erung des Gebirges. *Erdkunde* 8: 120.

Rundle, A. S. (1961). Evolution of the Mersey River Valley. Unpub. B.Sc. thesis, University of Tasmania.

Sexton, R. T. (1960). Notes on some cave surveys. *Bull. Tasm. Cavern. Club* 1 (4): 37-44.

Stevens, N. (1958). Palaeozoic geology of the Cooleman Caves district, New South Wales. *Proc. Linn. Soc. N.S.W.* 83: 251-8.

Sweeting, M. M. (1960). The caves of the Buchan area, Victoria, Australia. *Z. Geomorph.* Suppbd 2: 81-9.

Thomas, T. M. (1963). Solution Subsidence in south-east Carmarthenshire and south-west Breconshire. *Trans. Inst. Br. Geogr.* 33: 45-60.

Thomson, J. M. (1950). The Nullarbor caves system. *Trans. R. Soc. S. Aust.* 73: 48-51.

Tricart, J. and Cailleux, A. (1955). *Introduction à la géomorphologie climatique.* Paris.

—— and Silva, T. C. da (1960). Un exemple d'évolution karstique en milieu tropical sec; le morne de Bom de Jesus da Lapa (Bahia, Bresil). *Z. Geomorph.* 4: 29-42.

Verstappen, H. Th. (1964). Geomorphology of the Star Mountains. *Nova Guinea*, Geology, No. 5: 101-58.

Ward, L. K. (1946). *The Occurrence, Composition, Testing and Utilisation of Underground Water in South Australia and the Search for Further Supplies.* Bull. geol. Surv. S. Aust. No. 23.

Wilhelmy, H. (1958). *Klimamorphologie der Massengesteine.* Braunschweig.

Wright, R. (1964). Geomorphology of the West Kimberley Area. Ch. IV of *General Report on lands of the West Kimberley area, W.A.* CSIRO Aust. Land Res. Ser. No. 9.

13

Pre-basalt, Sub-basalt and Post-basalt Surfaces of the Hunter Valley, New South Wales

R. W. GALLOWAY

INTRODUCTION

Study of the geomorphological history of eastern New South Wales must take cognisance of the Tertiary basalt. Not only does it occupy extensive portions of the region but it also acts as a datum from which stages in the landscape evolution can be reconstructed. It buried and preserved the pre-existing surface and presented a relatively featureless surface on which a new drainage system evolved *ab initio*; it may have done this on more than one occasion.

The present essay attempts to assess the Cainozoic history of the Hunter Valley in relation to the widespread basalt occurrences. This requires reconstruction of the age and original extent of the basalt. When the basalt erupted it obliterated, but preserved, the landscape of the time. Later, this buried landscape was affected by considerable post-basalt tectonic movements and consequently its present form, as reconstructed from the altitude of basalt remnants, differs notably from the original. We must therefore distinguish between a pre-basalt land surface of lower Tertiary age and a sub-basalt surface formed in the earth movements which affected the basalt. Only the latter is available for study, and will be considered first, but the former may be reconstructed by subtracting the effects of post-basalt tectonics. The major post-basalt geomorphological events, the relation of drainage development to the basalt, and the legacy of the sub-basalt surface in the present landscape form the themes of this essay.

The Hunter Valley, which drains to the sea at Newcastle on the central coast of New South Wales, was selected for this study on account of the widespread occurrence of Tertiary basalt, the reasonably good map cover, and the knowledge of the area acquired during a regional survey by the CSIRO Division of Land Research (Story *et al.* 1963).

Thanks are due to Mr K. Fitchett of the Division of Land Research, who helped with the field-work, and to the Hunter Valley Research Foundation for some geological information.

THE BASALT

Figure 13.1 shows the known distribution of Tertiary extrusive volcanics and some intrusives in the Hunter Valley, compiled from air photographs supplemented by field observations. Two sets of volcanics are distinguished, here termed 'first basalt' and 'second basalt'. These bodies of volcanic rocks roughly correspond

293

to the 'Older basalt' and 'Newer basalt' of earlier workers, but the latter terms have not been used because their validity and applicability in particular cases are controversial.

(a) *The First Basalt*

The first basalt is by far the more extensive and covers some 3900 km² of the 21,000 km² of the Hunter Valley. Figure 13.1 indicates that it is rather more widespread than shown on previously published maps (Geol. Surv. N.S.W. 1962; Story *et al.* 1963). The greatest thicknesses occur along the northern margin of the area: 700 m at Mt Barrington and at the head of the Isis River, 825 m at Mt Murrurrundi, and probably well over 900 m under the Liverpool Range. Considerable thicknesses also exist near the southern boundary of the Goulburn Valley, where up to 150 m of basalt flows cap Mt Coricudgy and possibly 230 m rest on Kerry Mountain (Carne 1908). Towards the centre and west of the Goulburn Valley, the basalt thins to a few metres or disappears entirely. The present volume of basalt is about 500 km³.

For clarity, intrusions probably associated with the first basalt have been omitted from Figure 13.1. An extensive basalt outcrop at the junction of Growee and Bylong Creeks, previously mapped as a flow (Dulhunty 1937), is a sill and accordingly is not shown. A difficult problem is presented by Mt Dangar, an isolated hill which rises to 670 m a few kilometres northwest of the Hunter-Goulburn confluence and which dominates the surrounding dissected sandstone plateau by 250-275 m. The upper 135-150 m of Mt Dangar consist of dolerite which Browne (1933) suggested was a denuded fragment of some older (presumably Mesozoic) sill, whereas Süssmilch (1940) apparently regarded it as part of the Tertiary basalt sequence. While the texture would suggest that the rock is indeed intrusive, dolerite flows are known in the Mullaly area not far north of the Hunter Valley (Wilshire and Standard 1963).

By far the greater part of these volcanics consists of olivine basalt, but dolerite facies and flows of other composition do occur. Apart from the immediate vicinity of vents, pyroclastics have rarely been observed and the basalt seems to have poured out quietly in a highly liquid state.

The sources of the basalt in the southern half of the area are plugs and dykes. Plugs appear to have been the source in the northeast, since several occur in the Nundle area just outside the Hunter Valley (Crook 1961). The source of the extensive basalt in the northwest is not definitely known but it is assumed that a fissure or fissures underlie the Liverpool Range.

The age of the basalt is not known for certain but there is fairly general agreement that it is Lower Tertiary (David and Browne 1950). This accords with the type of plant remains occurring in sub-basalt and inter-basalt sediments, with the extent of post-basalt dissection, with the presence of laterite patches on the basalt surface, and with the radiometric dating of 34 million years for a basalt not far away in southern New England (Cooper, Richards, and Webb 1963).

Between basalt flows in the north of the area, now exposed at points from Cassilis to Pages Creek, there are sedimentary layers and soils; similar materials are frequently found under the basalt. The sediments include siliceous gravel, sand, and clay, sometimes consolidated into conglomerate, sandstone, and shale,

and sometimes contorted by the passage of molten basalt over them. These sediments indicate that eruption of the first basalt took place in stages, interrupted by intervals of weathering, erosion, and deposition. At least two such inter-basaltic intervals are known just to the northeast of the Hunter Valley (Crook 1961) but it is probable that they were relatively short and they do not require serious modification of the view that the basalt flows were parts of essentially one geological event. The final flows of the first basalt obliterated all relief that may have formed during these intervals.

The original extent of the basalt can be reconstructed on the assumption that the scattered occurrences of today are survivals of a former continuous sheet. Unfortunately we have no definite proof of this assumption on which much of the following discussion must rest, but it is in accord with the evidence from the near-horizontality of the flows that the lava was highly liquid and capable of spreading widely over low gradients. The present maximum thickness of the basalt in each locality gives a minimum value for the original thickness, taking no account of possible lowering of the surface by erosion.

In the northeastern third of the area there is little doubt that basalt averaging at least 450 m in thickness was originally present everywhere, since all high summits are capped by remnants of thick flows. On the southern and western sides of the Barrington Tops great slabs of basalt now rest on the ridges and clearly once extended far beyond their present limits (Plate XXVIIa). North of the Goulburn River the near-horizontal basalt flows of the Liverpool Range must have extended much further south and with greater thickness than now. South of the Goulburn, the large number of patches on ridge tops is strong evidence that a continuous sheet once existed there, but near the river itself only some hills have basalt caps and others, equally suited by form and altitude, have none. This means that in the central Goulburn Valley the basalt was originally only patchy or that post-basalt erosion has largely removed it. In this connection the evidence from Mt Dangar, discussed above, is crucial: if its lava cap is indeed part of the general Tertiary volcanics it implies an original thickness of over 300 m of basalt in the Goulburn Valley, most of which has been removed by erosion. On the other hand, there is evidence that some Lower Tertiary auriferous deep leads in the Gulgong area, only 20 km west of the head of the Goulburn, were never covered by basalt (David and Browne 1950).

In the centre of the Hunter Valley, the presence of basalt flows at about 670 m on top of Woodlands Trig. (Raggatt and Whitworth 1932) indicates that basalt was widespread here too, though not necessarily very thick if the wide lowland to the north was excavated after the eruption.

Silcrete boulders (known as 'grey billy') on wide benches 35-40 m above the Hunter River near Denman and Jerrys Plains have been ascribed to silicification of terrace sand and gravel by basalt (Raggatt 1938). However, in association with the basalt cap on the summit of Woodlands Trig. a few miles away, this implies a thickness of some 520 m of basalt: it seems unlikely that such an immense thickness could be removed entirely, yet leave the thin underlying stratum of silcrete preserved. A more likely explanation is that a much later, local basalt flow, now removed, silicified the underlying material, but it seems equally probable, as Süssmilch (1940) has pointed out, that the silcrete is a weathering phenomenon related to the climate of the later Tertiary or early Pleistocene, and has no connection with basalt.

In the southeast of the Hunter Valley there is little evidence from which to reconstruct the former extent of the basalt: three small patches of basalt are shown in Figure 13.1 in the Paterson-Dungog area but their age and nature are uncertain. However, in the extreme south, Tertiary volcanics cap Mt Warrawolong and also Mts Yengo and Wareng, just outside the area (Standard 1961). These summits are the highest in their locality and the implication is that if other hills as high had survived, they too would carry basalt. The presence of these caps suggests that basalt may once have extended widely over the lower Hunter and that it was perhaps even continuous with that around the Barrington Tops. Since the basalt has been largely removed by erosion in the upper Hunter, farthest from the sea, it is not surprising to find that it has practically disappeared from the southeast, which lies much nearer to the baselevel of erosion.

Thus, according to the available evidence, the main basalt covered at least two-thirds of the Hunter Valley and possibly the entire area. It was very thick (over 600 m) in the north, and moderately thick (tens of metres) in the southwest. In the west, centre, and east it was probably fairly thin, though it could have exceeded 300 m if the lava cap on Mt Dangar were part of the one Tertiary volcanic sequence. Conservatively estimating the original mean depth at 150 m and the area at 15,500 km^2 gives an initial volume of over 2300 km^3; twice this figure is not impossible.

(b) *The Second Basalt*

Long after the major basalt outpourings, there was a minor revival of vulcanicity with the development of flows in the Goulburn Valley which now survive as a series of small patches perched above the river for 80 km downstream from Crowie. At least two flows occurred (Plate XXVIIb) and the height of their base above the present river gradually increases downstream from about 20 m at Crowie to 110 m at Baerami. The present gradient of the river between these points (neglecting meanders in alluvium) is about 1 in 500 while that of the valley delineated by the basalt patches is about 1 in 1000. This low gradient indicates a highly fluid lava, but the possibility of some later warping cannot be entirely excluded. Extrapolation of the valley floor delineated by the basalt patches eastwards towards Denman and Jerrys Plains indicates that the basalt, if it ever reached so far, was some 70 m above the silcrete discussed earlier and so could not have caused the silicification. It is not known if all this basalt issued from the vent at Crowie mapped by Dulhunty (1937) or if other vents existed downvalley from this point. Dulhunty apparently regarded the Crowie basalt as part of the main Tertiary volcanic sequence. If this were so one would expect to find similar patches in similar sites in adjacent parts of tributary valleys, such as Merriwa Creek, but no such patches exist. The basalt is strictly confined within the deep inner valley of the Goulburn in what must have been the lowest part of the landscape at the time of the eruption, 100 m or more below the remnants of the earlier, first basalt flows which near the Goulburn River are now found only on interfluves. The position in the landscape and the degree of dissection suggest that the second basalt is probably Pliocene or early Pleistocene.

At about the same time a few necks developed north, east, and southeast of Scone; they are shown on Figure 13.1 since they throw light on the Cainozoic tectonic evolution of the area.

Having thus deduced on geomorphic grounds that there are two distinct ages of Tertiary volcanics in the Hunter Valley, there is a risk of circular argument in using this in turn to support further geomorphological dating. Nevertheless, in the absence of any more reliable method, this must be done. Different ages of Tertiary basalts in New South Wales have long been recognised (e.g. Harper 1909; David and Browne 1950) on similar geomorphological grounds.

THE SUB-BASALT SURFACE

(a) *Compilation of the Map*

The map of the sub-basalt surface (Fig. 13.1) was compiled from field observations, air photographs, contour maps, and scattered information in the literature. The field-work mainly consisted of mapping the extent of the basalt and fixing the altitude of its base by aneroid or by contour maps where available. Maps with contours at approximately 15 m at scales between 1/15,840 and 1/63,360 and of fair to good quality cover most of the eastern two-thirds of the area; in the western third the only available maps of reasonable accuracy are at a scale of 1/250,000 with contours at approximately 75 m. The reliability of the final map varies with the frequency of basalt occurrences, accessibility in the field, and the nature of the contour maps: the quality of the data does not encourage drawing form lines at intervals closer than 250 ft (75 m). Varying degrees of reliability in the form lines are indicated on Figure 13.1.

The biggest problem in preparing the map was to identify the true base of the basalt; thereafter fixing its altitude with an accuracy sufficient for the present purpose was comparatively straightforward. The basalt base is generally obscured by soil and rubble which can extend for remarkable distances downslope from the outcrop boundary: on the eastern slopes of Wheelbarrow Mountain for instance, mass movement has carried basaltic debris nearly 1 km down an average gradient of 1 in 10. Contemporary surficial movement, aided presumably by volume changes in the characteristic montmorillonitic clay, is attested by the piling up of rock debris behind logs and other obstructions on both cleared and timbered land, but at altitudes over 1100 m it seems that the extensive accumulations are largely fossil and may well be relics of Pleistocene periglacial mass movement. Good examples of stabilized rubble, in this case scree, occur along the eastern edge of the Nullo Mountain plateau. The best exposures of the basalt base were found on the crests of spurs, whereas in creek beds and valley bottoms the contact was obscured by slumped material. In the dry northeastern corner of the area occurrences of old soil immediately under the basalt generally showed clearly as light-toned scars both on the ground and on the air photographs, although confusion was possible with analogous layers between the basalt flows. In the densely forested, steep country south of the Barrington Tops (Fig. 13.2), on the other hand, the basalt base could not be identified from the air photographs, and the form lines depend on a few aneroid determinations. Sometimes the base of the basalt is marked by a horizontal shelf cut on the underlying rock. On the western side of

Nullo Mountain, where horizontally bedded sandstone underlies the basalt and provides particularly suitable structure, such a shelf, about 10 m wide, can be followed for several kilometres like a roadway, locally obstructed by basalt debris from the slopes above and cut across by gullies. This feature was a useful field indicator of the basalt base but was too small to be identified under trees on air photographs. Wider, but rather less well defined sub-basalt benches cut across steeply dipping shale in the upper Paterson Valley (Fig. 13.2).

Further information on the trend of the sub-basalt surface was derived by plotting the position and altitude of summits without basalt. Because of the uncertainty surrounding the Mt Dangar lava, data from this point have not been used in compiling the form lines.

13.2 *The upper Paterson Valley is bounded by basalt remnants resting on a distinct bench cut across folded Carboniferous sediments. Barrington Tops form the skyline*

(b) *General Form of the Sub-basalt Surface*

The sub-basalt surface portrayed in Figure 13.1 is undulating to accidented, with local relief about one-third to one-half the present values and generally with even slopes. The sub-basalt surface of southern New England mapped by Voisey (1942) has the same general character. The smooth forms have made possible reasonably satisfactory interpolation of the form lines over wide areas between points of known altitude. Locally, as north of Nullo Mountain and west of Scone, more broken relief existed and accurate reconstruction of the sub-basalt surface would require detailed mapping at a larger scale than was feasible in the present study. The lowest area lies under the Liverpool Range, and the highest on the southern edge of the Goulburn Valley and on Barrington Tops. A broad saddle lies over the central Hunter Valley.

(c) *The Effects of Post-basalt Tectonics*

The most extensive post-basalt tectonic activity occurred in the Goulburn Valley, where the southern half was uplifted and the northern half depressed. Uplift in the south is demonstrated by the occurrence of stream gravel under the basalt cap of Mt Coricudgy at about 1010 m above sea level: this gravel includes granite pebbles whose nearest source is 40 km away to the west at a much lower altitude, or 80 km away to the south at a comparable altitude: it is considered unlikely that post-basalt erosion has greatly lowered these possible sources. Depression in the north, under the Liverpool Range, is clearly indicated by the form lines in

Figure 13.1, particularly west of Wingen. The course of the form lines suggests that the sub-basalt surface below the central Liverpool Range is no more than 150 m above sea level, well below its altitude to the north and west, and lower than in the Goulburn Valley to the south. Thus the sub-basalt surface now forms a closed basin and post-basalt downwarping of at least 150 m is indicated. Doubtless this downwarping is in part due to the immense weight of basalt poured out to form the Liverpool Range and to corresponding evacuation of magma below, but it is also a continuation of pre-basalt tectonics responsible for the feature known as the Oxley Basin (Dulhunty 1940). This basin would have acted as a drainage focus in pre-basalt times, and consequently it is believed that the centripetally directed valleys apparent in the form lines of Figure 13.1 already existed then, though with gentler gradients, and are not solely due to post-basalt tectonics.

Other tectonic movements in the Goulburn Valley, possibly post-basalt, produced gentle anticlines along meridional or NNE-SSW axes under what is now the western watershed of the area and in the vicinity of Wollar. The form lines in Figure 13.1 portray shallow N- or NE-trending valleys but are insufficiently detailed to indicate to what extent they are the work of post-basalt tectonics as well as pre-basalt erosion. A series of similar meridional warps affecting the Triassic and Permian rocks extend as far east as the present coast and have controlled the courses of several major southern tributaries of the Hunter River, such as Growee Creek, Widdin Brook, and Wollombi Brook.

Major tectonic disturbance of the pre-basalt landscape has also occurred in the Murrurrundi-Wingen area, where pronounced faulting and warping, accompanied by minor vulcanism, have taken place. Both the WNW-ESE Murrurrundi fault and the meridional Wingen fault are probably old features reactivated in post-basalt times. Where the two fault trends intersect, a few miles northeast of Blandford, a basalt neck has developed. The sub-basalt surface dips sharply away from these faults towards the Oxley Basin, and indeed most of the height difference between the basalt base on either side of these fault zones noted by Browne (1924) in the Wingen area is due to this warping rather than to vertical displacement along the actual fault. There are also strong indications of a hitherto unrecorded powerful fault zone with downthrow to the south running eastwards from Parkville up Stewarts Brook towards the Barrington Tops. Evidence for this fault zone includes changes in drainage and strike patterns visible on the air photographs, the very steep south escarpment of the Blacktop massif, the occurrence along the line of the presumed dislocation of a minor neck 8 km north of Gundy, a small flow at Belltrees on the same line, and the higher altitude of the sub-basalt surface north of Stewarts Brook than on the south side of the valley. Probably a strike fault lies just west of the Isis River at the foot of a prominent meridional scarp (Plate XXVIII) and forms the eastern boundary of what is here termed the Blacktop horst. Uplift of at least 300 m is indicated at the southern end of the horst, decreasing to the north.

Pages River crosses this horst in a deep valley, the transgressive course of which has been superimposed from a former basalt cover of which relics still survive. The present depth of the valley, approaching 600 m, is largely a result of rapid post-basalt uplift which caused the river to deepen its superimposed course. The

XXVIIa Some 425 m of horizontal basalt flows forming Mt Woolooma on the right skyline rest on the quasi-horizontal sub-basalt surface cut across folded Carboniferous sediments. The top of the basalt may correspond to the post-basalt planation surface, and subsequent linear erosion has cut down into the sub-basalt rocks and picked out structural trends indicated here by straight crests and linear spurs.

XXVIIb Two flows making up part of the second basalt in the Goulburn Valley near Bylong. The lower flow is more weathered than the upper but it is not known if this is due to a considerable interval having occurred between the flows or to a difference in composition.

XXVIII *The broad Isis Valley has been excavated along the strike of Carboniferous rocks after removal of a basalt cover which still survives on the eastern side of the valley in the immediate foreground. The floor of the valley is occupied by low strike ridges picked out by linear erosion while the steep western side, visible in the background, is formed by the eastern escarpment of the Blacktop horst.*

horst is mostly built of resistant rocks, but southeast of Blandford it includes undulating country on relatively weak rocks now subject to rapid erosional attack from the surrounding lowlands. The survival of these weak rocks in such an exposed situation suggests that uplift has been fairly recent, presumably late Tertiary, and possibly contemporaneous with the second basalt in the Goulburn Valley.

On the south and southwest of the Barrington Tops the basalt flows and the sub-basalt surface slope very gently away from the massif, indicating that there has been at most only a very broad upwarping in post-basalt times; there is no evidence of the major fault postulated by Süssmilch (1940). On the west and northwest, on the other hand, there is evidence, in the close spacing of the form lines in Figure 13.1 and in some field observations, that there has been both warping and faulting which have been responsible for initiating the NE-SW depression followed by the upper Hunter River.

THE PRE-BASALT LAND SURFACE

(a) *Landforms*

Having estimated the extent of post-basalt tectonic movements, and allowing for their effects, form lines on the pre-basalt land surface appear as in Figure 13.3. The absolute altitude above the sea level of the time is not known, and the heights of form lines in Figure 13.3 are given relative to an assumed local datum of zero.

The whole area was characterised by low relief and the maximum height range was little more than one-quarter of the present 1600 m. The Goulburn Valley was a lowland sloping gently northwards and occupied by wide, shallow valleys in the northern half and by at least one narrow valley (A-B in Fig. 13.1) cut in the more resistant rocks to the south. This old valley ran NNW from Nullo Mountain towards the Goulburn and thence probably northwards. It has been cut across obliquely by the present generation of valleys and survives as strips of basalt perched on interfluves. The old valley was about 90-180 m deep (half as much as the present valleys) with steep sides where cut in resistant Triassic sandstone and of more open form on the softer Permian rocks. A broader, less well defined valley ran NNE from the Nullo Mountain area. A small relic of another valley (C-D in Fig. 13.1) is preserved in the extreme west of the Goulburn Valley in a basalt-filled channel cutting across the interfluve between Moolarben and Murragamba Creeks: it is too narrow to be shown by the form lines of Figures 13.1 and 13.3.

Another pre-basalt valley system may be preserved under basalt on top of the ridge enclosed by the great bend of the Goulburn NNE of Wollar. Here the basalt occurs as narrow meandering strips which in places are fairly thin but which elsewhere descend to unknown depths. The thin occurrences are definitely valley fills, but the deeper examples may be dykes, although the curvature in plan and the width of the outcrop are reminiscent of the incised gorge of Wilpinjong Creek immediately to the west. Further field-work is required to determine the nature of these basalt occurrences, and if they do prove to be infilled river valleys, to correlate them with other features of the sub-basalt surface and the geomorphological history of the Goulburn River.

v

It is surprising that other incised sub-basalt valleys have not been preserved in the lithologically and topographically uniform belt of Triassic sandstone south of the Goulburn and Hunter Rivers. It could be that the present generation of valleys are mostly aligned along the same trends as the pre-basalt valleys and have destroyed them, leaving only the broad indications portrayed in the form lines of Figure 13.3.

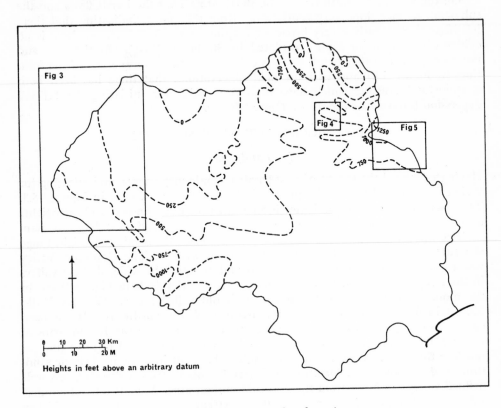

13.3   Form lines on pre-basalt surface

In the northeastern third of the Hunter Valley reconstruction of the pre-basalt relief is complicated by the widespread post-basalt tectonic disturbance, but it seems probable that valleys radiated from the Barrington Tops area, which was already high-standing. The implication that a broad valley passed NNW up what is now the Isis River can be regarded only as very tentative, and the drainage in this area may in fact have run in the same direction as the present streams. It is clear that the present-day meridional valley running from Aberdeen to Blandford did not exist, since three west-flowing valleys are preserved under the basalt on its western side southwest of Scone, at Owens Gap, and north of Wingen.

In the southeastern third of the Hunter Valley there are insufficient data to attempt any reconstruction of the pre-basalt relief.

(b) *Soils*

The pre-basalt landscape had a well developed soil which is now frequently exposed as light-coloured scars on slopes below the basalt. On the Triassic quartz sandstone widespread in the southern half of the Goulburn Valley the soil is a deep white sand, but on most other rocks, including unconsolidated Tertiary sediments, it consists of three layers, all rich in clay: a pale grey-brown upper layer, a brick-red middle layer, and a pale grey lower layer. The three layers are apparently the A, B, and C horizons of the soil, with the A horizon somewhat lightened through loss of its original organic content. The total depth ranges from 1 to 20 m, with the greatest thickness in valleys of the pre-basalt surface. A typical occurrence a few kilometres southeast of Timor on folded Devonian sediments had a light red B horizon of gritty clay with pH 8·5 over a white C horizon of sandy clay with numerous angular rock fragments and a pH of 8·0; presumably the original A horizon had been stripped before the advent of the basalt. A few ironstone nodules were encountered in the red horizon but they could not be described as a lateritic ironstone. Most likely the soil formed under tropical rainforest, although the relatively high pH is surprising. Similar soils occur as 'bole' between basalt flows, and related pedogenic reddening of a basalt layer towards the base of the volcanic sequence has been observed at many points from Cassilis eastwards to Pages Creek.

POST-BASALT GEOMORPHOLOGICAL EVOLUTION

Ever since the first basalt erupted the Hunter Valley has been subjected to erosion, except for minor vulcanism in the Goulburn Valley and around the Blacktop horst, and to deposition of riverine and estuarine alluvium. The erosion has reduced the basalt to perhaps a quarter or even an eighth of its original volume and cut deeply into the older rocks beneath; its history can be divided into three major stages. The deposition was related to Quaternary climatic changes and falls outside the scope of this essay: Quaternary events in the Hunter Valley have been briefly considered elsewhere (Galloway 1963).

(a) *Post-basalt Planation*

As on the New England tableland to the north (Voisey 1956), the eruption of the basalt was followed by an initial stage of erosion which produced a smooth, lateritised landscape here termed the post-basalt planation surface. In cutting this surface, erosion may merely have retouched the original constructional surface of the basalt, or (if Mt Dangar's lava cap is part of the Tertiary volcanics) it removed vast quantities of rock. Relics of the post-basalt planation surface, bearing traces of laterite, are preserved on major watersheds in the west and on the southern margin of the Merriwa tableland, where the almost horizontal sandstone and shale and distance from the present baselevel of erosion have favoured the formation and preservation of erosion surfaces. Near the Goulburn River, the post-basalt planation cut through the basalt and lightly bevelled the sub-basalt surface. The level summits of Barrington Tops and the Mount Royal Range may likewise be fragments of this erosion surface, though no laterite has been reported. Elsewhere in the Hunter Valley it has not been identified and has probably disappeared long since, but concordant crests in the Paterson and Williams valleys and, more especially, in the Wollombi catchment, and laterite capping Red Hill (290 m) east of Paterson, may be relics. It should be noted, however, that the presence of laterite is hardly diagnostic of a particular erosion surface, since lateritisation occurred at other periods in the Cainozoic.

There is some rather weak evidence that during the post-basalt planation there was westward migration of the Great Divide. Arguing from stream patterns, Taylor (1911) suggested that the divide at one time lay on the Barrington Tops and that the upper Hunter flowed westwards (presumably over basalt) up what is now the Goulburn Valley. West-flowing streams on fragments of the post-basalt peneplain now captured or about to be captured by the Hunter system, occur on the plateaux of the western Liverpool Range and Nullo Mountain and likewise point to a former more easterly position of the divide (Figure 13.1). However, by the time the post-basalt planation surface was completed, the broad outlines of today's eastward drainage pattern had been formed, although the present Goulburn headwaters in the Ulan district still flowed westwards towards the inland.

(b) *Late Tertiary Valley Planation*

During the next stage the post-basalt erosion surface was extensively dissected, presumably as a result of relative uplift, and the landscape evolved to nearly its present form with erosional plains forming in the major valleys. Dissection naturally advanced furthest along the major rivers and in weak rocks. The central lowland from Murrurrundi to the sea, already in existence in embryo form, was further opened up at this time on relatively unresistant Permian sediments. Downvalley from the Muswellbrook-Denman area, scarp retreat in the overlying Triassic sandstone has widened the lowland to over 30 km, and erosion has gone so far as to produce an undulating landscape that falls gently seawards from between 60-120 m at Singleton practically to sea level at Raymond Terrace. Upstream from Muswellbrook the lowland is narrower, since scarp retreat in the Triassic sandstone has been less effective because of steeper dips, less available relief, and shorter time.

In the generally resistant Carboniferous rocks of the northeast this stage of erosion produced straths up to 5 km wide, traceable, for example, along the Paterson and upper Hunter valleys.

Along the Goulburn, dissection was slow on account of distance from the sea and the presence of highly resistant, thick quartz sandstone. Erosion has gone no further than cutting gorges in hard rocks and forming small lowlands and straths, such as the Wollar basin and Bylong valley, on softer rocks. On the basalt of the Merriwa plateau, straths developed in the major valleys. During the course of the dissection, when the inner Goulburn Valley had been incised to about half its present depth of 90-180 m, the second basalt poured out as flows along the stream and was then itself dissected by continuing incision.

About this time, headward erosion by the Goulburn, aided perhaps by anticlinal warping west of Ulan, captured Moolarben, Murragamba, and Curra Creeks, and possibly upper Munmurra Brook, the headwaters of which still retain their old westward courses (Fig. 13.4). These captures brought the Great Divide to a little west of its present position. Currently in the Ulan area the gradient

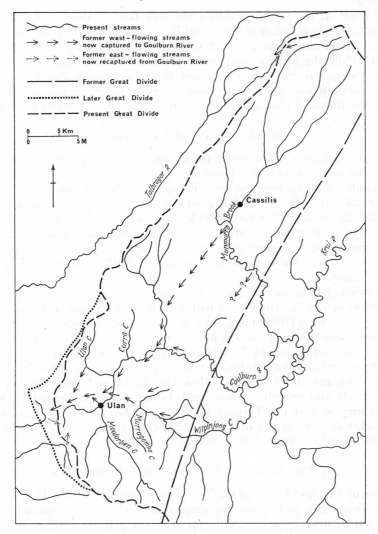

Present streams
Former west – flowing streams now captured to Goulburn River
Former east – flowing streams now recaptured from Goulburn River
—— — —— Former Great Divide
•••••••••• Later Great Divide
— — — — Present Great Divide

0   5 Km
0   5 M

Talbragar R.

Murnmurra Brook
Cassilis

Kruj R.

Ulan C.
Curra C.
Goulburn R.

Ulan
Moolarben c.
Murragamba c.
Wilpinjong C.

13.4   Stream captures in the Ulan-Cassilis area

advantage lies with streams west of the divide which have now reconquered some of their lost territory. The resultant slight eastward shift of the divide has left the highest summits in the district not on the present watershed but a little to the west. Similar shifts of the Great Divide in response to both local and distant lithological and tectonic controls can be found at many points in eastern Australia.

(c) *Late Cainozoic Valley Incision*

In the third major stage of post-basalt erosion, renewed linear incision cut narrow inner valleys in the floors of the lowlands and straths developed during the previous stage. At the present coastline the rock floor of this inner valley of the Hunter is nearly 90 m below sea level and it can be traced far up the main stream and its major tributaries as a trough of diminishing depth partially filled with alluvium. While the incision well below present sea level suggests a correlation with the Pleistocene glaciations, the fact that the inner valley extends so far inland (more than 300 km) from the coast suggests a longer period of development than the few hundred thousand years when glacial low sea levels prevailed.

(d) *Rate of Post-basalt Erosion*

On the basis of figures given above for the original and present volume of the basalt, it can be calculated that post-basalt erosion has removed some 1800-4100 km³ of basalt. By comparing the present contours with the sub-basalt form lines it can be calculated that a further 2700 km³ have been eroded from the older rocks below the basalt. Thus 4500-6800 km³ of rock have been removed since the time of the first basalt outpourings, which it is suggested occurred in Lower Tertiary time, some 35 million years ago. This implies an average rate of denudation over the whole catchment of 5 to 10 m in a million years: these seem very moderate values.

A surprisingly similar value can be deduced for the rate of erosion since emplacement of the Murrumbidgee batholith in southeastern New South Wales. According to Snelling (1960) the granite was emplaced at a depth of 2000-3000 m and it has a radiometric age of 396 million years (Evernden and Richards 1962): this implies an average rate of denudation of 5-7·5 m per million years.

On the other hand these deduced rates of geologic erosion are only about one-tenth of those calculated for the Mississippi basin and the Appalachians by Menard (1961) and one-fifth to one-tenth of the values presented by Schumm (1963). It may be that the Tertiary basalt in the Hunter Valley was originally much thicker than suggested here and that there was extensive post-granite sedimentation over the Murrumbidgee batholith.

(e) *The Nature of Erosion in the Hunter Valley*

Dissection of the post-basalt planation surface was dominated by processes of linear erosion which picked out and emphasised lithological contrasts, so giving rise to the structural control of landforms so apparent in the Hunter Valley today (Plates XXVIIa and XXVIII). In contrast, a lesser degree of structural control is apparent in the pre-basalt and post-basalt erosion surfaces in so far as we can reconstruct them, and sheet erosion processes may have played a greater part in their elaboration. As stated in the preceding discussion of late Tertiary valley planation, the change from dominantly non-linear to dominantly linear erosion was probably related primarily to relative uplift providing greater relief energy, but the possibility of climatic change giving the streams greater incisive power by furnishing more abrasive debris or greater discharge, should not be overlooked. The nature of the sub-basalt soils, indicative of humid tropical conditions, suggests that pre-basalt erosion may have been of the tropical sheetwash type recently discussed by Büdel (1959) and Cotton (1962). The occurrence of laterite remnants on the post-basalt planation surface may indicate that it was elaborated under sheetflood conditions, since many of the lateritic crusts in northern Australia are clearly detrital and the products of such a process.

DRAINAGE DEVELOPMENT IN RELATION TO THE BASALT

(a) *Discordant Streams*

It will be apparent from this outline of the post-basalt geomorphological evolution, that over the greater part if not all of the Hunter Valley the drainage has been superimposed from a more or less uniform basalt cover on to the various underlying older rocks. Consequently it is to be expected that many of the streams will be discordant, and indeed major discordances are not lacking. The outstanding case is the Goulburn River, which cuts across the meridional warps and the overall northward dips of the Oxley Basin. The lower Hunter below Denman must likewise be regarded as superimposed, since it transgresses the north-south grain of the Permian rocks and in the Gosforth area cuts across resistant Carboniferous lavas even though relatively weak Permian sediments just to the south offer a lower and easier passage. The Goulburn-lower Hunter axis may well be inherited from a major drainage line on the post-basalt planation surface. Taken as a whole, the upper Hunter above Aberdeen is likewise transgressive (Browne 1924) and may have originated along the post-basalt downwarp postulated on the northwest edge of the Barrington Tops. The transgressive course of Pages River across the Blacktop horst has already been mentioned.

(b) *Concordant Streams*

Such examples of discordance are exceptional, however, and drainage is usually well adapted to structure despite having been superimposed from basalt. The ways in which this adjustment has been achieved can be deduced from a study of valleys where they leave the basalt and pass on to other rocks. Three major situations exist.

(i) *Drainage Adjustment after Cutting Through the Basalt*

A drainage trend initiated on the basalt sometimes persists for some distance across adjacent older rocks, but adjustment is eventually achieved. In the northeast of the Hunter Valley in the upper Isis River-Pages Creek area there are indications that an old eastward drainage initiated on the basalt has now cut down into the underlying Palaeozoic sedimentary rocks: it retains its old direction for only a short distance before swinging SSE along the strike or joining a major river which does so.

Taken as a whole, the upper Hunter runs obliquely to the meridional strike and, as we have seen, is probably superimposed from the basalt. When examined more closely however, the overall transgressive course resolves itself into long stretches parallel to the strike of weaker rocks or parallel to prominent lineaments, and short sectors cutting across harder rocks at right angles to the strike (Fig. 13.5). Strictly speaking, the latter sectors transgress structure, but their directions give the stream the most direct course, and therefore the greatest erosive efficiency, just where the rocks are most resistant. This might be termed an adaptation, if not an adjustment to structure.

The adaptations described have been achieved after only moderate incision into the rocks beneath the basalt: less than 30 m in the upper Isis valley and no more than 120 m along the upper Hunter at Ellerston.

A rather different case is provided by Munmurra Brook in the west of the Hunter Valley. On leaving what is clearly a straight, structurally controlled, SSW-trending valley in basalt south of Cassilis this stream wanders off to the SSE (Fig. 13.1). In this case, the cause of the drainage change is an adjustment to the lithology of the underlying Mesozoic sediments. Just where the river now leaves the basalt a particularly resistant sandstone crops out, and apparently the stream deviated round this obstacle as it was exposed by removal of the basalt cover.

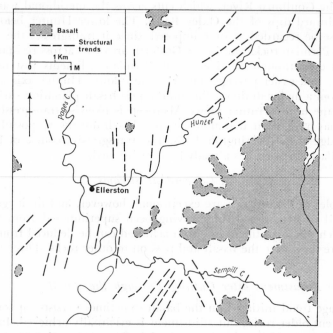

13.5   Relation of upper Hunter to structural trends and to basalt

Post-basalt adjustment of the drainage pattern to structure on the grandest scale is provided by the relationship of Kingdon Ponds Creek and the upper Pages River in the north of the area. The latter has a highly transgressive course super-imposed from the basalt surface and influenced by post-basalt uplift, but will eventually be captured in the vicinity of Blandford by Kingdon Ponds Creek, which is rapidly extending headwards along the strike of relatively poorly consoli-dated Permian rocks. When this capture does take place it will create a drainage pattern more logically related to the sub-basalt geology than the old pattern super-imposed from the basalt.

Sometimes adaptation to the sub-basalt structure requires only a slight change in the direction of streams leaving the basalt. A number of streams coming down from the Liverpool Range northwest of Scone flow southwards or south by east on the basalt, and swing to SSE courses parallel to a prominent joint pattern as soon as they pass on to older rocks. In this case, the slight adjustment required takes place immediately the geological boundary is crossed and there is no noticeable prolongation of drainage trends derived from the basalt across the older rocks.

(ii) Undercutting of the Basalt

This situation occurs where the present drainage is working headwards into the basalt from adjacent lower areas on other rocks. This is most clearly illustrated by the valley heads biting into the southern margin of the Barrington Tops plateau. Up on the tableland there is an old, east-trending drainage system: some 600 m below, younger south-trending valleys, closely related to the strike of the Carboniferous rocks, are undercutting the basalt. It is clear from Figure 13.6 that

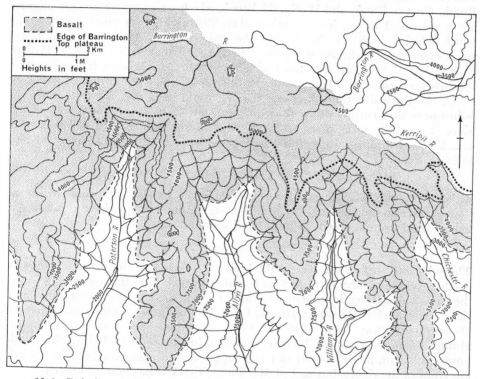

13.6 Relation of drainage to basalt on southern margin of Barrington Tops

the meridional trend of the younger valleys exists only below the basalt base, above which the valley heads are semi-circular basins resembling cirques and showing no particular structural trend. Presently these younger valleys will capture the east-flowing drainage on the plateau; indeed this has already happened in the case of the upper Chichester River. Other examples of this situation occur in the Nullo Mountain area, where headward erosion along structural lineaments in the Triassic sediments is undercutting the basalt and capturing streams with very different and older trends developed on the post-basalt planation surface.

A variety of this second situation occurs where the material under the basalt is not solid bedrock but unconsolidated soil and Tertiary sediments filling pre-basalt valleys. These materials are very subject to slumping, gullying, and erosion of all kinds, and in this way old drainage trends can be resurrected by selective headward erosion. This is best exemplified at the head of Timor Creek, but does not seem a widely significant process in drainage development since there has been little or no headward erosion along the basalt-filled valley (A-B in Fig. 13.1) south of Wollar.

(iii) Common Structure in the Basalt and the Underlying Rocks

This situation is theoretical and has not been definitely identified in the Hunter Valley. However, it may be that such north-flowing streams as Widdin Brook, Growee Creek, and Wollombi Brook, which, as stated above, are aligned along structural warps, have acquired their directions from post-basalt folding which affected both the basalt and the underlying sedimentary rocks. Some support for this conclusion is provided by the pre-basalt valley south of Wollar (A-B in Fig. 13.1), which does not follow these structures, thereby indicating that the structures came into being after the older valley had been filled by basalt.

Of the three situations discussed here it would seem that the first—drainage adjustment after cutting down through the basalt—is by far the most important. Since it generally takes place relatively rapidly, the existence in any area of a well adjusted drainage cannot be cited as evidence that a basalt cover did not formerly exist.

THE LEGACY OF THE SUB-BASALT SURFACE

Although the sub-basalt surface was fashioned in the Tertiary, as a consequence of its conservation under basalt it is still a significant element in the landscape today. The legacy is present in both landforms and soils.

(a) The Landform Legacy

The sub-basalt surface survives in the present landscape at the margins of basalt patches. Where post-basalt dissection has bitten deeply into the underlying rocks, the sub-basalt surface is present only as a narrow shelf or accordant spurs and ridge crests. Such shelves have already been described from Nullo Mountain and around Barrington Tops (Plate XXVIIa), and they also occur in the upper Hunter basin. On resistant Triassic sandstone in the southern half of the Goul-burn catchment, the sub-basalt surface is approximately preserved on the accord-ant crests of the ridges, but east of Martindale Creek it has been destroyed.

On the southern margin of the Merriwa plateau the post-basalt dissection has not advanced so far and the sub-basalt surface has been extensively preserved as flat areas on interfluves. It has been lightly retouched by post-basalt erosional and pedogenic episodes, but the smooth forms characteristic of that far-off time are inherited in the present landscape.

The relationship of the modern valley system to that of pre-basalt times is debatable. Dulhunty (1937) and David and Browne (1950) have suggested that the present major valleys are re-excavated, little modified descendants of the pre-basalt valleys. This suggestion rests largely on the belief that basalt flows close to the Goulburn River at Crowie and the siliceous 'grey billy' in the Singleton-Denman area are products of the main period of basalt eruption. On the other hand, reasons have been advanced in this essay for believing that the Crowie basalt is part of a very much later, relatively minor volcanic episode, and that the 'grey billy' may not be related to basalt at all. In the light of the evidence presented here the incised inner valley of the Goulburn developed long after the main basalt flows had been extensively eroded, and only some of the meridional tributary valleys may be re-excavated pre-basalt landscape features. The meridional valley of Kingdon Ponds Creek north of Aberdeen is clearly post-basalt in age, unrelated to the east-west valleys of pre-basalt times. Reconstruction of the old sub-basalt and inter-basalt valleys on the Merriwa plateau could have considerable economic significance since they often contain alluvial deposits forming excellent aquifers.

In the upper Hunter the south-flowing Isis River and Pages Creek broadly follow meridional pre-basalt valleys which, however, may have drained in the opposite direction, as suggested in Figure 13.3. If, on the contrary, the pre-basalt streams flowed southwards as today, they must have joined a trunk stream roughly along the line of the present upper Hunter, since the Barrington Tops massif, already high ground in pre-basalt times, barred their way. It may be, then, that there is a very considerable degree of inheritance of the pre-basalt valley pattern in this area, although the overall transgressive courses of the upper Hunter and Pages Rivers argue strongly against this and in favour of superimposition of the drainage pattern from a basalt cover.

In the southeastern third of the Hunter Valley information is too scanty to say whether or not there has been inheritance of pre-basalt valley trends, although there is a hint of this for the area on the southern side of the Barrington Tops in the form lines in Figure 13.3.

(b) *The Soils Legacy*

The legacy of the pre-basalt landscape in the present soils is most significant on the southern fringe of the Merriwa plateau. Here extensive areas of krasnozemic soils form what is locally known as 'red basalt country' and support the main wheat production in the Hunter Valley. The krasnozems are related, in part, to reweathering of the pre-basalt soil exposed by erosion of the basalt (McGarrity and Munns 1954; van de Graaff 1963), but there is possible confusion in this area with krasnozems related to inter-basalt soils, to a particular red-weathered basalt layer, and to lateritic weathering on the post-basalt planation surface. The share due to pre-basalt soils cannot be determined without further field-work.

Elsewhere in the Hunter Valley the pre-basalt soil now occupies only a minute proportion of the surface, but nevertheless it is of considerable interest since it contrasts so markedly with soils developed on the same rocks under the present climate. In the upper Hunter catchment in particular, the pre-basalt soil is remarkably infertile and supports only a poor flora with much bare ground. The scanty vegetation, the high proportion of clay, and the frequent occurrence of springs and seepage at the basalt base have induced active slumping and gullying, and serious soil erosion often commences at this level.

SUMMARY AND CONCLUSIONS

At the time of its outpouring in the Lower Tertiary the basalt cover of the Hunter Valley was much more extensive than now and may even have covered the entire area to an average depth of several hundred metres. Further detailed field-work, laying particular emphasis on petrological correlation of scattered outcrops, may help to define more accurately the original extent and thickness of the basalt and related volcanics, but there has been so much post-basalt erosion that a full reconstruction is probably impossible. In the light of the evidence from the Hunter Valley it seems likely that extensive areas of eastern New South Wales were once covered by basalt, though not necessarily all at the same time, and that the outpouring of basalt was one of the most significant events in the Cainozoic history of the entire area. Eastern Australia may well have ranked with the Deccan of India and the Columbia-Snake River plateau in the U.S.A. as one of the world's major Tertiary basalt provinces.

This study supports the views of other workers that there were two main periods of basalt eruption in the Hunter Valley, of early and late Cainozoic age respectively. The later phase was very much less extensive than the earlier one, and produced only minor vents and flows. Tectonic activity during and since the main period of vulcanism has been considerable. The pre-existing Oxley Basin in the western half of the area was further deepened by over a hundred metres, strong faulting affected the Wingen-Murrurrundi area, and there was probably faulting in the Barrington Tops area with downwarping along the northwestern edge of the massif.

The old land surface preserved under the basalt has been extensively disturbed by this tectonic activity but at the time it was covered by basalt it was an undulating lowland with wide, shallow valleys and deep soils. Only on the resistant Triassic quartz sandstone along the south of the area were narrower, more sharply incised valleys to be found. The main drainage trends were centripetal towards the Oxley Basin in the west and radial from the Barrington Tops in the east.

The first discernible stage in the post-basalt history was one of erosion which produced a gently rolling post-basalt planation surface on which a lateritic profile developed. The evidence is insufficient to determine whether this erosion was relatively slight or considerable and whether or not it was made up of several distinct substages. The post-basalt planation surface was in its turn deeply dissected and now survives only in the Goulburn Valley and on a few watershed sites elsewhere. The dissection picked out lithological differences and emphasised structural control of the relief. During the course of this dissection, which took place in at least two well marked stages, the second, relatively minor phase of vulcanism took place and a series of stream captures carried the Great Divide westwards to about its present position.

The pre-basalt drainage shows little relationship to the present pattern, except possibly in the northeast where the available evidence is indeterminate. The present drainage was initiated on the basalt, yet is generally well adapted to the structure of the exposed older rocks over which it now flows where the basalt has been removed. Adaptation has been achieved by adjustment to structure after superimposition from the basalt, by headward erosion from adjacent basalt-free areas, or by response to Cainozoic tectonic movements affecting both the basalt and the underlying rocks. The margins of extensive basalt sheets would be good places to study how streams become adapted to structure: the fact of adaptation is obvious but the processes are not.

It will be apparent that many of the conclusions reached in this essay are tentative and based on limited evidence: more detailed field-work is required in many directions. Ultimately similar studies could be undertaken throughout much of eastern Australia, since basalt occurs from Victoria to northern Queensland, and could throw light on the Cainozoic evolution of a vast area. Heretofore the value of basalt as a datum in geomorphological studies has been restricted by difficulties of dating and by the lack of agreement on the number, extent, and significance of the episodes of Tertiary vulcanism. It is to be hoped that radiometric dating will in the future enable these questions to be clarified, and thus open the way to constructing a fuller and more accurate history of the landscape of eastern Australia.

REFERENCES

Browne, W. R. (1924). Notes on the physiography and geology of the upper Hunter River. *J. Proc. R. Soc. N.S.W.* **58**: 128-44.

——— (1933). An account of post-Palaeozoic igneous activity in New South Wales. *J. Proc. R. Soc. N.S.W.* **67**: 9-95.

Büdel, J. (1959). Die Flächenbildung in den feuchten Tropen und die Rolle fossiler solchen Flächen in anderen Klimazonen. *Abh. dt. Geogr. Wurzburg* 1957: 89-121.

Carne, J. E. (1908). *Geology and Mineral Resources of the Western Coalfield*. Mem. Geol. Surv. N.S.W. No. 6, pp. 71-152.

Cooper, J. A., Richards, J. R., and Webb, A. W. (1963). Some potassium-argon ages in New England, New South Wales. *J. geol. Soc. Aust.* **10**: 317-24.

Cotton, C. A. (1962). Plains and inselbergs of the humid tropics. *Trans. R. Soc. N.Z.* **1**: 269-77.

Crook, K. A. W. (1961). Post-Carboniferous stratigraphy of the Tamworth-Nundle district, N.S.W. *J. Proc. R. Soc. N.S.W.* **94**: 209-13.

David, T. W. E., ed. Browne, W. R. (1950). *The Geology of the Commonwealth of Australia*. Vol. II, London.

Dulhunty, J. A. (1937). Stratigraphy and physiography of the Goulburn River district, N.S.W. *J. Proc. R. Soc. N.S.W.* **71**: 297-317.

——— (1940). Structural geology of the Mudgee-Gunnedah region. *J. Proc. R. Soc. N.S.W.* **74**: 88-98.

Evernden, J. F. and Richards, J. R. (1962). Potassium-argon ages in Eastern Australia. *J. geol. Soc. Aust.* **9**: 1-49.

Galloway, R. W. (1963). *Geomorphology of the Hunter Valley*. CSIRO Aust. Land Res. Ser. No. 8, pp. 90-102.

Geol. Survey N.S.W. (1962). *Geological Map of N.S.W.* Dept Mines, Sydney.

Graaff, R. H. M. van de (1963). *Soils of the Hunter Valley*. CSIRO Aust. Land Res. Ser. No. 8, pp. 103-35.

Harper, L. F. (1909). *Notes on the Physiography and Geology of the Northeastern Watershed of the Macquarie River*. Rec. Geol. Surv. N.S.W. No. 8, pp. 321-34.

McGarrity, J. W. and Munns, D. N. (1954). 'Anomalous' krasnozem in the Richmond-Tweed region, N.S.W. *Aust. J. Sci.* **17**: 69-70.

Menard, H. W. (1961). Some rates of regional erosion. *J. Geol.* **69**: 154-61.

Raggatt, H. G. (1938). Note on the silicified terrace sands ('grey billy') in the Hunter Valley (N.S.W.) *J. Proc. R. Soc. N.S.W.* **72**: 318-24.

———— and Whitworth, H. F. (1932). The intrusive igneous rocks of the Muswellbrook-Singleton district. Part II. The Savoy Sill. *J. Proc. R. Soc. N.S.W.* **66**: 194-233.

Schumm, S. A. (1963). *The disparity between present rates of denudation and orogeny.* U.S. Geol. Surv. Prof. Pap. 454-H.

Snelling, N. J. (1960). The geology and petrology of the Murrumbidgee batholith. *Q. Jl geol. Soc. Lond.* **116**: 187-217.

Standard, J. C. (1961). A new study of the Hawkesbury Sandstone; preliminary findings. *J. Proc. R. Soc. N.S.W.* **95**: 145-6.

Story, R., *et al.* (1963). *General Report on the Lands of the Hunter Valley.* CSIRO Aust. Land Res. Ser. No. 8.

Süssmilch, C. A. (1940). The geomorphology of the Hunter River district, N.S.W. *Proc. Linn. Soc. N.S.W.* **65**: 301-22.

Taylor, G. (1911). *The Physiography of Eastern Australia.* Bur. Meteorol. Aust. Bull. No. 8.

Voisey, A. H. (1942). The Tertiary land surface in southern New England. *J. Proc. R. Soc. N.S.W.* **76**: 82-5.

———— (1956). Erosion surfaces around Armidale, N.S.W. *J. Proc. R. Soc. N.S.W.* **90**: 128-33.

Wilshire, H. G. and Standard, J. C. (1963). The history of vulcanism in the Mulally district, N.S.W. *J. Proc. R. Soc. N.S.W.* **96**: 123-8.

14

Landforms of the Newer Volcanic Province of Victoria

C. D. OLLIER

INTRODUCTION

(a) *Petrographic and Geomorphological Provinces*

The idea of petrographic provinces is well established, and it has long been realised that composition of parent magma has an effect on the nature of volcanic landforms. Thus andesitic volcanoes are commonly explosive, making steep pumice cones; rhyolites have very viscous lavas which may produce steep tholoids; basalt eruptions are usually quietly effusive with a minimum of pyroclastics, and give rise to lava plains and shields. Geomorphologists have perhaps not been ready enough to recognise geomorphological provinces within a single petrographic province, for it is apparent that the same petrologic type is not always associated with the same landforms in detail. Thus Hawaii and Iceland are both basaltic, but very different physiographically, while the basaltic areas of the Snake River (U.S.A.) and Victoria are different again.

The *Catalogue of the Active Volcanoes of the World* produced by the International Vulcanological Association provides a descriptive catalogue of great geomorphological value, but areas of extinct volcanoes tend to be described in more general style and it is fairly hard to find simple accounts of geomorphological provinces. Eardley (1962) has divided the Columbia-Snake River basalts into a number of groups, each of which has a certain degree of physiographic character, and this sort of division is not only useful, but probably has some deeper vulcanological significance. Thus more recognition and detailed study of geomorphological provinces would probably add to knowledge of vulcanicity itself.

It is thought that the Western District volcanics of Victoria make a geomorphological/petrographic province, characterised by olivine basalt, extensive flows, central type eruptions, numerous but small volcanoes, and a low explosion index.

(b) *The Setting*

Rocks of the western Victorian volcanic province are known as the 'Newer Volcanics' to distinguish them from the 'Older Volcanics' which are found mainly in Gippsland, eastern Victoria. The Older Volcanics are Lower Tertiary and only eroded remnants are left; the Newer Volcanics are mainly Pleistocene and Recent.

Since the volcanics were erupted throughout this period of time, we cannot be too precise in defining the pre-volcanic topography, but the broad outlines are clear. The Otways, of Mesozoic rocks, and the Coastal Plains, of Cainozoic sediments, limit the volcanic province on the south. The southern part of the province itself consists of a low plain underlain by a trough of Tertiary sediments. This region is called the Western District Plains. It once contained extensive lakes, and Lake Corangamite and its neighbours occupy depressions on the site of what was once a much larger lake (Currey 1964). The northern part of the province is the area known as the Western Highlands, which consists of a dissected plateau of Palaeozoic rocks sloping down to the north. These divisions are shown in Figure 14.1.

On to this topography the volcanics were strewn, but there was considerable tectonic movement both during and after vulcanicity. The Brisbane Ranges, for instance, are a post-volcanic fault-scarp with a throw of a hundred metres or more. Elsewhere the volcanics were monoclinally warped without faulting, as in the Geelong district. Many of the large valleys were blocked by lava flows, and drainage ponding and diversions caused further modification to the landscape.

The result is that at the present day the basic physiographic features remain—Coastal Plains, Western Plains, Western Highlands—but are now diversified by primary volcanic landforms—cones and flows—and by landscape modifications attributable in part at least to the volcanic activity.

DISTRIBUTION OF LAVA AND VOLCANOES

Figure 14.2 shows the extent of Newer Volcanics in western Victoria, and Figure 14.1 shows the distribution of the main points of eruption. There are a great many small points of eruption without names, grading down to insignificance, and as it is impossible to show them all, only named volcanoes are included in Figure 14.1.

The Newer Volcanics occupy about 15,000 km² on the plains and in the highlands. The lava distribution map (Fig. 14.2) shows what might be expected from the nature of the pre-basalt topography: widespread extensive areas of basalt on the plains and an irregular 'mosaic' in the highlands, where flows are often confined within deep valleys. This pattern is a little oversimplified, however. Recent work is showing that considerable areas of the plains are not, in fact, underlain by basalt, and the total extent of the lava sheets may be much less than was formerly supposed (Currey 1964). On the other hand, in the highlands there were occasions when lava accumulated to such depths that the deep valleys were completely filled and high level lava plains were formed.

The province is remarkable in having a large number of points of eruption, none of which grew to any great size. Almost all the volcanoes are less than 200 m above their base and the majority are less than 100 m. Points of eruption are particularly common on the highlands. Coulson (1953) recorded 123 points in 1500 km² in the Daylesford area and Edwards (1938) found 21 points of eruption in an area of 50 km² near Mt Holden, in the form of mounds 15 to 30 m above the plain. The small humps are not much larger than tumuli and it is not always certain whether they are real volcanoes with necks or merely adventitious eruptions, that is eruptions fed from lava in a flow and not from a neck connected more or less vertically to a magma chamber. On the other hand, important sources of lava may be marked by very small hills. Mt Hydewell, for instance, is 15 m high and has such gentle slopes that it seems almost insignificant, but from

XXIXa *(top) Mt Elephant, a scoria cone with simple crater*

XXIXb *(above) Mt Rouse, a scoria cone with incipient gullies forming part of a complex
volcano*

XXIXc *(below) Lake Keilambete, a maar*

XXIXd *(bottom) Mt Holden, an eroded volcano with crest formed by the old crater fill of
lava and a lava flow*

XXXb *Tumulus (lava blister) near Byaduk. The tumulus has cracked open, revealing jointing and layered lava below the skin. Photograph by M. C. Brown.*

XXXc *Lava cave at Mt Eccles with typical semi-circular roof and flat floor. Photograph by M. C. Brown.*

XXXa *Trentham Falls, formed where the Coliban River runs off columnar basalt on to bedrock*

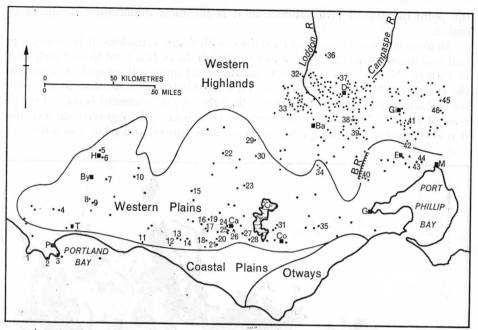

14.1 *Physiographic regions of southwest Victoria, named points of eruption in the Newer Volcanic Province and key to localities mentioned in the text*

Ba	Ballarat	D	Daylesford	L.C.	Lake Corangamite
B.R.	Brisbane Ranges	E	Exford	M	Melbourne
By	Byaduk	G	Geelong	P	Portland
Ca	Camperdown	Gi	Gisborne	T	Tyrendarra
Co	Colac	H	Hamilton		

Anakie	40	Mt Leura	26
Mt Atkinson	44	Mt Misery	42
Mt Bainbridge	5	Mondilibi	15
Bald Hill	8	Mt Monmot	29
Cape Bridgewater	1	Moolort (Stony Rises)	36
Bullenmerri	25	Munderong	13
The Cap	35	Mt Napier	7
Cobrico	20	Cape Nelson	2
Mt Cooterell	43	Mt Noorat	9
Mt Eccles	9	Mt Pierrepoint	6
Mt Eckersley	4	Mt Porndon	28
Mt Elephant	23	Pretty Sally Hill	45
Elingamite	21	Purrumbete	27
Mt Franklin	37	Mt Rouse	10
Gnotuk	24	Spring Hill	46
Cape Grant	3	Staughton Hill	18
Mt Greenock	32	Terang	17
Mt Hamilton	22	Three Sisters	33
Mt Holden	41	Tower Hill	11
Mt Hydewell	39	Wangoom	12
Keilambete	16	Warrion Hills	31
Larkins Hill	38	Mt Warrnambool	14
Lawaluk	34	Mt Widderin	30

W

the point of view of lava production it is the most important volcano in its region.

In some volcanic areas, especially those with fissure eruptions, it is common to find volcanoes falling along a number of straight lines. It is hard to find such lines in Victoria. Mt Eccles is in line with at least eight small hills or spatter cones and the elongate crater of Lake Surprise. This is probably the most distinct evidence for lineaments in Victoria. Boutakoff (1963) thinks the lineament is related to the edge of an underlying laccolith which has been indicated by gravity surveys, but it is also possible that the spatter cones are adventitious and related to a flow.

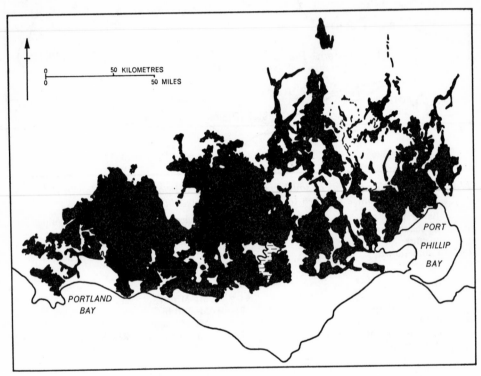

14.2 Distribution of Newer Volcanics

The Anakies are three elongate scoria hills which lie along a straight line, possibly related to jointing in the underlying granite. East of Colac there are at least five small vents which run in an east-west line, parallel to an escarpment to the south. A number of north-south lines may be recognised in the arrangement of the maars of the Camperdown district, but all these 'lines' contain very few points and may be only imaginary.

Coulson (1953) attempted to construct a map of lineaments for the 123 points of eruptions of the Daylesford district, but Ollier and Joyce (1964) could find no clear lineaments either there or on the Western Plains.

There are, however, notable concentrations of volcanoes. One is along the line

Geelong-Colac-Portland, which coincides with the axis of the Tertiary trough (Fig. 14.3). The other is in the Ballarat-Daylesford area, which is the centre of the volcanics of the Western Highlands plateau.

Although almost all the Newer Volcanics are found in west and central Victoria there are a few scattered eruptions in the east, including Morass Creek near Benambra, Seven Creeks near Euroa, and a probable occurrence at Gelantipy (Hills 1939). The volcanics of South Australia, including Mt Gambier and Mt Schank, are clearly related to the Victorian volcanics but are perhaps even younger.

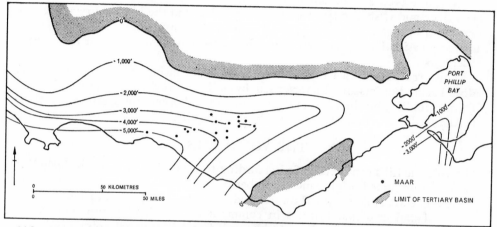

14.3   Contours on the base of Tertiary sediments (in feet) and the distribution of maars. The shaded line marks the approximate Tertiary shoreline.

PETROLOGY

Both the Older and the Newer Volcanics of Victoria are basaltic, with olivine-basalt dominant, but the Older suite is distinct from the Newer both in the nature of many of the rock types and in the probable composition of its parent magma. The Older Basalt is a 'plateau magma' type, like Kennedy's (1933) 'olivine basalt', while the parent magma of the Newer Volcanics appears to have some pronouncedly tholeitic features.

According to Edwards (1938) the Newer Volcanics offer an 'Intra-Pacific' suite of rocks illustrating an alkaline line of magmatic descent. Many rock types have been recorded, from limburgites to solvsbergites, but the great majority are olivine-labradorite basalts which have been classified as follows:

Trentham type—olivine-labradorite basalt. No large phenocrysts of labradorite.

Gisborne type—as above but more granular and with large phenocrysts of labradorite.

Malmsbury type—iddingsite-labradorite basalt, with original olivine as phenocrysts and in the groundmass.

Footscray type—as above, but olivine only in phenocrysts, and groundmass is iron-rich and glassy.

Ballan type—andesine-iddingsite basalt.

There are complete transitions between the Footscray type and the Malmsbury and Ballan types.

Detailed petrographic descriptions have been given by Edwards (1938), who studied the central Victorian area, by Coulson (1953, Daylesford area; 1938, Geelong basalts; 1941, Portland basalts) and by Yates (1954, Ballarat area) amongst others.

The classification above is petrographic, and not necessarily genetic, for iddingsitised and olivine basalts may be found in different parts of the same flow (J. M. Bowler, personal communication).

Nevertheless, as a broad generalisation, it has been maintained that the Trentham and Gisborne types are generally older, and the Malmsbury and Footscray types younger. There is a gradual transition from the more acid members to the more basic; the former tend to be constricted flows and the latter the effusive sheetflows.

This occurrence of a Pacific suite of rocks in a continental area is of interest. Most Pacific borders are characterised by andesitic rocks and have undergone Tertiary folding, but in Victoria the volcanic rocks border and overlie a trough of Tertiary sediments that have not suffered an orogeny.

THE VOLCANOES

The volcanic hills can be classified according to a number of features, including shape and presumed origin, and a number of terms have been applied to certain groups. The Mt Holden type (Edwards and Crawford 1940) refers to a group with structural and erosional features in common; the Portland group (Ollier and Joyce 1964) refers to a number of old, eroded and ill-exposed volcanoes in the west. However, for most purposes a traditional classification as used below is quite adequate in Victoria.

(a) Basalt Cones

These are usually hills of gentle slope, made up of a number of lava flows with no apparent scoria. Mt Hamilton (Fig. 14.4) is the only perfect lava cone; it is 80 m high, with a large crater 400 m wide and 30 m deep. The crater has steep inner walls which are unbreached, but the outer slopes have gradients of only about 4° and merge into the plain around. Mt Cotterill is an example near Melbourne and Moolort an example from the north. All basalt hills except Mt Hamilton are weathered and have little or no sign of a crater. On the flanks of Mt Hamilton and Mt Widderin lava tunnels are found.

(b) Basalt Discs

Basalt without scoria seems to have been erupted at Lawaluk; but this is a steep-edged, flat-topped disc of lava rather than a simple cone. Mondilibi is probably of the same type, and the lava sheet within the ring barrier of Mt Porndon (Skeats and James 1937) is possibly a similar, though larger feature (Fig. 14.4). The Warrion Hills are a basalt complex forming an elevated plateau with a diameter of nearly 2 km, and with steep sides with many lava outcrops.

Basalt hills are not as common as scoria hills and in general appear to be older.

(c) *Scoria Cones*

The ideal scoria cone is a single cone with steep, straight sides and a crater at the top. Mt Elephant (Fig. 14.4; Plate XXIXa), Mt Franklin, and Greenock Hill are very good examples. The even height of the crater rim often causes the hills to

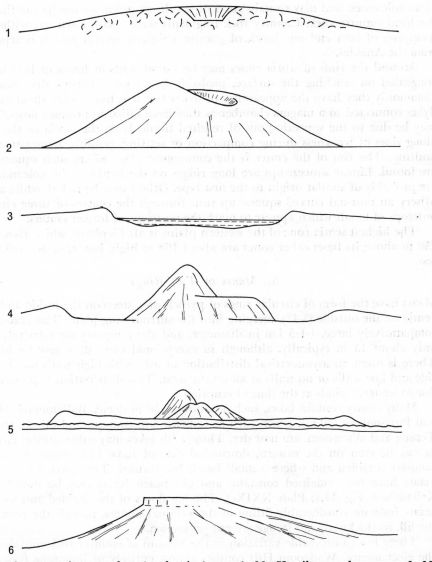

14.4 Diagrammatic examples of volcanic forms. 1. Mt Hamilton, a lava cone. 2. Mt Elephant, a breached scoria cone. 3. Keilambete, a maar. 4. Mt Leura, scoria cones nested within a maar. 5. Mt Porndon, extensive stony rises overlain by a lava disc with later scoria cones in the centre. 6. Mt Holden, an eroded volcano capped by lava that originally filled a crater.

look flat-topped from a distance. Many are multiple cones, where eruptions from a number of closely spaced vents overlap to form irregular hills, and in some cases it is not easy to find the actual points of eruption. The ejectamenta show a wide range of variation from coarse bombs and blocks to fine ash. Sometimes the scoria is welded together, especially around crater rims. Bombs are common on some volcanoes, and may contain cores of basalt, granular olivine (peridotite), or the local country rock. Country rock fragments were also thrown out without a wrapping of lava and one block of granite weighing several tonnes is reported from the Anakies.

Around the rims of scoria cones may be found walls or heaps of lava which congealed on reaching the surface, probably being more viscous than normal. Commonly they have the appearance of dykes but it is hard to see them as true dykes connected to a magma chamber as they have failed to produce flows. They may be due to the squeezing out of residual liquid from the scoria of the cone along lines of weakness during compaction or settling, possibly accompanied by faulting. The rim of the crater is the commonest place where such squeeze-ups are found. Linear squeeze-ups are long ridges on the flanks of the volcano, and are probably of similar origin to the first type. Others may be radial, while at Mt Misery an unusual curved squeeze-up runs through the centres of three circular outcrops of basalt which appear to mark the positions of former craters.

The highest scoria cone of the western plains is Mt Elephant, which rises some 250 m above its base; other cones are about 160 m high, but most are 100 m or less.

(d) *Maars or Tuff Rings*

Maars have the form of circular rings of pyroclastics, steep on the inside and very gentle on the outside (3-4°), merging into the surrounding plain. The craters are comparatively large, 1-1·5 km in diameter, and the ramparts are relatively low, only about 15 m typically, although in exceptional cases they may be higher. There is often an asymmetrical distribution of ash, with high walls on the east side and low walls or no walls at all on the west. This distribution is presumably due to westerly winds at the time of eruption.

Many maars contain lakes, such as Gnotuk (30 m deep), Bullenmerri (80 m), and Purrumbete (50 m). Some, such as Cobrico, are swamps, and others, such as Terang and Wangoom, are now dry. Those with lakes may suffer littoral erosion, as can be seen on the eastern, downwind side of Lake Elingamite, where the rampart is cliffed and where a small beach has formed. The water levels in the maars have not remained constant, and old beach levels may be found as at Keilambete (Fig. 14.4; Plate XXIXc). The flat floors of the drained and swampy maars indicate considerable filling of the original craters, though the nature of the fill, its thickness, and its age are not yet known.

There is a considerable variation in the amount of country rock contained in the ejectamenta. Wangoom Hill consists almost entirely of limestone fragments in the southern part at least, but there are also pieces of dense black basalt. The Lake Elingamite rampart is mainly pyroclastic but has a few fragments of limestone, while that of Purrumbete is almost entirely volcanic ash.

The pyroclastic material shows distinct bedding, which dips outwards from the crater at the same low angle as the groundsurface. The bedding of the ash indicates periodic variations during a single eruption and the sorting of material during its descent. Bedding is often perfect, disturbed only by occasional bombs (Plate XXXId). In a few places cross-bedding in the outward-dipping ash indicates that wind action has also played a part in the sorting and deposition.

Inward-dipping bedding of the ash on the inside of the crater rim is steeper than the bedding on the outside, and shows much landsliding and cross-bedding. It is much more common for the outward-dipping ash beds to be truncated at the inner edge, as at Tower Hill. This is most probably due to collapse of the crater walls into the empty vent after the eruption, but whether this is on a scale sufficient for the maars to be regarded as calderas is open to question.

The separation of maars from scoria cones can at times be difficult, and a continuous series can be postulated, from large, perfectly circular, and shallow lakes with low ramparts to high scoria cones with small irregular lakes. However, transitional types are unusual, and the separation of maars from scoria cones does seem to have some significance. With the exception of a few doubtful cases the maars are concentrated in the Camperdown area on bedrock of Tertiary limestone, and on a flat plain where groundwater is near the surface. It seems quite probable that reaction of hot lava with groundwater gave rise to violent eruptions, causing the large craters and fine pyroclastics of the maars. If there was further eruption after the first violent activity it would not react with groundwater, and at Mt Warrnambool and Mt Leura (Fig. 14.4) there are normal scoria cones on the sites of earlier maars. It is also noteworthy that the maars are close to the axis of the Tertiary trough.

(e) Calderas

Calderas are large depressions, usually over 2 km wide, due to volcanic subsidence. It is generally agreed that Tower Hill is a caldera, though of minimum size and very like a maar, with a multiple scoria cone inside it. Other suggested calderas, such as Mt Warrnambool and Mt Leura, are regarded by Ollier and Joyce (1964) as maars.

Boutakoff (1963) has described Bridgewater Bay, Nelson Bay, and Grant Bay (all near Portland) as collapse calderas 3 km or more in diameter, and has shown the existence of a fault along the western edge of Bridgewater Bay. Filling with sediment and breaching by the sea have given rise to the present bays, where submarine contours indicate probable eruption points within the caldera. These suggested calderas are of Lower Pleistocene age, much older than the maars.

(f) Complex Volcanoes

Some hills do not fit simply into the classification given above because of complications during eruption. Several eruptions may occur in close proximity, giving rise to a multiple volcano; but as, in the Newer Volcanic Province, the several hills tend to be all of about the same size, it is not possible to distinguish main and parasitic cones. Generally, the parts of a multiple volcano are similar in composition, as at the Three Sisters, a multiple scoria cone.

Mt Rouse (Plate XXIXb) is an example of a composite hill, with an elongate crater in a scoria hill, and with a smaller and more distinct crater with a basalt rim on the south. The composite Mt Porndon (Fig. 14.4) has a large basaltic shield with a diameter of about 3 km, in the centre of which are a number of scoria hills, partly arranged in concentric arcs. Staughtons Hill consists of a maar, a scoria hill, and a basalt-rimmed separate crater. Most composite hills appear to consist of individual hills which are genetically related, but it is possible that some, such as Staughtons Hill, are due to the accidental superimposition of unrelated eruption points of different ages. Petrological work could be instructive here.

Some volcanoes of the Portland area do not fit into any of the types described so far. They are smoothly rounded hills of bedded tuff, with basalt plugs and flows.

FEATURES OF THE VENTS

Craters may be absent or obscure, or may be perfect as at Mt Noorat and Mt Elephant amongst the scoria cones and at Mt Hamilton among the lava cones; they may also be relatively deep as at Mt Noorat (150 m) and Mt Leura (100 m). Many maars have craters as much as 3 km across, but other craters are smaller, usually less than 400 m.

Breached crater rims are common in scoria volcanoes. Larkins Hill is a scoria cone from which a lava tongue emerges through such a gap, but in most examples there is no lava flow and the breach has therefore not been formed by lava break-through. Some breaches may occur by slumping of the wall into or away from the crater. At Mt Elephant an accumulation of scoria debris lies downslope from the breach, but in most cases there is no evident accumulation. Some authors have indicated a preferred direction of breaching, usually maintaining that most breaches are on the west side and correlating this with supposed wind direction at the time of eruption. Ollier and Joyce (1964) found a random direction of breach, with, if anything, a maximum to the north and northwest. Some dumb-bell-shaped hills appear to have resulted from breaching of the crater at both ends, as at Mt Eckersley. Mt Monmot consists of two adjacent craters, the western crater breached to the west, and the eastern one to the east. Mt Eccles is the only markedly elongated crater, and from this a well defined flow emerges.

Many craters are flat-bottomed due to a fill of debris and alluvium; others, such as Noorat, have simple concave bottoms with very little fill; some, such as Monmot, have a convex boss or spatter cone in the middle of the crater.

A small spatter cone south of Mt Eccles has an open vent (Fig. 14.5) in which a small crater leads into a constriction about 5 m wide. Below, the shaft opens out like an inverted wineglass to a depth of almost 30 m, with a floor of large, loose, scoriaceous blocks, and with walls festooned with lava stalactites. Withdrawal of magma after eruption is clearly indicated (Ollier 1964b).

THE LAVA FLOWS

The lava flows that poured over the western plains were not entirely uniform, and several types of flow occurred, associated with certain landforms.

(a) *Lava Sheets*

These gave rise to the flattest lava surfaces, and were formed by very liquid lava flowing over a pre-existing plain. Gradients of as little as 1:500 are not uncommon. Large areas were covered, but an examination of bore records shows that an average flow was only about 8 m thick. Hanks (1955) in the region north of Melbourne, and Condon (1951) in the Mt Cotterill area, were able to map distinct flows and to show that even apparently flat sheets of lava were made up of many individual lobes. On the Western Plains, the original topography probably helped the rapid lateral spread of the lavas. In the highlands, deep valleys had to be filled by basalt before extensive lava plains could form; nevertheless, some quite large plains were formed. Some bore records indicate several flows separated by layers of ejectamenta and sediment.

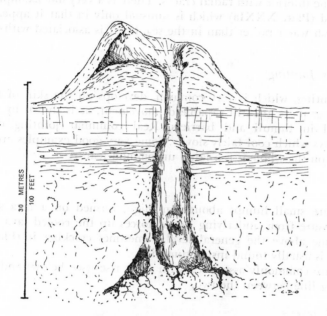

14.5   *A spatter cone with open vent close to Mt Eccles. Vertical exaggeration 2·5 ×. The small cone of welded spatter overlies dense layered lava which in turn overlies massive lava that is very vesicular at the bottom of the shaft.*

(b) *Constricted Flows*

Some lava flows followed valleys and still bear the imprint of the valleys, being thicker but narrower than the sheetflows. The youngest flows of this type, such as the Harman valley flow at Byaduk, still occupy their valleys and have not been affected by subsequent erosion. Others have lateral streams, such as the Tyrendarra flow from Mt Eccles. The lava that flowed down the old valleys must have been very liquid, for it flowed at least 24 km in the case of Byaduk, and over 50 km in the Mt Eccles flow. Some confined flows are small, but those in the Campaspe and Loddon valleys are several kilometres wide and over a hundred metres thick.

(c) *Minor Volcanic Landforms*

In and on the lava flows there are a number of structures and features of interest, some of which are of importance in understanding the nature of lava flow. The commonest features are so well known that they need little description, and emphasis will be placed on those features more peculiar to this province.

(i) *Pillow Lava*

Where lava flows into water it solidifies into the peculiar form of pillow lava, consisting of rounded masses of lava, each having a tachylitic, chilled edge and a more crystalline interior with radial cracks. There is a very fine example of pillow lava at Exford (Plate XXXIa) which is unusual only in that it appears to have formed in fresh water rather than in the sea, for it is associated with thin bands of alluvium.

(ii) *Columnar Jointing*

Crude jointing, which is very common, develops on the skin of a lava flow while the lower parts are still capable of movement, as is shown by tilted joint planes found in tumuli and barriers. Real columnar jointing develops in stationary flows which cool fairly slowly. Some very good examples are known in Victoria, but on the whole it is a fairly uncommon feature.

(iii) *Tumuli*

Tumuli are small humps about 3 m high, formed on a lava sheet where localised pressure from underlying liquid forces up the cooled lava skin into a bulge or dome above the general level, sometimes cracking it (Plate XXXb). Massive lava is usually found inside tumuli.

Tumuli are commonly associated with stony rises (see below) and there is no clear dividing line between the two.

(iv) *Lava Blisters*

So-called lava blisters have the form of very exaggerated tumuli, rising very steeply from their base, with cracks across their tops due to the great bending they have suffered. The best examples, near Byaduk, have been described by Skeats and James (1937), who believed they were formed by gas pressure due to steam generated where a lava flow crossed a swamp. Since no hollow blisters have been found, and indeed lava has been extruded from some, this special explanation does not seem necessary. The lava blisters are now believed to be tumuli of exaggerated type, but still due to local lava pressure and not to steam generated beneath the flow (Ollier 1964a).

(v) *Steam Bubbles*

Boutakoff (1963) has found depressions 10-15 m in diameter which he calls 'steam bubble' structures. These depressions are hemispherical or egg-shaped, surrounded by concentric joints, and occur in the Lower Pleistocene basalt along the coast to the west of Portland. Boutakoff believes they are cavities left by steam and gas bubbles escaping from a viscous lava.

(vi) *Pressure Ridges* (Fig. 14.6)

Barriers and pressure ridges are elongate ridges of basalt crust pushed up by movement of the underlying lava (Skeats and James 1937). Some are transverse to the flow and are formed in one operation by drag below the crust. The Great Barrier of the Harman valley flow (Fig. 14.7) is the best example; it is curved downstream, indicating differential flow between the centre and the sides of the lava stream. Others are lateral to flows, and late withdrawal of lava may be partly responsible for their construction.

(vii) *Side Curtains*

These are produced when cooling lava in a valley flow is pushed towards the edges by the hot lava stream, forming ridges parallel to the valley side. Boutakoff (1963) has found such side curtains on the Tyrendarra flow, especially above bottlenecks in the valley.

(viii) *Depressions*

When lava is drained from beneath an early formed skin, the crust may sag. If withdrawal takes place on a large scale, broad enclosed depressions may be formed. Two such depressions about 1 km wide occur near Exford.

(ix) *Stony Rises* (Fig. 14.6)

Much of the ground in certain volcanic regions is very irregular, although tending to a plain on a broad scale. Hummocks and depressions, channels and ridges, make a completely confused topography called 'stony rises' with relief of about 10 m usually. There appear to be several varieties. Some are individual narrow flows of lava emerging from the base of a broad lava sheet, well exemplified on the southern shores of Lake Corangamite. Differential draining of lava from beneath the skin of a partly congealed lava plateau causes elongated depressions if the surface sags, and this type of stony rise is the most common. The drained channels can coalesce, so that the ridges break up into a number of isolated hillocks with accordant, often flat summits. 'Stony rises' occur in clearly demarcated areas with sharp transition to flat plains.

(x) *Lava Caves*

Many lava caves are known from the Newer Volcanics (Ollier and Brown 1965). Descriptions of individual caves, together with surveyed plans and sections have been published in the *Victorian Naturalist* (Gill 1944, 1959; Ollier 1963a, 1963b, 1964a, 1964b).

When lava flows, the surface in contact with the air cools more quickly than the inside, and therefore solidifies faster, and most geologists agree that caverns are formed in basalts by draining out of liquid below the solidified upper surface of a flow. Victorian lava caves are of this type, but the simple explanation above does not account for all the observed shapes and structural features of the caves

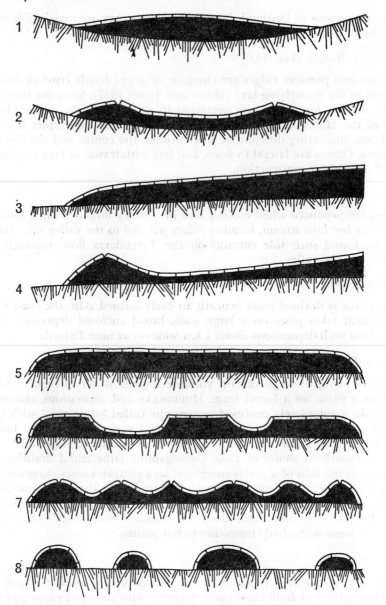

14.6 *Minor features of lava flows: 1. Cross-section of a flow with a skin. This may sag in the centre and rise near the edges to form lateral barriers. 2. In long section. 3. There may also be differential sagging, pushing up the toe of the flow as in 4. 5. Cross-section of a wide flow which collapses later along many channels. If these are widely spaced, flat-topped stony rises may be formed as in 6. If collapse is close a haphazard type of stony rise with some breaching is formed. 7. A number of individual, closely spaced lobes of lava. 8. Another form of stony rise.*

and surrounding flows, and a more involved explanation has been suggested by Ollier and Brown (1965). The idea of Skeats and James (1937) that the caves formed as great hollow lava blisters which were buried under later flows is no longer acceptable.

Some lava caves occur on the flanks of cones, some occur in valley flows (Plate XXXIb), some on wide lava plains, and some on smaller lava plains built by earlier eruptions of adjacent volcanoes.

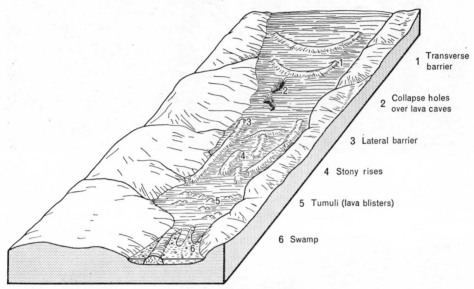

1 Transverse barrier

2 Collapse holes over lava caves

3 Lateral barrier

4 Stony rises

5 Tumuli (lava blisters)

6 Swamp

14.7   Features of the Harman valley lava flow, Byaduk

The caves range in size from small tubes a decimetre or so across, which are mere tributaries to the main caves, up to very large caves. The main chamber at Skipton Cave (Mt Widderin) is 60 m long, has a maximum width of 20 m and is 8 m high. Church Cave, Byaduk, contains a chamber roughly 50 m long and 8 m high. Mt Hamilton Cave has no great chambers but has a total length of passages amounting to about 900 m (Fig. 14.8).

In plan the caves are usually conspicuously elongated in the direction of lava flow; they may be straight tubes or branching, and may have swellings and constrictions. Some show bulbous endings to the tunnels, either at the upstream or at the downstream end. The tunnels usually slope gently down away from the magma source, but occasionally the slope is in the opposite direction, as at the entrance to Turk Cave, Byaduk.

In cross-section there is usually a well defined floor, which may be quite flat, above which the cave roof is typically arched (Plate XXXc). No circular cross-sections have been found. Two caves have asymmetrical cross-sections and structures, indicating plastic deformation of original outlines.

The flows enclosing tunnels are divided into layers varying from about a metre to about a decimetre in thickness and parallel to the surface, each of compact basalt separated by trains of vesicles or in some cases by definite partings. The layers do not represent successive flows, nor the partings joints, but are due to shearing during laminar flow just before solidification. This has been called 'layered-lava' by Ollier and Brown (1965).

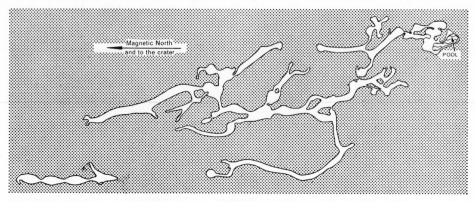

PLAN

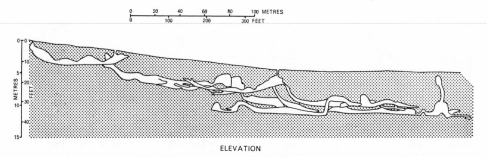

ELEVATION

14.8 Mt Hamilton lava cave

The cave roofs are strongly discordant with the layering, and the layers reach the cave walls without being noticeably deflected. Concealing these layers in many instances is a lining or skin of basalt, plastered on to a roof and walls which display flow marks and wrinkles, and lava stalactites.

FLOW CHARACTERISTICS OF THE LAVAS

Following eruption, lava flows downhill under gravity, and a crust is formed on the surface by cooling. Movement of partly congealed lava is laminar and a layering may be produced, with individual layers separated by partings and vesicles, and by more liquid lava. The rate of cooling of lava is often too slow for the laminae to be preserved, but in the regions where lava tunnels are present the flow layers invariably accompany them and are well formed (Plate XXXIc).

The distinction between layered-lava and massive lava is of some petrological significance. Very fluid lavas reach their position of rest as liquids, and during solidification there can be vertical segregation of minerals and differentiation of rock type. This cannot happen in layered-lava.

When layered-lava is formed, the more congealed lava goes into the layers and the more liquid lava (accompanied by many volatiles) is concentrated between the laminae. At this point something very unusual and unexpected happens.

The liquid lava becomes further segregated and comes to occupy cylindrical tubes running through the layered-lava. The tubes are completely full of liquid which exerts a hydrostatic pressure, so the tunnels can change level at times and the liquid can flow upwards for short stretches. The mobile liquid lava eventually becomes concentrated into a few major cylindrical lava streams which are a continuing source of heat, and the hot liquid contents may even erode or melt some of the earlier layered-lava. However, all these processes are contemporaneous; solidification and remelting, flow and hydrostatic pressure, are all working together. The result is a cylinder of liquid lava flowing through tubes cut in virtually solid layered-lava.

The lava may solidify in this form, but often, due to a breach in the toe of the flow and/or cessation of supply from the volcanic source, the liquid lava will escape from the confining tubes.

If the roof of the tube is strong enough a tunnel or cave will be preserved. Alternatively, the roof may sag down as lava is withdrawn. The broad depressions in lava plains are not associated with layered-lava and tunnels, but are due to withdrawal of very fluid lava on a large scale. Collapse over lava tubes forms stony rises, and the nature of stony rises country shows that there was widespread collapse over many branching and anastomosing tunnels. Isolated collapsed tunnels are quite rare. The collapses described here are primary, that is they happen while the lava is still molten: there are also plenty of secondary collapses that occur when the basalt is cold and brittle.

Repeated rupture and healing of the toe of the lava flow will cause constant changes in the hydrostatic pressure in the tubes, as will the varying amounts of lava supplied from the source. In full tubes the shape and size of the passages may be modified by fluid lava under pressure, forcing more viscous material into bubble-like shapes and giving rise perhaps to some of the domes and bulbous swellings noted in the caves. In partially drained caves, changes in pressure of the lava beneath the cave floors can cause bucklings, blisters and ridges. Changes in pressure may affect the crust of the lava, forcing it up into tumuli (including so-called lava blisters). These have a fairly haphazard distribution, but they seem to be especially abundant near the edges of flows, and some are aligned as if along underlying tubes. Lateral barriers are formed by withdrawal rather than by pressure, while arcuate transverse barriers and side curtains are due to drag on a nearly solidified crust. Barriers and tumuli are common at the end of flows, perhaps due to pressure at the end caused by collapse of the crust behind.

THE NATURE OF THE VULCANICITY

On the foregoing evidence the commonest local sequence of eruption would appear to have been an outpouring of lava to give a lava plain or confined flow, followed by formation of scoria cones at the end of vulcanicity. There are, however, many complications and exceptions, giving rise to basalt cones, basalt discs and strato-volcanoes.

Some of the maars, such as Wangoom, represent single explosive eruptions neither preceded nor followed by extrusion of lava, while others have scoria cones built later at the same centre of eruption.

The scoria cones are probably monogenetic, that is the result of one continuous series of eruptions rather than of the numerous eruptions, widely separated in time, which are typical of pyroclastic volcanoes.

Small pyroclastic volcanoes can be formed from fluid magmas when the pressure behind the magma is too weak for a lava stream to be poured out, so they often form during the last phase of a mixed eruption, and thus overlie previous lava streams.

It is commonly supposed that sheets forming lava plains are erupted from fissures. This could be so in the Western District, but erosion has not yet revealed any such dykes. Certainly the Older Volcanics in eastern Victoria were fed by many dykes, but most of the Newer Volcanic eruptions appear to be of central vent type. The lava plains mapped by Hanks (1955) and by Condon (1951) have been shown to consist of individual lobes which can be traced to distinct points of eruption. Mt Rouse, Mt Porndon, Mt Napier and the Warrion Hills are all surrounded by expanses of flows and stony rises which are almost certainly derived from those points of eruption, and there are many other examples. The form of the cones suggests central vent eruption, and the lack of lineaments is regarded as evidence against fissure eruption. It must be borne in mind that the cones represent only the last period of activity, and that the earliest type of eruption may have been different, but the balance of evidence indicates that we have a region of central vent eruptions.

Ollier and Joyce (1964) found the explosion index E (percentage of pyroclastics in all erupted material) to be about 1 per cent. This is remarkably low (cf. 3 per cent for the Pacific according to Rittmann (1962)), but reflects the fact that the lava flows, though thin, are extensive, while the more noticeable scoria cones are really much smaller in total volume. According to its explosion index, the volcanic activity should be most like the Hawaiian or Icelandic type of eruption, but the Victorian eruptions are not of Hawaiian type (lava shield) and there is little evidence of fissure eruptions of Icelandic type. The scoria cones of Victoria were probably formed by explosive eruptions of Vulcanian or Strombolian type, and maars were formed when lava reacted with groundwater.

The Newer Basalts may thus represent a distinct type of geomorphic/petrographic province, characterised by extensive plains of basaltic lava, and by many small, monogenetic, central vent volcanoes formed in the last stages of vulcanicity.

WEATHERING, SOILS, AND EROSION OF THE VOLCANICS

(a) *Weathering and Soils*

The youngest flows are remarkably fresh, with virtually no soil cover, as in the northern flow from Mt Eccles. Stony rises, wherever they occur, are little altered or eroded, so are believed to be fairly young features, and the volcanoes from which the parent lavas were erupted are therefore fairly young also.

XXXIb Cave entrance in the flat floor of a lava flow in the Harman valley at Byaduk

XXXId Quarry in scoria at Mt Porndon, showing bedding, small-scale faulting, and an accumulation of bombs

XXXIa Pillow lava at Exford overlying older, more weathered basalt

XXXIc Layered lava at Byaduk; on the left is a 'tunnel' that failed to drain

The older flows show much spheroidal weathering and development of later-ites and deep soils. Basalts of the Portland area are deeply lateritised (Boutakoff 1963) and laterites are found in the Hamilton area (Gibbons and Gill 1964). A wide variety of soil types is found on the basalts. Leeper *et al.* (1936) and Baldwin (1950) have described a sequence of mainly dark-coloured clays and loams in catena. Over much of the Western Plains, red soils are dominant, mainly kras-nozems and red-brown earths. Buckshot (pisolitic iron oxide) may be present, and is perhaps a criterion of older flows.

Weathering and soil formation are governed by many factors besides age and parent material, and krasnozems, red-brown earths, and black earths may all be found on the basalt from one volcano. Complicated soil profiles are quite common, and the significance of many observed soil relationships is not known. Gibbon and Gill (1964), however, have attempted the recognition and classification of land systems, distinct assemblages of landforms and soils, which to a large extent indicate the relative ages of different flows.

(b) *Erosion of the Volcanoes*

In the youngest volcanoes even small-scale features are preserved intact. Near Mt Eccles, small spatter cones have perfectly preserved ropy lava and stalactites, even in exposed positions.

The scoria cones have little runoff, owing to their porosity, and they naturally show little erosion. Scoria cones with welded agglomerate near the vent may show a distinct rim around the crater due to general surface lowering of the unwelded scoria of the flanks.

In many of the older volcanoes there has been general rounding rather than gullying, and the original forms are obscure. Some are low and rounded with ill-defined breached craters, while volcanoes of the Portland area, including both lava volcanoes and tuff cones, are rounded hills with little indication of original shape.

Volcanoes of the highland area show some gullying, but within the area of the plains gullies are rare. The greater rainfall on the higher ground may be responsible for this difference. A number of volcanoes in the Gisborne district display considerable erosion (Edwards and Crawford 1940) and the hills are capped by lava sheets which possibly occupied craters originally (e.g. Mt Holden, Plate XXIXd). The well known erosional sequence, from volcano stage through planeze stage and residual mountain stage to the final skeleton stage, is not found in this volcanic province.

(c) *Erosion of Valley Flows*

When lava flows into pre-existing valleys the drainage system is disrupted to some extent. For a while the river may flow over the lava in an ill-defined course depending on minor irregularities in the lava surface. At this stage a thin layer of alluvium may be deposited haphazardly on the basalt, and this may account for the plentiful quartz and other unlikely minerals found in some 'basalt' soils. Eventually, however, the river will incise a well defined valley either across the lava or around it.

The most common modification is for a river to be displaced from its bed to a position at the edge of a lava flow, when it is called a lateral stream. Sometimes twin lateral streams develop, one on each side of the flow, and sometimes, as in the case of the Loddon, the river flows across the lava following approximately its old course (Fig. 14.9).

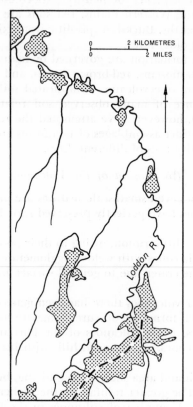

14.9   Deep lead (dash line) and residuals of lava, showing drainage modifications on the Loddon River

Some of the very young flows, such as the Harman valley flow at Byaduk, do not have lateral streams at all. Others, such as the Tyrendarra flow from Mt Eccles, even though young, have well developed lateral streams. The amount of incision of lateral streams will depend on the size of the catchment, amount of runoff, and other factors besides age. When there is sufficient available relief, lateral streams may incise valleys over a hundred metres deep. This has happened in some valleys near the Brisbane Range fault-scarp, where streams have cut valleys 130 m below the old lava fill.

On the plains, the lack of available relief and lower rainfall has minimised erosion, and the considerably greater amount of erosion in the highlands does not necessarily indicate greater age.

In the highlands, the old river courses now covered by basalt are known as 'deep leads', and many of these were traced with great care during the working of buried auriferous alluvium. Maps of old deep leads in conjunction with geological and topographical maps provide an opportunity for study of 'case histories' in the evolution of the drainage of the highlands (Harris and Thomas 1934).

Figure 14.9 shows part of the course of the Loddon River and its associated outcrops of basalt. To the south the old valley is still filled with basalt and the deep lead has been mapped, predictably, along the centre of the flow. The present river is here lateral in part, and elsewhere flows on top of the basalt. Further downstream, that is to the north, it seems that the river originally meandered over the lava surface, but that it has now cut down to a level below the deep lead, leaving remnants of lava as flat-topped hills in meander cores.

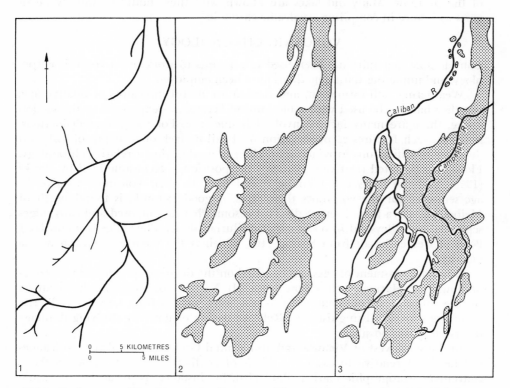

14.10   Drainage modifications of the Campaspe River. 1. A map of the original drainage pattern as indicated by deep leads. 2. The maximum extent of lava. 3. The present-day drainage with the Coliban River on the west and the Campaspe River on the east. For Caliban *read* Coliban.

Figure 14.10 shows a more complicated sequence of events. The area was originally drained by the Campaspe, which took most drainage, and by the small Coliban River in the north. The old courses are traced on deep lead maps. After the valleys were filled with basalt, no tributaries from the west seemed able to cross the basalt to join the Campaspe; they were diverted north as a lateral stream, and eventually joined the Coliban. The original Coliban became much larger and cut through its lava in the same way as the Loddon. The Campaspe, deprived of its tributaries, failed to cut down very much and still flows over the basalt in most of its upper reaches, occasionally crossing on to bedrock. Waterfalls are usually developed where rivers flow off basalt on to bedrock (Plate XXXa).

Sometimes basalt coming down a main valley is sufficiently liquid to flow up tributary valleys, and sometimes it simply blocks them without filling them. If this happens the lava-dammed stream expands into a lake. In Melbourne there are several examples of lakes formed where the Yarra or its tributaries were blocked by lava flows from the north (Hills 1959). The lakes accumulate silt which remains as alluvial flats when the lakes are drained, as they inevitably are, by downcutting of the overflow. Many old lakes are known, and they should eventually be of great assistance in compiling a volcanic chronology.

VOLCANIC CHRONOLOGY

Considerable ingenuity has been used in attempts to work out a volcanic chronology, and numerous dating methods have been employed.

Weathering, soil formation, and erosion are useful indicators of relative age, but they have to be used with some caution because, as explained in the section above, there are many factors involved besides age. For the grosser deductions, however, such features as preservation of detail or lack of it, depth of soil, and drainage modifications provide useful clues in establishing a relative chronology. Flows may be dated relatively by their superposition, a technique used by Hanks (1955), and the flows can then be traced back to their volcanoes to give an age sequence for the volcanoes themselves. A good example is found north of Melbourne. Lava from Pretty Sally Hill is somewhat decomposed and caps ridges separated by valleys cut into sub-basaltic Silurian shale. The valleys contain later flows of fresher basalt from Spring Hill, which is the youngest volcano in the vicinity.

A rough assessment of ages can be based on the degree of preservation of cones or flows—the Harman valley flow from Mt Napier, for instance, shows an aa surface still almost complete, whereas old flows such as from nearby Mt Pierrepoint are scarcely distinguishable. Relative dating of flows by studying drainage diversion is also possible.

In the southwest of Victoria and also around Geelong a number of volcanoes can be dated relative to extensive sheets of aeolian calcarenite which make a convenient stratigraphic marker. Bald Hill, for instance, is pre-aeolianite, while nearby Mt Eccles is post-aeolianite.

Cape Grant and Cape Nelson have been dated by reference to a 30 m marine platform which truncates tuffs and plugs and which is believed to be of Middle Pleistocene age (Boutakoff 1963). Mt Eccles has been dated relative to a 5 m raised beach which rests on part of the flow from that mountain.

If material underneath a volcano or flow can be dated, the maximum age of the volcano is set. Too often in the past there has been a tendency to assume that the underlying deposits give an *actual* age for the volcanics when there is probably a significant unconformity between the underlying material and the volcanics. Some flows have been dated as Lower Pliocene or earlier on such a misreading of evidence. This distinction is of less importance when the underlying material is of recent age, for other dating methods become available. At Mt Gambier in South Australia, implements and hearths have been found beneath the volcanics, and archaeological dating and radiocarbon dating are possible. In a number of places in Victoria, too, artefacts have been found beneath volcanic material (Gill 1953). The younger volcanoes are certainly within the range of C14 dating and are believed to be about 5000 years old. A radiocarbon dating for Mt Gambier was 4700 years, and shells from beneath tuffs near Gnotuk were dated at about 13,700 (Gill 1955).

A few fossils have been recovered from within volcanic deposits, but not in sufficient numbers to be of much use in dating. Fossils found in lava caves give only a minimum age of the flow, for the volcano and caves may have been in existence a long time before they were occupied. Wakefield (1964) has described this line of enquiry in detail.

Many craters and maars have swampy deposits in their bottoms, and there are many swamp deposits around the margins of flows due to drainage modifications. This suggests that pollen analysis might eventually be used for relative dating of the volcanics. Preliminary tests have been made, and although only a little pollen is present in crater samples, the method appears to be feasible. It will, however, take a considerable time to build up a pollen sequence.

Palaeoclimatology is a rather indirect way of dating, but has been used a little. Buckshot gravel, laterite, and certain soil types have been taken as indicators of former climates and tentatively fitted into a Pleistocene chronology. The asymmetric distribution of ash around Wangoom and Mt Warrnambool indicates transport by a west wind, from which Gill (1950) deduced that the eruption took place during the last period of glaciation when west winds would be more prevalent over Victoria.

With all these possible means of dating Victorian volcanoes, it should be possible in time to build up a detailed chronology. This will be of considerable interest, for it is not often possible to get the complete history of a volcanic province from beginning to end—most volcanic provinces which are sufficiently well preserved are still active. At the present time, however, although there are numerous isolated observations, actual progress in establishing a chronology has been small and only a few generalisations can be made. The Portland group consists of old volcanoes, that is pre-aeolianite, well rounded and weathered, and presumably older Pleistocene. This group is in the west of the state, but within this area is Mt Eccles, a fresh, young volcano, probably the youngest in the state. Other post-aeolianite and very young volcanoes are found further west still in South Australia (Mt Gambier and Mt Schank), and not far away are Mt Rouse and Mt Napier, which are both comparatively young, although perhaps older than Mt Eccles. These are in turn younger than Mt Pierrepoint and Mt Bainbridge, which are old and weathered remnants.

The maars appear to be fairly young, as do many of the scoria cones of the plains, but the relative ages are hard to deduce at present. In the Melbourne-Geelong region there are no very young volcanoes and most of them are rather old. Comparison of plains volcanoes with those of the uplands is difficult, but most of the vulcanicity in the Ballarat and Daylesford regions is perhaps of the middle period—younger than the Portland group but older than the maars or Mt Eccles. The eroded volcanoes of the Gisborne area are evidently fairly old, comparable perhaps with the Melbourne group.

Perhaps the most remarkable feature of Victorian vulcanicity is its complete cessation. Older Basalts were erupted in Victoria through long periods in the Tertiary; the Newer Basalts were erupted throughout the Pleistocene and extended into the Recent. The last eruption probably took place only 5000 years ago, and yet now there are no fumaroles, no hot springs, no anomalous temperature gradients or seismic effects, in fact nothing to indicate how recently the volcanic activity ceased. Fortunately for Victoria, but a little disappointingly for her geologists, who are just too late to see active eruptions, one must conclude that the whole province is extinct.

REFERENCES

Baldwin, J. G. (1950). A soil survey of the Shire of Whittlesea, Victoria. *Proc. R. Soc. Vict.* **62**: 173-96.

Boutakoff, N. (1963). *The geology and geomorphology of the Portland area.* Geol. Surv. Vict. Mem. 22.

Condon, M. A. (1951). The geology of the Lower Werribee River, Victoria. *Proc. R. Soc. Vict.* **63**: 1-24.

Coulson, A. (1938). The basalts of the Geelong district. *Proc. R. Soc. Vict.* **50**: 251-7.

—— (1941). The volcanoes of the Portland district. *Proc. R. Soc. Vict.* **53**: 394-402.

—— (1953). The volcanic rocks of the Daylesford district. *Proc. R. Soc. Vict.* **65**: 113-24.

Currey, D. T. (1964). The former extent of Lake Corangamite. *Proc. R. Soc. Vict.* **77**: 377-86.

Eardley, A. J. (1962). *Structural Geology of North America.* New York.

Edwards, A. B. (1938). Tertiary volcanic rocks of Central Victoria. *Q. Jl geol. Soc. Lond.* **14**: 243-320.

—— and Crawford, W. (1940). The Cainozoic volcanic rocks of the Gisborne district, Victoria. *Proc. R. Soc. Vict.* **52**: 281-311.

Gibbons, F. R. and Gill, E. D. (1964). Basaltic plains of Western Victoria, terrains and soils. *Proc. R. Soc. Vict.* **77**: 387-95.

Gill, E. D. (1944). Basalt cave at Panmure, Western Victoria. *Victorian Nat.* **60**: 167; **61**: 42.

—— (1950). An hypothesis relative to the age of some Western District Volcanoes. *Proc. R. Soc. Vict.* **60**: 189-94.

—— (1953). Geological evidence in Western Victoria relative to the antiquity of the Australian Aborigines. *Mem. natn. Mus. Vict.* **18**: 25-92.

—— (1955). Radiocarbon dates for Australian archaeological and geological samples. *Aust. J. Sci.* **18**: 49-52.

—— (1959). The Parwan Caves, Bacchus Marsh district, Victoria. *Victorian Nat.* **75**: 159.

Grayson, H. J. and Mahony, D. J. (1910). *The Geology of the Camperdown and Mount Elephant Districts.* Geol. Surv. Vict. Mem. 9.

Hanks, W. (1955). Newer volcanic vents and lava fields between Wallan and Yuroke, Victoria. *Proc. R. Soc. Vict.* **67**: 1-16.

Harris, W. J. and Thomas, D. E. (1934). The geological structure of the Lower Ordovician Rocks of Eastern Talbot, Victoria. *Proc. R. Soc. Vict.* **46**: 153-78.

Hills, E. S. (1939). The age and physiographic relationships of the Cainozoic volcanic rocks of Victoria. *Proc. R. Soc. Vict.* **51**: 112-39.

—— (1959). *The Physiography of Victoria*. Melbourne.

Kennedy, W. Q. (1933). Trends of differentiation in basaltic magmas. *Am. J. Sci.* **225**: 239-56.

Leeper, G. W., Nicholls, Ann and Wadham, S. M. (1936). Soil and pasture studies in the Mount Gellibrand area, Western District of Victoria. *Proc. R. Soc. Vict.* **49**: 77-138.

Ollier, C. D. (1963a). The Mount Hamilton lava caves. *Victorian Nat.* **79**: 331-6.

—— (1963b). The Skipton lava caves. *Victorian Nat.* **80**: 181-3.

—— (1964a). Tumuli and lava blisters of Victoria, Australia. *Nature, Lond.* **202**: 1284-6.

—— (1964b). Caves and associated features of Mount Eccles. *Victorian Nat.* **81**: 64-71.

——, and Brown, M. C. (1964). The Byaduk lava caves. *Victorian Nat.* **80**: 279-90.

—— and —— (1965). Lava caves of Victoria. *Bull. volcan.* **28**: 1-15.

——, and Joyce, E. B. (1964). Volcanic physiography of the western plains of Victoria. *Proc. R. Soc. Vict.* **77**: 357-76.

Rittman, A. (1962). *Volcanoes and Their Activity*. New York.

Skeats, E. W. and James, A. V. G. (1937). Basaltic barriers and other surface features of the newer basalts of western Victoria. *Proc. R. Soc. Vict.* **49**: 245-92.

Wakefield, N. A. (1964). Mammals past and present. *Proc. R. Soc. Vict.* **77**: 419-32.

Yates, H. (1954). The basalts and granitic rocks of the Ballarat district. *Proc. R. Soc. Vict.* **66**: 63-101.

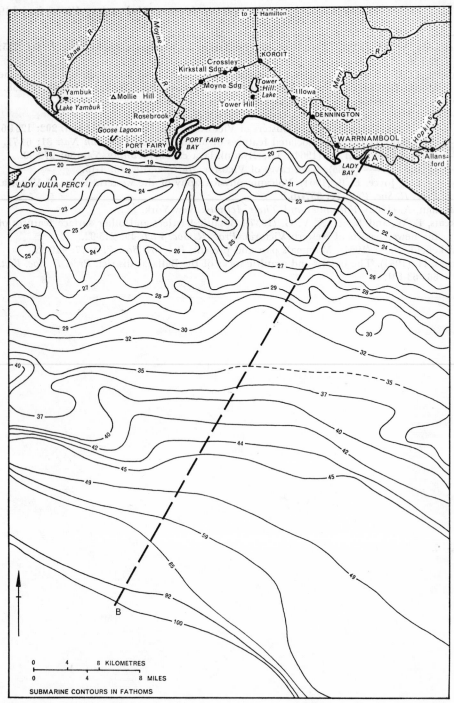

15.1   The Warrnambool-Port Fairy coast, and the continental shelf contoured from
        Admiralty chart soundings

15

Evolution of the Warrnambool-Port Fairy Coast and the Tower Hill Eruption, Western Victoria

EDMUND D. GILL

INTRODUCTION

Coasts are complex and polygenetic, and many processes over a long period of time have usually contributed to the features preserved. It is therefore difficult to distinguish forms due to present processes from those which are an inheritance from the past. Relict Pleistocene formations contribute to Holocene shorelines, and multiple cycling of materials often makes origins unclear. However, at Tower Hill, between Warrnambool and Port Fairy in Western Victoria, a Holocene volcano completely and rapidly obliterated the contiguous coast, smothering it with a thick blanket of volcanic ejectamenta so that coastal processes began anew. Moreover, former sources of coastal sand in that area, except one—the sea—were made unavailable. The whole geological and geomorphological setting was thus admirably simplified. When the volcanic ash was incorporated in new formations, the obvious mineralogical label of volcanic products was present for the geologist to read. In any series of sand layers nearby, the fresh, sharp-edged green olivine grains mark the time of the volcanic eruption as indubitably as the clearest historical record.

In support of the stratigraphic evidence, radiocarbon dating makes it possible to establish an absolute time scale. Datings have not yet been completed, but enough are available for a chronology of the main events since the eruption. This essay outlines what has been learnt of the evolution of the earlier coastline and of the new coastline since its formation some five millennia ago.

GEOLOGICAL BACKGROUND

The geological background consists of a horizontal formation of Miocene marine limestone capped with basalts of mostly Pleistocene age and fronted in the Warrnambool area by a large formation of Pleistocene aeolianite.

The Miocene limestone in the Warrnambool-Port Fairy area has been called both Port Campbell Limestone and Portland Limestone, and is exposed in the cliffs east of the area (Baker 1943, 1944). The section in the west bank of the Hopkins River estuary at Warrnambool has yielded a fauna indicating that this marine limestone is Upper Miocene in age (probably Cheltenhamian), and that there is a large time gap between the limestone and the overlying basalt.

Dr A. W. Beasley kindly determined the tuff minerals in various post-eruption sediments, and Miss J. Hope Macpherson determined the snail shells.

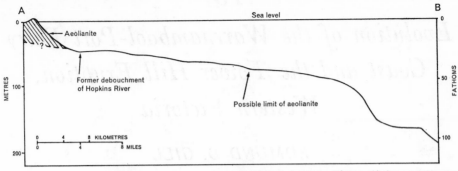

15.2   Profile across the continental shelf on A-B in Figure 15.1

The limestone is a yellow earthy rock (Caldwell 1937; Mahony 1937) in which leaching has destroyed the aragonitic fossils but left the calcitic ones; there has been much secondary deposition of carbonates, affecting the strength and solubility of the rock. This Port Campbell Limestone is underlain by calcareous clayey silt formations (Baker 1953) met also in deep bores and in the ejectamenta of volcanoes such as Tower Hill. The highly calcareous foundation has resulted in a high percentage of carbonates in the Tower Hill ejectamenta. Since limestone forms the basement of the area, karst features, including collapse dolines, are common and caves are numerous (Gill 1948).

Extensive basalt flows cover the Tertiary strata. The oldest basalts in the area are perhaps Upper Pliocene, but the majority are tentatively ascribed to the Pleistocene on the basis of their stratigraphy, geomorphology, degree of development of secondary iron and carbonate minerals, and their soils (Gibbons and Gill 1964; Gill 1964). The numerous flows have not all been differentiated, but the Yangery Basalt and Woodbine Basalt (Table 1) are recognised as distinct flows.

As a result of the Kosciusko Uplift, the streams have been strongly rejuvenated, resulting in deep incision through the basalt to the underlying marine strata. Sections in these streams and bores show that the basalt varies in thickness by as much as 60 m, and this may be taken as the degree of erosion before the extrusion of the basalts.

The surface formation on which Warrnambool is built is a large body of aeolianite (Mahony 1936a, b; Gill 1943) which fills an old marine embayment extending eastwards for about 20 km from Tower Hill. At Warrnambool this dune rock extends about 4 km inland; offshore, the sea floor descends fairly rapidly to 35-45 m, where there is a marked change in declivity (Figs. 15.1, 15.2) which may be interpreted as the limit of the aeolianite. Numerous debouchments of rivers can be deciphered from the submarine contours at about this depth, and may well mark a former shoreline. The formation reaches a maximum thickness of about 75 m, the result of the building of newer dunes upon the eroded remains of earlier dunes. Fossil soils are not uncommon in it.

GEOMORPHOLOGICAL SETTING

The extreme eastern limit of the former Warrnambool embayment is in the vicinity of Childers Cove, where the top of the cliffs is formed of aeolianite (Gill

TABLE 1

Stratigraphy of the Warrnambool-Port Fairy coastal area, Victoria

Structural relationships		Formation	Type locality	Facies	Age
	1	1. MOYNE ALLUVIUM	Tower Hill marsh surficial alluvium (Fig. 15.6a)	Paludal	Middle and Upper Holocene
	2	2. ARMSTRONG SAND	Calcareous, largely mobile dunes bordering Armstrong Bay (Fig. 15.6b)	Dune	Upper Holocene
	3	3. PITON SCORIA	Central cones, Tower Hill volcano (Fig. 15.6b)	Volcanic (explosive)	Upper Holocene
	4	4. TOWER HILL TUFF	Rim of crater, Tower Hill volcano (Fig. 15.6b)	Volcanic (explosive)	Upper Holocene
Conformable	5	5. PERTOBE COQUINA	Lake Pertobe, Warrnambool (Fig. 15.8)	Still water marine	Middle Holocene
Unconformable	6	6. DENNINGTON SAND	Calcareous dune with calcrete crust extending SE from Moulden Quarry (Fig. 15.7, E1)	Dune	Last Interglacial (Upper Pleistocene)
Conformable	7	7. PORT FAIRY CALCARENITE	Large drain crossing Princes Highway on N. boundary of Port Fairy (Fig. 15.5)	Shallow water marine to shoreline	Last Interglacial (Upper Pleistocene)
Conformable	8	8. WOODBINE BASALT	Rosebrook quarries (Fig. 15.5)	Volcanic (effusive)	Penultimate Glacial (Middle Pleistocene)
No known contact	9	9. WARRNAMBOOL AEOLIANITE	Cutting in Pertobe Road, Warrnambool (Fig. 15.8)	Dune	Penultimate Interglacial (Middle Pleistocene)
Upper contact conformable	10	10. SUNNYSIDE SAND	Under Woodbine Basalt near Killarney (Fig. 15.5, Bores 12, 13)	Shallow water marine	Penultimate Interglacial (Middle Pleistocene)
Conformable to unconformable	11	11. YANGERY BASALT	Conn's Lane, Parish of Yangery (Fig. 15.6c)	Volcanic (effusive)	Lower Pleistocene or late Pliocene
Disconformable to unconformable	12	12. PORT CAMPBELL LIMESTONE (= Portland Limestone)	Port Campbell cliffs (Portland cliffs)	Offshore marine (lime mud)	Upper Miocene (probably Cheltenhamian)

All the Quaternary names newly presented in this table have been approved by the Australian Stratigraphical Nomenclature Committee.

1947). Further west, the aeolianite constitutes the whole cliff, which may be as much as 60 m high, and the present coastline cuts across the aeolianite dune trend at a slightly oblique angle. Nearer Warrnambool the coast is low and lacks prominent features until Tower Hill is reached, where the highest cone of the group of cones and craters in the middle of the caldera rises above the rim, forming a notable feature recorded by the early explorers. The French explorer Baudin in the *Géographe* noted Tower Hill and called it *Piton de Reconnaissance,* whilst Flinders, who saw it shortly afterwards, called it a 'peaked hill' (Fowler 1914).

The Tower Hill volcano coincides with a marked change in the trend of the former coastline upon which it is situated (Figs. 15.1, 15.3). The two directions are related to fundamental lineaments in the structure of the bedrock (Boutakoff 1952) and their intersection may account for the site of the volcano. At its nearest, the perimeter of the crater is 2 km from the present coast.

The open bay caused by the change in coast direction near Tower Hill is called Armstrong Bay, while that on which Warrnambool is situated is called Lady Bay. The latter also appears to be open, but a bar of aeolianite runs across the mouth of the bay at shallow depth, causing waves to break and giving an area of comparatively quiet waters inside.

The beaches of the area are mostly sandy, with calcareous sand. In addition, aeolianite forms shore platforms and low cliffs on the east side of the Hopkins River and for 2·5 km west of Lady Bay. As is common in Victoria, the general southerly courses of the rivers hereabouts are interrupted near the coast by the sand accumulations, both old and new. Thus the Hopkins River flows south to the edge of the basalt plain, and then west for 8 km at the inland edge of the aeolianite to debouch at Hopkins Point (Fig. 15.4). However, a former course can be traced southeastwards behind the aeolianite to Childers Cove, in the opposite direction to the present flow near the mouth.

The Merri River is even more tortuous in its course (Figs. 15.3, 15.4; Plate XXXIIb). From Wollaston it flows 5 km west between the basalt and the aeolianite to Dennington, where it flows south through a gap in the Pleistocene dune line and then turns east again to emerge at Warrnambool. At times since the eruption of Tower Hill, the Merri has continued west another 6 km from the gap to emerge at Tower Hill beach in Armstrong Bay. The lagoon at 'The Cutting' is a remnant of that course, and is today invaded by storm waves which surmount the sand bar at its seaward end.

Alluvium has collected in the abandoned coastal channels to form swamps.

PLEISTOCENE SHORELINES

Sea level is constantly changing, and has never been more mobile than in the Quaternary; it is only in a relative way that we can speak of still-stands. The most real concept of sea level is a dynamic one, and the most appropriate geomorphology here is historical rather than descriptive.

The seaward edges of the limestone, basalt, and aeolianite in the study area have been modified again and again by advances and retreats of the sea. Time after time sea level rose and older formations were eroded, coastal cliffs were formed and modified, and new masses of sediments emplaced. When the sea

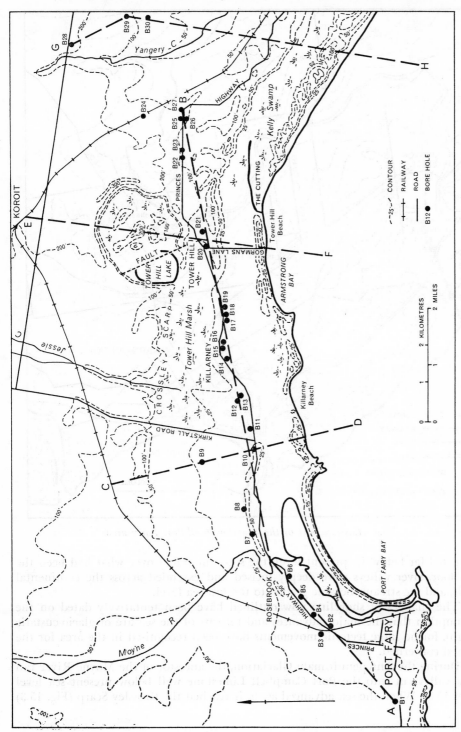

15.3   *Western part of the Warrnambool-Port Fairy area, based on Port Fairy Sheet 1/63,360 Military Map. The contours are not precise. Section lines of Figures 15.5 and 15.6 are shown*

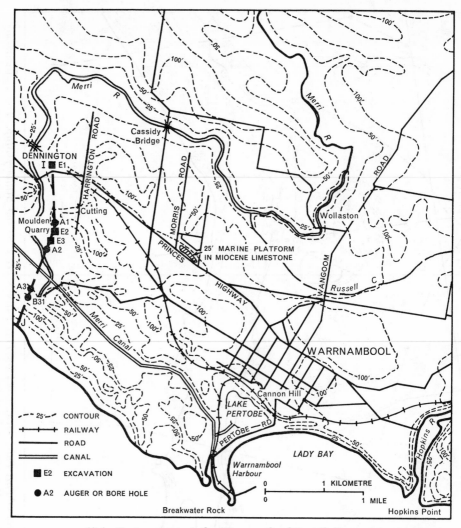

15.4   Eastern part of the Warrnambool-Port Fairy area

retreated far below its present level, the shore migrated over what had been the sea floor, river valleys were deeply incised and extended across the continental shelf, and the streams became graded to the low sea level.

The changes of shoreline now outlined have been tentatively dated on the assumption that the major advances and retreats of the sea are of glacio-eustatic origin, for no large tectonic movements have been recognised in the area for the period concerned.

During the Antepenultimate Glaciation, the ancestor of the Moyne River ran in a valley cut into the Port Campbell Limestone well below present sea level (Fig. 15.5). When the sea advanced again it reached the Crossley Scarp (Fig. 15.3)

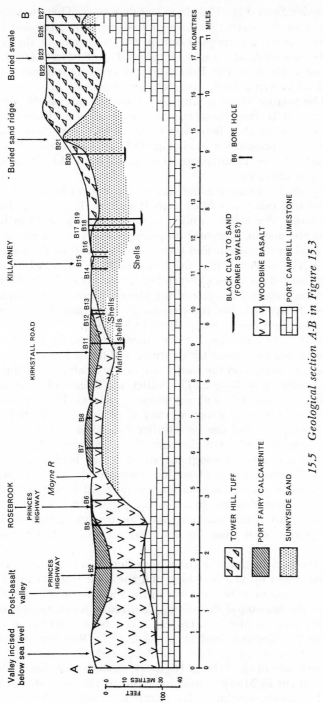

15.5 *Geological section A-B in Figure 15.3*

and the Sunnyside Sand (Figs. 15.5, 15.6) was deposited. There was no Tower Hill volcano then, and the scarp ran through the area now occupied by the crater (Fig. 15.3). The limestone cropping out on the east sector of the crater rim was then probably an island, which may be called Tower Island. The Crossley Scarp continued round north of the Princes Highway at Dennington and north of Russell Creek at Warrnambool, intersecting the present coast east of Allansford (Fig. 15.1). The marine Miocene limestone cropping out on the west side of the Hopkins estuary at Warrnambool was also apparently an island, which may be called Belvedere Island after Belvedere Cave which occurs there. The Sunnyside Sand extends above present sea level (Fig. 15.5) and so is judged to represent an interglacial period—the Penultimate Interglacial—and this is in keeping with what is known of the fauna.

The Sunnyside Sand was trenched during the low sea level of the Penultimate Glaciation and this valley was filled with Woodbine Basalt (Fig. 15.5) on which Port Fairy is built. The valley so filled is graded to at least 30 m below present sea level. Miocene marine limestone cropping out at Goose Lagoon west of Port Fairy is marginal to this basalt and forms the west wall of the valley. At Mollie Hill, 10 km NNW of Port Fairy, the basalt is 30 m thick, while to the east it spreads out in front of the Crossley Scarp but without reaching it (Figs. 15.5, 15.6a). The basalt extends about 5 km east of the Moyne River and is commonly held to be a flow from Tower Hill, but the sections disprove this, since there is no basalt on the summit of the Crossley Scarp (Figs. 15.5, 15.6a).

As soon as the Woodbine Basalt was emplaced during the Penultimate Glacial, it began to be eroded by streams with a strong fall to the low sea level of the time. A valley so formed occurs on the north side of Port Fairy, as is shown by Figure 15.5 where it is pierced by Bore 2. This valley was filled with Port Fairy Calcarenite which rises to about 7·5 m above present sea level. This formation possesses marine species indicative of waters warmer than the present, such as the gasteropod *Ninella torquata* and the foraminifer *Fabularia lata* (Collins 1953, 1956; Gill 1955a; Valentine 1965). On the corner of the Princes Highway and Bank Street, Port Fairy, is a beach conglomerate of basalt boulders, calcareous sand, and broken shells about 7·5 m above low water mark (LWM). Shells from this deposit exceed the range of radiocarbon dating (Gill 1955a), and this, together with the warmer water elements in the fauna, suggests a Last Interglacial age (cf. Jennings 1959). This is now supported by an ionium dating of 125,000 years obtained on marine shell from the Port Fairy Calcarenite by Professor J. W. Valentine.

Just as at the present time the coast from Port Fairy to Tower Hill is characterised by sand ridges up to 7·5 m high and the coast from Tower Hill to Warrnambool by dunes up to 30 m, so it was in the Pleistocene (Plate XXXIIb). Thus at Dennington the horizontal Port Fairy Calcarenite forms the flat on which the village is built, while at Moulden Quarry it can be seen to pass up into a dune formation, the Dennington Sand (Figs. 15.4, 15.7). Remains of sand ridges of similar age can be seen at Port Fairy and Rosebrook.

On the north side of the Princes Highway, as shown in Figure 15.4, there is a marine platform cut in Miocene limestone and of the order of 7·5 m above the present one. Pleistocene marine shells, calcareous sand, and flat beach pebbles of

XXXIIa (above) Crater and nested cones of the Tower Hill volcano. Photograph by Alex Wilkins.

XXXIIb (right) Aerial view of the coast by the Merri River, with Dennington at top right. Kelly Swamp lies behind the mobile coastal dunes, and the ridge inland from the swamp is of Warrnambool Aeolianite and/or Dennington Sand. Published with permission of Department of Lands and Survey, Victoria.

One Half Mile

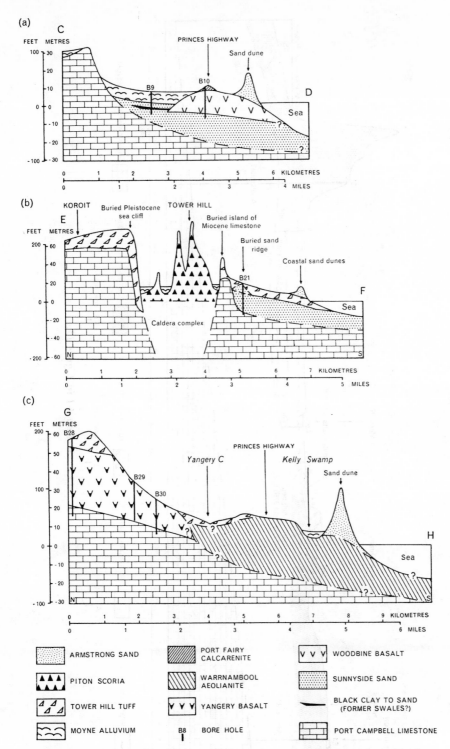

15.6 (a) Section C-D in Figure 15.3. (b) Section E-F in Figure 15.3. (c) Section
      G-H in Figure 15.3. (The rocks shown as Warrnambool Aeolianite may
      also include Port Fairy Calcarenite and Dennington Sand.)

Y

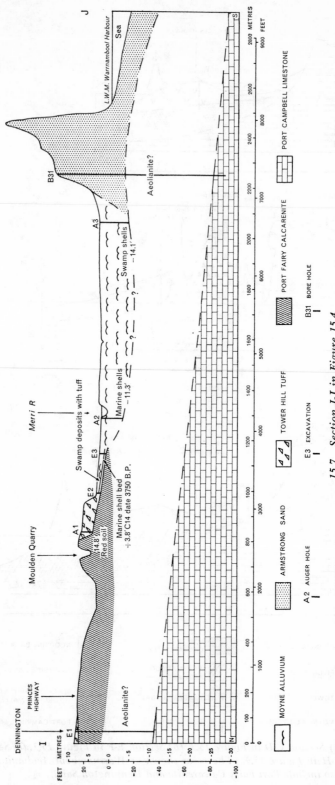

15.7 *Section I-J in Figure 15.4*

calcrete, the 'discoid beach gravel' of Hatai and Saito (1963), form a thin layer over the platform. Just west of this site, at the corner of Morris Road (Fig. 15.4), there is a boulder bed with fine to coarse sand and shells—a facies of the Port Fairy Calcarenite. Numerous excavations in this area have encountered the shell beds, and there is one other report of the boulder bed, extending 2·5-7 m above sea level. In the Last Interglacial there was thus a marine embayment in the Dennington area. The Yangery Basalt limits the embayment to the west and the Warrnambool Aeolianite limits it to the east.

THREE PHASES OF DUNE BUILDING

As the sand of this coast is highly calcareous, percolating waters leach the carbonates, which are precipitated as the sand dries out, forming a cement between the sand grains. Since this lithification is a function of time, the disparate effects of different periods of lithification on different dune systems can be recognised. In recent years, cutting by heavy machinery has revealed the following three phases of dune building (Table 2).

TABLE 2

Characteristics of dune formations

Formation	Age	Lithification	Soils	Snails
Armstrong Sand	Holocene	None	Grey juvenile	*Austrosuccinea* and introduced European snails
Dennington Sand	Last Interglacial	Calcrete crust Soil pipes	Terra rossa	
Warrnambool Aeolianite	Penultimate and earlier Interglacials	Complete Soil pipes	Terra rossa	*Chloritobadistes* in aeolianite; *Magilaoma*, etc. in fossil soils

(a) *Armstrong Sand*

This comprises the modern dunes of unconsolidated sand that fringe the coast. Lithification is practically absent, a few rhizoconcretions being the only structures involving redeposition of carbonate. The Armstrong Sand is Holocene in age, and where radiocarbon dates are available, as at Tower Hill beach, it can be shown to be Upper Holocene.

(b) *Dennington Sand*

This formation consists of dunes left by the retreat of the Last Interglacial sea, and characterised by a case-hardening of calcrete. Thus in Moulden Quarry, the type locality for the formation, the crust on the Dennington Sand consists of 0·6-0·9 m of calcified red soil and calcrete breccia. Calcareous concretions are present in the sand below this, while above is 1 cm of mammillary calcite followed by 20 cm of tuffaceous black soil. The Dennington Sand, with an armour of calcrete and soft sand beneath, constitutes the ridge extending southeast from Moulden Quarry and rising to a little over 30 m above sea level.

A high cutting in Harrington Road, Dennington (Fig. 15.4) shows a thick layer of Tower Hill Tuff with brown volcanic soil overlying Dennington Sand which has a hard calcrete capping surmounted by a buried terra rossa.

Thus the dunes of the Last Interglacial can be recognised by the fact that they grade down into the Port Fairy Calcarenite, that they are associated with a shoreline 7·5 m above the present, that they have a crust of calcrete, and that they bear a terra rossa soil which is not found on younger dunes.

The shell beds here named respectively the Port Fairy Calcarenite and the Pertobe Coquina were not originally distinguished (Gill 1943). The shell beds on the Hopkins River (Gill 1943) belong to the former and have since been traced under the coastal hills east of the Hopkins River mouth; these hills are now interpreted as Last Interglacial Dennington Sand. It is not yet known whether the interior of the hill is free sand, though there are suggestions of this in small cuttings; the coastal sections do not help because sea water and coastal spray bring about the lithification of the surficial rock. This process can be distinguished from pedogenic lithification in that lithification by the sea is comparatively even and does not alter the colour of the rock by heavy localised encrustations, while that by soil-forming processes produces bands of tough, whitish calcrete attaining 1·5 m in thickness. Thus an emerged marine platform can be distinguished from a platform left by differential erosion of pedogenic calcrete, and former land surfaces can often be recognised when boring aeolianite.

Since the events of the Last Interglacial, calcification has occurred, including the formation of solution pipes, and there has been a retreat of the sea far below the present level, causing incision of deep channels which were later filled with sediments during the Flandrian Transgression. These sediments are still unconsolidated and unoxidised, unlike those of the Last Interglacial high sea level, which were drained during the Last Glacial low sea level, thus allowing consolidation and admission of air for oxidation.

(c) *Warrnambool Aeolianite*

In contrast to both the Armstrong Sand and the Dennington Sand, the whole Warrnambool Aeolianite formation is lithified, and where evenly cemented it has been quarried as a building stone. At Steere Quarry, on the south side of the Princes Highway in Warrnambool, the aeolianite is more than 21 m thick and overlies a layer of coarse, loose, poorly sorted, nearly horizontally bedded sand (probably Sunnyside Sand) which represents a former beach. As the Warrnambool Aeolianite is older than the Last Interglacial shorelines incised into it, the formation must be at least Middle Pleistocene (Zeuner 1959). As the Dennington Sand was left by the retreat of the sea from the high stand of the Last Interglacial, so the Warrnambool Aeolianite was probably left when the sea was retreating from earlier high levels. Discontinuities and fossil soils in the formation show that more than one phase of dune building was involved, and so the aeolianite is believed to comprise both Middle and Lower Pleistocene deposits.

On the ridge running northwest from Dennington, Warrnambool Aeolianite, possibly with Dennington Sand, is overlain by Tower Hill Tuff. In road cuttings, a terra rossa with some development of soil pipes can be seen under the tuff.

HOLOCENE SHORELINES

The youngest formation of emerged marine sediments in this area is the Pertobe Coquina, which consists of sand with varying percentages of shell. These sediments are unconsolidated, not deeply incised, not oxidised below sea level, less leached than older coquinas, and the fauna does not contain the warmer water species of the Port Fairy Calcarenite. The Pertobe Coquina is also associated with eroded marine platforms of very low level often cut in the Port Fairy Calcarenite (Figs. 15.7, 15.8) and therefore younger, and mid-Holocene radiocarbon dates are consistently obtained for it.

The seaward edge of the aeolianite on which Warrnambool stands ends abruptly in a former sea cliff at Cannon Hill (Fig. 15.8) overlooking the flats on which Lake Pertobe is situated and which rise only 3 m above LWM in Lady Bay. Cut into the base of the former cliff is a platform 1·5 m above LWM, and on the platform is the Pertobe Coquina, consisting of a layer of red sand followed by grey sand with marine fossils. The coquina is overlain in turn by peaty sand with swamp fossils (Fig. 15.8).

Shells of *Homalina deltoidalis* from the grey sand have been radiocarbon dated as 5840 ± 320 years B.P. (Ac-14). The Pertobe Coquina continues out and thickens under Lake Pertobe, where it is revealed in the banks of the Merri Canal. Here shells of the same species from just above HWM have yielded a radiocarbon date of 6500 ± 200 years B.P. (Ac-15). Tower Hill Tuff overlies the shell bed at Cannon Hill and is piled against the old sea cliff.

The Pertobe Coquina occurs in similar circumstances near Dennington, where a platform has been cut in the Port Fairy Calcarenite and a marine bed without tuff minerals has been deposited on its outer part. Shells from Excavation 2 (Fig. 15.7) from 25-53 cm gave a radiocarbon date of 3750 ± 150 years B.P. (GX-0058). This date is discussed later in connection with the age of the Tower Hill eruption. Overlying this shell bed is the alluvium of Kelly Swamp, which belongs to the formation called Moyne Alluvium; these sediments are rich in tuff minerals from the Tower Hill volcano.

At Killarney beach, both basalt and overlying Port Fairy Calcarenite have been planed off near the shore to give a platform about a metre above sea level, which probably belongs to the mid-Holocene. It is covered by sand beach ridges behind which are marshy areas.

At Port Fairy, the Moyne River has eroded the Port Fairy Calcarenite, cutting it deeply during the last low sea level. In this channel, young shell beds have been emplaced, and these extend on to the Woodbine Basalt in the vicinity of the Princes Highway. Shell beds also underlie Port Fairy Botanic Gardens and the contiguous flats, where Rawlinson (1878) records,

> On portion of these flats W. of the River Moyne, well shafts have been sunk to depths varying from 14 to 18 ft. deep, and an original sea bed disclosed, with abundance of recent shells.

The fossils collected are in the National Museum of Victoria, and their type of preservation shows they do not belong to the Port Fairy Calcarenite.

Similarly at Goose Lagoon west of Port Fairy, where there has been downcutting at the edge of the Woodbine Basalt, young shell beds are found resting on

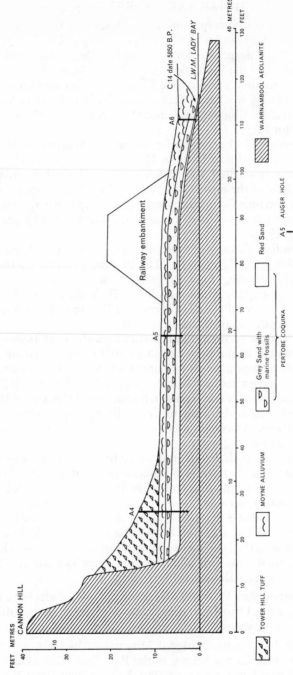

15.8   *Section from Cannon Hill through flats near Lake Pertobe, showing deposits overlying a fossil shore platform*

a basalt platform. Further evidence of the Last Glacial low sea level is seen in a deep channel of the Merri River south of Dennington and in the submarine contours which depict a continuation of the channel further south (Fig. 15.1). At Cassidy Bridge (Fig. 15.4) the present bed of the river is 6·3 m below LWM and the top of the Tower Hill Tuff is at 12·4 m below LWM; however, the thickness of the tuff, and so the full depth of this former channel, is not known.

TOWER HILL ERUPTION

The next event was a climactic one that rapidly and drastically changed the nature and shape of the coast—the Tower Hill volcanic eruption (Hart 1901; Gill 1950). The volcano, of olivine basalt magma, was violently explosive, and formed what is believed to be the largest volcanic crater in Australia (Plate XXXIIa; Fig. 15.3), 3·2 km long and 2·4 km wide, and about 11 km around the oval rim. The ash spread is to the northeast, down the present-day prevailing wind (Gill 1950); hence Tower Hill is one of a group of younger volcanoes which contrast with an older group with ash spreads to the east and southeast (Gill 1950). That the eruption was short-lived and fiercely explosive is shown by the ring of ejectamenta of up to 75 m of mostly thinly bedded tuff and lapilli without any signs of significant intermission such as buried soils or appreciable leaching of carbonates. However, at the top of the rim, filled-in washouts, disconformities, and unconformities provide evidence of a slowing tempo of eruption and intervening small-scale erosion. Here also is up to 1 m of coarse agglomerate, comprising basaltic bombs, pieces of baked Miocene limestone, angular pieces of scoria, blocks of tuff and lapilli, as well as pieces of basalt and ropy lava, believed to belong to the phase when the central cones were constructed.

Although the eruptive activity was more or less continuous, it varied in intensity as is proved by the variation in the ejectamenta from fine ash to cinders, and also by the fact of the stratification itself. In the middle of the large crater is a complex of perhaps 20 smaller craters and peaks (Plate XXXIIa). This multiplicity of eruption points has to be explained.

The ejectamenta that constitute the central group of cones (Piton Scoria) contrast with those in the rim of the volcano described above (Tower Hill Tuff) in that they are mostly unstratified. One mound on the east side consists of an agglomerate similar to that already noted on the rim. A valley running approximately NW-SE, parallel to a crater fault, divides the central complex into two unequal parts (Fig. 15.3). At the southeast end of this valley there is a small pahoehoe lava flow, the only one known in the volcano. This short arcuate flow of vesicular lava containing pieces of bedrock serves to emphasise the difference between the rim structure and the central complex, for the phase that ejected the former was one of much higher energy level than that which formed the central complex, and the two phases of volcanic activity must have been characterised by different gas/lava ratios. The existence of these two phases, and the sudden break between them, must also be explained in any satisfactory theory of the genesis of the volcano.

The rim deposits are like those found in maars such as in the classic Eifel area of Western Germany, and in local maars in Western Victoria, such as Lake

Keilambete. Tower Hill is not considered to be a maar, however, on account of its size, which is greater than that of any known maar.

The biggest maar in the Eifel is the Laacher See; diameter 2½ km (1½ miles), depth 53 m. This maar is a little exceptional insofar as it produced only trachytic tuffs, and not basaltic ones as the other maars. The next biggest is the Meerfelder Maar, diameter of the bottom 1480 m (less than a mile), depth 17 m. Some well-known and often-visited maars have a diameter of 300-600 m. The deepest has 74 m depth. (M. Schwarzbach personal communication; see also Hopmann, Frechen, and Knetsch (n.d.)).

A further point is that Tower Hill is nested, and there are no nested maars in the type area of the Eifel.

It is envisaged that breaks in the bedrock caused by the intruding magma admitted water so that water vapour became the prime mover. Steam blast eviscerated the underlying rock and produced the Tower Hill Tuff. Beneath the Port Campbell Limestone, which is fairly competent albeit weakened by karst, lies the friable marl which is very readily disintegrated. The Tower Hill ejectamenta in fact contain a remarkable amount of comminuted calcareous bedrock, and samples of volcanic cinders from Mt Leura, Mt Noorat, and Tower Hill, treated with acid, lost respectively 3, 4, and 16 per cent of their dry weight. Hollowed out by steam blast, the whole structure collapsed when the steam pressure was reduced. The collapse is likely to have involved Port Campbell Limestone to a depth of the order of 150 m, and a similar thickness of underlying marl (Chapman 1925). Tower Hill is too large to be a simple gas vent, and has been described as a nested caldera (Hills 1940). This volcano may be said to have started as a maar, but to have developed into a caldera largely by reason of the nature of the rock beneath.

Through the debris that choked the original vent, many small vents developed, building the multiple cones that constitute the central complex. By this stage the greater part of the energy of the volcano had been expended, and in its remaining life it built only cinder and scoria cones.

Such a history accounts for the great size of the crater, the nested cones, the strong dissimilarity between the ejectamenta of rim and central complex, and the occurrence of bedrock in the agglomerate.

The extreme southwest corner of the crater has a breached appearance, and it is pertinent to enquire if a cold lahar broke through and spread sediments across Tower Hill marsh. However, at the east end of Tower Hill marsh, 3·5-4 m of stratified wind-borne ash such as is found in the rim occur under the black alluvium, so apparently there was no lahar.

Even allowing for the fact that the prevailing southwest winds took most of the ash away from this corner, the rim is lower than one would expect. The low rim and the lower part of the crater floor adjacent are believed to be due to a fault, shown in Figure 15.3. At the north end of the fault line is a quarry which reveals a monocline, and in the rim south of this quarry there are other evidences of disturbance. The saddle in the rim at the south end of the fault line may also be due to faulting. It is estimated that the downthrow on the fault was between 6 and 8 m to the southeast.

A complete lake in the caldera was shown on maps of 1846-50, and rather later by Brough Smyth (1858). Photographs taken in 1912 show the crater to have been dry except for the southwest corner, which never dries, and this situation also existed at the time of the military survey in 1942, when the floor of the Tower Hill crater was an extensive swamp with a lake called Tower Hill Lake in the southwest corner. Since 1946 water has again covered the whole of the caldera floor. These fluctuations appear to be connected with series of wetter and drier years. In 1902 it was feared that the lake would again dry up, and residents proposed that Jessie Creek should be diverted into the crater. About 1945, when the lake was dry, an auger was put down 3 m into the peaty sediments without reaching their base; a study of these sediments and of their fossil content would enhance our knowledge of the later history of the volcano.

DATING OF THE TOWER HILL ERUPTION AND LATER EVENTS

All early writers (e.g. Bonwick 1858; Brough Smyth 1858; Wilkinson 1865) correctly stressed the recency of this eruption, and the writers of the present century have reiterated this (e.g. Skeats 1909; Chapman 1929; Hills 1938). The author (Gill 1943, 1950, 1953) referred the Tower Hill Tuff to the Holocene because it overlies Holocene shell beds, rests against a fossil cliff but a metre or so above sea level, follows the contours of the existing countryside, and has not been cut through completely by the Merri River, as upstream from Woodford and at Cassidy Bridge. The rim of Tower Hill looks very fresh and is not eroded except for some very shallow groovings that probably developed after the volcano was cleared of trees, because they are so straight and regular. No doubt the highly permeable nature of the tuff also helps to account for this fresh appearance.

Long search has failed to reveal any materials in the ejectamenta suitable for radiocarbon dating, but the time of the eruption has been approximately determined by dating samples from above and below the volcanic products (Table 3).

TABLE 3
Radiocarbon dates relating to the Tower Hill eruption

Sample	Site	Date in Years B.P.	14C Lab. No.
(a) Materials from above the Tower Hill ejectamenta:			
Marine shells	Midden in lower soil, Tower Hill beach	4315 ± 195	GX-0059
Charcoal	Midden in lower soil, Tower Hill beach	5120 ± 120	GaK-610
Marine shells	Midden in upper soil, Tower Hill beach	1750 ± 115*	GX-0060
Charcoal	Midden in upper soil, Tower Hill beach	2800 ± 100	GaK-611
(b) Materials from below the Tower Hill ejectamenta:			
Bones	Bushfield, N. of Warrnambool	6605 ± 190	GX-0151
Marine shells	Merri Canal, Warrnambool	6500 ± 200	Ac-15
„ „	Lake Pertobe, Warrnambool	5850 ± 320	Ac-14
„ „	SE. of Moulden Quarry, Dennington	3750 ± 150	GX-0058

* An earlier sample from the upper soil was dated 538 ± 200 years B.P. by the solid carbon method (Libby 1952; Gill 1955b), but the sample was probably rather young for this method of assay.

Materials from below the Tower Hill ejectamenta provide maximum dates for the eruption. Of these dates (Table 3b) the one of the shells from the neighbourhood of Moulden Quarry is discrepantly young. Thin *Homolina deltoidalis* shells which showed signs of leaching were necessarily used and there may have been ionic exchange with younger carbonate from overlying sediments. The dated bones from Bushfield (Gill 1953) are correlated with similar mineralized bones found by Keble in sediment mixed with tuff over which were several feet of tuff. If the date were reliable, it would thus date the time of the eruption. However, the date listed is from the CO_2 fraction and the provenance of the mineralization is uncertain; the organic fraction, which is perhaps less trustworthy still, yielded a date of 5850 ± 320 years B.P. The remaining two dates are thus the best to rely on and they suggest the eruption was later than 6000 years B.P.

Of the dates for materials above the Tower Hill Tuff, the charcoal dates are probably the more reliable and that from the lower soil is the one most relevant to the present purpose. However, the charcoal accumulated some time after the end of the eruption because the soil containing it rests on sand which overlies eroded consolidated tuff; the wood, which was apparently burnt in aboriginal fires to yield the charcoal, would, however, not range much in time itself. As an unknown interval must be added to the date of 5120 for this charcoal, the most reasonable date for the eruption in terms of the present evidence is between 5500 and 6000 B.P.

The Tower Hill volcano is thus older than the Mt Gambier volcano, because charcoal from the A horizon of a soil under that tuff gave a radiocarbon date of 4710 ± 70 years B.P. Mt Gambier and Tower Hill belong to a series of young volcanoes scattered along the coastal plain.

The relationship of the Tower Hill Tuff to sea levels may now be considered. The tuff overlies emerged marine shell beds at Lake Pertobe, Merri Canal, and elsewhere. There is a series of such stratified shell beds that has been traced across the state; these beds are at comparable elevations above LWM whether they occur in basins or on horsts, suggesting that for the period of time involved the tectonic movements have been negligible. The radiocarbon dates for the shells range from 4000 to 6000 B.P. approximately; hence they all fall within the Post-glacial Thermal Maximum (Gill 1955c, 1965).

At Tower Hill beach, after the tuff was lithified, the sea cut a platform in it about 0·5 m above the outer edge of the present platform and extending inland about 300 m (Gill 1953). On the platform and behind the present shore are two rows of sand ridges formerly about 8 m high, but heightened this century after the introduction of marram grass. On the seaward side of each of the ridges, in a limited area east of Gorman Lane (Fig. 15.3), there is a ridge of tuff blocks washed from the shore platform by the sea. Beneath the two sand ridges is a horizontal juvenile soil containing a rich assemblage of materials belonging to aboriginal occupation—marine shells, hearth stones, flint scrapers, basalt axes, bones of marsupials, birds, fish, seals, and whales (Mahony 1912), and implements made of bone. The soil is formed in calcareous sand, and if sand ridges existed at the time it formed they must have been further seaward, with sea level lower—a conclusion already reached from the sedimentary structure of the tuff. In places this soil is divided into a series of up to four soils, owing to the building at that time of low sand rises on which further soil development occurred and midden material accumulated. Later, sand ridges were formed over this soil, probably migrating inland as the sea rose again, and a younger soil developed on the sand ridges, following the surface slopes. Both older and younger soils are calcareous humic sands, but the lower one is gleyed (B. E. Butler personal communication). The two soils were 2 m apart vertically where the C14 samples were taken (Fig. 15.9). The radiocarbon dates (Table 3) are averages of the ages of the shells selected, or the charcoal collected, and give no measure of the duration of soil formation. However, the difference of about 2500 years in age gives an idea of the time elapsed between the two periods. The shell dates are younger than the charcoal dates. The shells were on the whole higher in the soil than the charcoal, so this could account for part of the difference.

The marine shells from the older soil, characterised by *Plebidonax deltoides,* belong to a sand facies, while those from the younger soil, characterised by *Subninella undulata,* belong to a rock facies. This difference may denote a change in shore conditions or it may merely reflect a change in human food habits; our information is not yet complete enough to say.

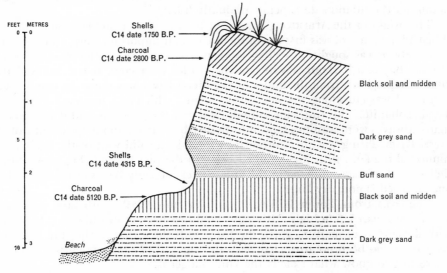

15.9   Section at Tower Hill beach, Armstrong Bay, showing two dated fossil soils

Two soils similar to those at Tower Hill beach occur in the dunes between Dennington and Tower Hill; they are characterised by having great numbers of the land snail *Austrosuccinea australis,* and by both being on sloping surfaces, indicating that considerable ridge growth took place before the first soil layer was formed. Similar soils have been noted in coastal dunes and ridges as far west as the South Australian border. These soils are indicators of relatively stable conditions, and they are useful for defining the formations of sand that have not been disturbed by coastal erosion.

COASTAL SAND AND ITS ORIGIN

The calcareous Armstrong Sand, with 80-95 per cent carbonates (Mahony 1917), characterises the modern coastline. From Tower Hill to Warrnambool the coast runs southeast, approximately normal to the prevailing southwest winds, and has dunes of the order of 30 m high (Plate XXXIIb). There is a surf zone about 300 m wide on a shelving sandy bottom, and berms up to 1·5 m high have been seen. In windy weather the sand on the beach is reduced by being blown on to the dunes. Since European occupation, the dunes have become largely mobile, as Plate XXXIIb shows. On the leeward side, in the middle of the air photo, are two large blow-outs reaching the drain along the mid-line of Kelly Swamp; they illustrate two stages in the evolution of blow-outs. The eastern one has just become stable with the growth of a grass cover, including the native *Spinifex hirsutus* and the introduced marram grass (*Ammophila arenaria*), in the wind-scoured axial hollow. The grass cover took 25 years to develop. The western blow-out shows a more advanced stage and is vegetated with scrub to a considerable extent. The original inland margin of the dunes is being obscured as the number of blow-outs increases, though it can still be traced locally by the position of fossil soils. The swamp on the inland side is being gradually filled.

The origin of the Armstrong Sand is of both academic and economic interest. When Warrnambool was first established it was an important port, and so professional advice was sought on its development (Barrow 1853). The main drawback of Lady Bay as a harbour was its tendency to fill with sand. It was believed that sand brought down from the dunes by the Merri River was the main trouble, and so a canal was cut along the next swale inland, which was bordered by consolidated aeolianite. This costly measure did not ease the problem, and it was decided that sea waves were washing sand into the harbour from about the mouth of the Merri River. Piling was therefore driven to make a solid wall of the bridge that connected the land with Breakwater Rock and the pier beyond (Fig. 15.4). Nevertheless sand still accumulated in the quiet waters of Lady Bay, so that where ships once moored is now dry land.

The coast from Tower Hill to Port Fairy runs WSW, with sand ridges not much more than 7·5 m high. Although the dunes have grown higher this century with the spread of marram grass, the fossil soils show that during the past 5000 years there has been no gross change in the amount of sand present; it would be interesting to know what exactly the sand budget is.

When the Tower Hill volcano erupted, its products completely covered the existing coast in its vicinity. At the cemetery on the Princes Highway 1800 m east of the crater rim, there are 30 m of ejectamenta resting on a swamp floor in a former swale. Seaward of this is a fossil dune, as both surface contours and bore data prove. Seaward again is a sand flat, probably recently exposed by retreat of the sea from the Post-glacial maximum. It is envisaged that a similar flat formerly existed seawards of the aeolianite dunes between Tower Hill and Dennington, but that the eruption laid down a thick carpet of ejectamenta, obliterating the former landscape and cutting off all landward sources of sand. The sand forming the dunes and ridges on top of the Tower Hill Tuff must therefore have come from the sea.

Coastal drift westwards carries sand derived from erosion of aeolianite, both above and below sea level, and from other sources.

There has been controversy concerning the direction of the resultant drift in the area, but drift westwards explains the disposition of the sands more satisfactorily, for if drift were from the Port Fairy area the sand supply would be limited, since it there forms merely a thin layer on basalt. The present coast is slightly oblique to the trend of the aeolianite dunes, and Lady Bay is a re-entrant formed by the breaching of such an old dune line. As it is more open to a westerly drift it naturally collects sand, and the flat containing Lake Pertobe is witness to the effectiveness of the bay as a sand-trap. The control of sand in Warrnambool harbour depends on maintaining the natural balance of sand removal and deposition; any structure obstructing drift will encourage sand accumulation. The records of Barrow (1853) and others show that there are seasonal fluctuations in the amount of sand, and it would appear that these have at times been confused with permanent changes.

SNAILS AND DUNE HISTORY

Shells of land snails help to elucidate the history of the dunes. In the Pleistocene aeolianite in the quarry in the southeast corner of Albert Park, Warrnambool, helicid snails were collected from the dune rock as distinct from the interposed terra rossa soils. There are three formations of dune rock in the quarry, separated by fossil soils, some of which have soil pipes. The snail found in the lowest, partly crystalline dune rock is *Chloritobadistes victoriae* (Cox), the habitat of which is dry forest. The same species was collected from aeolianite at a depth of 12 m in Canterbury Road, Warrnambool. By contrast, the fossil terra rossa soils in the aeolianite contain snails typical of humid sites, including *Magilaoma penolensis*, *Strangesta rugosa*, *Elsothera funerae*, and *Pernagera tamarensis*. They occur in immense numbers in fossil soils on dune slopes as well as on flats. It would appear from this that the habitats during sand accumulation were relatively dry and those during soil formation were relatively wet. The fossil soils are often a metre thick, and their formation must have involved the solution of a considerable thickness of aeolianite.

It is sometimes difficult to tell whether the loose sand in the mobile dunes was emplaced after European occupation or before. Two indicators have been found helpful. The grey dune soils rich in *Austrosuccinea australis* to the exclusion of practically every other species, and comparable with soils at Tower Hill beach dated 1700-2800 and 4300-5100 years B.P., show the original configuration of the dunes. Secondly, some layers of sand contain introduced snails, and so it is known that they were emplaced after European occupation. It may be that there is a micro-stratigraphy available based on the order in which the various snail species were introduced. The snail *Helicella* (*Cochlicella*) *barbara* appeared first in the sections examined, whilst the introduced snail *Euparypha pisana* occurs in incredible numbers on the calcarenite dunes at the present time. A collection in the vicinity of Bore 31 (Fig. 15.7) also included the introduced *Helicella caperata* and *Helix aspersa* and some of the native *Austrosuccinea australis*.

MOYNE ALLUVIUM

The youngest deposit in the Tower Hill marsh is the Moyne Alluvium, a clayey to sandy carbon-rich horizon which continues to accumulate, although at a much slower rate since the marsh was drained. Alluvium in the marsh varies in thickness from 1 to 4 m. The peaty sediments in the floor of the Tower Hill crater to the north are also referred to the Moyne Alluvium.

An extensive deposit attributed to this formation occupies Kelly Swamp (Fig. 15.3), where 2 m of swamp deposits overlie Tower Hill Tuff. The top 1·2 m consists of peaty swamp alluvium with tuff minerals and numerous mollusc shells including *Lenameria tenuistriata* (Sowerby) and *Notospisula parva*. Stratified Tower Hill Tuff crops out at the inland end of The Cutting, and so apparently a channel, younger than the tuff and presumably once used by the River Merri, follows the trend of the aeolianite bank. It is envisaged that after the Tower Hill eruption altered the coastline in the vicinity of the volcano, the Merri drained towards Warrnambool and Lady Bay, but that sand later accumulated in its channel and diverted the river westwards behind the dunes to Armstrong Bay.

The alluvium under Lake Pertobe and mentioned above is also referred to the Moyne Alluvium, but similar deposits extend under the tuff at the foot of Cannon Hill (Fig. 15.8). The alluvium of the Russell Creek flats (Fig. 15.4) is also referred to the Moyne Alluvium. In this area, thin alluvium was found to merge downwards into 1 m of light brown sand resting on tuff, and on the south side of the creek east of Wangoom Road 1·8-2·4 m of clayey alluvium rests on calcareous sand with carbonate nodules. The latter appears to be a beach sand, being far too coarse for dune sand. Marine shells have been reported from this flat, so that the area behind the aeolianite dunes may have been invaded by the Last Interglacial (7·5 m) sea.

CONCLUSIONS

Tabular formations of Upper Miocene marine limestone, and basalt mainly of Pleistocene age form the country rock of the area studied, and the seaward edge of these formations has been repeatedly modified during the Quaternary period of changing sea level.

The earliest records are of the Lower Pleistocene low sea level of the Antepenultimate Glacial, when an ancestor of the Moyne River cut a channel far below present sea level. At high sea levels during the Lower and Middle Pleistocene, the Warrnambool Aeolianite accumulated in a broad coastal embayment across the area, probably forming during early stages of the retreats of the sea, and Upper Pleistocene and Holocene shorelines have largely been eroded into it. During the transgression of the Penultimate Interglacial the original Crossley Scarp was formed and the Sunnyside Sand of Middle Pleistocene age was deposited. Sea level fell once more during the Penultimate Glacial, and the Moyne River cut a channel to about 30 m below present sea level at Port Fairy. This channel was filled with Woodbine Basalt, into which further channels were cut in turn. During the Upper Pleistocene the Crossley Scarp was refashioned in the high sea level of the Last Interglacial, and the Port Fairy Calcarenite was deposited on the coastal flats below. Dunes of Dennington Sand were formed as the sea began to retreat. The Port Fairy Calcarenite and the Woodbine Basalt were further incised during the low sea level of the Last Glacial, and the channels formed were filled in turn during the succeeding Flandrian Transgression. At the maximum sea level, correlated with the Post-glacial Thermal Maximum, the Holocene Pertobe Coquina was deposited.

During the Upper Holocene the eruption of the Tower Hill volcano occurred, forming a maar of Tower Hill Tuff, and this collapsed to form a caldera. Subsequent volcanic activity deposited the Piton Scoria as a complex of cones in the caldera. The Tower Hill ejectamenta obliterated the contiguous coast and so initiated a new cycle of events. Dunes of Armstrong Sand and river and swamp deposits of Moyne Alluvium were deposited on the Tower Hill Tuff. Minor fluctuations of sea level occurred in these later stages.

Thus during the Quaternary the evolving coastline has grown seawards due to the emplacement of basalt and large calcareous sand formations, in spite of fluvial erosion during low sea levels and marine attack during high sea levels. Redeposition of carbonate in these sands has formed resistant aeolianite with hard calcrete cappings. At present, consistent with observations elsewhere, sea level appears to be rising, and a soil of the order of 5000 years old at Tower Hill beach is now being rapidly destroyed, although it must have formed on the present shore away from the direct influence of the sea. Thus the picture of coastline evolution afforded by this study is a dynamic one.

REFERENCES

Baker, G. (1943). Features of a Victorian limestone coastline. *J. Geol.* **51**: 359-86.
—— (1944). The geology of the Port Campbell district. *Proc. R. Soc. Vict.* **56**: 77-111.
—— (1953). The relationship of *Cyclammina*-bearing sediments to the Older Tertiary Deposits southeast of Princetown, Victoria. *Mem. natn. Mus. Vict.* **18**: 125-34.
Barrow, J. (1853). Map of Lady Bay, Warrnambool. Paper No. C38. Vict., *Votes & Proc. Leg. Council*, 1853-4, Vol. 3.
Bonwick, J. (1858). *Western Victoria: Its Geography, Geology and Social Condition*. Geelong.
Boutakoff, N. (1952). The structural pattern of south-west Victoria. *Min. geol. J. Vict.* **4**: 21-9.
Brough Smyth, R. (1858). On the extinct volcanoes of Victoria, Australia. *Q. Jl geol. Soc. Lond.* **14**: 227-35.
Caldwell, J. J. (1937). Limestone deposits, Port Fairy. *Rec. Geol. Surv. Vict.* **5**: 581-2.
Chapman, F. (1925). Tertiary fossils from bore cores, Port Fairy. *Rec. Geol. Surv. Vict.* **4**: 481-3.
—— (1929). *Open Air Studies in Australia*. London.
Collins, A. C. (1953). Pleistocene foraminifera from Port Fairy, western Victoria. *Mem. natn. Mus. Vict.* **18**: 93-105.
—— (1956). A recent record of the genus *Fabularia* Defrance. *Contr. Cushman Fdn. foramin Res.* **7**: 105.
Edwards, A. B. (1938). The Tertiary volcanic rocks of central Victoria. *Q. Jl geol. Soc. Lond.* **94**: 243-315.
Fairbridge, R. W. (1961). Eustatic changes in sea level. *Physics Chem. Earth* **4**: 99-185.
Fowler, T. W. (1914). Notes on the discovery of the Victorian coastline. *Rept Aust. Ass. Adv. Sci. (14th Mtg)*, pp. 343-57.
Gibbons, F. R. and Gill, E. D. (1964). Terrains and soils of the basaltic plains of far western Victoria. *Proc. R. Soc. Vict.* **77**: 387-95.

Gill, E. D. (1943). The geology of Warrnambool. *Proc. R. Soc. Vict.* **55**: 133-56.

——— (1947). Some features of the coastline between Port Fairy and Peterborough, Victoria. *Proc. R. Soc. Vict.* **58**: 37-42.

——— (1948). Structure and origin of Guano Cave, near Warrnambool, Victoria. *Victorian Nat.* **65**: 187-91.

——— (1950). An hypothesis relative to the age of some Western District volcanoes, Victoria. *Proc. R. Soc. Vict.* **60**: 189-94.

——— (1951). Aboriginal kitchen middens and marine shell beds. *Mankind* **4**: 249-54.

——— (1953). Geological evidence in western Victoria relative to the antiquity of the Australian aborigines. *Mem. natn. Mus. Vict.* **18**: 25-92.

——— (1955a). Radiocarbon dates for Australian archaeological and geological samples. *Aust. J. Sci.* **18**: 49-52.

——— (1955b). Aboriginal midden sites in Western Victoria dated by radiocarbon analysis. *Mankind* **5**: 51-5.

——— (1955c). The Australian 'arid period'. *Aust. J. Sci.* **17**: 204-6.

——— (1964). Rocks contiguous with the basaltic cuirass of Western Victoria. *Proc. R. Soc. Vict.* **77**: 331-55.

——— (1965). Quaternary geology, radiocarbon datings, and the age of australites. *Special Paper, geol. Soc. Am.* **84**: 415-32.

Hart, T. S. (1901). Notes on a visit to Tower Hill, Koroit. *Victorian Nat.* **17**: 157-60.

Hatai, K. and Saito, M. (1963). Selective accumulation of beach gravels. *Rec. oceanogr. Wks Japan* **7**: 95-100.

Hills, E. S. (1938). The age and physiographic relationships of the Cainozoic volcanic rocks of Victoria. *Proc. R. Soc. Vict.* **51**: 112-39.

——— (1940). *The Physiography of Victoria*. Melbourne.

Hopmann, M., Frechen, J., and Knetsch, G. (n.d.). *Die vulkanische Eifel*. Bonn.

Jennings, J. N. (1959). The coastal geomorphology of King Island, Bass Strait, in relation to changes in the relative level of land and sea. *Rec. Queen Vict. Mus.* (N.S.) **11**: 1-39.

Libby, W. F. (1952). *Radiocarbon Dating*. Chicago.

Mahony, D. J. (1912). On the bones of the Tasmanian Devil and other animals, associated with human remains near Warrnambool: with a note on the dune sand. *Victorian Nat.* **29**: 43-6.

——— (1917). Shell sand in the Warrnambool District. *Rec. Geol. Surv. Vict.* **4**: 10-11.

——— (1936a). Portland cement materials near Port Fairy. *Rec. Geol. Surv. Vict.* **5**: 275-8.

——— (1936b). Clays, limestones and sands near Warrnambool. *Rec. Geol. Surv. Vict.* **5**: 278-81.

——— (1937). Limestone deposits, Port Fairy. *Rec. Geol. Surv. Vict.* **5**: 582-4.

Rawlinson, T. E. (1878). Notes on the coast line formation of the Western District, etc. *Proc. R. Soc. Vict.* **14**: 25-34.

Schofield, J. C. (1960). Sea level fluctuations during the past 4,000 years as recorded by a chenier plain, Firth of Thames, New Zealand. *N.Z. Jl Geol. Geophys.*, **3**: 467-85.

Skeats, E. W. (1909). The volcanic rocks of Victoria. *Rept Aust. Ass. Adv. Sci. (Brisbane Mtg)* **12**: 173-235.

Valentine, J. W. (1965). Quaternary mollusca from Port Fairy, Victoria, Australia and their palaeoecologic implications. *Proc. R. Soc. Vict.* **78**: 15-74.

Wilkinson, C. S. (1865). In Report of the Director of the Geological Survey of Victoria to September 1864. Paper No. 44, pp. 21-8. *Vict. Parl. Pap.* 1864-5, Vol. 4.

Zeuner, F. E. (1959). *The Pleistocene Period*. London.

XXXIII *The Gippsland Lakes from Jemmys Point, near Lakes Entrance, showing the former cliffed coastline on the right, and the inner and outer barriers enclosing coastal lagoons*

16

Coastal Lagoons of Southeastern Australia

E. C. F. BIRD

INTRODUCTION

Coastal lagoons may be defined as areas of shallow water that have been partly or wholly sealed off from the sea by the formation of barriers, usually of sand or shingle, built above high tide level by the action of waves. On the Australian coast the barriers consist mainly of sand; they are surmounted by dune topography, and bordered on the seaward side by long, gently-curving sandy beaches. They have been built across river mouths and in front of coastal inlets and embayments to enclose lagoons of various shapes and sizes on the southeastern coast of Australia between Adelaide and Brisbane, on the coast of Western Australia south of Perth, and locally on the coasts of Queensland and Tasmania. This essay is concerned with the geomorphological problems posed by coastal lagoons and barriers that enclose them in southeastern Australia (Fig. 16.1).

The smallest and simplest lagoons are found where the mouth of a river has been ponded back by a wave-built barrier. Such a barrier may be breached occasionally by storm waves, or when river floods pour out over it after heavy rain, but it is soon rebuilt by waves when fine weather returns. Lagoons of this type, known in South Africa as 'blind estuaries' (Day 1951), occur at the mouths of most of the rivers draining to the ocean coast of Victoria. Other lagoons are long and narrow, parallel to the coast and separated from the sea by barriers built up in front of the former coastline; the Coorong, bordering Encounter Bay in South Australia, is of this type (Fig. 16.2). Lagoons which show a branched configuration, elongated at an angle to the coast, have formed where drowned valleys have been enclosed at their mouths by a barrier; an example is Lake Tyers in Victoria (Fig. 16.4a). The largest and most complicated lagoons are found where broad embayments have been sealed off from the sea by one or more barriers, as in the Gippsland Lakes in eastern Victoria (Fig. 16.3; Plate XXXIII).

A geomorphological study of the Gippsland Lakes (Bird 1963, 1965) has shown the range of factors that must be taken into account in dealing with the evolution of coastal lagoons. It is necessary to seek evidence of the geological and geomorphological history of the area, and the sequence of changes in level of land and sea which have led to coastal submergence and the drowning of the lower parts of valleys to form inlets and embayments. The growth of coastal barriers must then be related to the effects of tides, waves, and currents in delivering sediment, shaping the depositional forms, and determining the position and dimensions of tidal entrances. Within a lagoon it is possible to relate changes in configuration to the effects of wind-generated waves and currents, and the currents produced by rivers and tides. It has been shown that ecological conditions, particularly water salinity, are of great importance in the geomorphological evolution of coastal lagoons, for they control the extent to which vegetation can colonise

z

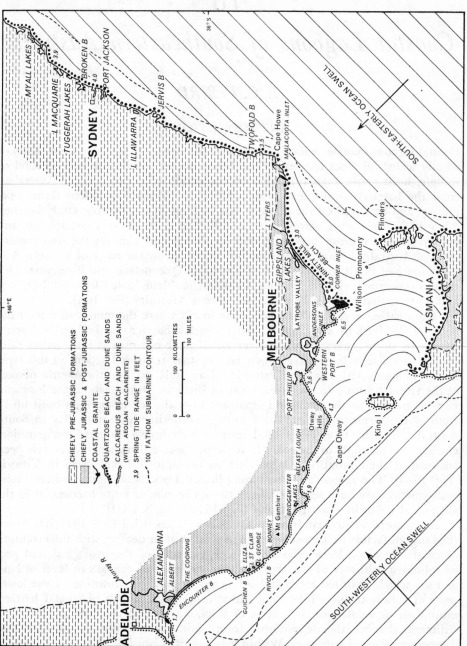

16.1 Coastal environmental features in southeastern Australia

lagoon shores, impeding erosion and influencing patterns of sedimentation. Where salinity is low, reedswamp communities spreading from the lagoon shore trap sediment and build up swamp land; where it is high, salt marsh vegetation may play a similar role. It is also necessary to take account of any direct or indirect effects of human interference. In the Gippsland Lakes shoreline erosion has been accentuated following die-back of reedswamp that formerly encroached from the shores, the die-back being a consequence of ecological changes accompanying increasing salinity since 1889, when an artificial entrance cut through the enclosing barrier permitted sea water to flow into lagoons that were previously relatively

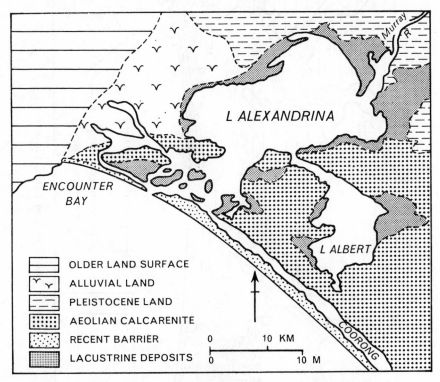

16.2   Murray-mouth lagoons (after De Mooy 1959)

fresh. Similar changes have taken place around Belfast Lough, a lagoon at the mouth of the Moyne River in western Victoria, which has become more saline following dredging in the channel that leads out of it to the sea at Port Fairy. This erosion is therefore an indirect consequence of human interference. On the other hand, Lakes Alexandrina and Albert, at the mouth of the Murray River in South Australia (Fig. 16.2), have become fresh since 1940, when barrages were completed, sealing off gaps in the barrier that formerly allowed sea water to enter, and geomorphological processes at work on the shores of these lagoons have changed with the spread of fresh-water reedswamp vegetation, which impedes erosion and facilitates sedimentation. Lake Bonney, also in South Australia, has

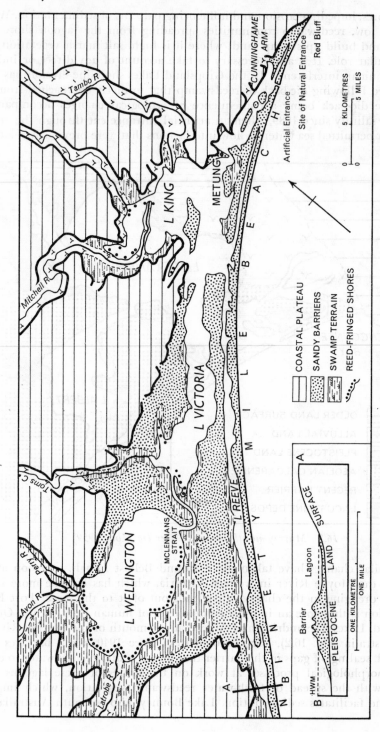

16.3   *The Gippsland Lakes, Victoria*

changed considerably since 1958, when an outflow channel was cut through the enclosing barrier, lowering its surface about 2·5 m, so that low-lying land adjacent to the lagoon could be drained. It is now a smaller, shallower lagoon, bordered by the emerged margins of its former floor.

Comparative studies of the various lagoons on the coast of southeastern Australia have indicated marked contrasts in form, but it is clear that each lagoon is essentially the product of coastal submergence followed by the development of an enclosing barrier, generally with a tidal entrance, permanent or intermittent. Similar processes operate in similar situations within each lagoon, and it is possible to analyse the contrasts between lagoons in terms of their geomorphological history and the influence of hydrological, geological, climatic, and ecological factors, taking account of the effects of human interference. It would be premature to attempt a comprehensive survey of the geomorphology of these coastal lagoons when so much detailed work remains to be done, but it may be useful at this stage to describe and illustrate the various factors that influence lagoon geomorphology, and show how they affect the geomorphological processes at work in coastal lagoons.

HYDROLOGICAL FACTORS

The hydrological characteristics of a coastal lagoon are determined partly by its configuration and the nature and dimensions of entrances from the sea, and partly by the balance between fresh-water inflow from rain and rivers (related to climate, particularly precipitation and evaporation) and salt-water inflow from the sea (related to tide range and consequent tidal ventilation of the lagoon). Lagoons with entrances that are permanently open, permitting inflow of sea water and outflow of river floods, may be classed as estuarine, being systems within which salt water from the sea meets and mixes with fresh water from rain and rivers. An example on the Victorian coast is Anderson Inlet, at the mouth of the Tarwin River, an estuarine lagoon with a broad, permanent entrance and extensive sandbanks exposed at low tide. Lagoons with more restricted or temporary tidal entrances are less like estuaries, for they are less influenced by tidal movements and more protected from the effects of ocean waves. Geomorphologically, they may resemble inland lakes. Lake Macquarie, for example, on the north coast of New South Wales, is essentially a marine lake (Fig. 16.4b); its shores are almost tideless, the barrier excludes ocean waves, and water salinity is similar to that of the sea, except where fresh water dilutes it near the mouths of inflowing creeks. The Myall Lakes, further north, are still more like inland lakes, for they are linked to the sea only through a long, narrow, winding channel (the Lower Myall River, leading into Port Stephens), and marine influences are almost excluded. Usually the water is fresh or slightly brackish, but during prolonged droughts the salinity increases as sea water enters along the connecting channel. The Bridgewater Lakes, west of Portland in Victoria, are fresh-water lagoons completely cut off from the sea by a high barrier of dunes.

In drier regions, lagoons completely cut off from the sea are less likely to become fresh, for loss of water by evaporation tends to increase their salinity. Some become hypersaline, with salinity higher than that of sea water (which here has mean salinity 35 per mille sodium chloride), and after long periods of drought

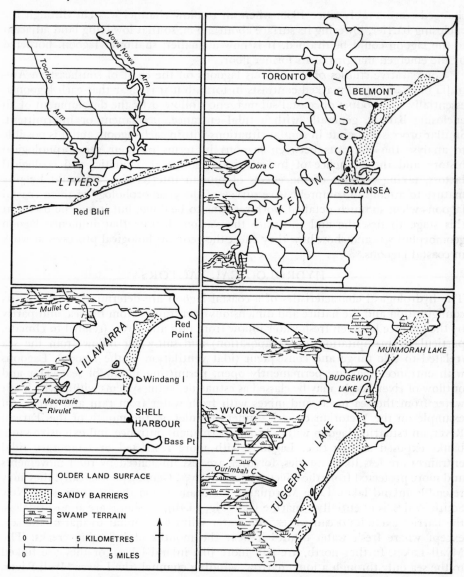

16.4 Some Australian coastal lagoons: (a) Lake Tyers, Victoria. (b) Lake Macquarie, N.S.W. (c) Lake Illawarra, N.S.W. (d) Tuggerah Lakes, N.S.W

they may dry out completely as salt flats. Lake Eliza and Lake St Clair, on the South Australian coast near Robe, are enclosed saline lagoons of this type, and hypersaline conditions are often found during the dry summer months at the southern end of the Coorong, away from the lagoon entrance, where tidal ventilation is too weak to prevent high salinity developing in the evaporating waters.

Most of the coastal lagoons of southeastern Australia show seasonal variations in hydrology, marked by fluctuations in water level and salinity. These are most pronounced in the South Australian lagoons, where water levels fall and high salinity concentrations develop during the dry summer months. In Victoria, where summer droughts are less frequent, hypersaline conditions are rarely found in coastal lagoons, while in northern New South Wales the incidence of summer rains prevents the development of high salinities.

GEOLOGICAL AND GEOMORPHOLOGICAL FACTORS

There is a fundamental geological contrast between the New South Wales coast north from Cape Howe, and the coasts of Victoria and South Australia west to the mouth of the Murray (Fig. 16.1). The New South Wales coast runs generally parallel to the strike of Palaeozoic and older Mesozoic formations and was uplifted late in Tertiary times; it is a 'steep coast', backed by high ground deeply incised by river valleys, and the land is thought to have been stable during Quaternary times. Southern Victoria and the adjacent parts of South Australia consist of younger formations, Jurassic and later, which have been folded and faulted by tectonic movements continuing into Pleistocene and even Recent (Holocene) times; the coast is more varied, and shows the effects of Quaternary deformation.

Changing sea levels have influenced the evolution of the coast. The indented coastline of southeastern Australia is due largely to submergence of the margins of the continent during Holocene times, when a world-wide marine transgression accompanied the Post-glacial amelioration of climate and the melting of ice sheets and glaciers in other regions. This transgression followed a series of oscillations of sea level through Pleistocene times, the sea reaching high levels and sub-merging the coast during interglacial phases, and falling away to low levels, so that the coast emerged, during each glacial phase. The Holocene marine trans-gression has been investigated in various parts of the world, and stages in the sea-level rise have been identified from shoreline deposits encountered at succes-sive levels in borings made in coastal plains and deltas, chiefly in Europe and North America. Radiocarbon dating of organic materials associated with these deposits has provided a chronology of the marine transgression. According to Fairbridge (1961) the sea stood 100 m below its present level when the transgres-sion began about 17,000 years ago, and reached the present level about 6000 years ago.

There have been conflicting views on sea-level history during the past 6000 years. Some believe that the sea attained a higher level, about 3 m above the present, before falling back during a 'Recent emergence' (Fairbridge 1948); others consider that sea level attained the present level within the past 6000 years without any higher Holocene stand (Shepard 1961). The problem remains contro-versial. Some features of barriers and terrain adjacent to lagoons on the south-eastern coast of Australia can be interpreted as evidence of emergence during Holocene times, but it remains to decide if these really are indicative of a change in the relative levels of land and sea, and if so, whether the change is due to elevation of the land or a fall in sea level.

The major submergence in Holocene times is not in doubt. Its effects are well displayed on the coast of New South Wales, where the drowned parts of valleys form branched inlets such as Port Jackson (Sydney Harbour), and Broken Bay at the mouth of the Hawkesbury River. In Victoria, tectonic movements continuing into Holocene times have apparently influenced the outlines of embayments invaded by the marine transgression: Port Phillip Bay occupies a 'sunkland', an area of tectonic subsidence bordered by Selwyn's Fault, an active fault along which earthquakes still occur (Keble 1946); its outlines are thus due partly to deformation of the land and partly to submergence by the sea. Western Port Bay and Corner Inlet, further east, have also been influenced by Holocene tectonic movements, while the former embayment occupied by Lake Wellington, one of the Gippsland Lakes, shows a marked protrusion westwards into the Latrobe Valley Syncline, another region of tectonic subsidence. The evolution of the coast of the southeast of South Australia has been influenced by tectonic deformation, the Mt Gambier area having risen as the Murray-mouth region subsided (Sprigg 1952, 1959), but the effects of this transverse tilting on the outlines of coastal embayments and lagoons have still to be worked out.

In their present form, the coastal lagoons of southeastern Australia post-date the Holocene marine submergence, but it is possible that some were formed originally during episodes of submergence in Pleistocene interglacial phases, when barriers were built across the mouths of coastal inlets and embayments. In South Australia, the Coorong is evidently the latest in a series of long, narrow lagoons enclosed by successive barriers on a coast that has emerged during Quaternary times. Its predecessors are marked by tracts of lagoon and swamp (now largely drained and reclaimed) lying between successive emerged sand barriers in the country behind the southern part of Encounter Bay. Other lagoons are enclosed by barriers believed to be of Pleistocene age (see below). These may have drained out during the later glacial phases, when sea level was low, leaving basins which were flooded again when the sea rose in Holocene times. The majority of coastal lagoons, however, are simply the product of barrier formation across inlets and embayments formed by the Holocene marine transgression.

THE FORMATION OF COASTAL BARRIERS

It was once thought that coastal barriers were built by powerful 'ocean currents', sweeping sand along the coast and forming spits which were prolonged until they enclosed lagoons in river mouths, inlets, and embayments (Gregory 1903; Halligan 1906), but it is now realised that waves and wave-induced currents are more important than mass movements of ocean water in transporting sand and building up beaches and barriers (Jennings 1955) and that the gently curving outlines of sandy shores have been determined by constructive ocean swell, refracted into curved patterns as it approaches the coast (Davies 1959). Some barriers have certainly been formed by the prolongation of spits, stages in their intermittent growth being marked by former terminal recurves traceable on the landward side; others have been initiated offshore as chains of barrier islands, united as the intervening gaps were sealed off by deposition.

It has been shown (Bird 1963, 1965) that the Gippsland Lakes (Fig. 16.3; Plate XXXIII) were first enclosed by a spit prolonged across the mouth of an embayment, then widened by accretion of sand on the seaward side. This became an inner barrier when a chain of barrier islands which subsequently formed a mile or so offshore were linked to form an outer barrier, backed by a long, narrow lagoon (Lake Reeve), and bordered on the seaward side by the Ninety Mile Beach. Borings through these coastal barriers have shown that they consist of unconsolidated sediment, banked against the partly submerged Pleistocene land surface (inset, Fig. 16.3). They are not being driven landward in the manner of shingle barriers such as Chesil Beach on the south coast of England (Steers 1953); once formed, they remain in position, the seaward margin prograding when the waves deposit sand and retrograding during phases of marine erosion. The inner shores bordering the enclosed lagoon often show promontories of various kinds, some of which are the terminations of recurved spits, while others are formed where mobile dunes spill over into the lagoon, or where sand is washed through low-lying parts of the barrier by stormy seas or exceptionally high tides. Waves and currents generated within the lagoon soon modify the configuration of these in-facing barrier shores.

The coasts of southeastern Australia are 'high wave energy coasts', exposed to the effects of ocean swell. West of Wilson Promontory the ocean swell arrives from the southwest, and is refracted in coastal waters so that it anticipates and eventually fits the curved shorelines of sandy beaches and barriers (Davies 1960); east of the promontory, and on the New South Wales coast, ocean swell arriving from the southeast is similarly refracted to fit the outlines of sandy shores (Bird 1961a). The small tide range on much of the coast of southeastern Australia has facilitated the formation of barriers. Large tides generate strong ebb and flow currents which have a disruptive effect, maintaining tidal entrances through barriers, while small tides produce weaker currents, the effects of which are more easily overcome by constructive wave action, entrances being deflected or sealed off by sand deposition. The contrast is well illustrated along the Ninety Mile Beach, for at the northeastern end, where the spring tide range is slightly less than a metre, barriers enclose the Gippsland Lakes in a former embayment, whereas at the southwestern end, where spring tide range is about 2·5 m, the barriers are interrupted by broad tidal entrances to a similar embayment at Corner Inlet.

Large quantities of sand have been delivered to this coast during Quaternary times. West of Wilson Promontory, the beach and dune sands are predominantly calcareous, consisting mainly of shell debris (often more than 90 per cent calcium carbonate), while east of the promontory and on the New South Wales coast the sands are predominantly quartzose (less than 10 per cent calcium carbonate), derived from decomposed and disintegrated acid igneous and arenaceous sedimentary rocks. This sedimentological contrast, which has never been satisfactorily explained, extends to King Island in Bass Strait, where the west coast sands are calcareous and those on the eastern shores quartzose (Jennings 1959), and is found also on Flinders Island (Dimmock 1957). It may be significant that calcareous sands are found on shores bordering the ocean province dominated by southwesterly swell and quartzose sands on shores that receive ocean swell from the southeast (Fig. 16.1).

The contrast in sediment types is important geomorphologically, for calcareous sands become lithified by internal deposition of calcium carbonate to form a calcarenite (often known as dune limestone or calcareous aeolianite) whereas quartzose sands, leached of calcium carbonate by percolating rainwater, remain unconsolidated. Old dunes and beach ridges of lithified calcareous sand are thus more durable, and less likely to be rearranged or dispersed, than similar landforms of equivalent age built of unconsolidated quartzose sand; attacked by marine erosion, calcarenite forms rugged cliffs.

The delivery of sand to the coast is due partly to wave action and partly to the effects of wind. In calm weather, constructive ocean swell supplies sand to the shore, building a beach ridge (berm) which may afterwards develop by accretion of wind-blown sand as a foredune parallel to the shoreline. Colonisation of berms by dune grasses plays an important part in the building of foredunes because the grasses trap blown sand. Davies (1957) has described how successive parallel beach ridges are formed by a process known as 'cut and fill' where constructive and destructive wave action alternate on a generally prograding sandy shore, and several barriers have been prograded in this way, the parallel beach ridges being surmounted by foredunes which rise as much as 30 m above sea level. On the broad barriers of the East Gippsland coast successive ridges mark 'lines of growth' parallel to the Ninety Mile Beach, and provide evidence of the form of the barriers at earlier stages in development (Bird 1961a). Locally, the parallel ridges have been interrupted by blow-outs and rearranged into parabolic dunes, particularly on the seaward margin, where shoreline erosion has attacked the youngest foredunes and initiated blow-outs and irregular waves of mobile sand, migrating landwards. The onset of erosion on these sandy shores is a very recent phenomenon, attributed to a contemporary rise in sea level, possibly accompanied by increased storminess in coastal waters (Davies 1957; Bird 1960).

Dunes and beach ridges parallel to the shoreline may be taken as evidence that sand has been supplied by wave action on a prograding shore in the manner described by Davies, but where there are irregular masses of coastal sand the supply may alternatively have been derived from unconsolidated deposits exposed on the emerged sea floor during Pleistocene glacial phases when sea level was low, and carried on to the coast by wind action. This hypothesis has been advanced to explain the calcareous dunes, now lithified, that pass beneath present sea level in western Victoria (Hills 1939). These must have been formed when the sea stood at a lower level relative to the land, but it is difficult to explain how barriers can be built up across the mouths of embayments by this process, for there is no obvious reason why sand blown landwards from an emerged sea floor should be arrested at the entrance to an emerged embayment. It is more likely that coastal barriers have been built from sand accumulated during Pleistocene and Holocene marine transgressions, when the advancing sea encountered unconsolidated deposits and carried them landwards.

Some lagoons are enclosed by more than one barrier. Where this is so the inner barriers are certainly older, and may be of Pleistocene age, formed during interglacial phases when the sea stood at or above its present level. A barrier of Pleistocene age must have survived dissection by sub-aerial erosion during the last glacial phase of low sea level and escaped destruction by waves when the sea rose again in Holocene times. Barriers of calcareous sand built up during Pleistocene times on the shore of Encounter Bay in South Australia evidently enclosed lagoons in an embayment at the mouth of the Murray. The present lagoons (Lake Albert and Lake Alexandrina) are separated from the sea by an intermittent inner

barrier of calcarenite and a younger outer barrier consisting of generally unconsolidated calcareous sand, built up in front of the Coorong (Fig. 16.2): according
to De Mooy (1959), the inner barrier is of Pleistocene age, formed during an interglacial phase when sea level was relatively high. Lagoons that were enclosed by
this barrier must have drained out when sea level fell during the last glacial phase
and the Murray extended its course through one of the gaps in the barrier and
out across the emerged sea floor; the present lagoons were formed as the sea returned in Holocene times, when an outer barrier was added along the shores of
Encounter Bay (Sprigg 1952). Between Robe and Beachport, on the southeast
coast of South Australia, lagoons are separated from the sea by a broad barrier of
aeolian calcarenite, probably built up during Pleistocene times, and now cliffed
by marine erosion on the seaward side. North of Robe, this barrier has been
breached by marine erosion, and a former lagoon has been opened up as Guichen
Bay, while south of Beachport another beach has been enlarged to form Rivoli
Bay. Lake Bonney, further south, also lies behind a calcarenite barrier, and must
have formed originally during Pleistocene times.

East of Wilson Promontory and on the New South Wales coast, barriers of
quartzose sand developed during Late Pleistocene times, when the sea stood at, or
slightly above, its present level. These barriers were modified in outline and
dissected by stream incision during the succeeding Last Glacial phase of lowered
sea level, and newer, outer barriers were built up offshore as the Holocene
marine transgression carried the sea back to its present general level. The Gippsland Lakes are enclosed by an inner barrier, which is largely an inheritance from
Late Pleistocene times, and an outer barrier, which was constructed when the
Holocene submergence came to an end.

Old dunes and beach ridges of quartzose sand show evidence of podzolisation,
which begins when the surface layers are leached of any shelly material (calcium
carbonate) present by percolating rainwater. The iron oxides that give fresh sand
its yellow colouring are then dissolved and carried down through the sand.
Organic matter derived from dune vegetation is also washed down through the
sand, and accumulates at depth, usually in the zone of seasonal fluctuations of the
watertable, in the form of a lightly cemented sandrock or 'coffee rock' horizon.
A proportion of the downwashed iron oxides is also deposited in this horizon,
which is essentially the B horizon underlying the leached A horizon of a deep
ground-water podzol. The degree of podzolisation is suggestive of the relative age
of dunes or beach ridges developed from the same parent material, but this
evidence must be treated with caution, for the depth of leaching also depends on
several other factors, including the level of the watertable, the initial content of
carbonates, the pedogenic effects of vegetation that colonises the dunes, and the
climatic history of the area. On quartzose sand deposits, deep podzol profiles with
coffee rock at depth are typical of dunes or beach ridges formed in Late Pleistocene times, whereas Holocene dunes have rarely been podzolised to this extent.
However, podzols have developed on the oldest beach ridges at Woy Woy,
regarded by Burges and Drover (1953) as a system of Holocene origin developed
on quartzose sand with a very low initial shell content. On calcareous sands and
calcarenites the high base status of the parent material reduces the rate of podzolisation, and deep podzol profiles are rarely found.

In face of all these variable factors, and until the stratigraphy and palaeontology of the Australian Quaternary are better known, the most reliable evidence of the age of barrier systems will come from radiocarbon dating of wood or shell samples found inter-bedded in beach ridges or dunes.

LAGOON ENTRANCES

Before dealing with the specific problems of lagoon geomorphology, it will be useful to consider the features of entrances that interrupt barriers and allow passage of water in and out of lagoons. The width and depth of an entrance to a coastal lagoon are determined by the contest between currents flowing through the entrance and the effects of onshore and longshore drifting of sand, which tend to seal it off. Currents are generated in several ways. There are tidal currents produced by tides entering and leaving the lagoon, their strength increasing with tide range; there are currents due to outflow from rivers, particularly after heavy rain, when floods build up the level of the lagoon so that water pours out through the entrance; and there are currents generated by wind action when onshore winds drive sea water into the lagoon, or offshore winds drive lagoon water out through the entrance. Movement of coastal sand is due largely to waves and wave-induced currents in the nearshore zone, waves that arrive parallel to the coast moving sand from the sea floor shorewards on to beaches and into lagoon entrances, while waves that reach the shore at an angle cause longshore drifting of sand, deflecting entrances and perhaps closing them altogether.

The position and dimensions of lagoon entrances change frequently in response to variations in the processes at work in and around them. When explorers arrived at the Gippsland Lakes in the eighteen-forties they found a small natural entrance at Cunninghame Arm near the eastern end of the lagoon system, which was sealed in calm weather, when onshore and longshore drifting of sand overcame the effects of transverse currents. It used to remain closed until heavy rains flooded the rivers and raised the level of the lakes so that water spilled out over the barrier. The difficulties of navigating so variable a passage led to a local demand for an artificial entrance, and in 1889 a gap was cut through the outer barrier at what is now Lakes Entrance. This gap, bordered by stone jetties, is a permanent artificial entrance, maintained by currents; a looped sand bar offshore testifies to the efforts of wave action to seal it off. After 1889, the natural entrance fell into disuse, and is now permanently closed (Bird 1961c).

A number of other lagoons on the southeast coast of Australia have intermittent entrances, sealed off during the dry season when outflow from rivers and creeks is low and tidal currents are insufficient to prevent the waves depositing sand. Some entrances remain sealed for several years, until a storm or an exceptional flood reopens them, or until an artificial outlet channel is cut through the barrier.

Lagoon entrances on high wave energy coasts are generally located where wave action is weak, and transverse currents therefore more effective. The entrance to Lake Illawarra is protected by Windang Island immediately offshore (Fig. 16.4c), while the entrances to several lagoons on the South Coast of New South Wales are situated at the southern end of sandy bays, close to rocky headlands, where the dominant southeasterly ocean swell is much refracted, and therefore weakened (cf. Bascom 1954). Other entrances are 'rock-defended', being located close to offshore reefs or foreshore rock outcrops that break up constructive waves and prevent them completing the barrier at a particular point.

The dimensions of lagoon entrances determine the extent of tidal ventilation in a lagoon and influence the pattern of salinity; the effects are represented schematically in Figure 16.5. Tide range within a lagoon diminishes rapidly away from an entrance, the more remote sections of large lagoon systems being unaffected by marine tides. In the Gippsland Lakes, the range of spring tides at Lakes Entrance is slightly less than a metre, but at Metung it is less than 30 cm and tides are not perceptible in Lake Victoria and Lake Wellington. There are, however, irregular changes of level due to heavy rain or river flooding, and marked oscillations during and after periods of strong wind. Similar variations have been observed in other coastal lagoons.

Within an estuarine lagoon it is possible to recognise three zones defined in terms of tides and salinity (Fig. 16.5). The first, tideless and relatively fresh, lies close to river mouths and far from tidal entrances. The second has brackish water, often with a marked salinity range, but is still relatively tideless, and the third, close to the entrance, has more saline water and stronger tidal effects. As will be seen, the three zones are distinct ecologically and geomorphologically; their proportions differ from one lagoon system to another, according to the size and shape of the lagoon, the fresh-water income from rainfall and runoff, and the extent of tidal ventilation, determined largely by tide range and the dimensions of tidal entrances. Salinity is of geomorphological importance because saline water is an electrolyte which coagulates and precipitates fine-grained sediment carried into lagoons in suspension by rivers, thus influencing patterns of sedimentation, and because of the ecological effects of salinity on shoreline vegetation, which also influences patterns of sedimentation.

SEDIMENTATION IN LAGOONS

Sediment is carried into coastal lagoons by rivers, by tidal currents entering from the sea, and by winds. Deposits in lagoons also include material of organic origin, such as shells, guano and peat, and in relatively arid regions, saline lagoons such as the Coorong receive chemical precipitates of salt, calcite and dolomite (Aldermann *et al.* 1957). In one way or another, most lagoons enclosed by barriers are being gradually filled in and replaced by depositional coastal plains.

Lagoons fed by rivers receive sediments ranging from coarse sand to silt and clay. The coarser material is deposited as the river enters the lagoon, and may be added to lagoon beaches and spread around the shore by wave action; the finer sediment is carried out into the lagoon and deposited on the floor, progressively reducing the depth. In the vicinity of tidal entrances, sand washed in from the sea forms sandbanks exposed at low tide, and on the inner shores of the barrier, sand blown over in mobile dunes or washed over in storms or very high tides forms fans of sediment, which are spread along the shore by waves. Sediment also circulates within a lagoon system, material eroded from parts of the lagoon shore being deposited elsewhere on prograding sections of the shore, or on the lagoon floor, while a certain amount may be carried out to sea through the entrance by outflowing floods or ebbing tides.

Patterns of sedimentation are related to the sources of sediment and to processes at work in and around lagoons. In the Gippsland Lakes, relatively coarse sediment is found on the bordering beaches and in channels leading from river mouths towards the tidal entrance, while finer sediment occupies intervening areas of the lagoon floor less subject to wave and current turbulence. Deltas built of sand, silt, and clay project into the lagoon at the mouths of rivers, those of the Latrobe, Avon, and Tambo Rivers being cuspate in form, while the Mitchell delta, built into more sheltered water in the northern part of Lake King, consists of elongated 'silt jetties'. The rivers that have built these deltas all

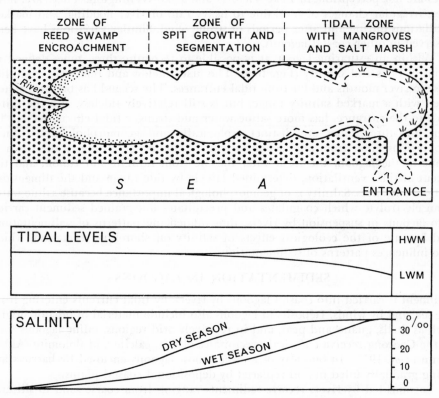

16.5 Diagram of zonation in an estuarine lagoon

show a marked seasonal régime, the deltas being channel-side levees built up and prolonged into the lagoon by sedimentation during floods. Further examples of deltas built into lagoons include those at the mouth of Macquarie Rivulet in Lake Illawarra (Fig. 16.4c), and the Ourimbah Creek and Wyong Creek deltas in the Tuggerah Lakes (Fig. 16.4d).

SWAMP LAND ENCROACHMENT

Shoreline vegetation has a strong influence on patterns of sedimentation in coastal lagoons. Salt marshes and mangrove swamps border the more tidal and saline shores, particularly in the vicinity of entrances, and sediment carried into these halophytic communities on the rising tide is filtered out by the vegetation and retained after the tide has fallen. Patterns and rates of sedimentation in salt marshes and mangrove swamps have so far received little attention in Australia, but certain general conclusions can be drawn from observations in estuaries and lagoons. Mangrove swamps are better developed in estuaries open to the sea than in the more enclosed lagoons, partly because of the diminished tide range in lagoons and the consequent reduction of the intertidal shore zone, and partly because of reduced salinity. This explains the absence of mangroves from the Gippsland Lakes, compared with their widespread occurrence on the tidal shores of Corner Inlet, 80 km away to the southwest. The same restrictions limit the extent of intertidal salt marshes in coastal lagoons, where brackish shores with little or no tide are often lined by the shore rush, *Juncus maritimus,* which spreads slowly into sheltered, shallow water, but merely occupies the water's edge on more exposed shores, where it has little effect on sedimentation.

In less brackish water, *Juncus maritimus* gives place to reedswamp communities with such species as *Phragmites communis,* and other reeds, rushes, and sedges, and in suitable conditions, reedswamp communities spreading from lagoon shores into water up to 1·5 m deep have an important effect on sedimentation, trapping silt and floating debris and contributing organic matter so that new land is built up. Swamp land encroachment has been an important process on the shores of the Gippsland Lakes (Bird 1961b), and to a lesser extent in other Australian coastal lagoons.

Reedswamp encroachment and patterns of lagoon-shore sedimentation are inter-related, for sediment deposited in the reeds provides physical support and nutrients for the growing vegetation, which then spreads farther into the lagoon, trapping more sediment. Lagoons that are freshened and supplied with silt by rivers often show vigorous reedswamp encroachment, and may become completely replaced by swamp land. On the shores of the Gippsland Lakes (Fig. 16.3) swamp land encroachment is accompanied by a vegetation succession, the land built up in the reedswamp being invaded from the rear by swamp scrub communities dominated by dense stands of Swamp Paperbark (*Melaleuca ericifolia*), which may in turn give place to woodland communities similar to those present on the surrounding land (Bird 1962a).

The development of swamp land on lagoon shores is only possible where ecological conditions favour reedswamp encroachment; if the reeds are not present, sedimentation near the lagoon shore is reduced. Ecological studies have shown that a number of factors limit reedswamp encroachment. *Phragmites communis* is unable to colonise water more than about 1·5 m deep, and does not spread into lagoons until the depth has been reduced to that level by sedimentation; the uniform reduction of lagoon depth as sedimentation proceeds may result in a sudden advance of reedswamp when the appropriate depth is attained simultaneously over a wide area. Strong waves or current scour impede swamp encroachment, so that a reed fringe is generally broader on sheltered parts of a lagoon shore, thinning out where exposure is greater: reeds have encroached farther on the southern and western shores of Lake Wellington, sheltered from the prevailing westerly winds, than on the more exposed northern and eastern shores. Direct human interference, such as reed cutting, is limited in Australia, but a swamp fringe can be damaged by boat scour or by water pollution. The most significant limit in coastal lagoons, however, is salinity: the reed fringe is best developed in fresh water around river mouths, and tends to thin out and disappear towards entrances from the sea where the lagoon becomes more saline.

In the Gippsland Lakes, reed-fringed shores are found in Lake Wellington and in parts of Lake Victoria and Lake King, remote from the artificial entrance, and there is evidence that reedswamp was formerly more extensive here, for Gregory (1903), who visited these lagoons in 1900, reported a reed fringe on shores where there is now no bordering vegetation, and where erosion is in progress. This change has been correlated with an increase in salinity of the Gippsland Lakes since the opening of the artificial entrance in 1889 (Bird 1961b), the reedswamp which formerly bordered much of the shoreline of Lake King and Lake Victoria having died back during the last few decades. Swamp land that had been built up within the reeds is now being eroded away by waves: the Mitchell and Tambo deltas in Lake King, which formerly had a reedswamp fringe, are being eroded, whereas the deltas of the Latrobe and Avon in Lake Wellington, farther from the artificial entrance, are still reed-fringed and still growing. Shoreline vegetation has therefore strongly influenced the pattern of sedimentation in the Gippsland Lakes, permitting the encroachment of swamp land and the growth and persistence of river deltas; the relationship between geomorphology and vegetation is clearly demonstrated by the erosion that has resulted from die-back in shoreline reedswamp when ecological conditions have become less favourable (Bird 1962b). The opposite effect is seen in the lagoons at the mouth of the Murray, in South Australia, where exclusion of sea water by barrages completed in 1940 has freshened the lagoons, stimulating the growth and spread of reedswamp on shores that were formerly eroding (Bird 1962c).

SEGMENTATION

As embayments become enclosed by barriers, the effects of ocean swell and tides are gradually excluded. Waves and currents generated in lagoons are then due largely to winds blowing over the lagoon surface, and depend on the direction and strength of winds and the length of fetch (open water) across which they are effective. Where there is no shoreline vegetation, beaches bordering the lagoon shore are subject to erosion and longshore drifting by waves, the drifting being strongest where the waves arrive at an angle of about 45°. Embayments are eroded, and sediment moved along the shore is built into miniature spits, bay barriers, cusps and cuspate forelands, which gradually change the configuration of the lagoon. The spits may grow to such an extent that a lagoon which was at first long and narrow becomes divided into a series of smaller, round or oval lagoons, linked by narrow straits or cut off completely. Price (1947) termed this process *segmentation*, and it has been described and analysed in more detail by Zenkovitch (1959), with examples from Soviet Russia.

Figure 16.6, based on diagrams published by Zenkovitch, shows three stages in the segmentation of a long, narrow lagoon cut off from the sea by a depositional

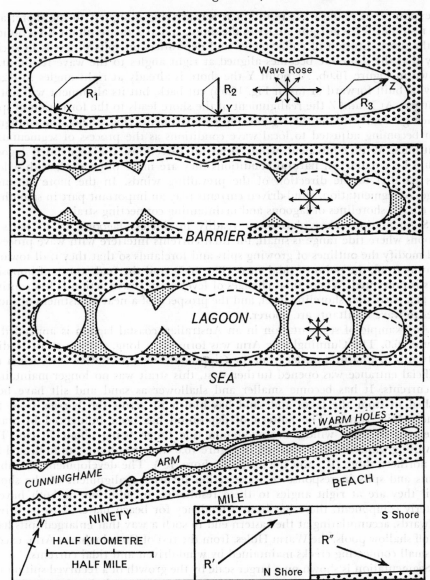

16.6   *The process of segmentation (after Zenkovitch 1959), with an illustration
from the Cunninghame Arm, near Lakes Entrance, Victoria*

barrier. It is assumed that winds are of equal strength and frequency from all
directions; the strength of waves generated in the lagoon then depends on length
of fetch, and is expressed by the *wave rose* drawn in Figure 16.6a. A *wave resultant*
can be determined for any part of the lagoon shore by taking account of the arc

AA

of exposure: at X the wave resultant is R1, arriving obliquely to the shore; at Y the resultant R2 is at right angles to the shore, and at Z the resultant R3 is oblique to the shore. Erosion of embayments and deposition on spits proceeds in such a way that the shoreline becomes aligned at right angles to the wave resultant, as shown in Figure 16.6b. At point Y the shore is already at right angles to R2: it may be built forward or (as in Fig. 16.6b) cut back, but its alignment will not be changed. At X and Z the realignment of the shore leads to the formation of spits, which gradually divide the lagoon into compartments (Fig. 16.6c), the configuration becoming adjusted to local wave conditions as the process of segmentation continues. With equivalent winds from all directions, the segmented lagoons would be circular; in natural conditions they are more often oval, with a long axis parallel to the direction of the prevailing winds. In the more advanced stages of segmentation, wind-driven currents play an important part in smoothing the curved shorelines of lagoons and maintaining connecting straits.

Segmentation takes place most readily in tideless lagoons, or in parts of lagoons where tide range is small, for tidal currents interfere with wave processes and modify the outlines of growing spits and forelands so that they trail towards, or away from, the point of tidal entry (Fig. 16.5), and the coalescence of opposing spits is prevented. Where tidal changes of level occur, wave action is less continuous at a particular shoreline level, and the prospects of a neat adjustment of shorelines to wave resultants are poorer.

An example of segmentation in an Australian coastal lagoon is appended to Figure 16.6. The Cunninghame Arm was formerly a long, narrow strait leading eastwards to a natural outlet from the Gippsland Lakes, but after 1889, when the artificial entrance was opened further west, this strait was no longer maintained by currents. It has become smaller and shallower as sand and silt have been washed in from the lakes and sand has blown in across the barrier from the Ninety Mile Beach. The pattern of deposition has been influenced by waves generated by local winds, the maximum tide range being about 75 cm. The prevailing winds are westerly, and in Figure 16.6 wave resultants are indicated for the northern shore (R') and the southern shore (R''). The development of embayments and spits in response to wave action involves realignment of the shores until they are at right angles to these resultants. In addition, as both have a westerly component, there has been a tendency for beach material to be driven eastwards, accumulating at the eastern end in such a way that enlarged spits have cut off shallow pools, the Warm Holes, from the rest of Cunninghame Arm, except for small connecting creeks maintained by wind-driven and tidal currents.

Segmentation is shown on a larger scale by the growth of a recurved spit on the eastern shore of Lake Wellington, which has been almost isolated from the rest of the Gippsland Lakes, except for the link maintained by currents through McLennan Strait (Fig. 16.3). This lake has a maximum diameter of 17·6 km WSW-ENE and its oval outline reflects the prevalence of westerly winds (Bird 1961a). Erosion of embayments and growth of intervening cuspate forelands on the shores of Lake Victoria and Lake Reeve are further signs of segmentation in progress, while on the South Australian coast, the lagoons between Robe and Beachport (Lakes Eliza, St Clair, and George) have been formed by the segmentation of a long, narrow lagoon, originally similar to the Coorong further north.

CONCLUSIONS

The geomorphology of a coastal lagoon system thus depends on a range of hydrological, geological, climatic and ecological factors. The configuration is determined initially by the shape of the inlet, embayment, or drowned valley formed during submergence, and the shape of the barriers that develop across its mouth. Its subsequent evolution may take one of several courses. If the barrier is complete, or the entrance small or impermanent, so that marine influences (ocean waves, tidal movements and salinity) are excluded, the lagoon will develop in the manner of a fresh-water lake. Sediment carried in will be deposited on the lagoon floor, and if reedswamp develops around the shores, swamp land encroachment will lead to a contraction of the water area accompanying the reduction in depth. The shape of contracting lagoons is related to wave conditions, and in turn to the winds that generate waves on the lagoon, swamp land encroachment being greater on sheltered parts of the lagoon shore.

More brackish but relatively tideless lagoons have little or no shoreline vegetation, and are bordered by beaches, spits, and related features built and shaped by the action of lagoon waves. The growth of these depositional features may eventually divide the lagoon into a chain of smaller segments, each with a configuration related to wind and wave patterns, the segmented lagoons being elongated in the direction of the prevailing winds. Lagoons which have permanent entrances from the sea and are affected by tidal movements are usually bordered by salt marsh or mangrove swamps in the zone between tide marks. Their floors are marked by shoals, emerged at low tide, and channels shaped by the ebb and flow of tidal currents. Such lagoons are similar to estuaries at the mouths of rivers where no enclosing barrier exists, and may be regarded as estuarine lagoons.

Many lagoons are estuarine in the vicinity of a tidal entrance, brackish and tideless in a central zone, and fresh, dominated by the effects of inflowing rivers, away from the tidal entrance. The three modes of geomorphological evolution may thus be represented within a single lagoon system, as in the Gippsland Lakes, in the manner shown schematically in Figure 16.5. The close relationships between ecological conditions and geomorphological development are best seen in the estuarine zone, where salt marsh and mangrove vegetation influence sedimentation, and in the fresh-water zone, where encroaching reedswamp influences sedimentation. The relationships are most obvious where a change in ecological conditions, due perhaps to human interference, results in a change in geomorphological development: a freshened coastal lagoon develops bordering reedswamp and begins to contract in area, while a lagoon becoming more brackish loses its reed fringe, suffers shoreline erosion of swamp land, and becomes segmented as bordering spits and embayments develop.

Finally, a change in geomorphological evolution on a coast where lagoons have developed may lead to the breaching of barriers by marine erosion and the opening up of lagoons as coastal embayments. Guichen Bay and Rivoli Bay, on the South Australian coast, are believed to have originated in this way following dissection of the barrier of aeolian calcarenite which still encloses the lagoons between Robe and Beachport.

In this review of lagoon geomorphology the hydrological, geological, climatic, and ecological factors which influence their development have been discussed, the processes at work in and around lagoons described, and probable modes of evolution deduced. Many problems await solution, but it is hoped that further light will be thrown on these in the course of more detailed geomorphological studies of the various kinds of lagoons found on the coast of Australia.

REFERENCES

Aldermann, A. R., Skinner, H., and Catherine, W. (1957). Dolomite sedimentation in the south-east of South Australia. *Am. J. Sci.* **255**: 561-7.

Bascom, W. (1954). The control of stream outlets by wave refraction. *J. Geol.* **62**: 600-5.

Bird, E. C. F. (1960). The formation of sand beach ridges. *Aust. J. Sci.* **22**: 349-50.

—— (1961a). The coastal barriers of East Gippsland, Australia. *Geogrl J.* **127**: 460-8.

—— (1961b). Reed growth in the Gippsland Lakes. *Victorian Nat.* **77**: 262-8.

—— (1961c). Landform changes at Lakes Entrance. *Victorian Nat.* **78**: 137-46.

—— (1962a). The swamp paper-bark. *Victorian Nat.* **79**: 72-81.

—— (1962b). The river deltas of the Gippsland Lakes. *Proc. R. Soc. Vict.* **75**: 65-74.

—— (1962c). The utilisation of some Australian coastal lakes. *Aust. Geogr.* **8**: 199-206.

—— (1963). The physiography of the Gippsland Lakes, Australia. *Z. Geomorph.* **7**: 233-45.

—— (1965). *The Geomorphology of the Gippsland Lakes.* A.N.U. Dept Geogr. Publ. G/1.

Burges, A. and Drover, D. P. (1953). The rate of podzol development in sands of the Woy Woy district, N.S.W. *Aust. J. Bot.* **1**: 83-94.

Davies, J. L. (1957). The importance of cut and fill in the development of sand beach ridges. *Aust. J. Sci.* **20**: 105-11.

—— (1959). Wave refraction and the evolution of shoreline curves. *Geogrl Stud.* **5**: 1-14.

—— (1960). Beach alignment in southern Australia. *Aust. Geogr.* **8**: 42-4.

Day, J. H. (1951). The ecology of South African estuaries: I—a review of estuarine conditions in general. *Trans R. Soc. S. Afr.* **33**: 53-91.

De Mooy, C. J. (1959). Notes on the geomorphic history of the area surrounding Lakes Alexandrina and Albert, South Australia. *Trans. R. Soc. S. Aust.* **82**: 99-118.

Dimmock, G. M. (1957). *The Soils of Flinders Island, Tasmania.* CSIRO Aust. Soils and Land Use Ser. No. 23.

Fairbridge, R. W. (1948). The geology and geomorphology of Point Peron, Western Australia. *J. Proc. R. Soc. West. Aust.* **34**: 35-72.

—— (1961). Eustatic changes in sea level. *Physics Chem. Earth* **4**: 99-185.

Gregory, J. W. (1903). *The Geography of Victoria.* Melbourne.

Halligan, G. H. (1906). Sand movement on the New South Wales coast. *Proc. Linn. Soc. N.S.W.* **31**: 619-40.

Hills, E. S. (1939). The age and physiographic relationships of the Cainozoic volcanic rocks of Victoria. *Proc. R. Soc. Vict.* **51**: 112-34.

Jennings, J. N. (1955). The influence of wave action on coastal outline in plan. *Aust. Geogr.* **6**: 36-44.

—— (1959). The coastal geomorphology of King Island, Bass Strait, in relation to changes in the relative level of land and sea. *Rec. Queen Vict. Mus.* (N.S.) **11**: 1-39.

Keble, R. A. (1946). The sunklands of Port Phillip Bay and Bass Strait. *Mem. natn. Mus. Vict.* **14**: 69-122.

Price, W. A. (1947). Equilibrium of form and forces in tidal basins of the coast of Texas and Louisiana. *Bull. Am. Ass. Petrol. Geol.* **31**: 1619-63.

Shepard, F. P. (1961). Sea level rise during the past 20,000 years. *Z. Geomorph.* Suppbd **3**: 30-5.

Sprigg, R. C. (1952). *The geology of the South-East province, South Australia, with special reference to Quaternary coastline migrations and modern beach developments*. Bull. Geol. Surv. S. Aust. No. 29.

——— (1959). Stranded sea beaches and associated sand accumulations of the upper South-East. *Trans. R. Soc. S. Aust.* 82: 183-93.

Steers, J. A. (1953). *The Sea Coast*. London.

Zenkovitch, V. P. (1959). On the genesis of cuspate spits along lagoon shores. *J. Geol.* 76: 169-77.

17

Coral Reefs of the Australian Region

RHODES W. FAIRBRIDGE

INTRODUCTION

Around the margins of the Australian continent and its dependent territories are to be found representatives of almost every type of coral reef, as well as such close relatives as algal reefs and sandstone reefs.

In the past, there has been some confusion about the definition of 'reef', which is now largely resolved thanks to numerous studies. Traditionally, to a navigator or hydrographer, a reef was any rocky prominence of the sea floor that might endanger shipping; only some of these were recognisably of coral or other organic origin. Discoveries of fossil reefs, particularly during oil boring, led to the recognition of large organic structures that must, at one time, have formed prominences on the sea floor. Where the sea was so deep that they did not cause waves to break, they were not surrounded by clastic debris as are most modern coral reefs; these would hardly have been a menace to Palaeozoic shipping! Accordingly, the term 'bioherm' was proposed (Cumings 1932) for any kind of massive organogenic structure on the sea floor; geologists tend to use bioherm when the term reef is inappropriate, that is where there is no sign of wave obstruction.

We may define a coral reef then as a complex organogenic framework of calcium carbonate, primarily of corals, which forms a rocky eminence on the sea floor and customarily grows upwards to the tide limit. It thus causes waves to break, and consequently the internal spaces in this branching framework are packed with fragments of reef material, coralline algae, broken-up mollusca, echinoid debris, and foraminifera. The principal reef builders today are the Madreporarian (or Scleractinian) colonial corals of the class Zoantharia, phylum Coelenterata. Formerly, the same ecologic niche was occupied by other classes or phyla. Calcareous algae often grow over and around the coral colonies, helping to hold them together and sometimes misleading observers into thinking that they are the actual frame-builders. Some very fine chalky mud may be chemically precipitated carbonate, either formed at low tide when isolation and higher temperatures raise the local relative concentration of salts in sea water or, after consolidation, when diagenetic circulation brings additional carbonate solutions to be precipitated and help fill in the pore spaces.

Coral reef rock is therefore a very porous material with a large variety of components, mainly organogenic, with chiefly inorganic cementing materials.

Both the outer reef periphery and the lagoon are marked by loose clastic debris that has largely been wave-broken and washed off the reef. This detritus is thus known as bioclastic or coral sand when fresh, or as calcarenite when cemented. A special type of coral sand is found on beaches; after repeated concentration of the interstitial sea water under the hot tropical sun over many low tide periods,

386

the sand becomes cemented into a beachrock, beach sandstone, or littoral calcarenite. Another special type is found in calcareous dune sands or cemented as aeolian calcarenite.

Owing to the rapid changes of sea level during the Quaternary glacial-interglacial oscillations, considerable belts of such dune sands accumulated at various levels along the coasts of Australia, and calcareous sands became readily cemented by percolating rainwater during 'pluvial' phases. Many such aeolian calcarenite ridges now form coastal or offshore reefs, the so-called sandstone reefs or 'Coastal Limestone' reefs. Since these dunes formed particularly in the mid-latitudes, farther south than normal coral reefs, they tend to be complementary to the latter in distribution, hence most of the northern and northeastern coasts are marked by coral reefs, and the southern and southwestern coasts by sandstone reefs (Teichert 1946; Fairbridge 1948a; Fairbridge and Teichert 1952).

Calcareous algae always contribute to coral reefs but also form independent algal reefs, particularly in places which are warm but for some reason unfavourable for coral growth. Such spots include Shark Bay, which is mostly too saline for coral growth (Logan 1961), and parts of the mid-Queensland coast near Cairns where heavy rainfall leads to reduced salinity in the wet season and to excessive turbidity from sediment in suspension.

REEF TYPES

Traditionally we follow Darwin's classical divisions into fringing, barrier, and atoll reefs, but in practice it is found that there are additional types or subtypes, the most important being known generally as platform and patch reefs.

(a) *Fringing Reefs*

These were regarded by Darwin as the basic reef type, forming a thin veneer or shelf in shallow water at or near the shore of the mainland or around offshore islands. Large runoff and heavy sedimentation along the mainland coasts tend to make these less attractive for fringing reefs than the offshore islands. Good examples are seen in the Whitsunday Group, the Lizard Islands, and the Murray Islands off the Queensland coast. The nearshore surface of the reef is often so veneered by terrigenous sediments as to obscure the corals and inhibit growth in the pools (Plate XXXIVa).

(b) *Platform and Patch Reefs*

These reefs are generally rounded or ovoid, the large ones over about 2 km long being called platforms (Plate XXXIVb), the smaller generally patch reefs, or variously 'shelf', 'bank', 'table', and 'hummock' reefs. They are found growing up from water of moderate depth (generally 20-40 m) on the continental shelves, sometimes dotted here and there in almost random manner, but more often in recognisable belts, suggesting an evolution from old shorelines. Probably they originated on headlands and capes during temporary negative or steady phases during the Post-glacial sea-level rise and then grew on upwards as the sea level continued to rise.

Where such reefs are small they form a simple rounded patch, sometimes only a hundred metres across. Under influence of wind, wave, and current, they gradually build a downwind sediment train (Hedley and Taylor 1908; Fairbridge 1950a), and then as they enlarge, twin spurs of horns develop from the reef, giving successively a horseshoe-shaped and then a horse's hoof structure. The interior hollow is gradually filled with smaller reef patches and sediment. Under reversing monsoon winds, the lee side often closes around to form an atoll-like reef, but the centre is not marked by a deep lagoon, only by shallow pools. This type of reef is sometimes called a pseudo-atoll, but its origin is distinct from that of atolls and it is best designated 'platform reef with shallow lagoon or pools'. Many examples of a progression from a small reef patch to a big reef platform may be seen in the northern sector of the Great Barrier Reef (Fig. 17.1).

(c) *Barrier Reefs*

According to Darwin slow subsidence of a fringing reef would cause the corals to grow upwards and outwards, and as the land behind gradually submerged, a lagoon would form between it and the growing barrier. According to Daly (1915) it was the Post-glacial rise of sea level that caused the submergence. It appears that in many parts of the world both factors (basement subsidence and rise of sea level) are contributing.

In some places these reefs are long ribbon reefs, in others, discontinuous modified platform reefs. The passes or channels between them represent Pleistocene stream valleys that crossed the continental shelf before the Post-glacial eustatic rise and separated the initial fringing reefs. These passes have strong tidal currents and are thus subject to constant sediment scour and hence kept open (Plate XXXVb).

Barrier reefs are always strongly asymmetric in plan and section, steep-to on the ocean side, often dropping abruptly away to 2000 m or so, and grading off gently towards the land with a sediment wedge dotted by small reef patches, pinnacles, and coral heads (Plate XXXVIa). Depths in the lagoon may drop here to 60 or 80 m.

Marshall (1931) has written of two distinct reef energy environments; the interior facies is his 'calm water type', the exterior facies is his 'rough water type'. The latter is marked by very vigorous surf action which leads to a piling up of the water, permitting calcareous algae to grow to several feet above the normal reef surface. This forms an algal or *Lithothamnion* rim which helps further to protect the inner environment. Under rather rare calm weather conditions one can walk along the outer rim. The outer face is cut by numerous radial grooves or surge channels down which there is a constant flow of abrading sand, while in between are spurs or buttresses marked by growing coral and *Lithothamnion* (or other calcareous algae such as *Porolithon*).

The finest example of a barrier reef in the world is that of Queensland, which stretches 1900 km from the Gulf of Papua to the Tropic of Capricorn. In eastern Papua there is another fine barrier complex that also rings the Louisiade Group as the Tagula Barrier Reef (Davis 1922). During the Post-glacial rise of sea level there were several important secondary oscillations of level which led to coastal changes. With renewed submergence new fringing

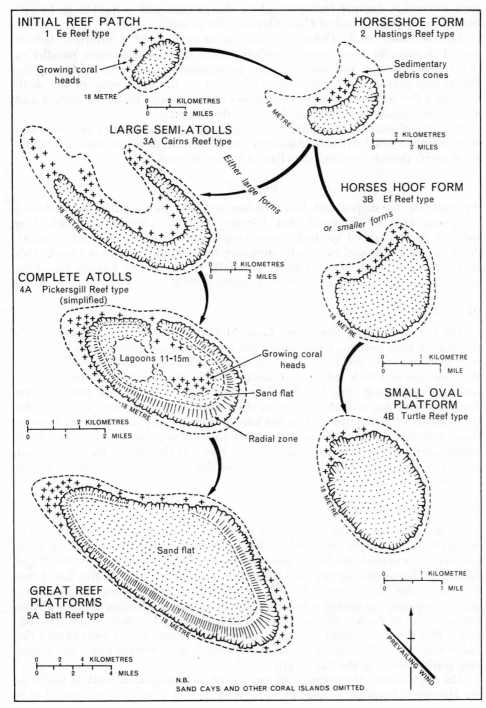

INITIAL REEF PATCH
1 Ee Reef type

Growing coral
heads

18 METRE

0   2 KILOMETRES
0   2 MILES

HORSESHOE FORM
2 Hastings Reef type

Sedimentary
debris cones

18 METRE

0   2 KILOMETRES
0   2 MILES

LARGE SEMI-ATOLLS
3A Cairns Reef type

18 METRE

Either large forms

0   2 KILOMETRES
0   2 MILES

HORSES HOOF FORM
3B   Ef Reef type

or smaller forms

18 METRE

COMPLETE ATOLLS
4A   Pickersgill Reef type
(simplified)

Lagoons 11-15m

Growing coral
heads

Sand flat

18 METRE

Radial zone

0   1   2 KILOMETRES
0   1   2 MILES

0   1 KILOMETRE
0   1 MILE

**SMALL OVAL
PLATFORM**
4B Turtle Reef type

18 METRE

**GREAT REEF
PLATFORMS**
5A Batt Reef type

Sand flat

18 METRE

0   2   4 KILOMETRES
0   2   4 MILES

0   1 KILOMETRE
0   1 MILE

PREVAILING WIND

N.B.
SAND CAYS AND OTHER CORAL ISLANDS OMITTED

17.1   Evolution of patch and platform reefs from examples in the Great Barrier Reef

reefs sometimes became incorporated in the pattern and a double or looped barrier developed, as east of Cape Melville, for example.

Off the Sahul Shelf (Timor Sea) there is an example of a 'drowned' barrier reef. This one, for some reason (probably local tectonic subsidence parallel to the Timor Trough), did not maintain its regular upward growth during the Post-glacial period and forms a submarine rim on the outer edge of the shelf. Only in a few scattered spots did vigorous colonial groups reach the surface and form contemporary reefs (Cartier, Ashmore, Browse, etc.).

Reports of barrier reefs near Northwest Cape ('Point Cloates Barrier') and other points around Western Australia are incorrect; these are basically 'sandstone reefs', though in places they have a veneer of coral.

(d) *Atolls*

An atoll is a ring-shaped reef, like a ribbon reef bent into a circle and enclosing a lagoon. Darwin suggested that fringing reefs which surround subsiding volcanic islands passed gradually into ring-shaped barrier reefs, and as subsidence continued, passed eventually into ring reefs without a central island. This is certainly the origin of some atolls, especially in the Society Islands, but there are several other types (Agassiz 1903; Fairbridge 1950a).

(i) *Shelf Atolls*

On the Queensland Shelf near Cape Melville there are several shelf atolls that do not have volcanic foundations, but appear to have grown up as horseshoe type platform reefs and later closed, or from pre-existing platform reefs by eustatic oscillation which led to truncation and the initiation of a new fringing reef and upgrowing ring. On the Sahul and Rowley Shelves off northwestern Australia there are several large atolls rising from depressed outer sectors of the shelf between 400 and 600 m. It is not known whether they have volcanic foundations, whether they are set on salt dome prominences, or whether they have simply grown up from Pleistocene platform reefs. At the surface they are similar to mid-Pacific atolls, but they definitely rise from the shelf instead of having foundations at 1200-1500 m.

(ii) *Compound Atolls*

In several parts of the world large continental crustal segments have slowly subsided, so that barrier reefs and platform reefs have grown upwards in the same manner as in oceanic atolls, for example in the South China Sea, in the Tiger Islands of Indonesia, in the Maldives, and Laccadives, and in the Coral Sea Plateau in the Australian region. These reefs often have compound tops. Evidently they grew up during subsidence, but were exposed during the last glacial low sea level to form a differentially weathered crest. MacNeil (1954) has suggested that this crest would be higher on the outside and would tend to give the old 'stump' an atoll form. Often many little rings have formed along the initial ring (called 'faros' in the Maldives).

On the Western Australian shelf a group of such compound atolls is found in the Houtman Abrolhos Islands. Here parts of the old stump are exposed, deeply weathered and penetrated by deep holes (former karst pipes). Here there has been no subsidence, so that they are classifid as a 'compound shelf atoll' group.

(iii) Oceanic Atolls

These are the so-called 'mid-Pacific type', which rise from isolated volcanic cones in the deep ocean basins (seamounts or guyots), with 1200-1500 m of accumulated reef growth, which may date back as far as the Cretaceous. These are quite rare in the Australian region, but a few are known in the Coral Sea and in the northern part of the Tasman Sea (Elizabeth, Middleton Atolls). It is interesting that oceanic atolls often have U-shaped gashes, attributed to landslides down volcanic slopes; shelf atolls are more often perfect and smoothly rounded (Fairbridge 1950c).

REEF ISLANDS

Since the days of Captain Cook, the pioneer explorer of the Great Barrier Reef, the islands have been known as 'high islands' and 'low islands'. The 'high' are of continental (e.g. Lizard and Whitsunday Islands) or volcanic rocks (e.g. Murray Islands), and the 'low' are strictly coral islands. The latter fall into five categories, shown in Figure 17.2 (Fairbridge 1950a).

(a) Simple Sand Cays

Called 'keys' in the Caribbean, these are mere accumulations of loose coral sand and beachrock, generally situated on the lee side of a coral platform where intersecting refracted waves have a minimum of energy, and liable to be washed over at high tide.

(b) Vegetated Sand Cays

These are similar to the above but are larger and more mature and are covered by a well established vegetation including quite large trees (*Tournefortia, Pandanus, Casuarina*). The sand sometimes blows up into little dunes, but it is the beachrock which gives stability to the cay; otherwise it would be washed away during hurricanes. The writer has shown that the cement of these modern beachrocks is aragonite; some older beachrocks are exposed in places and in the last 3000 years or so the cements have inverted to calcite.

Well known examples of populated cays are Green Island off Cairns (Plate XXXVa), and Heron Island in the Capricorn Group. The latter is the site of the Research Station of the Great Barrier Reef Committee of Brisbane.

(c) Shingle Cays

These are similar to sand cays in that they are simply accumulations of wave-tossed debris and 'negro heads' (dead coral heads thrown on to the reef by storms), but they are normally situated on the windward side of platform reefs. The heavy coral cobbles and shingle are often cemented into a wave-resistant breccia or conglomerate. The coral shingle initially forms a discontinuous beach ridge or 'rampart'. At break-through points storms carry the shingle on to the reef flat to form radial spits. Short ridge sections and long tails give some of these spits a

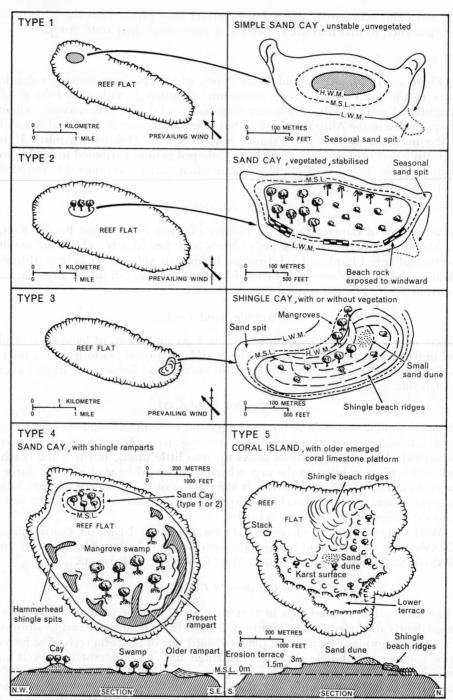

17.2 *Evolution of coral island types from the continental shelf areas of Australia*

hammerhead appearance, so they are called hammerhead spits. On small reef platforms the intersection of wavelets across the reef flats at high tide causes these hammerhead spits to develop long curving tails.

(d) *Sand Cays with Shingle Ramparts*

There is a very interesting belt of small reef platforms in the inner part of the Great Barrier Reef lagoon, from the latitude of Cairns almost to Torres Strait, with both shingle cays and sand cays, for example Low Isles, Two Isles, Three Isles, and Hope Island. These were first called the 'low wooded island reefs' by Captain Cook. In the protected lee of the shingle ramparts, which may build up in several zones or generations, there is an opportunity for floating mangrove seedlings to take root. In the more exposed areas *Avicennia* is the principal genus; in the areas with deeper muddy bottom it is the stilt-rooted *Rhizophora*. Together they play an important role in modifying the inner reef environment, for they provide an accumulation of organic debris. Bacterial decay then sets in, liberating CO_2 and making carbonic acid, so that in the mangrove muds the pH may drop to 5. Under these conditions, the coral sands and limestones are rotted and the interior of the reef flat may be dissolved out.

(e) *Emerged Reef Islands*

On the better protected or more mature reefs there are widespread traces of some older reefs at three distinct higher levels (Plate XXXVIc). These emerged reef limestones form the nuclei of many atoll islands across the Pacific and Indian Oceans; indeed, the Polynesian navigators would have had few places on which to land were it not for the negative shifts of sea level that have resulted in these emerged platforms! It is difficult to date coral accurately, but related beaches with molluscan shells give excellent radiocarbon dates, and on this evidence the three principal high levels have been dated to be Holocene as follows:

Peron Submergence (3 m, possibly several oscillations)
6000-3500 B.P.

Abrolhos Submergence (1·5 m, also oscillations)
2700-2100 B.P.

Rottnest Submergence (0·5 m, also oscillations)
1500-900 B.P.

In places there is a pre-Würm (i.e. pre-Wisconsin or Sangamon) reef complex which is found from 3-8 m, thus causing confusion with the post-Würm 3 m level.

These Holocene submergences alternated with emergences, and by diving below the lagoons it is possible here and there to detect traces of old shorelines at various depths to —3 or —4·5 m. The last important low level was about —2 m in Roman times (about 1800 B.P.) and this has been confirmed by archaeological work on old harbours around the Mediterranean.

In some places fragments of the old emerged reef terraces are being quarried away by the waves and remnants lie scattered over the reef flat, forming another type of 'negro head'. There has long been an interesting controversy about the origin of these coral blocks. Saville-Kent (1893) claimed that they were jetsam, thrown up by the waves. Agassiz (1898) claimed that they were corroded remnants of such former coral limestone platforms. So it turns out, after all, they were both right, each in his own area.

Examples of emerged reef islands are seen off Queensland amongst the low wooded island reefs, and on the outer barrier at Raine Island, and in Western Australia in the Abrolhos Group.

ECOLOGICAL CONTROLS OF CORAL GROWTH

There are some curious anomalies in the distribution of corals around Australia. The basic problem is this: the largest and one of the richest reef environments of the world lies along the northeast coast; one of the poorest and most barren along the northwest. Since there has been no long-lasting barrier to east-west migration in the Indo-Pacific realm, it seems reasonable to ascribe these anomalies in part to ecological controls. However, in spite of much fine work (Yonge 1940, 1963) considerable basic research is still lacking.

Fundamental ecological controls of coral reef growth are as follows:

(a) *Temperature*

Corals in Moreton Bay (Qld) at 27°30′S. survive in water that reaches 15·5°C. in winter, according to Hedley (1925a). At Rottnest Island (W.A.) at 32°00′S. there is a reef that withstands a mean September (winter) temperature of 16°C. For brief periods temperatures drop to 13° or less. In the tropical area, at Murray Islands, Mayer (1918) observed a minimum reef-flat temperature as low as 22°C. Temperatures in reef pools may exceed 38°C. without doing any apparent damage to the organisms.

(b) *Salinity*

Corals are of course stenohaline, that is intolerant of salinity change. On the Murray Islands, Mayer (1918) found that a few hours exposure to a 50 per cent dilution of sea water would kill most species, and a 50 per cent increase is also fatal. At Shark Bay, where the salinity reaches 4·8 per cent, there is a complete absence of corals. A tropical hurricane coinciding with low tide will cause a fresh-water layer to form over the sea, causing wholesale destruction over reef flats, as was shown by Hedley (1925b) and Rainford (1925) in the Bowen region. The high rainfall around the Gulf of Carpentaria and along the Arnhem Land coast during 'the Wet', and the extensive mangroves have no doubt much to do with the relative paucity of coral there, except on offshore islands.

(c) *Aeration*

A large supply of oxygen is essential for coral growth and the best circulation is provided in the region of breakers. Along the Great Barrier Reef the southeast trade winds blow almost constantly on shore, inducing vigorous circulation. Along the north coast we are in the belt of alternating winds, and the trades blow offshore for 7-8 months, leaving circulation at a minimum. However, vigorous aeration need not be very significant, since the symbiotic algae, zooxanthellae, keep oxygen levels high in corals during hours of photosynthesis, regardless of general circulation (Yonge, 1940).

(d) *Hydrogen Sulphide and Other Chemical Factors*

In the stagnant bottoms of some closed lagoons and mangrove swamps there is free H_2S and the Eh drops to minus 200-400 mv; also pH may drop to 5. Both conditions are lethal to corals, but since they are established in geographic situations (ring reefs, etc.) induced by vigorous initial coral growth, they may be counted out as general controls of coral growth offshore.

(e) *Sediment*

Although soft sediment is known to be unfavourable to corals, observations show that some coral planulae (larvae) settle on any hard object, such as a molluscan shell, embedded in mud; further, experiments by Marshall and Orr (1931) showed that corals totally buried could sweep themselves clear of sediment in a few hours. The writer has noticed that at times during the wet season the lagoon of the Great Barrier Reef can become completely clouded by a red muddy suspension, evidently without fatal effects. Nevertheless, fringing reefs are notably absent along much of the mainland shore in the very high rainfall areas.

(f) *Light*

Reef corals are notably phototropic, if for no other reason than because of their algal symbiotes, the zooxanthellae. In the Great Barrier Reef lagoon most flourishing corals are found in less than 9 m, and turbidity may play an important role here. Orr (1933) observed that the Secchi Disk was visible only to 12 m in the Inner Channel, as against 39 m in the Outer Channel at about the latitude of Cairns. However, one may note that the pellucidity of the waters of the northwest coast does not seem to be an adequate inducement to coral colonisation.

(g) *Exposure*

As is well known, corals are killed on exposure, yet it is observed that in regions of excessively large tidal range, they exude a protective mucus which carries them over the period of low tide exposure. With very large tides along both northeast and northwest coasts, this factor does not appear to be inhibiting (Basset-Smith 1900).

(h) *Aspect*

Coral larvae are free-floating plankton and accordingly they will be carried where the current goes. It is well established that the eastern Pacific is impoverished in corals since the Equatorial Currents set mainly westwards, and the easterly sets are not fed by regions of high coral supply. It seems to be significant that the Great Barrier Reef region is supplied by the East Australian Current that sweeps through the reef-choked waters of Melanesia and the Coral Sea. On the west coast in summer, there is a north-setting cold current from the reefless Southern Ocean. In winter there is a warm south-setting current, but it swings in from the easterly Indian Ocean which is essentially reefless except for Cocos Island. Surface waters are blown offshore all along this coast by the steady southeast trade winds. It is felt therefore that this aspect, and thus the relation to winds and currents, is an extremely important control of corals for Australia.

(j) *Nutrients*

Coral food consists of zooplankton, but the availability of the latter depends upon the inorganic nutrient supply. The supply of such mineral salts is normally low in the tropical oceans. Phosphorus is critical; it averages 4 mg/m^3 in the Great Barrier Reef lagoon as compared with 14 in the English Channel (Orr 1933).

It seems to be significant that in neither the northeast nor the northwest of Australia is there significant upwelling, such as could introduce such salts. On the other hand, the east coast is marked by a relatively young orogenic belt, recently revived, so that there is a vigorous chemical erosion of primary igneous rocks accompanied by heavy rainfall and rapid transportation to the sea. Behind the northwest coast, on the other hand, there is an ultra-stable Precambrian hinterland of little relief, and younger, flat-lying sediments, very low rainfall, and an essentially sluggish geomorphological régime. In the absence of proper oceanographical studies, it is nevertheless suggested that this is probably the key factor in discouraging coral growth in the northwest.

EUSTATIC AND TECTONIC CONTROLS OF REEF GROWTH

Glacio-eustasy as a cause of sea-level change must no longer be regarded as one of a number of working hypotheses, but as a quantitatively demonstrated fact although many details remain to be established. The basic tenets are now part of every geologist's working principles, and the great verbal battles of Darwin and Murray, and in this century of Davis, Daly, Hoffmeister, and others, are of historic interest only.

The last glacial low sea level was of the order of —100 m and possibly more (Fig. 17.3). Between 17,000 and 6000 years B.P. (shown by numerous radiocarbon dates) the sea rose to some 3 m above its present level (Fairbridge 1961a). Since then there have been numerous oscillations of the order of 500-1000-1500 years, and of lower orders such as 22 and 11 years.

It is the opinion of the writer that the larger cycles of glacial/interglacial type are to be correlated with the Milankovitch astronomical cycles (precession, obliquity, etc. — 21,000, 40,000, and 92,000 years), but this is difficult to prove; the radiocarbon dating of the last cycle, however, allowing for melt-retardation, seems to be just about right for the last 50,000 years (Fairbridge 1961b), and for even earlier cycles according to results of new dating procedures.

There appears to be a second-order series of cycles, controlled also by celestial mechanics, that is basically about 567 years and its multiples, corresponding to the periodic alignment of the earth-moon-sun in almost coincident orbits; both tidal and climatic effects are to be expected.

The third order eustatic cycles deduced from recent studies are the sunspot cycles (simple, 11 year; the 'Hale Cycle' of 22 years; the 'Gleissberg Cycle' of about 80 years (Fairbridge 1961c)). Modern rocket and artificial satellite studies have shown conclusively that peaks of solar activity, marked by sunspot maxima, coincide with peaks of ultraviolet radiation (up to twice the normal value). The ultraviolet radiation breaks up oxygen molecules in the upper atmosphere to produce ozone and the ozone-H_2O-CO_2 concentration here forms a 'thermal

XXXIVa Typical fringing reefs at Lizard Island, modified by quartzose sand from continental-type island beaches

XXXIVb The southeast (windward) side of a very large platform reef (Batt Reef, off Cairns), showing 'trickle zone' over which the waves wash, to build up coral debris in the interior, the 'central sand flat'

XXXVa Green Island, a vegetated cay, about 700 m long, off Cairns, is an ideal holiday resort and research centre. Note the varied ecological situations, coral heads, algal flats, sanded zones, and beach rock along the shore. Vertical air photograph by R.A.A.F.

XXXVb Ribbon reefs and passages through the outer line of the Great Barrier Reefs. Overhanging corals face the deep passages, but rounded coral heads grow on the gentle lee side.

blanket' (with 'greenhouse effect') and thus controls the thermal balance of the earth.

During the first half of the twentieth century, there was a steady rise in the peaks of sunspot numbers (up till 1958), accompanied by a rise in the mean earth surface temperature of 1°C. (Mitchell 1963) and numerous other important climatic effects, such as a rise of 50 per cent of surface evaporation over the Bay of Bengal. Meanwhile, glaciers have been melting extensively, sea temperatures rising, Arctic Sea ice retreating, and mean sea level rising at a mean 1·2 mm/yr.

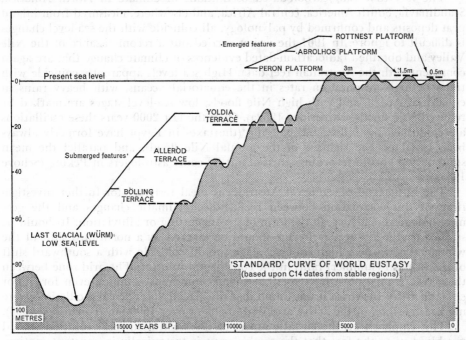

17.3   *Eustatic curve over the last 20,000 years B.P. (datum year 1950 A.D.) based on C¹⁴ dates from stable coastlines; similar but somewhat lower curves offered by Shepard and others include data from subsiding areas. Note that the emergent features are named after Australian sites; the submergent levels are based on Scandinavian terminology.*

The eustatic correlation seems unmistakable. However, a study of the long-term sunspot patterns and sea-level oscillations over the last 6000 years suggests that the temperature rise of the last half century is merely a minor positive recovery superimposed on a generally negative mean curve over this period. Over this longer term, the mean temperature has dropped 2·5°C., coinciding with the Milankovitch prediction from celestial mechanics, and mean sea level has dropped 3 m.

Radiocarbon dates from many parts of the world appear to confirm that between 6000 B.P. and the present, there has been an oscillating drop of MSL with intermediate 'highs' about 3 m, 1·5 m, and 0·5 m, with negative swings (i.e.

BB

downward eustatic trends) in between, to —3 m or —4·5 m. The geomorphology of the emerged coral limestone terraces and the related 'raised' beaches, beach-ridges, emerged peat swamps, etc., seems to allow no alternative explanation. Nevertheless, geologists working around the Mississippi delta have rejected the idea of mid-Holocene high sea levels. They claim that there must have been tectonic uplift that has affected Australia uniquely (Russell 1963; Shepard 1964). However, radiocarbon dates from such diverse places as Brazil, Morocco, Madagascar, Borneo, and Vietnam confirm the Australian dates.

The fact that radiocarbon-dated oscillations of climate in North America, Scandinavia, South America, central Africa, and elsewhere, measured from inland peat deposits and confirmed by palynology, all coincide with the sea-level changes is difficult to ignore. In 1961 the writer carried out a reconnaissance of the Nile Valley and obtained radiocarbon-dated evidences of climate change that are again consistent with the Australian reef data. High sea levels apparently coincide with times of high evaporation rates in the equatorial oceans, with heavy rains in equatorial Africa, and with high Nile floods; low sea-level stages are marked by reduced Nile floods (Fairbridge 1962a). Over the last 2000 years these oscillations are confirmed by 'Nilometer' gauging (the taxes in Egypt have formerly always been based on the richness of the annual Nile flood), and parallel the mean sunspot and aurora recordings carried out by court astrologers in Peking (Schove 1955).

The hinterland of semi-arid Australia is ideal territory for further investigations of this correlation between reef-deduced climatic changes and the geomorphological evidence, in the form of stream-cutting or alluviation. It should be stressed that a low sea-level stage should be marked by a northward shift of the winter rains, while a high sea-level stage should coincide with a southward shift of the tropical (summer) rains in the continental interior. The arid zone between these two 'fronts' must have oscillated many hundreds of miles, even for minor climatic shifts. In Africa it was found that the glacial/interglacial oscillations were marked by shifts of the active arid dune belts of over 1600 km (Fairbridge 1964).

This emphasis on the eustatic aspect of the Australian reef evolution should not blind us to the fact that the earth's crust is tectonically in constant motion. There are daily earth-tides (lunar effect) of about 0·3 m in amplitude to which even the most stable sectors of the crust react. Secular effects, mainly related to the re-establishment of isostatic equilibrium, may be revived from time to time, for many millions of years after the apparent completion of an orogeny. We may safely predict that the east coast of Australia will be more active than the west. Youthful vulcanicity around Mt Gambier, South Australia, has tilted the Pleistocene aeolianite beach-ridges in a striking manner. The very youthful orogeny of northern New Guinea is evidently responsible for the uplift of coral limestones which around Finschhafen reach 300 m above sea level.

Tests of contemporary mobility can be made by repeated geodetic levelling and with tide gauges. Information in both of these fields in the Australian continent is seriously lacking. Nevertheless there are already sufficient records available to permit preliminary analyses. These must then be checked against the geophysical data on isostasy obtained by gravity surveys. One may note that while the rest of the world's tide gauges show this rising trend of sea level during the last half century, the Sydney gauge suggests the reverse. This means that either the earth's crust at Sydney is rising or some oceanographic phenomenon is upsetting the local pattern. Such a cause could be related to the East Australian Current. This stream sets to the south, and consequently, under the Coriolis Force, bears slightly to the left (east). The sea surface is thus geodynamically tilted down on the west or coastal side. An acceleration of the current would increase this tilt and make the land appear to rise. A determination as to which explanation is correct would require careful team studies (geologists, geodesists, geophysicists, and oceanographers). A similar problem exists in eastern North America, where the crust is also partly active and where there may be a deceleration of the Gulf Stream (Fairbridge and Krebs 1962).

When the Holocene coral reef limestones are being studied, especially where they are so beautifully exposed along the Great Barrier Reef complex, it is essential that great care be exercised before claiming either eustatic, tectonic, or oceanographical causes. Evidently all three are real and active. It is therefore necessary to determine relative rates and thus to resolve which are the dominant factors. It is believed that the maximum mid-Holocene high sea level was about 3 m above the present. Therefore, if a reef or terrace dated at 5000-3000 B.P. is found at 4·5 m above its contemporary equivalent, there is a 1·5 m altitude anomaly to be explained. To study the geomorphology of the Queensland coast and say that evidently there has been differential uplift since the Mio-Pliocene is not enough. Was this uplift still in progress during the last 5000 years? Since the Coral Sea Plateau was subsiding during the same time, where was the fulcrum? Much can be done by the statistical approach. If raised coral reefs occur at constant heights over known positive and negative tectonic trends, evidently those zones are insufficiently active to leave measurable traces over the 5000 year period involved.

It must be evident from this discussion that the study of reefs and their related reef limestone terraces can open the way to a vast field of understanding of the former climates and tectonic evolution of the continent.

REGIONAL DISTRIBUTION OF REEFS

Four geotectonic groups of reefs can be recognised in the Australian region:

Epicontinental reefs, with rather stable foundations and with eustatic features dominant, for example Queensland (Great Barrier Reef complex), Northern Territory, and Western Australia.

Mobile belt reefs, with moderately or highly unstable foundations and with eustatic factors often obscured, for example in a gently subsiding zone in the eastern Papua-Tagula-Louisiade barrier reef, and in the strongly uplifted zone of the Finsch Coast.

Quasicratonic reefs, where there has been *en bloc* subsidence of appreciable areas of former continental crust, for example Coral Sea Plateau.

Oceanic volcanic reefs, where the foundations of atolls lie along the known volcanic trends and by implication are of similar nature (i.e. 'mid-Pacific type'), for example Elizabeth Atoll and others in the N-S trend of Norfolk Island, Cocos-Keeling Atoll in the northeastern Indian Ocean. These are subsiding examples. In some examples, such as Christmas Island, Nauru, and Ocean Island, subsidence has been followed by uplift. Colonised by oceanic birds, they have become phosphate islands.

(a) *Great Barrier Reef Complex*

Extending 1900 km from the Gulf of Papua (lat. 9°S.) almost to Sandy Cape (lat. 24°S.), the Great Barrier Reef is the largest and most continuous reef complex in the world (Fig. 17.4). In the latitude of Torres Strait (10°S.) it is 160 km wide; in the middle, between Cape Melville and Cairns, it narrows to 30-50 km; and widens again to a 'fish-tail' in the south, in the latitude of Swain Reefs (22°S.) to 300 km. Roughly, it embraces about 460,000 km². It rises from the continental shelf of Queensland (Bryan 1928) as a veneer 120-150 m in thickness under the coral islets, as demonstrated by bores put down for the Great Barrier Reef Committee (Fig. 17.5). The first, in 1926 at Michaelmas Cay off Cairns, showed 121 m of shallow-water corals and reef debris, stopping at 183 m in terrigenous sands. The second, in 1937 at Heron Island in the Capricorn Group, reached the base of the coral at 154 m and then continued to 223 m, likewise in terrigenous glauconitic quartz sands and foraminiferal calcareous sands with beach-rock layers of Pleistocene age. No dolomite was found (Richards and Hill 1942). Recently an oil exploration bore put down at Wreck Island (north of Heron Island) penetrated 122 m of reef material, then Pleistocene and Tertiary sediments, to reach basement at 546 m.

Early investigators led by Jukes (1847), believed the reefs to represent a giant wedge several thousands of metres thick, but the morphology alone shows this is not so. The underlying continental shelf emerges as an independent and pre-existing structure both in the north, where coral growth is inhibited by muddy brackish water, and in the south, where corals are limited by winter temperatures.

The rock basement of the shelf emerges in such offshore islands as the Lizard Group (only 16 km inside the outer barrier), the Flinders Group, at Palm Island, Magnetic Island, and in the Whitsunday Group. This basement is probably Precambrian in the north and of Palaeozoic metasediments in the south. The eastern borders of the Tasman Geosyncline are not found on the mainland and may well lie buried in this shelf region or under the Coral Sea Plateau. If the former eastern hinge zone of the geosynclinal belt can be located, it may have some significance for petroleum exploration. Most palaeo-geographical reconstructions call for the subsidence of a former 'Tasmantis' a dismembered continent that extended to Melanesia and New Zealand (Fairbridge 1961d).

In the coral limestone itself no early Pleistocene indications of high terraces have been identified. Most of the material is thus late glacial or Holocene, and the visible emerged coral limestone terraces seem to be exclusively mid-Holocene. We reach the rather astonishing conclusion that the bulk of this vast complex was formed during a mere 10,000 years.

The entire eastern Australian seaboard discloses evidence of tremendous Pleistocene block faulting (Andrews 1910, 1922; Steers 1929); the Mio-Pliocene peneplain has been uplifted to about a thousand metres and tilted westwards, so that at the watershed in certain places near Cairns one can stand in gullies that will drain eventually to the Indian Ocean, yet at the same time observe the full

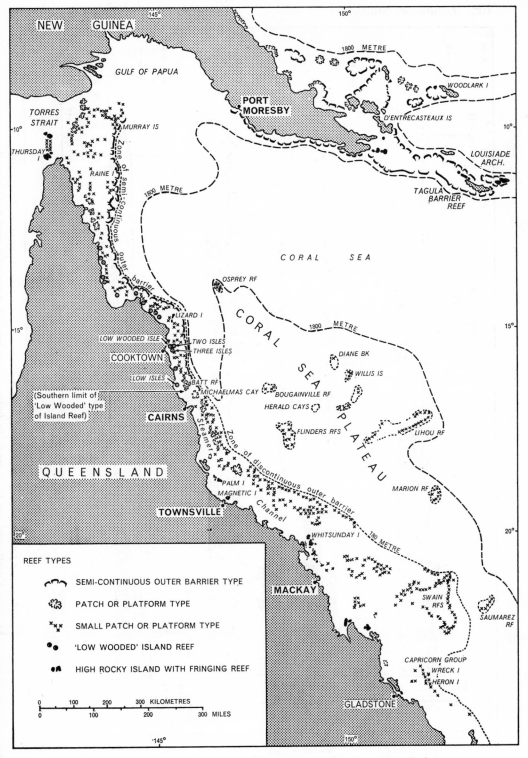

17.4 Great Barrier Reefs, Coral Sea, and southeastern New Guinea

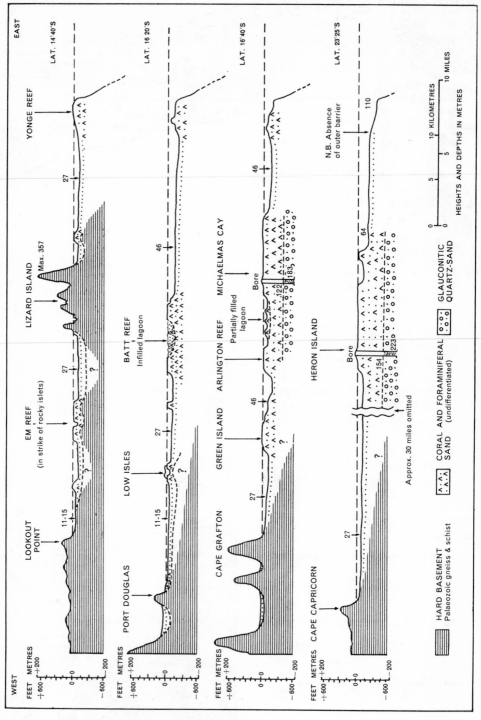

17.5　*Four profiles through the Great Barrier Reefs, showing two experimental bore sites. No attempt has been made to indicate locations of the continental border faults.*

expanse of the Barrier Reef below, the outer margin of which is further faulted down to depths of 1800 m or more. The reef bores suggest that the last important movements of this giant taphrogeny occurred less than 50,000 years ago.

Curiously enough, vulcanicity is only associated with this fracturing in one area, the Murray Islands opposite Torres Strait. The lavas are reported to contain some blocks of dolomite, which represents a basement type not seen elsewhere (Haddon *et al.* 1894).

The thickness of the reef material disclosed by the bores suggests that there is a factor of subsidence (perhaps of 30 m or so) in addition to the eustatic factor. Darwin, supported energetically by Davis (1917), claimed that the whole amount was tectonic subsidence; Agassiz (1898, 1903) spoke for growth from an antecedent platform; Daly (1915) introduced the eustatic factor. It turns out that each was partially correct.

The Barrier Reef complex may be divided conveniently into two sectors, a northern and a southern, as follows:

(i) Northern Sector of the Great Barrier Reef

This is mainly a long narrow shelf in the south, beginning at the latitude of Trinity Opening near Cairns (16°30'S.) and widening out considerably in the Torres Strait-Murray Islands area (10°S.). One may distinguish the following belts:

(*1*) *Outer Barrier or Ribbon Reefs.* These were called 'linear reefs' by Jukes (1847). Each is 300-450 m wide, consisting of stretches 3-24 km long separated by quite narrow passes. From the air they look like a continuous rampart extending for nearly 800 km and marked by foaming breakers. East of Cape Melville they are looped to form a double rampart with an inner lagoon 18 km wide. At Wreck Bay (12°S.) there is an extraordinary re-entrant, suggesting perhaps a large land-slide scar. At 11°35'S. is Raine Island, the only emerged reef island on the whole outer barrier; Jukes observed that it consists of calcareous aeolianite, with an emerged beachrock terrace here ascribed to the 3 m mid-Holocene stage. The aeolianite, by analogy with other offshore occurrences in Australia (e.g. Abrolhos, Rottnest), is probably of late glacial (Würm) age, when sea level was low enough to permit wide beaches to form and dune accumulations to develop. At the Murray Islands (lat. 10°S.) too, there are 3 m and intermediate terraces. The typical ribbon reef, however, is free from islands, and is marked only by a prominent algal ridge—the *Lithothamnion* rim. The extremities of each sector are marked by recurving horns where the swell from the Pacific is refracted into the passes. The best descriptions of a typical example, Yonge Reef, are provided by Stephenson *et al.* (1931) in the report of the British Museum Barrier Reef Expedition which visited the area in 1927-8.

(*2*) *Outer Channel.* An almost reefless channel, about 65 m deep, separates the ribbon reefs from the next belt. Presumably such channels represent zones over which the rising Post-glacial sea passed very rapidly, not giving time for the establishment of reef colonies. It is now too deep for the major reef-builders.

(*3*) *Belt of Platform Reefs.* This is the belt of horseshoe to ovoid platforms, many of which are 15-25 km long. In the sector from Cairns to Cape Flattery

(15°S.) the platforms are elongated NW-SE and certainly reflect the southeast trade-wind direction (Fig. 17.6). Platform reefs occupy, and indeed almost block, Torres Strait; here they are oriented east-west on account of the oceanic currents, which reverse seasonally with the alternation of wind régimes. Islands are almost totally lacking except where continental rocks appear in the high islands of the Lizard Group (14°40′S.), and in Torres Strait. In Batt Reef, Stephenson *et al.* (1931) have best described a typical example of a platform reef.

(*4*) *Belt of Low Wooded Island Reefs.* These form an independent line of reefs a few kilometres westward of the zone of large platform reefs. They are distinguished by their small size, but are capped by islands which generally include nuclei of emerged coral limestone with extensive shingle ridges, spits, or islets and vegetated sand cays (Fig. 17.7). These are amongst the few habitable barrier reefs islets outside Torres Strait. In this essay they have been described briefly under reef-island types (d) and (e); detailed descriptions include those by Stephenson *et al.* (1931), Spender (1930), Steers (1929, 1937, 1938), and by Fairbridge and Teichert (1947, 1948).

These small but complex platform reefs grow up from the inner part of the Great Barrier Reef lagoon in depths of only 18-27 m. Since, in these turbid waters, coral growth is inhibited below 11-13 m, it is evident that the reef foundations were established during a lower stand of sea level, probably originating as fringing reefs on current-swept headlands at about Alleröd time, 11,000 years ago. The sea floor between these reefs is now being shallowed with grey terrigenous sands and muds from the nearby rivers. It is interesting, for comparison with ancient fossil reefs in limestone facies, that these isolated reefs are entirely surrounded by non-carbonate sediments.

(*5*) *Inner Channel.* The low wooded island reefs are separated by a channel 8-16 km wide from the mainland. This is almost entirely free of reefs, probably as a result of the very rapid rise of world sea level between the short cool period that followed the Alleröd and the beginning of the $+$ 3 m stage at 6000 B.P. In this 5000-year period sea level rose nearly 30 m, at certain stages averaging about 45 mm a year. Under such conditions most corals would be rapidly 'drowned', would have their growth slowed, and would become easily buried by terrigenous sediment. This is fortunate for commercial shipping, and the Inner Channel, being thus free from reefs, is a safe passage all the way up to Torres Strait.

(*6*) *Fringing Reefs.* These are common on headlands and rocky sectors from Cairns to Cape York, but in the broad bays marked by sandy beaches or mangrove swamps, they are absent. The reefs are poor and often almost smothered by sediment, and in places they are algal rather than coral reefs.

(*ii*) *Southern Sector of the Great Barrier Reef*

This extends from Trinity Opening near Cairns (16°30′S.), south to Swain Reefs and the Capricorn and Bunker Groups, as far as Lady Elliot Island (24°10′S.) near Sandy Cape. Again there are distinct belts, but these differ in important respects from those of the northern sector:

(*1*) *Outer Barrier Platform Reefs.* Ribbon reefs are not seen south of Trinity

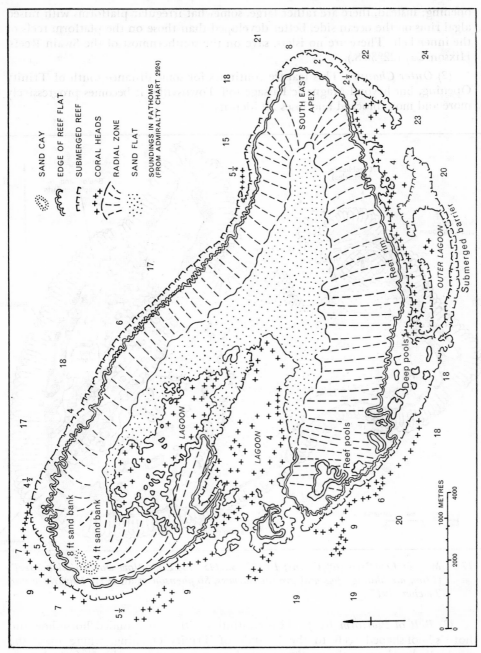

17.6 *Sketch map of Pickersgill Reef (15° 52′ S.), a platform reef that suggests evolution from a shelf atoll, a nearly complete ring, with lagoon remnants partly filled with coral heads, and sand*

opening; instead, there are rather large, somewhat irregular platforms with raised algal rims on the ocean side, better developed than those on the platform reefs of the inner belt. There are no islets, save on the southernmost of the Swain Reefs, Hixson Cay (22°30′S.).

(2) *Outer Channel*. This feature continues for some distance south of Trinity Opening, but beyond Magnetic Passage (off Townsville) it becomes progressively more and more blocked and loses all identity.

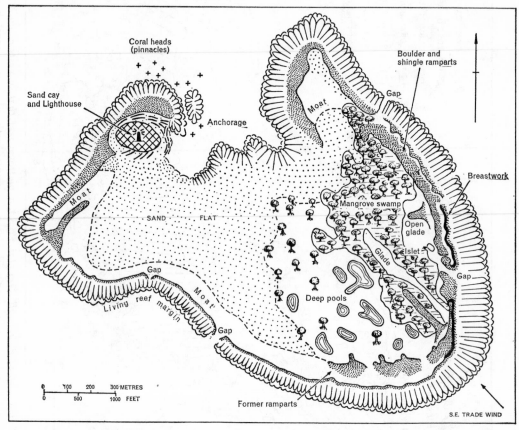

17.7 *Map of Low Isles (off Cairns; 16° 23′ S., 145° 34′ E.), a 'low wooded island reef'. (From air photographs and ground surveys, Stephenson et al. 1931; Fairbridge and Teichert 1947.)*

(3) *Belt of Platform Reefs*. This continues with well rounded horseshoe and horse's-hoof-shaped reefs to the latitude of Trinity Opening, where these too gradually break up in the southeast into large masses of irregular reef patches.

As the continental shelf widens in the south, the reef platforms form series of large loops as well as irregular patterns. It is suggested that these may represent former island areas that became ringed by fringing reefs about Alleröd time.

These reefs have since become partly overgrown by reef patches, giving shape to the later ring developments, such as Swain Reefs.

In the southern fork of the 'fishtail' of the southern sector of the Great Barrier Reef, there appear two isolated and distinctive clusters of platform reefs, mainly capped by vegetated sand cays. These are the Capricorn and Bunker Groups, typified by Heron Island (Steers 1937, 1938).

(4) Inner Channel. Low wooded island reefs disappear completely in the southern sector and the inner channel broadens out to 110 km in the wide Capricorn Channel that slopes down gradually into the northern end of the Tasman Sea basin. It seems to be tectonically controlled.

(5) Fringing Reefs. These are almost absent from the mainland coast of the southern sector, but occur in places around high islands like those of Whitsunday Group. A small patch occurs in a quite isolated spot at Peel Island in Moreton Bay near Brisbane. However, this is not a strictly open sea environment and presumably is kept warm by the restricted nature of the bay.

(b) *Coral Sea Reefs*

The Coral Sea occupies a complex structural basin between Queensland, New Guinea, and the other Melanesian islands. It contains the Papua Trough in the north and the New Caledonia Trough in the east, both probably representing modern geosynclines, since they can be followed as direct extensions of the Papuan Geosyncline, and occupy foredeeps along the foot of the youthful orogenic belt that runs through New Guinea, the Louisiades, and New Caledonia, eventually to New Zealand.

Apart from these troughs, there are several fairly flat-topped, complex submarine plateau areas, ranging from 350 to 1800 m in depth, with randomly scattered large reefs (mostly shelf-type atolls or compound atolls) reminiscent of the Tiger Islands in the Flores Sea, of Chesterfield Reef in the South China Sea, of the Maldives and Chagos, rather than typical mid-Pacific reefs. There is no trace of submarine volcanic foundations, and the plateau blocks would appear to have subsided slowly during the Pleistocene, and possibly earlier periods, permitting upward reef growth to maintain itself. The principal submarine plateaux are:

(i) *The Coral Sea Plateau*

This flat-topped structure of intermediate depth (Fairbridge 1962b) is separated from the Queensland Shelf by a long narrow slot which I have called 'Queensland Trench', the form of which suggests a great hinge-fault trough sloping down from 350 m in the southeast to 3500 m where it joins the Papua Trough. The plateau itself appears to be tilted down bodily to the north, so that the reefs like Saumarez and Marion in the southeast with their foundations at only 350-550 m, are followed progressively to the northwest by deeper and deeper foundations, as in Lihou, Flinders, Herald Cays, Willis, Diane, Bougainville, and Osprey Reefs. The last drops impressively down to nearly 3650 m on three sides.

(ii) *The Bellona Plateau*

This occupies a shoal area extending from 18° to 23°S. and 155° to 163°E.

(Fairbridge 1962b), being separated by only narrow troughs from the southeastern limits of the Coral Sea Plateau and the ridge of New Caledonia. Its reefs are a mixture of shelf atolls, partly drowned and modified by subsidence, and platform reefs. Outstanding are the Chesterfield Reef, Bellona Reef, Bampton Reef, Observatory Cay, Minerva Reef, Darling Reef, Fairway Reef, Henry Miller Reef, Kenn Reef, Wreck Reef, and Cato Reef. Only the first five rise from less than 1800 m.

(iii) Oceanic Reefs of the Coral Sea and North Tasman Sea

Scattered atolls are also observed in certain quite distinctive belts outside the submarine plateaux. The most remarkable of these lineaments is a north-south line that I have called Middleton Ridge (Fairbridge 1962b). From south to north it extends through Ball Pyramid, Lord Howe Island, Elizabeth Reef, Middleton Reef, Capel Bank, and Kelso Bank; and then joins the Bellona-Chesterfield trend.

There seems little doubt, from the emerged volcanic nature of Ball Pyramid and Lord Howe Island, that these are normal mid-Pacific type atolls or drowned atolls with volcanic foundations. Where Middleton Ridge joins the Bellona Plateau it intersects a semi-continental crustal structure, which may have been modified by volcanic plugs.

(c) New Guinea Reefs

In spite of its tropical rainfall, most of the shores of New Guinea (including Papua and New Britain) are lined by fine fringing reefs, except at the mouths of streams. The broad muddy delta of the Fly River is exceptional in being quite reefless.

The barrier reef off the southeast coast of Papua, and running all around the Louisiade Archipelago in the Tagula Barrier Reef, is extraordinarily little-known despite its impressive size. It measures 1000 km in length and in the Louisiades it is 50 km across from barrier-front to barrier-front. Its interior is dotted with platform reefs and patches.

The mid-Holocene 3 m reef limestone is widespread, but along the Finsch coast very active uplift has led to a regular 'staircase' of emerged reefs, and both Gibb Maitland and Behrmann have reported emerged reefs more than 300 m above sea level.

(d) Sahul and Arafura Shelf Reefs

Sometimes the term 'Sahul Shelf' is applied to the entire northern Australian shelf region, one of the broadest continental shelves in the world. However, it has been suggested (Fairbridge 1953) that the eastern part, coinciding with the Arafura Sea, be designated Arafura Shelf, the centre section, including the Timor Sea and Sahul Banks proper, the Sahul Shelf, and the southwestern sector off the Kimberley coast, the Rowley Shelf (Fig. 17.8). Fringing reefs are common on headlands, but most bays and estuaries are dominated by mangrove; offshore reefs are scarce.

Both the Arafura Shelf (820,000 km²) and Sahul Shelf (300,000 km²) are underlain by mainly Precambrian basement with superimposed shallow basins of Palaeozoic and younger rocks. The hinterland is low and semi-arid, though heavy summer rains fall near the coast. The bottom topography of the shelf shows an interesting pattern of Pleistocene river channels (Fairbridge 1951) analogous to

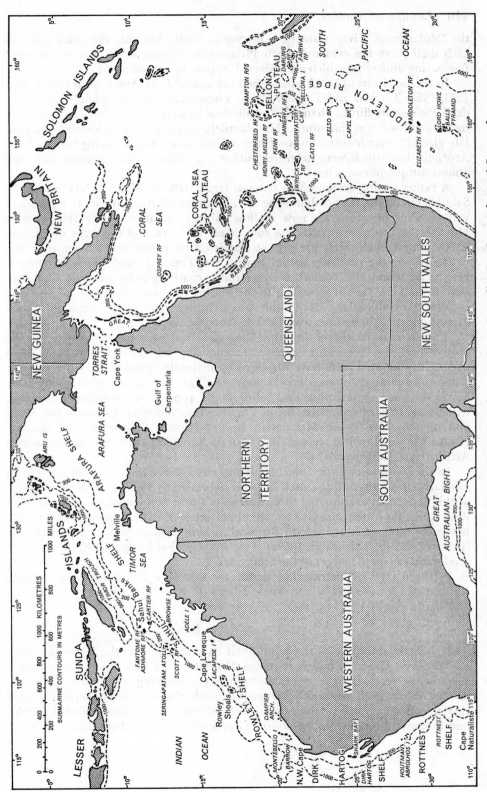

17.8 *Sketch map showing the wide continental shelves north of Australia. For Lacapede read Lacepede.*

the 'Molengraaff River' system of the Sunda Shelf. Towards the outer parts of each shelf there has evidently been Pleistocene warping which has led to some fascinating anomalies which are reflected in part by reef patterns.

In the northeast of the Arafura Shelf are situated the Aru Islands (Fairbridge 1951, 1953; Termier and Termier 1963). These islands are completely crossed by deep Pleistocene fluvial channels and disclose upwarped late Tertiary shelf sediments and fossil reef limestones. The channels, or sungeis, are evidently valleys of late glacial antecedent streams that maintained their courses during uplift of the Aru axis, but which were drowned during the Holocene transgression, and are almost unique phenomena.

A rather similar tectonic axis extends from Melville Island WNW across the Sahul Shelf. Again, the north-flowing rivers maintained their courses in antecedent valleys, some of which are now shallow submarine canyons over 180 m deep. However, in this case the axis was completely drowned and there are no islands. In the Sahul Shelf, reefs are almost restricted to a drowned barrier reef that extends along the northern border against the Timor Trough. This structure is very active seismically, is marked by a strong negative gravity anomaly similar to that of the Java Trench according to the Vening Meinesz submarine surveys, and is backed by the island of Timor, where Molengraaff (1930) reported raised Pleistocene coral limestones over 1000 m above sea level.

The drowned barrier of the Sahul Shelf rises from near the 180 m line, but the abrupt shelf edge is certainly depressed tectonically and may be up to about 360 m deep. Only isolated reefs have managed to maintain themselves at the surface: Cartier, Ashmore, Fantome, Troubadour, etc. They are mainly platform reefs or partly drowned shelf atolls. The Sahul Banks proper are completely drowned, with about 18 m of water over them. They are thus rather analogous to the Alexa and related reefs of the Melanesian Border Plateau (Fairbridge and Stewart 1960), or to the drowned reefs of the southeast Borneo Plateau and the Spermonde Archipelago (Umbgrove 1947).

In the southwest of the Sahul Shelf there is a broad re-entrant of the 180 m submarine contour, and the shelf break is depressed to 460-550 m. Near the edge of this depression are situated three fine shelf atolls: Seringapatam, and the Scott Reef atolls; the latter consist of one small perfect atoll with no passage and a large horseshoe atoll with a break to the north. Seringapatam is also a perfect ring (Plate XXXVIb, Fairbridge 1950a; Teichert and Fairbridge 1948). There is a small sand cay on the larger of the Scott reefs.

Platform reefs of intermediate depth are seen in a few quite isolated spots, for example Browse Island and Adèle Island (Figs. 17.9, 17.10; see also Teichert and Fairbridge 1948).

(e) *Rowley Shelf Reefs*

This shelf lies southwest of the Sahul Shelf and extends from the Kimberley coast to Northwest Cape. Although it covers 243,000 km², it has but few coral reefs; nevertheless, sections of it are extraordinarily interesting. Outstanding are the Rowley Shoals, shelf atolls rising from just inside the tectonically depressed shelf margin at 550 m. They are three ovoid atolls of considerable size, Mermaid, Clarke, and Imperieuse, oriented north-south. They seem to lie just about on an extension

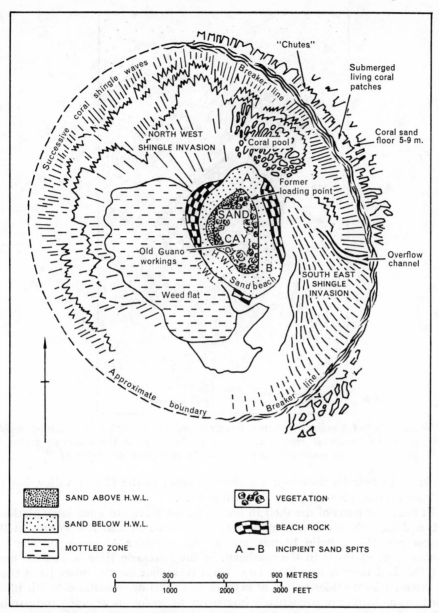

17.9 Browse Reef and Island, Sahul Shelf, (14° 07′ S., 123° 34′ E.), with an almost circular reef platform, reflecting well distributed wind control

of the axis of the Canning basin on the hinterland, a broad downwarp of the Precambrian Shield which has been slowly subsiding on and off since the Palaeozoic, and thus also has thin veneers of Mesozoic and Tertiary formations. There is a

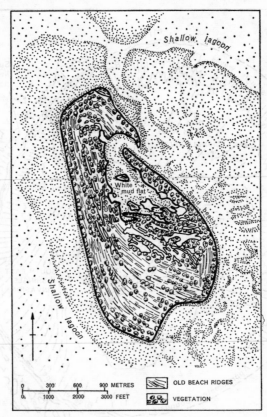

Shallow lagoon

White mud flat

Shallow lagoon

| 0 | 300 | 600 | 900 METRES |
| 0 | 1000 | 2000 | 3000 FEET |

OLD BEACH RIDGES

VEGETATION

17.10 *Adèle Island, a mature structure, largely of successive beach ridges built up mainly from the northwest monsoon, as it is protected from the southeast trades by proximity to the mainland, and modified by mangrove development*

cluster of Jurassic leucite-lamproite volcanic plugs in the Fitzroy valley, but no evidence for volcanic stocks near the shelf margin.

In the inner parts of the shelf in the southwest there are some large platform reefs and high islands with fringing reefs, as off Onslow and Roebourne, in the Barrow and Monte Bello Islands, and in the Dampier Archipelago. There is another large platform in the northeast, in the Lacepede Islands. For the most part the shelf floor is free from large coral reefs, but on the other hand there are extensive banks (biostromes) of bryozoa and pearl oysters (Basset-Smith 1900). The bryozoa banks are particularly interesting to geologists as being comparable with the bryozoan reefs of the Palaeozoic. It should be noted that the inscription 'crl' (coral) extensively found on the hydrographic charts often refers to coralline algae and bryozoa.

(f) *Dirk Hartog Shelf Reefs*

The Dirk Hartog Shelf is defined as extending from Northwest Cape to the northern limit of the Abrolhos Islands, thus covering 50,000 km² (Carrigy and

XXXVIa   Sequence of features observed on a ribbon reef, from the ocean side. Note the double moats, the reef crest, and the colour contrast between the deep water off the precipitous outer margin and the pale hues on the coral-studded lagoon side.

XXXVIb   Portion of a fine shelf atoll on the Sahul Shelf, Seringapatam Atoll. Note the contrast between the radial ('trickle') zone of truncated (dead) reef material and the sanded zone with coral heads to the interior. The hammerhead spits represent accumulations of relatively loose reef debris trailing back from the reef crest, debris originally broken off from the outer growth zone, marked by breakers.

XXXVIc   Pre-Würm (? Sangamon) emerged coral reef and lagoon limestone in the Houtman Abrolhos Islands (W.A.), 3-7·5 m above present low tide level, secondarily planed off near the shore by the Peron Submergence, which also reached 3 m; raised beaches on the interior of similar platforms date by C^{14} from about 5000 B.P.

Fairbridge 1954). Fringing and patch reefs are scarce here, but colonies of corals are found extensively, forming thin veneers over the aeolianite 'sandstone reefs' along the shore and also offshore, as for example in the Maude-Cloates Barrier, off Cape Cuvier, and here and there off Dirk Hartog Island and in the northern part of Shark Bay where there is better circulation.

(g) *Rottnest Shelf Reefs*

The Rottnest Shelf extends from the Houtman Abrolhos Islands to Cape Leeuwin and embraces 50,000 km², generally being rather narrow, only 50-100 km in width, with the shelf break about 180-200 m. As with the Dirk Hartog Shelf there are many aeolianite 'sandstone reefs' along the shore and offshore, in places veneered by reef patches. The most southerly of these coral patches is the Parker Point reef of Rottnest Island (Teichert 1950) at 30°S.

Near the northern limit of this shelf are the Houtman Abrolhos Islands (Fig. 17.11), a unique group of compound shelf atolls at 28-29°S. (Teichert 1946; Fairbridge 1948b). They contain a pre-Würm reef foundation which became extensively degraded by karst solution with large sinkholes during the eustatic low sea level of the last glaciation. During the early Holocene they were recolonised, they carry widespread relics of the 3 m, 1·5 m, and 0·5 m mid-Holocene high sea-level stages, and have become the type area for these impressive features. Patches of aeolianite also reflect the Würm low sea level, as in Rottnest Island and elsewhere along the coast (e.g. Pt Peron). The raised shell beaches at these places offer opportunities for radiocarbon-dating (Fairbridge 1948a, 1961a).

VALUE OF AUSTRALIA'S REEFS IN THE STUDY OF THE EARTH'S HISTORY

A reef is generally a fascinating and beautiful natural phenomenon in itself, and it offers all sorts of biological and ecological problems. However, in the field of geology more than any other study, reefs have contributed information of world-wide significance:

Palaeozoic and Mesozoic fossil reefs, which are of great economic significance, especially for the oil industry, are epi-continental platform reefs and shelf atolls, but not oceanic atolls; therefore the widespread development of these types in the Australian region calls for special study, in preference to the mid-Pacific types.

The Australian reefs almost exclusively rise from 'antecedent platforms' that were only geologically recently established. Much of the Queensland shelf probably had its last movements during the late glacial stage, and the antecedent canyon development of the Sahul and Arafura shelves is probably of about the same age. Although Australia is often described as a long-stable continent, these marginal belts seem to have suffered very recent and vigorous re-activation. From this may be learned important lessons for the geomorphological history of continents.

In the history of the earth's crust, it is often claimed that while continents may enlarge, ocean basins remain essentially constant. The disposition of shelf and compound atolls over such areas as the Coral Sea Plateau strongly suggests that this is a section of what Stille calls 'quasicratonic crust' which is suffering

CC1

regeneration in that it is currently subsiding *en bloc* to form a new oceanic depression. It is in part the site of a lost continent known as Tasmantis. Fundamental geophysical problems such as continental stretching, ocean expansion, convection currents, and subcrustal attenuation are involved.

The dating of eustatic 'highs' and 'lows' recorded by reef terraces can be related to fluvial sedimentation, soil history, and other climatologically controlled

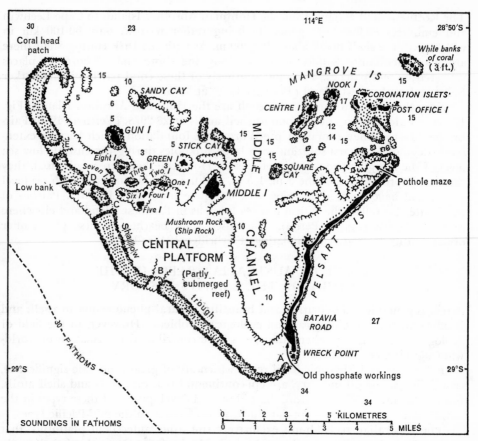

17.11   Principal reef group of the Houtman Abrolhos Islands (Pelsart), illustrating the compound atoll type, a complex of pre-Würm reefs, affected by karst weathering during the glacial low sea-level stage and veneered by aeolianite and younger reef and beach ridge accumulations.

aspects of continental geomorphology. The interrelations of alluviation and/or downcutting with the history of the reefs through thalassostatic reactions can be helpful in contributing to our ideas on the climatic history of the continent and indeed to fundamental problems of solar control and the principles of palaeoclimatology.

Coral reefs also provide the sites for potentially very interesting geochemical, biochemical, and microbiological studies. In spite of considerable progress with reef ecology, much remains to be learned about calcification, namely the organic fixation of calcium carbonate, and about the geochemistry and mineralogy of the reef carbonates. The solid solutions of magnesium in calcite and of strontium in aragonite still present some perplexing problems. Inversion of the metastable aragonite and high magnesium calcite, and the formation of dolomite are fascinating phenomena. The questions of the solution of reef limestone by salt spray, which is theoretically saturated with respect to calcite, and the corrosion of reef foundations by mangrove cannot be regarded as closed (Revelle and Fairbridge 1957; Revelle and Emery 1957).

In this brief review I have tried to stress Australia's tremendous wealth of coral reefs and related features of widespread interest.

REFERENCES

Agassiz, A. (1898). A visit to the Great Barrier Reef of Australia in the steamer 'Croydon'. *Bull. Mus. comp. Zool. Harv.* **28**: 95-148.

———— (1903). On the formation of barrier reefs and of the different types of atolls. *Proc. R. Soc.* (Lond.) **71**: 412-14.

Andrews, E. C. (1910). Geographical unity of Eastern Australia in Late and Post Tertiary time. *J. Proc. R. Soc. N.S.W.* **44**: 420-80.

———— (1922). A contribution to the hypothesis of coral reef formations. *J. Proc. R. Soc. N.S.W.* (Pres. Address) **56**: 10-38.

Basset-Smith, P. W. (1900). On the formation of coral-reefs on the N.W. coast of Australia. *Proc. zool. Soc. Lond.* 1899: 157-9.

Bryan, W. H. (1928). The Queensland Continental Shelf. *Rep Gt Barrier Reef Comm.* **2**: 58-69.

Carrigy, M. A. and Fairbridge, R. W. (1954). Recent sedimentation, physiography and structure of the continental shelves of W. Australia. *J. R. Soc. West. Aust.* **38**: 65-75.

Cumings, E. R. (1932). Reefs or bioherms? *Bull. geol. Soc. Am.* **43**: 331-52.

Daly, R. A. (1915). The glacial-control theory of coral reefs. *Proc. Am. Acad. Arts Sci.* **51**: 155-251.

Davis, W. M. (1917). The Great Barrier Reef of Australia. *Am. J. Sci.* **194**: 339-50.

———— (1922). The Barrier Reef of Tagula, New Guinea. *Ann. Ass. Am. Geogr.* **12**: 97-151.

Fairbridge, R. W. (1948a). The geology and geomorphology of Point Peron, Western Australia. *J. R. Soc. West. Aust.* **34**: 35-72.

———— (1948b). Notes on the geomorphology of the Pelsart Group of the Houtman's Abrolhos Islands. *J. R. Soc. West. Aust.* **33**: 1-43.

———— (1950a). Recent and Pleistocene coral reefs of Australia. *J. Geol.* **58**: 330-401.

———— (1950b). Landslide patterns on oceanic volcanoes and atolls. *Geogrl J.* **115**: 84-8.

———— (1951). The Aroe Islands and the continental shelf north of Australia. *Scope (J. Sci. Union, Univ. West. Aust.)* **1** (6): 24-9.

———— (1953). The Sahul Shelf, Northern Australia; its structure and geological relationships. *J. R. Soc. West. Aust.* **37**: 1-33.

———— (1961a). Eustatic changes in sea level. *Physics Chem. Earth* **4**: 99-185.

———— (1961b). Convergence of evidence on climatic change and ice ages. *Ann. N.Y. Acad. Sci.* **95** (1): 542-79.

———— (1961c). Radiations solaires et variations cycliques du niveau marin. *Revue Géogr. phys. Géol. dyn.* (2nd Ser.) **4**: 2-14.

———— (1961d). The Melanesian Border Plateau, a zone of crustal shearing in the S.W. Pacific. *Publs. Bur. cent. Seism. int. ser.* A, fasc. 22 (Helsinki, 1960): 137-49.

—— (1962a). New radiocarbon dates of Nile sediments. *Nature, Lond.* **196**: 108-10.

—— (1962b). Basis for submarine nomenclature in the South-West Pacific Ocean. *Dt. hydrogr. Z.* **15**: 1-15.

—— (1964). African ice-age aridity. *Problems in Palaeontology* (London, Wiley-Interscience) **2**: 357-63.

—— and Krebs, O. B. jun. (1962). Sea Level and the Southern Oscillation. *Geophys J.* **6**: 532-45.

—— and Stewart, H. B. jun. (1960). Alexa Bank, a drowned atoll on the Melanesian Border Plateau. *Deep Sea Res.* **7**: 100-16.

—— and Teichert, C. (1947). The Rampart System at Low Isles, 1928-1945. *Rep. Gt Barrier Reef Comm.* **6**: 1-16.

——, —— (1948). The Low Isles of the Great Barrier Reef: a new analysis. *Geogr. J.* **3**: 67-88.

——, —— (1952). Soil horizons and marine bands in the coastal limestones of Western Australia. *J. Proc. R. Soc. N.S.W.* **86**: 68-87.

Haddon, A. C., Sollas, W. J., and Cole, G. A. J. (1894). On the geology of Torres Straits. *Trans. R. Ir. Acad.* **30**: 419-76.

Hedley, C. (1925a). The natural destruction of a coral reef. *Rep. Gt Barrier Reef Comm.* **1**: 35-40.

—— (1925b). The surface temperature of Moreton Bay. *Rep. Gt Barrier Reef Comm.* **1**: 149-50.

—— and Taylor, T. G. (1908). Coral reefs of the Great Barrier, Queensland. *Rep. Australas. Ass. Advmt Sci.* **2**: 397-413.

Jukes, J. B. (1847). *Narrative of the Surveying Voyage of H.M.S. Fly . . . During the Years 1842-1846.* Vol. 1, p. 423, London.

Logan, B. (1961). *Cryptozoon* and associated stromatolites from the Recent, Shark Bay, Western Australia. *J. Geol.* **69**: 517-33.

MacNeil, F. S. (1954). The shape of atolls: an inheritance from subaerial erosion forms. *Am. J. Sci.* **252**: 402-27.

Marshall, P. (1931). Coral reefs—rough-water and calm-water types. *Rep. Gt Barrier Reef Comm.* **3**: 64-72.

Marshall, S. M. and Orr, A. P. (1931). Sedimentation on Low Isles Reef and its relation to coral growth. *Scient. Rep. Gt Barrier Reef Exped.* **1**: 93-133.

Mayer, A. G. (1918). Ecology of the Murray Island coral reef. *Carnegie Inst. Washington, Publ. 213, Tortugas Lab. Pap.* **9**: 1-48.

Mitchell, J. M. (1963). On the world-wide pattern of secular temperature change. *Changes of Climate* (Rome Symp., UNESCO) , pp. 161-81.

Molengraaff, G. A. F. (1930). The coral reefs in the East Indian Archipelago, their distribution and mode of development. *Proc. Pacif. Sci. Congr.* (4th, Java, 1929), **IIA**: 55-89; **IIB**: 989-1021.

Orr, A. P. (1933). Physical and chemical conditions in the sea in the neighbourhood of the Great Barrier Reef. *Scient. Rep. Gt Barrier Reef Exped.* **2**: 37-86.

Rainford, E. H. (1925). Destruction of the Whitsunday Group Fringing Reefs. *Aust. Mus. Mag.* **2**: 175-7.

Revelle, R. and Emery, K. O. (1957). *Chemical erosion of beach rock and exposed reef rock.* U.S. Geol. Surv. Prof. Pap. 260-T, pp. 699-709.

—— and Fairbridge, R. W. (1957). Carbonates and carbon dioxide. *Geol. Soc. Am. Mem.* **67** (1): 239-96.

Richards, H. C. and Hill, D. (1942). Great Barrier Reef bores, 1926 and 1937.—Descriptions, analyses, and interpretations. *Rep. Gt Barrier Reef Comm.* **5**: 1-122.

Russell, R. J. (1963). Recent recession of tropical cliffy coasts. *Science* **139**: 9-15.

Saville-Kent, W. (1893). *The Great Barrier Reef of Australia,* pp. 1-387. London.

Schove, D. J. (1955). The sunspot cycle, 649 B.C. to A.D. 2000. *J. geophys. Res.,* **60:** 127-46.

Shepard, F. P. (1964). Sea level changes in the past 6000 years: possible archaeological significance. *Science* **143:** 574-6.

Spender, M. (1930). Island-reefs of the Queensland Coast. *Geogrl J.* **76:** 193-214, 273-97.

Steers, J. A. (1929). The Queensland Coast and the Great Barrier Reefs. *Geogrl J.* **74:** 232-57, 341-67.

—— (1937). The coral islands and associated features of the Great Barrier Reefs. *Geogrl J.* **89:** 1-28, 119-46.

—— (1938). Detailed notes on the islands surveyed and examined by the Geographical Expedition to the Great Barrier Reef in 1936. *Rep. Gt Barrier Reef Comm.* **4:** 51-96.

Stephenson, T. A., Tandy, G., and Spender, M. (1931). The structure and ecology of Low Isles and other reefs. *Scient. Rep. Gt Barrier Reef Exped.* **3:** 17-112.

Teichert, C. (1946). Contributions to the geology of Houtman's Abrolhos, Western Australia. *Proc. Linn. Soc. N.S.W.* **71:** 145-96.

—— (1950). Late Quaternary sea-level changes at Rottnest Island, Western Australia. *Proc. R. Soc. Vict.,* **59:** 63-79.

—— and Fairbridge, R. W. (1948). Some coral reefs of the Sahul Shelf. *Geogrl Rev.* **38:** 222-49.

Termier, H. and Termier, G. (1963). *Erosion and Sedimentation* (trans. D. W. and E. E. Humphries). London and Princeton.

Umbgrove, J. H. F. (1947). Coral reefs of the East Indies. *Bull. geol. Soc. Am.* **58:** 729-78.

Yonge, C. M. (1940). The biology of reef-building corals. *Scient. Rep. Gt Barrier Reef Exped.* **1:** 353-91.

—— (1963). *The Biology of Coral Reefs. Advances in Marine Biology.* New York.

Index

(a) AUTHORS CITED

419

(b) PLACE NAMES

(c) GENERAL